WORDLY WISE
3000

Book **2**

Kenneth Hodkinson
Sandra Adams

EDUCATORS PUBLISHING SERVICE
Cambridge and Toronto

Cover design by Hugh Price

Educators Publishing Service
800.225.5750
www.epsbooks.com

Printed in the U. S. A.
ISBN 0-8388-2432-3
978-0-8388-2432-0

22 23 CUR 10 09 08 07

Lesson 1

Word List
Study the definitions of the words below; then do the exercises for the lesson.

accustom
ə kus´ təm

v. To make familiar.
[Every fall the students *accustom* themselves to the new schedule.]
accustomed *adj.* 1. Usual.
[We sat in our *accustomed* places.]
2. Used to. [My eyes soon became *accustomed* to the dark.]

alert
ə lʉrt´

adj. Watchful; wide-awake.
[The shortstop was not *alert* and missed the catch.]
v. To warn to be ready.
[A sign *alerted* drivers to the flooded road ahead.]
n. A warning signal.
[Because of the forest fires, the nearby towns have a fire *alert*.]

assign
ə sīn´

v. 1. To select for a position or for what has to be done.
[For this year's basketball team, the coach *assigned* me to play as a forward.]
2. To give out, as a piece of work to be done.
[Our science teacher usually *assigns* two chapters a week as homework.]
assignment *n.* Whatever is given out as work to be done.
[What was the *assignment* for tomorrow's history class?]

budge
buj

v. To move or shift.
[The old, metal trunk was so heavy we could not *budge* it.]

burly
bʉr´le

adj. Big and strongly built.
[Most football players are quite *burly*.]

companion
kəm pan´ yən

n. One who spends time with or does things with another.
[My grandmother was always an interesting *companion* when we went to the city for the day.]

compatible
kəm pat´ ə bəl

adj. Getting along well together.
[Julie and I didn't mind sharing a room because we were so *compatible*.]

concept
kän´ sept

n. A general idea or thought about something.
[In designing the stage set for the school play, I started with the *concept* of a Japanese tea house.]

distract
di strakt´

v. To draw one's thoughts or attention away from the subject at hand.
[The police sirens *distracted* me, so I didn't hear what you said.]
distraction *n.* Something that draws one's thoughts or attention away.
[I do my homework during study period when there are no *distractions*.]

jostle
jäs´ əl

v. To push or shove.
[I dropped my packages when someone in the crowd *jostled* me.]

obedient
ō bē´ dē ənt

adj. Doing what one is asked or told.
[When giving orders, a ship's captain expects the crew to be *obedient*.]
obedience   *n.* The state or condition of doing what one is told.
[We are trying to teach our Labrador retriever *obedience*.]

obstacle
äb´ stə kəl

n. Something that prevents one from moving forward.
[The *obstacle* holding up traffic was a tree blown over by last night's storm.]

patient
pā´ shənt

adj. Willing to wait without complaining.
[The audience was very *patient* even though the show started thirty minutes late.]
n. A person in a doctor's care.
[The *patients* in this part of the hospital are recovering from operations.]
patience   *n.* A willingness to wait for someone or something without complaining.
[Having to stand in line for an hour to buy tickets really tested my *patience*.]

pedestrian
pə des´ trē ən

n. A person who is walking; someone traveling on foot.
[*Pedestrians* should use the crosswalk to avoid accidents.]

retire
rē tīr´

v. 1. To stop working because one has reached a certain age.
[The jewelry company usually gives its workers a small gift when they *retire*.]
2. To go to bed.
[I was not feeling well, so I *retired* early.]
retirement   *n.* The state of no longer working.
[My Uncle Eli regularly saved money for his *retirement*.]

1A Finding Meanings

Choose two phrases to form a sentence that correctly uses a word from Word List 1. Write each sentence in the space provided.

1. (a) become familiar with it.
   (b) do it carefully.
   (c) To accustom oneself to something is to
   (d) To distract oneself by doing something is to

   _____

2. (a) is under a doctor's care.
   (b) A patient is a person who
   (c) A companion is one who
   (d) gives hope to others.

   _____

3. (a) An assignment is
   (b) A concept is
   (c) a general idea about something.
   (d) something that stands in the way.

   _____

4. (a) has traveled a lot.
   (b) A pedestrian is someone who
   (c) spends time with another person.
   (d) A companion is someone who

   _____

5. (a) An alert is   (c) work given out to be done.
    (b) a meeting arranged in advance.   (d) An assignment is

6. (a) Patience is   (c) help and support given to another.
    (b) Obedience is   (d) the willingness to wait without complaining.

7. (a) is big and strong.   (c) An alert person is one who
    (b) gets along with others.   (d) A burly person is one who

8. (a) Obedience is   (c) a drawing away of one's attention.
    (b) Retirement is   (d) a time when one no longer works.

9. (a) To jostle someone is   (c) To distract someone is
    (b) to warn the person of danger.   (d) to bump up against that person.

10. (a) go to bed.   (c) To retire is to
    (b) To budge is to   (d) do as one is told.

1B Just the Right Word

Improve each of the following sentences by crossing out the italicized phrase and replacing it with a word (or a form of the word) from Word List 1.

1. They expected their children to be *willing to do as they were told.*

2. My grandparents plan to travel to other countries when they *give up working at their jobs.*

3. They refused to *make the slightest move* even though we pleaded with them to step aside.

4. If you and your roommate are not *able to get along*, you should split up.

5. Elido sounded the *signal that warned of danger* when he saw smoke.

6. We made our way around the *objects that were blocking our way* and continued on our journey.

7. A buzzing mosquito can be a *thing that draws your attention away* when you are trying to read.

8. The camp director *gave out jobs and sent* us to the kitchen crew.

9. You see very few *people out walking* this early in the morning.

10. My sister is more *willing to accept delays without complaining* than I am.

1C Applying Meanings

Circle the letter of each correct answer to the questions below. A question may have more than one correct answer.

1. Which of the following could be an *obstacle?*
   - (a) lack of money
   - (b) a fallen tree
   - (c) poor eyesight
   - (d) a pleasant voice

2. In which of the following places would a *pedestrian* be?
   - (a) on the sidewalk
   - (b) inside a car
   - (c) in a favorite armchair
   - (d) on a plane

3. Which of the following could *distract* someone?
   - (a) loud noises
   - (b) whispering
   - (c) dreams
   - (d) the radio

4. Which of the following usually learn *obedience?*
   - (a) dogs
   - (b) soldiers
   - (c) cats
   - (d) children

5. Which of the following must be *alert?*
   - (a) a watchman
   - (b) a baby-sitter
   - (c) a driver
   - (d) a pilot

6. Which of the following would you expect to be *compatible?*
   - (a) friends
   - (b) partners
   - (c) enemies
   - (d) teammates

7. Which of the following could be *assigned?*
   - (a) jobs
   - (b) rooms
   - (c) seats
   - (d) birthdays

8. Which of the following might make a good *companion?*
   - (a) a dog
   - (b) a canoe
   - (c) a friend
   - (d) a meal

1D Word Relationships

In each of the groups below, circle the two words that are synonyms. (Synonyms are words that have the same or almost the same meaning.)

1. SILENT   OBEDIENT
   ALERT   WATCHFUL

2. DISTRACTION   HOMEWORK
   ATTENTION   ASSIGNMENT

3. BUDGE   FORSAKE
   FIND   MOVE

4. ACCUSTOMED   PATIENT
   USUAL   STRANGE

5. DISTRACT   SHOVE
   JOSTLE   COMPLAIN

6. PATIENT   UNCOMPLAINING
   BURLY   WEAK

7. ALERT   RETIRE
   TIRE   WARN

8. OBSTACLE   CONCEPT
   IDEA   ACTION

9. STRONG   SMOOTH
   COMPATIBLE   BURLY

10. ASSIGN   SELECT
    REMEMBER   RETIRE

1E Narrative

Read the narrative below; then complete the exercise that follows.

FRIENDS FOR LIFE

The **concept** that trained dogs could act as eyes for those who could not see developed at the beginning of the twentieth century in Germany in an unusual school. The pupils were not humans, but dogs who were taught how to lead people who were blind. The idea caught on quickly, and guide dogs, or Seeing Eye dogs as they are also known, began to be trained in many countries. They are now a familiar sight. These **patient** and loyal animals lead their blind **companions** everywhere they go, permitting them to make their way in the world almost as well as sighted persons.

Not every breed of dog makes a good guide. Seeing Eye dogs must be **alert** at all times, so dogs that are easily **distracted** are not suitable. Labrador retrievers, German shepherds, and boxers make excellent guides because they are smart, easy to train, and usually get along well with people. During its training, the dog is taken to many kinds of busy places. This is to get it **accustomed** to anything that might happen. A dog is trained in large stores, noisy airports, and crowded restaurants. It rides on buses and in taxis. It is pushed and poked, and it learns to ignore anything that might cause its attention to wander.

The Seeing Eye dog is responsible for steering its owner carefully past any **obstacles.** On busy sidewalks, the dog must skillfully weave its way around other **pedestrians** to make sure its owner doesn't get **jostled.** A guide dog is trained to come to a stop just before it reaches a curb; this is the way it tells its owner to take a step up or down. But even though it learns to be **obedient,** a guide dog is also taught that sometimes it must disobey. For example, if its owner tells it to cross a street when a car is coming, it won't **budge** until it is safe to cross. While it is being trained, a guide dog is never punished for making a mistake; instead it is encouraged to do better by being rewarded when it behaves correctly.

When the training is complete, a guide dog is **assigned** to its new owner. The two of them need to be **compatible** because they will be together for a long time. The size, weight, and nature of both are taken into account. A **burly** person might be more comfortable with a large dog while a person who spends most of the day inside probably will not want to be matched with a frisky dog that needs plenty of exercise. From the beginning, a strong bond needs to form between the dog and the owner.

The Seeing Eye headquarters in Morristown, New Jersey, was the first, and is still the largest, school for guide dogs in the United States. Every year several hundred blind people spend a month there learning how to work with the dogs they have been matched with. Usually a guide dog stays with its owner for about ten years before it **retires.** Then, it often may go to live with friends of the owner and stay with them as an ordinary family pet for the rest of its life.

Answer each of the following questions in a sentence. If a question does not contain a vocabulary word, use a vocabulary word in your answer. Use each word only once. Questions and answers will then contain all fifteen words (or forms of the words) from this lesson's word list.

1. What was the **concept** behind the Seeing Eye dog movement?

   _____

2. When does the relationship between guide dog and owner officially begin?

   _____

3. What sort of dog might a **burly** person be matched up with?

   _____

4. Why do you think a powerful dog would not be matched with someone who is not very strong?

   _____

5. Where are you most likely to see **pedestrians**?

   _____

6. **Obedience** is important in dogs kept as pets. Why is this not always true of guide dogs?

_____

7. Why is pushing and poking a guide dog necessary during its training?

_____

8. What is the meaning of **alert** as it is used in the narrative?

_____

9. How will a guide dog respond if it is ordered to cross a street with heavy traffic?

_____

10. Why are guide dogs unlikely to get excited when another dog approaches?

_____

11. What is the meaning of **patient** as it is used in the narrative?

_____

12. Name three **obstacles** that a guide dog might have to deal with on the street.

_____

13. Why do guide dogs need to keep a watchful eye on other people in crowded places?

_____

14. What is the meaning of **retires** as it is used in the narrative?

_____

15. Why would it be somewhat surprising to see a guide dog without its owner?

_____

WORDLY WISE

Alert comes from the Italian *all'erta,* which meant "acting as a lookout on a watchtower." The person in the watchtower had to be *alert* (*adjective,* meaning "watchful"); the person would *alert* the others in the event of danger (*verb,* meaning "to warn") by sounding the *alert* (*noun,* meaning "warning signal"). To be *on the alert* means "to be watchful and ready."

If you live with or travel with a **companion,** you will probably eat your meals together. This was the case with the Romans too. The word comes from the Latin prefix *com-,* which means "with," and the word *panis,* which is Latin for "bread." To the Romans, a *companion* was a person with whom one shared a meal, of which bread was one of the main items.

A **pedestrian** is a person who gets around on foot. A *pedal* is a lever operated by the foot. A *quadruped* is a creature with four feet, while a *centipede* supposedly has 100 feet (it actually has about seventy). All of these words come from the Latin *ped-,* whose meaning you can probably guess.

Lesson 2

Word List
Study the definitions of the words below; then do the exercises for the lesson.

aroma
ə rō´ mə

n. A smell or odor, especially a pleasant one.
[The *aroma* of hot buttered popcorn made our mouths water.]

beverage
bev´ ər ij

n. A liquid, other than water, used as a drink.
[When we ordered our *beverages,* I chose lemonade.]

bland
bland

adj. 1. Lacking a strong flavor.
[Patients with stomach problems eat *bland* foods like chicken soup and mashed potatoes.]
2. Not irritating, exciting, or disturbing.
[The doctor's *bland* manner soon calmed the crying child.]

brittle
brit´ l

adj. Easily broken; not flexible.
[Candy canes are *brittle* and should be handled with care.]

cluster
klus´ tər

n. A number of similar things grouped together.
[*Clusters* of brightly colored flowers grew along the side of the road.]
v. To gather or come together in a group.
[The children *clustered* around the storyteller.]

combine
kəm bīn´

v. To join or bring together.
[We *combine* oil and vinegar to make the salad dressing.]
combination *n.* A joining or bringing together.
[Our team's victory resulted from a *combination* of hard work and good luck.]

consume
kən sōōm´

v. 1. To use up.
[Piano practice *consumes* all of Alex's free time.]
2. To eat or drink.
[A horse *consumes* fifty pounds of hay a day.]
3. To do away with or destroy.
[The forest fire *consumed* over two thousand acres in Oregon.]

crave
krāv

v. To have a strong desire for.
[When he was a teenager, Abraham Lincoln *craved* knowledge so much that he would walk miles to borrow a book he had not read.]
craving *n.* A strong desire.
[After the hike, we all had a *craving* for lots of cool water.]

cultivate
kul´ ti vāt

v. 1. To prepare land for the growing of crops.
[Before the spring planting, farmers *cultivate* the soil.]
2. To grow or to help to grow.
[Ana *cultivates* tomatoes every year in her garden.]
3. To encourage development by attention or study.
[Parents can *cultivate* a love of nature in their children by taking them on hikes in the country.]

equivalent
ē kwiv´ ə lənt

adj. Equal to.
[Although the decimal 0.5 and the fraction $\frac{1}{2}$ appear to be different, they are *equivalent* amounts.]
n. (eks´ pôrt) That which is equal to.
[One year of a dog's life is the *equivalent* of seven human years.]

export
ek spôrt´

v. To send goods to another country for sale.
[Colombia *exports* coffee to countries all over the world.]
n. (eks´ trackt) Something exported.
[Grain is an important *export* of the United States.]

extract
ek strakt´

v. 1. To remove or take out.
[Dr. Bogasian will *extract* my wisdom tooth next week.]
2. To obtain with an effort.
[I *extracted* a promise from them to leave us alone.]
n. Something removed or taken out.
[Vanilla *extract* comes from the seedpods of vanilla plants.]

introduce
in trə do͞os´

v. 1. To cause to know; to make known by name.
[Let me *introduce* you to my companion, Jane Willow.]
2. To bring to the attention of, especially for the first time.
[It was our friends in Hawaii who *introduced* us to scuba diving.]
3. To bring into use.
[The invention of the airplane *introduced* a new way of traveling.]
introduction *n.* (in trə duk´shən) 1. Something spoken or written before the main part.
[We read the *introduction* before going on to the rest of *The Woman in White*.]
2. The act of being made known by name.
[After my *introduction* to the others in the room, I relaxed and enjoyed the party.]

purchase
pur´ chəs

v. To buy.
[My parents *purchase* a new car every five years.]
n. 1. Something that is bought.
[Store detectives may ask you to show sales slips for your *purchases* as you leave.]
2. The act of buying.
[Because of a bicycle's cost, I looked at and rode several before I made a *purchase*.]

tropical
träp´ i kəl

adj. 1. Of, from, or similar to the regions near the equator.
[Ecuador, which lies on the equator, is a *tropical* country.]
2. Hot and moist.
[The chill autumn temperatures outside made the air at the indoor pool feel *tropical*.]

2A Finding Meanings

Choose two phrases to form a sentence that correctly uses a word from Word List 2. Write each sentence in the space provided.

1. (a) An aroma is
    (b) a pleasant smell.
    (c) A cluster is
    (d) a drink.

2. (a) to give it away.   (c) To crave something is
   (b) to use it up.   (d) To consume something is

3. (a) An extract is something   (c) An equivalent is something
   (b) that is bought.   (d) that is equal to something else.

4. (a) A cluster is   (c) a group of similar things.
   (b) An export is   (d) something that is given away.

5. (a) A combination is   (c) a strong desire.
   (b) An introduction is   (d) a making known by name.

6. (a) Something that is brittle   (c) Something that is bland
   (b) lacks a strong flavor.   (d) bends easily.

7. (a) is to borrow it from that person.   (c) To introduce someone to a book
   (b) is to make that person aware of it. (d) To purchase a book for someone

8. (a) obtain it with an effort.   (c) To extract an offer is to
   (b) reject it.   (d) To crave an offer is to

9. (a) breaks easily.   (c) has a strong smell.
   (b) Something that is tropical   (d) Something that is brittle

10. (a) A beverage is   (c) something that is eaten.
    (b) A purchase is   (d) something that is bought.

2B Just the Right Word

Improve each of the following sentences by crossing out the italicized phrase and replacing it with a word (or a form of the word) from Word List 2.

1. Milk, juice, and other *liquids suitable for drinking* are on sale at the booth.

2. This machine *takes out* the juice from oranges.

3. These computers are being *sold to other countries* at the rate of two hundred a day.

4. Rollerblades were *first brought into use* in the U.S. in the 1980s.

5. The *mixing together* of blue and yellow paint produces green.

6. Plants will not grow well if the soil has not been *properly prepared for the growing of crops.*

7. The summer climate in Washington, D.C., is almost *like that near the equator.*

8. After my cousins *paid money in order to own* a dog, they all helped to feed, train, and exercise it.

9. It was clear that Uncle Paul *had a strong desire for* a piece of my mother's pumpkin pie.

10. Every morning chickadees *gather in a group* around our bird feeder.

2C Applying Meanings

Circle the letter of each correct answer to the questions below. A question may have more than one correct answer.

1. Which of the following is a *bland* food?
   (a) oatmeal   (c) white bread
   (b) hot chili   (d) pepperoni pizza

2. Which of the following can be *purchased?*
   (a) good health   (c) automobiles
   (b) diseases   (d) energy

3. Which of the following can be *cultivated?*
   (a) corn   (c) an interest in science
   (b) water   (d) the soil

4. Which of the following has an *aroma?*
   (a) the number 7   (c) a famous person's name
   (b) freshly ground coffee   (d) a rose

5. Which of the following can be *consumed?*
   (a) vegetables   (c) fuel
   (b) sleep   (d) plants

6. Which of the following is a *beverage?*
   (a) milk   (c) chocolate ice cream
   (b) water   (d) hot chocolate

7. Which of the following are *equivalent* to a dollar?
   (a) fifty cents   (c) four quarters
   (b) ten dimes   (d) twenty nickels

8. Which of the following are *exported* from the U.S.?
   (a) kangaroos   (c) parrots
   (b) grains   (d) medicines

2D Word Relationships

In each of the groups below, circle the two words that are antonyms. (Antonyms are words that have opposite or nearly opposite meanings.)

1. MOVE   PURCHASE
   CLUSTER   SELL

2. COMBINATION   DISTRACTION
   CRAVING   DISLIKE

3. CLUSTER   ASSIGN
   CULTIVATE   SCATTER

4. COMBINE   SAVE
   SEPARATE   EXPORT

5. PROMISE   DESTROY
   RESCUE   CULTIVATE

6. EXTRACT   SUPPORT
   EXPORT   INSERT

7. BRITTLE   FLEXIBLE
   HOT   TROPICAL

8. LARGE   BLAND
   IRRITATING   OBEDIENT

9. WET   TROPICAL
   DISTANT   COLD

10. BLAND   UNEQUAL
    SMOOTH   EQUIVALENT

2E Narrative

Read the narrative below; then complete the exercise that follows.

WHEN MONEY GREW ON TREES

Do you wish that chocolate grew on trees? Well, it does. The trees are cocoa trees and they grow in **tropical** countries. Of course, you wouldn't recognize the little pale-colored and bitter-tasting beans of the cocoa tree as chocolate, but they are the raw material from which candy bars are made.

Cocoa trees were first **cultivated** in Central and South America, but are now grown in many other parts of the world, including West Africa, the Caribbean, and southern Asia. They grow best in areas with a year-round temperature of around eighty degrees and an annual rainfall of eighty inches or more. Because the young trees need to be sheltered from direct sunlight, banana plants, which are taller, are often grown between the rows to provide shade.

Pods as big as footballs grow from the branches and trunks of the trees. Inside each pod is a **cluster** of twenty to forty cocoa beans, each inside its own thin shell. Workers cut the pods from the trees by hand and split them open to remove the beans, which are separated and stored in boxes for about a week. When the beans are brown and have a slight chocolate **aroma**, they are ready to be dried, either in the sun or in ovens. After the drying is completed, the beans are put in sacks and **exported** to countries all over the world.

Now they are ready to be made into chocolate. First, the beans are roasted. This makes the shells **brittle** and easy to separate from the beans, which next are ground into a paste. This paste contains a lot of fat, called cocoa butter, which is **extracted**. What remains is cocoa powder, used for making chocolate cakes, cookies, and puddings. The soft, sweet chocolate in candy is made by **combining** the cocoa powder with cocoa butter, sugar, and dried milk.

The Spanish explorers who traveled through Central and South America in the 1500s were the first to **introduce** chocolate into Europe. The Aztecs, who lived in what is now Mexico, ground up cocoa beans and made the paste into a cold **beverage**. They must have thought it tasted **bland** because they mixed it with chili peppers and other spices. Not surprisingly, the name "chocolate" comes from an Aztec word meaning "bitter drink." Montezuma, the Aztec king, seems to have had a **craving** for it because, according to Aztec records, he **consumed** up to fifty cups of chocolate a day!

The Aztecs also used cocoa beans as money. A rabbit cost ten beans, while a slave could be **purchased** for a hundred; that would have made the value of a human being **equivalent** to ten rabbits! This may seem surprising, but here is something else to think about: the Aztecs really did live in a land where money grew on trees.

Answer each of the following questions in a sentence. If a question does not contain a vocabulary word, use a vocabulary word in your answer. Use each word only once. Questions and answers will then contain all fifteen words (or forms of the words) from this lesson's word list.

1. How can one satisfy a **craving** for chocolate?

   _____

2. What are two ways that cocoa is used today?

   _____

3. What is the meaning of **cultivated** as it is used in the narrative?

   _____

4. Why do cocoa trees grow only in **tropical** countries?

   _____

5. To which countries are cocoa beans **exported**?

   _____

6. In addition to using cocoa beans for a drink, in what other way did the Aztecs use them?

   _____

7. How is chocolate candy made?

   _____

8. What would you find if you split open a pod of the cocoa tree?

   _____

9. How do workers know when the cocoa beans are ready to be dried?

   _____

10. What is the meaning of **consumed** as it is used in the narrative?

    _____

11. When can the shells of cocoa beans be removed easily from the beans?

    _____

12. How is ground cocoa bean paste turned into cocoa powder?

    _____

13. How and when did Europeans learn about chocolate?

_____

14. What is the meaning of **bland** as it is used in the narrative?

_____

15. Why could an Aztec receive five rabbits in exchange for fifty cocoa beans?

_____

WORDLY WISE

Aroma once meant a spice. Spices have strong and pleasant smells, and in time the meaning of the word changed. An aroma became the pleasant smell of the spice rather than the spice itself. Later the word came to mean any smell, but especially one that is pleasant.

◆ ◆ ◆ ◆ ◆ ◆ ◆

The word **export** is formed from the Latin prefix *ex-*, meaning "out," and the Latin root *port*, meaning "carry." Goods being *exported* are *carried* by boat or plane *out* of the country. The antonym of *export* is *import*. To *import* goods is to bring them *into* a country. (The United States *imports* many cars from Japan.)

◆ ◆ ◆ ◆ ◆ ◆ ◆

The Latin *tractus* means "drawn" or "pulled" and forms the root of several English words. A *tractor* is a vehicle used to pull farm machinery. A *protracted* explanation is one that is drawn out and goes on too long. This root joins with the Latin prefix *ex-*, meaning "out," to form the word **extract.**

◆ ◆ ◆ ◆ ◆ ◆ ◆

The adjective **tropical** is formed from the word *tropic*. The Tropic of Cancer and the Tropic of Capricorn are two imaginary lines going around the earth, north and south of the equator. They are three thousand miles apart, and the area of the world between them is called the tropics. Most of Africa and Central and South America and parts of Asia are in the tropics.

Lesson 3

Word List

Study the definitions of the words below; then do the exercises for the lesson.

ancestor
an´ ses tər

n. 1. A person from whom one is descended.
[My *ancestors* came from Italy.]
2. An early kind of animal from which later ones have developed; a forerunner.
[The dog-sized mesohippus is the *ancestor* of the modern horse.]

carnivore
kär´ ni vôr

n. A flesh-eating animal.
[*Carnivores* have sharp, pointed teeth that enable them to tear the meat they eat.]
carnivorous *adj.* (kär niv´ ər əs) Flesh-eating.
[Although dogs are *carnivorous,* they will often eat other foods besides meat.]

comprehend
käm prē hend´

v. To understand.
[If you don't *comprehend* the question, let me know and I will word it differently.]
comprehension *n.* The act of understanding; the ability to understand.
[Pawel cannot speak Spanish very well, but his *comprehension* is quite good.]

duration
door ā´ shən

n. The time during which something lasts or continues.
[We stayed in our house for the *duration* of the heavy downpour.]

evident
ev´ ə dənt

adj. Easy to see and understand; obvious, clear.
[It is *evident* from your manner that you are not happy to see me.]

extinct
ek stiŋkt´

adj. 1. No longer existing or living.
[The giant woolly mammoth became *extinct* about ten thousand years ago.]
2. No longer active.
[Mount Saint Helens was believed to be an *extinct* volcano until it suddenly became active in 1980.]

ferocious
fə rō´ shəs

adj. Savage; fierce.
[Doberman pinschers make *ferocious* guard dogs.]
ferocity *n.* (fə räs´ ə tē) The state or quality of being fierce.
[The *ferocity* of the storm surprised us.]

gigantic
jī gan´ tik

adj. Very large; like a giant in size.
[The *Spruce Goose* was a *gigantic* airplane that made only one flight.]

obscure
äb skyoor´

v. To cover up or keep from being seen.
[Clouds *obscured* the moon.]
adj. 1. Hard to see; hidden.
[The boat was an *obscure* shape in the mist.]
2. Not easy to understand.
[The poem was full of *obscure* words like "clough" and "moraine."]

option
äp´ shən

n. Choice, or something that is available as a choice.
[We had the *option* of practicing soccer during the lunch break or after school.]
optional *adj.* Left to choice.
[Bill said we should attend the meeting, but staying on for the party afterward was *optional.*]

premature
prē mə chŏŏr´

adj. Too early; happening or arriving before the proper time.
[*Premature* babies require special care before they are allowed to leave the hospital.]

preserve
prē zʉrv´

v. 1. To save; to keep from harm; to protect.
[This law will help to *preserve* the old forests in the national parks.]
2. To keep from rotting or spoiling.
[Steve and Martha *preserve* the peaches from their orchard by canning them.]

prey
prā

n. 1. An animal that is hunted for food.
[Chickens are the natural *prey* of foxes.]
2. One that is helpless or unable to resist attack; a victim.
[Be alert when you travel so that you will not be *prey* to thieves.]
v. 1. To hunt (animals) for food.
[Wolves *prey* on the weakest deer in the herd.]
2. To take from or rob using violence or trickery.
[The pick pockets *preyed* on newly arrived tourists, who were usually concentrating on their new surroundings.]

puny
pyōō´ nē

adj. 1. Weak.
[Lifting weights can change *puny* muscles into powerful ones.]
2. Lacking in size, strength, or power.
[My one dollar offering seemed *puny* compared to what others gave.]

survive
sər vīv´

v. 1. To stay alive where there is a chance of dying or being killed.
[Only three passengers *survived* the plane crash.]
2. To continue living or existing through a threatening situation.
[Only two of the eight maple trees in our yard *survived* the hurricane.]
survivor *n.* One who stays alive while others die.
[*Survivors* of the shipwreck floated on life rafts until the helicopter could pick them up.]

3A Finding Meanings

Choose two phrases to form a sentence that correctly uses a word from Word List 3. Write each sentence in the space provided.

1. (a) it is easy to see.
   (b) If something is evident,

   (c) If something is premature,
   (d) it has lasted for a long time.

_____

2. (a) from whom one is descended.
   (b) who does not eat meat.

   (c) An ancestor is someone
   (d) A survivor is someone

_____

3. (a) To prey on wildlife is to
   (b) To preserve wildlife is to

   (c) keep it from harm.
   (d) have a complete understanding of it.

_____

4. (a) A gigantic volcano is one that   (c) is no longer active.
   (b) An extinct volcano is one that   (d) is hidden from view.

5. (a) is to let it get away.   (c) To prey on something
   (b) To obscure something   (d) is to hunt it for food.

6. (a) The comprehension of something is   (c) the length of time it is delayed.
   (b) the length of time that it lasts.   (d) The duration of something is

7. (a) that is very big.   (c) A puny figure is one
   (b) that is well known.   (d) A gigantic figure is one

8. (a) is one that has not died out.   (c) A practice that is optional
   (b) is one that seems strange.   (d) A practice that survives

9. (a) one that leaves nothing out.   (c) An obscure report is
   (b) A premature report is   (d) one that is hard to understand.

10. (a) A ferocious creature is   (c) An extinct creature is
   (b) one that has died out.   (d) one that eats only meat.

3B Just the Right Word

Improve each of the following sentences by crossing out the italicized phrase and replacing it with a word (or a form of the word) from Word List 3.

1. The house was *hidden from view* by a thick hedge.

2. My two-horsepower engine is *lacking in power* compared to the fifty-horsepower one in your boat.

3. It is *easy to see* from the dishes in the sink that someone has already eaten lunch.

4. The film captures the *fierce behavior* of a mother tiger defending her cubs.

5. The pirate Blackbeard *attacked and robbed the people* on ships in the Caribbean.

6. To announce the holiday schedule now would be *to do so before the time is right*.

7. After the flood, the *people who remained alive* returned to their homes to clean away the mud.

8. Alberto had no other *choice open* but to take the test on Friday, even though he was still sick.

9. We did not stay for the *entire time* of the concert because Madelaine was too tired.

10. Lions and tigers are *animals that eat meat*.

3C Applying Meanings

Circle the letter of each correct answer to the questions below. A question may have more than one correct answer.

1. Which of the following would be *optional* on most cars?
   (a) brakes   (c) air conditioning
   (b) tires   (d) tape deck

2. Which of the following can be *preserved*?
   (a) freedom   (c) letters
   (b) fruit   (d) clouds

3. Which of the following can become *extinct*?
   (a) languages   (c) plants
   (b) volcanoes   (d) animals

4. Which of the following is an *ancestor*?
   (a) your brother   (c) your great-grandmother
   (b) your daughter   (d) your grandson

5. Which of the following are *carnivorous*?
   (a) wolves   (c) cows
   (b) rabbits   (d) frogs

6. Which of the following can be *premature*?
   (a) a death   (c) an announcement
   (b) a holiday   (d) a baby

7. Which of the following might be *ferocious?*
   (a) a polar bear
   (b) a teddy bear
   (c) a hungry dog
   (d) a hungry baby

8. Which of the following might be hard to *comprehend?*
   (a) a computer game
   (b) a shopping list
   (c) a foreign language
   (d) a card game

3D Word Relationships

In each of the groups below, circle the two words that are synonyms.

1. EXTINCT   GIGANTIC
   HUGE   ANCIENT

2. WEAK   CARNIVOROUS
   PUNY   STUPID

3. CHOICE   FEROCITY
   PROOF   OPTION

4. DURATION   UNDERSTANDING
   DISTRACTION COMPREHENSION

5. OBVIOUS   WISE
   EVIDENT   ALERT

6. SAVAGE   DISTANT
   OBSCURE   FEROCIOUS

7. CARNIVORE   VICTIM
   COMPANION   PREY

8. HIDDEN   EXTINCT
   BLAND   OBSCURE

9. FORERUNNER   ANCESTOR
   EQUIVALENT   OBSTACLE

10. SURVIVE   CLUSTER
    SAVE   PRESERVE

3E Narrative

Read the narrative below; then complete the exercise that follows.

THE LAST DINOSAURS

When people think of dinosaurs, the one that comes to mind most frequently is *Tyrannosaurus rex*, a **gigantic** monster almost fifty feet in length and weighing five tons. With curved eight-inch talons on its feet and a huge jaw lined with teeth as long and as sharp as steak knives, it was thought to have been the most terrifying of all the **carnivorous** dinosaurs. Imagine the surprise, then, when scientists digging in eastern Utah in 1992 found **preserved** in the rock the remains of a dinosaur that could well have been a match for *Tyrannosaurus rex*.

Named *Utahraptor*, this **ferocious** creature was "only" twenty feet long, but it had twelve-inch hooked claws on each of its hind legs. Unlike *Tyrannosaurus rex*, which had surprisingly short and **puny** forelimbs, *Utahraptor* had large, powerful arms equipped with ten-inch claws. With these it could grasp its **prey**. Once it had brought its victim down, it could slash with the terrible claws on its hind feet. Nor was flight an **option** for an animal being attacked; with its sturdy back legs *Utahraptor* could probably outrun any other creature. A contest between these two powerful creatures of the dinosaur world never took place, however. All of the *Utahraptors* had been dead for fifty million years before *Tyrannosaurus rex* ever appeared.

It is difficult to **comprehend** the vast stretch of time that dinosaurs lived on the earth—well over a hundred and fifty million years. *Tyrannosaurus rex* was among the last of the dinosaurs; it died out sixty-five million years ago. Human beings have been around for only two or three million years. It will be a long time before we equal the **duration** of the dinosaurs' stay on earth.

No one knows why these creatures became **extinct**, but it seems **evident** from the record left in the earth's crust that it happened fairly suddenly. We know that a meteorite, a large mass of rock or metal from outer space, hit the earth in what is now Mexico about sixty-five million years ago, making a crater almost two hundred miles across. Dust from such an impact would have **obscured** the light from the sun for many weeks and caused freezing temperatures. Much of the earth's plant life would have died, making it difficult for many animals to **survive.**

However, it would be **premature** to say for certain that this was what brought an end to the dinosaurs; scientists are still studying the subject. Indeed, the discovery in China of the bones of *Sinornis*, a feathered dinosaur that perched and flew, has led some scientists to claim that this creature may be the **ancestor** of today's birds. If this turns out to be true, then it would be possible to say that the dinosaurs never died out at all.

Answer each of the following questions in a sentence. If a question does not contain a vocabulary word, use a vocabulary word in your answer. Use each word only once. Questions and answers will then contain all fifteen words (or forms of the words) from this lesson's word list.

1. How do scientists know that *Utahraptor* ever lived?

    _____

2. What was the **duration** of the age of the dinosaurs?

    _____

3. When did the last of the dinosaurs die out?

    _____

4. What are some things scientists now **comprehend** about *Utahraptor?*

_____

5. What is the meaning of **prey** as it is used in the narrative?

_____

6. How did *Tyrannosaurus rex* compare in size to *Utahraptor?*

_____

7. What is the meaning of **survive** as it is used in the narrative?

_____

8. What were the **options** of a creature attacked by *Utahraptor?*

_____

9. Were the forelimbs of *Tyrannosaurus rex* as powerful as those of *Utahraptor?*

_____

10. Why is it **premature** to say for certain what brought an end to the dinosaurs?

_____

11. Did the dinosaurs die out over a long period of time?

_____

12. Why would a meteorite crashing into the earth affect the sunlight?

_____

13. Why do some scientists say a dinosaur may be the **ancestor** of birds?

_____

14. How would you describe the eating habits of *Tyrannosaurus rex* and *Utahraptor?*

_____

15. Why would other creatures probably try to avoid *Utahraptor?*

_____

WORDLY WISE

A **carnivore** is a meat-eating animal, especially a mammal that hunts for its food. Certain plants that eat insects, such as the Venus's-flytrap, are also *carnivorous*. The word comes from the Latin word *carn,* which means "meat" or "flesh." *Chili con carne* is a Spanish phrase in which the word *carne* comes from the same Latin word; the phrase means "chili with meat."

Things that are hard, such as stone, iron, or bones, are slow to decay or wear away, and so they last a long time. The Romans saw how these two qualities, of being hard and lasting a long time, were related. The Latin words *durus* "hard," and *durare,* "to last a long time" show this connection and form the root of several English words. In addition to **duration,** there is *endure,* which means "to last a long time." In the United States, the separation of church and state is a concept that has *endured* for more than two centuries. *Durable* goods are items such as cars and refrigerators that are expected to last a long time.

The Latin phrase *puis ne* means "born afterward" and was applied to Roman children of noble birth who followed the first-born. Since Roman titles and property passed to the oldest, the other children, those who were *puis ne,* were considered to be less powerful. The phrase passed into English as our adjective **puny.**

Lesson 4

Word List
Study the definitions of the words below; then do the exercises for the lesson.

accurate
ak´ yər ət

adj. 1. Able to give a correct reading or measurement.
[This clock is so *accurate* that it gains less than one second a year.]
2. Without mistakes or errors in facts.
[In science class we make *accurate* drawings of the plants we study.]
accuracy *n.* Correctness, exactness.
[I question the *accuracy* of your report because others have described the accident quite differently.]

approximate
ə präk´ si mət

adj. Not exact, but close enough to be reasonably correct.
[My *approximate* weight is a hundred and ten pounds.]

course
kôrs

n. 1. The path over which something moves.
[The space shuttle is now on a *course* for the moon.]
2. A way of acting or behaving.
[Because it is raining so hard, our best *course* is to wait in the car until the storm ends.]
3. A subject or set of subjects to be studied.
[The high school science *course* includes several field trips.]

depart
dē pärt´

v. To leave; to go away from a place.
[The bus for Detroit *departs* at ten o'clock.]
departure *n.* The act of leaving.
[We were sad after the *departure* of our friends.]

despair
də spâr´

v. To lose hope.
[When neither the library nor the bookstore had it, I *despaired* of ever finding the book I wanted.]
n. A total lack of hope.
[The look of *despair* on their faces told me that the situation was worse than I had feared.]

destination
des tə nā´ shən

n. The place to which something or someone is going.
[Tell the clerk your *destination* when you buy your ticket.]

deteriorate
dē tir´ ē ər āt

v. To make or become worse.
[Smoking causes the lungs and heart to *deteriorate*.]

gale
gāl

n. 1. A very strong wind.
[Last night's *gale* tore several tiles off the roof.]
2. A loud outburst.
[We heard *gales* of laughter coming from the party.]

horizon
hər ī´ zən

n. The apparent line in the distance where the sky meets the sea or land.
[We watched the setting sun sink slowly over the *horizon*.]
horizontal *adj.* (hər i zänt´ l) Going straight across from side to side.
[The shoeboxes were in a *horizontal* row at the back of the closet.]

jubilation
jōō bə lā´ shən
n. A feeling or expression of great joy.
[The end of World War II brought *jubilation* to most of Europe.]
jubilant   *adj.*   (jōō´ bə lənt) Very happy.
[My family was *jubilant* when Aunt Jean survived the heart operation.]

navigate
nav´ ə gāt
v. To calculate or direct the movement of a ship or aircraft.
[Phoenician sailors *navigated* by measuring the position of the sun and stars.]
navigation   *n.* The science or practice of navigating.
[Clocks and sextants are instruments used in *navigation*.]

nostalgia
näs tal´ jə
n. A longing for a certain time in the past.
[Seeing the photographs of my first dog filled me with *nostalgia*.]
nostalgic   *adj.* Having feelings of nostalgia.
[I became *nostalgic* when I heard you playing the song my grandfather used to sing to me.]

revive
rē vīv´
v. 1. To make or become strong again.
[A short rest will *revive* you.]
2. To bring back into use or fashion.
[The show *revives* a number of songs from the fifties.]

sever
sev´ ər
v. 1. To break off.
[When the plane that crashed was proven to be on a spy mission, the two countries *severed* all ties with each other.]
2. To cut in two.
[Irving accidentally *severed* the garden hose while mowing the lawn.]

voyage
voi´ ij
n. A long journey by sea or in space.
[The *voyage* across the Pacific will take three weeks.]
v. To make a journey by sea or in space.
[Long before Columbus, the Vikings *voyaged* across the Atlantic Ocean to reach North America.]

4A Finding Meanings

Choose two phrases to form a sentence that correctly uses a word from Word List 4. Write each sentence in the space provided.

1. (a) get worse.
   (b) To deteriorate is to
   (c) To revive is to
   (d) feel slightly uneasy.

_____

2. (a) An accurate account is
   (b) one that is obscure.
   (c) A jubilant account is
   (d) one that is without errors.

_____

3. (a) make it strong again.
   (b) To sever a friendship is to
   (c) To revive a friendship is to
   (d) look back on it with fond memories.

_____

4. (a) A destination is   (c) a setting out from a place.
(b) A course is   (d) the path over which something moves.

5. (a) Something that is horizontal   (c) is falling into a state of disrepair.
(b) is not exact.   (d) Something that is approximate

6. (a) the act of leaving.   (c) A destination is
(b) A departure is   (d) a long journey by sea.

7. (a) a lack of understanding.   (c) Nostalgia is
(b) a feeling of longing for the past. (d) Despair is

8. (a) A voyage is   (c) a strong wind.
(b) a small boat.   (d) A gale is

9. (a) Jubilation is   (c) the directing of a ship's movement.
(b) Navigation is   (d) the length of time something lasts.

10. (a) To despair is to   (c) return to one's starting point.
(b) To voyage is to   (d) feel a sense of hopelessness.

4B Just the Right Word

Improve each of the following sentences by crossing out the italicized phrase and replacing it with a word (or a form of the word) from Word List 4.

1. The *loud outbursts* of laughter from the next room distracted me from my work.

2. I will be responsible for *working out the direction the boat should be headed* when we sail to Bali.

3. The *place to which it is going* is shown on the front of the bus.

4. We *start on our journey* at ten o'clock tomorrow morning.

5. The ship met with stormy weather during the *long journey by sea* around Cape Horn.

6. Early this morning the *apparent line where the sky and sea meet* was obscured by the fog.

7. When the driver told me that the bus ride to Boston would take two hours, my friend said that was *close enough to be almost correct*.

8. Each *set of subjects to be studied* takes one year to complete.

9. I *completely broke off* my relationship with the company when I got a new job.

10. Nina and her best friend were *filled with joy* when they were assigned to the same tent.

4C Applying Meanings

Circle the letter of each correct answer to the questions below. A question may have more than one correct answer.

1. Which of the following can *depart?*
   (a) a train
   (b) a ship
   (c) a guest
   (d) a noise

2. Which of the following could you *sever?*
   (a) a branch of a tree
   (b) a puff of smoke
   (c) a relationship
   (d) a finger

3. Which of the following could be a *destination?*
   (a) a town in the Midwest
   (b) a friendship
   (c) next Tuesday
   (d) Hollywood

4. Which of the following is a *course?*
   (a) the earth's path around the sun
   (b) taking a wait-and-see attitude
   (c) "Introduction to Science"
   (d) the start of a race

5. On which of the following might you *voyage?*
   (a) an ocean liner
   (b) the space shuttle
   (c) a rowboat
   (d) a helicopter

6. Which of the following might make a person feel *nostalgic?*
   (a) thinking about the past
   (b) making plans for the future
   (c) looking at old photographs
   (d) meeting an old friend

7. Which of the following can be *accurate?*
   (a) a clock   (c) a drawing
   (b) a statement   (d) a weather forecast

8. Which of the following can be *navigated?*
   (a) a space ship   (c) a train
   (b) an airplane   (d) a boat

4D Word Relationships

In each of the groups below, circle the two words that are antonyms.

1. DESPAIR   JUBILATION   5. HORIZONTAL   DEPARTED
   ACCURACY   EFFORT   PREPARED   UPRIGHT

2. NAVIGATE   IMPROVE   6. DISTRACT   NAVIGATE
   DETERIORATE   CUT   REVIVE   COLLAPSE

3. PRESERVE   JOIN   7. DEPART   VOYAGE
   VOYAGE   SEVER   ARRIVE   CULTIVATE

4. ACCURATE   WRONG
   NOSTALGIC   GRATEFUL

4E Narrative

Read the narrative below; then complete the exercise that follows.

A DIFFICULT JOURNEY

In England in the early seventeenth century, people were not free to worship as they pleased. This was a matter decided for them by the government, and those who did not like this could leave. So it was that on September 6, 1620, a sailing ship called the *Mayflower* **departed** from Plymouth, England, with a hundred and two passengers.

Many of those on board were leaving in order to be free to worship in their own way. Later, they were called Pilgrims, the name for people who make long journeys because of a deep religious faith. Others on the ship were simply hoping to make a new life for themselves in America. The passengers, however, did not want to **sever** all ties with England. They had to pay back the money they had borrowed to make this journey, and they intended to do this by trading with the old country.

The *Mayflower*'s **destination** was Virginia, where others from England had settled thirteen years before. But getting there was no simple matter. In those days, when sailors were out of sight of land, they **navigated** by measuring the position of the sun and stars. When the sun told them it was noon, the clocks on board gave a different time, depending on how far east or west they had traveled. The difference in time was used to calculate their position. But their clocks and other instruments were not very **accurate**, and when clouds obscured the sun or stars, figuring out where they were and in what direction they were headed was not easy.

For the first couple of weeks of the *Mayflower's* **voyage**, gentle breezes carried the ship along, and the passengers sat on deck and enjoyed the sunshine. Later on, however, the weather **deteriorated**. Strong **gales** rocked the *Mayflower* and made life miserable for the passengers; many people became sick. One person died and was buried at sea. A woman named Elizabeth Hopkins had a baby in mid-ocean and named the child Oceanus. Day after day, the Pilgrims stared at the **horizon**, hoping for the sight of land to **revive** their spirits. Day after day, all they saw was endless sea and sky. Many **despaired** of ever reaching America. Then at last, after sixty-five days, they saw land. That day there was great **jubilation** on board the *Mayflower*.

The Pilgrims soon discovered, however, that they had been blown far off their proper **course** by the strong winds in mid-Atlantic. Instead of landing in Virginia, they found themselves on Cape Cod, **approximately** five hundred miles to the north. For several weeks they explored the coast of Cape Cod Bay, looking for a place in which to settle. They had little time because the bitterly cold winter weather was almost upon them.

Finally, in late December, they discovered a suitable spot. The passengers went ashore to plan the new settlement and build houses. The place where they landed had been visited earlier by English explorers, and the name they had given it may have made some of the Pilgrims **nostalgic**. It was called Plymouth.

Answer each of the following questions in a sentence. If a question does not contain a vocabulary word, use a vocabulary word in your answer. Use each word only once. Questions and answers will then contain all fifteen words (or forms of the words) from this lesson's word list.

1. What option was open to people in England who wanted to practice their own religion?

   _____

2. What is the meaning of **sever** as it is used in the narrative?

   _____

3. How long did it take the *Mayflower* to get from England to Cape Cod?

   _____

4. Where did those on board the *Mayflower* intend to land?

_____

5. What is the meaning of **accurate** as it is used in the narrative?

_____

6. **Approximately,** how many passengers were there on the *Mayflower?*

_____

7. When did the weather start to get worse?

_____

8. When might it have been dangerous for passengers to go on deck?

_____

9. Why did many passengers **despair** of reaching America?

_____

10. What problem would cloudy skies cause for the crew of the *Mayflower?*

_____

11. Where did the passengers first see land?

_____

12. What is the meaning of **revive** as it is used in the narrative?

_____

13. How might the religious Pilgrims have expressed their **jubilation** at seeing land?

_____

14. Name some of the things that the Pilgrims might have felt **nostalgia** for.

_____

15. What **course** was open to the Pilgrims when they found themselves on Cape Cod instead of in Virginia?

_____

WORDLY WISE

Don't confuse **course**, a noun that has several meanings, with the adjective *coarse*, which means "rough to the touch; crude; not fine." These two words are homophones; they are pronounced the same but have different meanings and spellings.

Winds have different names, depending on the speed at which they blow. A *breeze* goes from 4 miles per hour (a light breeze) to 31 m.p.h. (a strong breeze). A **gale** has a wind speed of from 32 to 63 m.p.h. A *storm* is a wind blowing between 64 and 73 m.p.h. A *hurricane* has a wind speed of over 74 m.p.h.

Both **revive** and *survive* (Word List 3) come from the Latin word *vivus*, which means "living, alive."

HIDDEN MESSAGE

In the spaces provided to the right of each sentence, write the vocabulary words from Lessons 1 through 4 that are missing in each of the sentences below. Be sure the words you choose fit the meaning of each sentence and have the same number of letters as there are spaces. The number following each sentence gives the lesson from which the missing word comes. If the exercise is done correctly, the shaded boxes will spell out the answer to this riddle:

How can mail carriers tell how many letters there are in a mailbox without looking inside?

1. I don't let anything _____ me while I'm working. (1)

2. A(n) _____ of mine fought in the Civil War. (3)

3. Cats _____ on mice, chipmunks, and birds. (3)

4. The bus's _____ was New York City. (4)

5. The dog looks _____, but it's quite harmless. (3)

6. Your eyes will soon _____ themselves to the dark. (1)

7. My parents hope to _____ a new car this year. (2)

8. The tires on the earth mover were _____. (3)

9. We have no other _____ but to continue. (3)

10. The _____ was admitted to the hospital this morning. (1)

11. A(n) _____ dog does not have to be told twice. (1)

12. If I _____ this storm, I'm never going sailing again. (3)

13. Last night's _____ blew several tiles off the roof. (4)

14. My _____ on the trip was an old school friend. (1)

15. The speck on the _____ turned out to be an island. (4)

16. I refused to _____ when told to give up my seat. (1)

17. A drink and a short rest will soon _____ us. (4)

18. Give me the _____ day of your arrival. (4)

19. The director will _____ you to your new section. (1)

20. Those trees _____ the view of the lake. (3)

21. Are you and your roommate _____? (1)

22. A large _____ of grapes hung from the vine. (2)

23. The _____ from Seattle to Sidney took a month. (4)

24. A single blow from an axe will _____ the rope. (4)

25. You can _____ mushrooms in any dark, damp place. (2)

26. We will _____ by the stars on our ocean crossing. (4)

27. I felt a sudden wave of _____ for the good old days. (4)

28. A driver needs to be _____ at all times. (1)

29. Do you _____ the meaning of the message? (3)

30. I plan to _____ early as I have to be up at six. (1)

31. Candy canes are very _____, so don't drop any. (2)

32. The _____ we had to follow was laid out for us. (4)

33. I went up and said, "Allow me to _____ myself." (2)

34. You can _____ peaches by canning them. (3)

35. The tiger is a(n) _____ and eats only meat. (3)

36. I'm trying to cut down on the fats that I _____. (2)

37. The Rockies were a(n) _____ to those heading west. (1)

38. The _____ of popcorn made our mouths water. (2)

39. What is the _____ of a dollar in Mexican money? (2)

40. Leather will _____ if it is not properly cared for. (4)

41. I felt someone in the crowd _____ me. (1)

42. Two _____ men piled the wood in the truck. (1)

43. Sam cannot understand the _____ of a budget. (1)

44. We _____ grain to many countries. (2)

Lesson 5

Word List

Study the definitions of the words below; then do the exercises for the lesson.

avalanche
av´ ə lanch

n. 1. A great mass of ice, earth, or snow mixed with rocks sliding down a mountain.
[The mountain climbers had a narrow escape when the *avalanche* swept over them.]
2. A great amount of something.
[Our company had an *avalanche* of orders after we used a television ad for our new game.]

blizzard
bliz´ ərd

n. A heavy snowstorm with strong winds.
[The Chicago airport had to close for two days because of the *blizzard*.]

challenge
chal´ ənj

v. 1. To invite others to take part in a contest.
[I *challenged* my friend to a game of chess.]
2. To cause a person to use a lot of skill or effort.
[This trail *challenges* even the best skiers.]
3. To question or to argue against, especially when something is unfair or unjust.
[Many doctors *challenge* the tobacco companies' claim that cigarette smoking is harmless.]

n. 1. An interesting task or problem; something that takes skill or effort.
[Living out of our backpacks for a week on the mountain was a real *challenge*.]
2. A call to take part in a contest.
[I accepted the *challenge* to run in the marathon.]

conquer
käŋ´ kər

v. 1. To get the better of.
[Swimming lessons at the YMCA helped me to *conquer* my fear of the water.]
2. To defeat.
[Hannibal's army *conquered* part of Spain in 219 B.C.]
conquest *n.* The act of defeating.
[The Norman *conquest* of England took place in 1066.]

crevice
krev´ is

n. A deep, narrow opening in rock caused by a split or crack.
[The *crevice* had filled with soil in which a cluster of small red flowers was growing.]

foolhardy
fool´ här dē

adj. Unwisely bold or daring.
[It would be *foolhardy* to go sailing during a gale.]

lure
loor

v. To tempt or attract with the promise of something good.
[In the early nineteenth century, the hope of owning land of their own *lured* many people to travel west to Ohio and Indiana.]
n. 1. Something that attracts.
[The *lure* of the sea led us to take up sailing.]
2. Artificial bait used for fishing.
[A large striped bass took the *lure,* and I hooked it.]

makeshift
māk´ shift

n. A temporary and usually less strong replacement.
[They used the trailer as a *makeshift* while their house was being rebuilt.]
adj. Used as a temporary replacement.
[We use the sofa as a *makeshift* bed when we have overnight guests.]

optimist
äp´ tə mist

n. One who looks at things in the most positive way; a cheerful, hopeful person.
[Pat and Jean are *optimists* and so, of course, they believed the plane would not leave without us.]
optimistic *adj.* Cheerful; hopeful.
[In spite of the injuries to our best players, I am *optimistic* about our chances of winning the big game.]
optimism *n.* A feeling of hope or cheerfulness.
[The patients' *optimism* helped them recover more quickly from their illnesses.]

previous
prē´ vē əs

adj. Earlier; happening before.
[Although I missed the last meeting, I attended the two *previous* ones.]

route
rōōt

n. 1. The path that must be followed to get to a place.
[Our *route* to Seattle takes us through Denver.]
2. A fixed course or area assigned to a sales or delivery person.
[Magali has over a hundred customers on her newspaper *route*.]

summit
sum´ it

n. 1. The highest part; the top.
[It took us three hours to climb to the *summit* of Mount Washington.]
2. A conference or meeting of the top leaders of governments.
[The *summit* of African heads of state will take place in Nairobi in late June.]

terse
tʉrs

adj. Short and to the point.
[When I said I was sure we would be rescued soon, my friend's *terse* reply was, "How?"]

thwart
thwôrt

v. To block or defeat the plans or efforts of.
[Heavy fighting *thwarted* the UN's attempts to deliver food.]

vertical
vʉrt´ i kəl

adj. Running straight up and down; upright.
[The black *vertical* lines in this painting are what one notices first.]

5A Finding Meanings

Choose two phrases to form a sentence that correctly uses a word from Word List 5. Write each sentence in the space provided.

1. (a) the way to reach the top.
   (b) a meeting of heads of state.
   (c) A lure is
   (d) A summit is

   _____

2. (a) An optimistic statement is one
   (b) that is released to the public.
   (c) A previous statement is one
   (d) that was made earlier.

   _____

3. (a) To lure someone is
   (b) To thwart someone is
   (c) to offer help or advice to that person.
   (d) to tempt that person with promises.

   _____

4. (a) an area assigned to a salesperson.   (c) a payment for something done.
   (b) A crevice is   (d) A route is

5. (a) To be thwarted is to be   (c) prevented from carrying out one's plans.
   (b) To be challenged is to be   (d) attracted by promises.

6. (a) An optimistic report is one   (c) that is written out.
   (b) that is hopeful.   (d) A terse report is one

7. (a) a call to take part in a contest.   (c) A challenge is
   (b) a severe snowstorm with high winds.   (d) An avalanche is

8. (a) A makeshift file is one that   (c) stores things upright.
   (b) A vertical file is one that   (d) gets narrower toward the top.

9. (a) A foolhardy remark is one   (c) that sounds threatening.
   (b) that is short and to the point.   (d) A terse remark is one

10. (a) a split or crack in rock.   (c) A blizzard is
    (b) a mass of falling rocks and snow.   (d) An avalanche is

5B Just the Right Word

Improve each of the following sentences by crossing out the italicized phrase and replacing it with a word (or a form of the word) from Word List 5.

1. Your *daring but unwise* leap off the boat almost cost you your life.

2. What kind of *artificial bait* is best for catching bluefish?

3. Being appointed chairman of the Joint Chiefs of Staff was the *highest point* of General Colin Powell's military career.

4. According to the radio, we can expect a *severe snowstorm with very strong winds* tonight.

5. I'm driving to Yellowstone this summer and wonder which would be the best *way to get there.*

6. The German army's *defeat of the armed forces* of France in 1940 took less than four weeks.

7. A *deep, narrow opening made by a split in the rock* provided a toehold for the climbers making their way up the cliff face.

8. Swimming across the lake will be quite a *difficult task requiring great skill and effort.*

9. What is the reason for Gail's *feeling that all will go well?*

10. Bruno didn't have a pillow, so he used a rolled-up coat as a *temporary replacement for one* and slept quite soundly.

5C Applying Meanings

Circle the letter of each correct answer to the questions below. A question may have more than one correct answer.

1. Which of the following might an *optimist* say?
   (a) "Things could be a lot worse!"   (c) "What's the use!"
   (b) "Don't count your chickens."   (d) "I know we can do it."

2. Which of the following might be a *lure* to a person?
   (a) the Broadway stage   (c) an ocean voyage
   (b) the presidency   (d) a tropical island

3. Which of the following might *challenge* a person?
   (a) competing in the Olympics   (c) driving a car
   (b) watching a TV show   (d) reading a book

4. Of which of the following could there be an *avalanche?*
   (a) letters   (c) gales
   (b) orders   (d) requests

5. Which of the following would you expect to be *vertical?*
   (a) a sleeping person   (c) the horizon
   (b) a front door   (d) a stairway

6. Which of the following might *thwart* someone?
   (a) support from a friend   (c) a flat tire
   (b) a sudden change in the weather   (d) lack of money

7. Which of the following is *foolhardy?*
   (a) skating on thin ice   (c) losing your wallet
   (b) riding without a seat belt   (d) smoking cigarettes

8. Which of the following can be *terse?*
   (a) a comment   (c) a phone conversation
   (b) muscles   (d) an aroma

5D Word Relationships

In each of the groups below, circle the two words that are synonyms.

1. AVALANCHE   BLIZZARD   6. CRACK   ROUTE
   SNOWSTORM   GALE   CREVICE   BAIT

2. SUMMIT   LURE   7. ASSIST   CHALLENGE
   TOP   PATH   QUESTION   CONQUER

3. FOOLHARDY   MAKESHIFT   8. OPTIMIST   RETURN
   GIGANTIC   TEMPORARY   PATH   ROUTE

4. THWART   TEMPT   9. DESPAIR   DEFEAT
   LURE   BOTHER   DISTRACT   CONQUER

5. EARLIER   ACCURATE   10. OPTIMISTIC TERSE
   VERTICAL   PREVIOUS   HOPEFUL   FEARFUL

5E Narrative

Read the narrative below; then complete the exercise that follows.

ON TOP OF THE WORLD

The world's greatest climbers have always been drawn to Mount Everest, but in trying to climb it, many have been **lured** to their deaths. Located on the border of two Asian countries, Nepal and Tibet, Everest is part of the Himalayan mountain chain north of India. It is just over twenty-nine thousand feet high. Other mountains are more difficult to climb and offer a greater **challenge,** but because it is the world's highest mountain, Everest has a special place in our imaginations.

Every attempt to reach the top requires careful planning and can cost over a quarter of a million dollars. Often climbers hire Nepalese guides called Sherpas, who are skilled and experienced mountaineers. Together they work out the **route** to take and set up camps along the way.

Because the air is so thin near the top, climbers need to bring oxygen with them, adding greatly to the weight that must be carried. In recent years, small groups of climbers have made attempts on Everest without oxygen and without relying on Sherpas. Their daring method has been to travel fast and light and to stay in temporary shelters as they make their way up and down.

Where the mountain rises **vertically**, climbers drive spikes into **crevices** in the rock and pull each other up with ropes. They must be very careful because a loose stone or even a loud noise can start an **avalanche**, burying those who are caught in its path or sweeping them to their deaths. In addition, climbers must be alert to the weather because it can change suddenly for the worse. **Blizzards** often strike with little warning, forcing climbers to scramble for **makeshift** shelter until the danger has passed.

The first people to reach the top of Mount Everest were Edmund Hillary of New Zealand and Tenzing Norgay, his Sherpa guide, in 1953. Teams of mountaineers had made at least eight **previous** tries; but all of them had been **thwarted** in their attempts to stand on the highest spot on earth, some by bad planning, some by bad weather, some by bad luck. The first woman to **conquer** Mount Everest was Junko Tabei, of Japan, in 1975; the first American woman to do so was Stacy Allison, in 1988.

Mountaineers are by nature **optimists**. They want to believe they will be able to reach the top. At times, however, if either their physical condition or the weather is deteriorating, they are forced to ask themselves if it would be **foolhardy** to continue. Their state of mind plays a big part in this decision, which must sometimes be made when they are only a few hundred feet from the **summit**. Many have chosen to continue, a decision that cost them their lives.

By 2001, just under fifteen hundred people had succeeded in climbing to the top of Mount Everest, but almost a hundred and fifty had died in the attempt. Why do it if it is so difficult and so dangerous? Someone once put this question to the English climber George Mallory, who made several unsuccessful tries to climb Mount Everest and died there with less than six hundred feet to go, in 1924, on what became his last attempt. He gave the **terse** reply, "Because it's there."

Answer each of the following questions in a sentence. If a question does not contain a vocabulary word, use a vocabulary word in your answer. Use each word only once. Questions and answers will then contain all fifteen words (or forms of the words) from this lesson's word list.

1. What would you think of someone who planned to climb Mt. Everest alone?

   _____

2. What is the meaning of **challenge** as it is used in the narrative?

   _____

3. Why would it be unwise to fire a gun while high up on Mount Everest?

   _____

4. Why would you expect conversations between climbers to be **terse**?

   _____

5. Why do climbers watch the weather carefully?

   _____

6. What weather conditions would make a mountain climber **optimistic**?

   _____

7. How are **crevices** useful to climbers?

   _____

8. What is the meaning of **route** as it is used in the narrative?

   _____

9. What should people do if caught in bad weather while climbing a mountain?

   _____

10. When do climbers need to use ropes?

    _____

11. What would happen to a team of climbers who couldn't raise enough money for an attempt on Mount Everest?

    _____

12. How did George Mallory explain the **lure** of Mount Everest?

_____

13. Why would Mallory have been familiar with Everest on his last climb?

_____

14. How do you suppose climbers know when they have reached the **summit**?

_____

15. Why would climbers feel jubilant while standing on the top of Everest?

_____

WORDLY WISE

Until 1881, a **blizzard** was a loud noise or blast. In that year the *New York Nation* said: "The hard weather has called into use a word which promises to become a national Americanism, namely *blizzard*. It [is the word for] a storm of snow and wind which we cannot resist away from shelter." That is how the word came to have its present meaning. To be called a blizzard, a storm must have winds above forty miles an hour, a temperature close to zero, and lots of fine snow.

The antonym of **optimist** is *pessimist*. Imagine two people looking at a glass of water. The *optimist* thinks the glass is half full; the *pessimist* thinks it is half empty.

Route is sometimes pronounced *ROOT* and sometimes *ROWT*; both are correct. Don't confuse this word with *rout* (pronounced *ROWT*), which means "a total and complete defeat."

♦ ♦ ♦ ♦ ♦ ♦ ♦

Vertical and *horizontal* (Word List 4) are antonyms. In a crossword puzzle the *horizontal* answers must fit perfectly with the *vertical* answers.

Lesson 6

Word List
Study the definitions of the words below; then do the exercises for the lesson.

abolish
ə bäl´ ish
v. To bring to an end; to do away with.
[Most people would support a plan to *abolish* weapons of mass destruction.]

agony
ag´ ə nē
n. Great pain of mind or body; suffering.
[The pinched nerve caused him *agony* for several weeks.]
agonizing *adj.* (ag´ ə nīz iŋ) Very painful.
[Watching their sick child in the hospital bed was *agonizing* to the parents.]

catapult
kat´ ə pult
n. A machine used in ancient wars that threw objects with great force.
[Roman *catapults* could throw six-pound objects almost a third of a mile.]
v. To move or be moved suddenly and with great force, as if by a catapult.
[The Groaners' latest song *catapulted* them to the top of the country music charts.]

character
kər´ ək tər
n. 1. The qualities that make a person or place different or special.
[Your friend's support during your long illness demonstrates her true *character*.]
2. A person in a story, movie, or play.
[Madame Defarge and Sydney Carton are the two *characters* I remember most clearly from *A Tale of Two Cities*.]
3. A letter or symbol used in writing or printing.
[The license plate number NKT605 contains six *characters*.]

denounce
dē nouns´
v. 1. To speak out against something; to criticize.
[The president *denounced* Congress for failing to approve the budget.]
2. To accuse someone of doing wrong.
[Carla *denounced* Victor, who sat next to her, for cheating on the test.]

escalate
es´ kə lāt
v. To go up or increase in size or scope.
[House prices *escalated* so much in the 1980s that many people could no longer afford to buy a home.]

grim
grim
adj. 1. Cruel; fierce.
[There were many *grim* battles during the Civil War.]
2. Unfriendly or threatening; stern.
[The coach's *grim* face expressed his displeasure at our team's poor performance.]
3. Unpleasant; disturbing.
[We heard the *grim* news that no one had survived the plane crash.]

harbor
här´ bər
n. A protected place along a seacoast where ships can find shelter.
[In the summer the *harbor* is busy with sailboats going in and out.]
v. 1. To give shelter to; to take care of by hiding.
[In most states, it is a crime to *harbor* someone wanted by the police.]
2. To hold and nourish a thought or feeling in the mind.
[Try not to *harbor* anger against the person who stole your bike.]

inflict
in flikt´
v. To cause something painful to be felt.
[The hurricane *inflicted* severe damage on coastal areas.]

loathe lōth	*v.* To hate or dislike greatly. [Mahatma Gandhi, the great Indian leader, *loathed* violence.] **loathing** *n.* A feeling of hatred. [Their *loathing* of cruelty to animals led them to set up a shelter for unwanted pets.]
meddle med´əl	*v.* To involve oneself in other people's affairs without being asked. [When my grandparents retired, they could have *meddled* in my parents' lives, but they didn't.] **meddlesome** *adj.* Given to taking part in others' affairs without being asked. [If you think I am being *meddlesome,* just tell me to mind my own business.]
monstrous män´strəs	*adj.* 1. Causing shock; horrible; wicked. [Hitler's *monstrous* plan to murder the Jews of Europe was carried out in concentration camps in Germany and Poland.] 2. Extremely large. [A *monstrous* statue of the Soviet leader Joseph Stalin, three times life-size, stood in the town square.]
rouse rouz	*v.* 1. To awaken, to wake up. [The children were sleeping so soundly that it was difficult to *rouse* them.] 2. To stir up; to excite. [Martin Luther King, Jr., *roused* the American people with his 1963 speech at the Lincoln Memorial, in Washington, D.C.]
steadfast sted´fast	*adj.* Unchanging; steady; loyal. [Rigo and Moni remained *steadfast* friends throughout their school years.]
translate trans lāt´	*v.* To put into a different language. [*The Little Prince,* which was written in French, was *translated* into English by Katherine Woods.]

6A Finding Meanings

Choose two phrases to form a sentence that correctly uses a word from Word List 6. Write each sentence in the space provided.

1. (a) involve oneself in the affairs of others.
   (b) hold certain thoughts in the mind.
   (c) To translate is to
   (d) To meddle is to

_____

2. (a) A harbor is something that
   (b) is expressed in another language.
   (c) hurls objects with great force.
   (d) A catapult is something that

_____

3. (a) feels resentment against others.
   (b) is not easily changed by others.
   (c) A monstrous person is one who
   (d) A steadfast person is one who

_____

4. (a) To loathe something is to   (c) express it in a different language.
   (b) To translate something is to   (d) present it for the first time.

5. (a) one that is very wicked.   (c) one that keeps getting put off.
   (b) An agonizing decision is   (d) A monstrous decision is

6. (a) a protected place for boats.   (c) A harbor is
   (b) anything that shocks or horrifies. (d) A character is

7. (a) To rouse someone is to   (c) wake up that person.
   (b) say that person's name out loud. (d) To denounce someone is to

8. (a) a person's special qualities.   (c) deliberate rudeness.
   (b) Character is   (d) Agony is

9. (a) find its causes.   (c) say that it is wrong.
   (b) To denounce a quarrel is to   (d) To escalate a quarrel is to

10. (a) To loathe something is to   (c) To abolish something is to
    (b) have an understanding of it.   (d) feel hatred for it.

6B Just the Right Word

Improve each of the following sentences by crossing out the italicized phrase and replacing it with a word (or a form of the word) from Word List 6.

1. Overnight, someone had put up a *gigantic and very unattractive* billboard across the street.

2. Americans in 1776 were *stirred into action* by Thomas Paine's writings.

3. I was in *very great pain* after I fell and twisted my ankle.

4. The school *did away with* the rules that prevented girls from playing on the baseball team.

5. Ida still *holds on to feelings of* mistrust toward Fern who made promises she knew she could not keep.

6. The *people written about* in Judy Blume's books seem like real people to me.

7. The burned-out buildings were a *disturbing and unpleasant* sign that the city had been under attack.

8. The quarrel between us *became more and more serious,* until we no longer spoke to each other.

9. The Beatles were *suddenly lifted* to world fame in the early 1960s.

10. The 1994 earthquake *was the cause of* heavy damage throughout much of Los Angeles.

6C Applying Meanings

Circle the letter of each correct answer to the questions below. A question may have more than one correct answer.

1. Which of the following might be *denounced?*
   (a) a plane's arrival
   (b) a scoundrel
   (c) an act of cruelty
   (d) a bad law

2. Which of the following can be *harbored?*
   (a) anger
   (b) a car
   (c) a runaway child
   (d) hatred

3. Which of the following can be *abolished?*
   (a) a rule
   (b) an idea
   (c) a law
   (d) a custom

4. Which of the following might *meddlesome* persons do?
   (a) keep to themselves
   (b) offer advice freely
   (c) ask a lot of questions
   (d) mind their own business

5. Which of the following can be *translated?*
   (a) paintings
   (b) music
   (c) books
   (d) laughter

6. Which of the following is a *character?*
   (a) Snow White
   (b) &
   (c) 9
   (d) optimism

7. Which of the following can be *grim?*
   (a) news   (c) weather
   (b) jubilation   (d) vegetables

8. Which of the following could be *agonizing?*
   (a) a bad toothache   (c) a persistent cold
   (b) the death of a friend   (d) a distraction

6D Word Relationships

In each of the groups below, circle the two words that are antonyms.

1. OPTIMISM   LOVE   6. PLEASANT   STEADFAST
   DISTRACTION   LOATHING   GRIM   ACCURATE

2. SUPPORT   DENOUNCE   7. BUDGE   TRANSLATE
   CATAPULT   ADJUST   ABOLISH   INTRODUCE

3. CHALLENGE   REDUCE   8. UNRELIABLE   STEADFAST
   ESCALATE   ROUSE   MEDDLESOME   ANGRY

4. STEADFAST   ATTRACTIVE   9. INFLICT   CALM
   MONSTROUS   DETERMINED   DISLIKE   ROUSE

5. OBEDIENCE   AGONY   10. FOOLHARDY   MEDDLESOME
   CHARACTER   JUBILATION   OBSCURE   SHY

6E Narrative

Read the narrative below; then complete the exercise that follows.

THE PEN *IS* MIGHTIER THAN THE SWORD

In the early nineteenth century, a number of Americans supported slavery, a practice that had been widely accepted since ancient times. Even people who **loathed** slavery, and there were a great many, thought that there was little that one person could do about it. They were wrong. Harriet Beecher Stowe, who was born in Litchfield, Connecticut, in 1811, was someone who caused important changes. She believed that slavery was a **monstrous** crime. While living in Ohio in the 1840s, she used her house to **harbor** slaves who had escaped from their southern owners and were making their way north to freedom. In 1850, after moving to Maine with her minister husband, she wrote a novel called *Uncle Tom's Cabin,* which not only awakened people to the horrors of slavery but also **catapulted** her to world fame.

Her book painted a **grim** picture of slave life. Readers shared the **agony** that the slave mother Eliza felt when she accidentally overheard that her only child was to be sold to a slave trader. They eagerly followed Eliza's adventures after she escaped with her child, crossing the half-frozen Ohio River by jumping from one broken piece of ice to the next, with armed men and yelping dogs close behind. They breathed a sigh of relief when Eliza and her child reached Canada and freedom.

Another **character** in the book is the wise and kindly slave, Uncle Tom. He was sold to Simon Legree, a man who took pleasure in **inflicting** severe punishment on his slaves. When Legree ordered Uncle Tom to give a whipping to a sick and weak female slave who had failed to pick enough cotton, Tom refused. So Legree had him whipped instead. Later, when Uncle Tom **steadfastly** refused to tell Legree where two of his runaway slaves were hiding, Legree had him beaten so severely that he died. Readers wept.

Uncle Tom's Cabin sold millions of copies and was **translated** into many different languages. It was also made into a play that was performed all over the world. The book helped **rouse** the people of America, especially those in the North, into demanding an end to slavery. Of course, not everyone looked with favor on *Uncle Tom's Cabin.* It was banned in the South, and slave owners and their supporters accused Harriet Beecher Stowe of **meddling** in their lives. She ignored their protests and continued to **denounce** slavery in speeches, articles, and books.

The quarrel between North and South over the question of slavery **escalated.** In 1863, in the middle of the Civil War, President Abraham Lincoln signed an order **abolishing** slavery in states then under Confederate control. Harriet Beecher Stowe's novel played no small part in bringing about the war that ended slavery. Her life shows that just one determined person can make a difference.

Answer each of the following questions in a sentence. If a question does not contain a vocabulary word, use a vocabulary word in your answer. Use each word only once. Questions and answers will then contain all fifteen words (or forms of the words) from this lesson's word list.

1. What differing views did Americans have of slavery?

   _____

2. What happened to the quarrel between North and South over slavery?

   _____

3. What event occurred thirteen years after *Uncle Tom's Cabin* was written?

   _____

4. Why did Harriet Beecher Stowe suddenly become famous?

_____

5. Which act described in the narrative do you think is the most **monstrous**?

_____

6. Why were some people who didn't know English able to read *Uncle Tom's Cabin?*

_____

7. Why is it inaccurate to describe Harriet Beecher Stowe as **meddlesome**?

_____

8. How did Harriet Beecher Stowe stand up to the supporters of slavery?

_____

9. What is the meaning of **character** as it is used in the narrative?

_____

10. Why do you think Harriet Beecher Stowe wrote *Uncle Tom's Cabin?*

_____

11. What is the meaning of **harbor** as it is used in the narrative?

_____

12. How would you say Eliza's **agony** differed from Uncle Tom's?

_____

13. What is it about Simon Legree that makes him so unpleasant?

_____

14. How did Uncle Tom answer when Simon Legree demanded to know where the runaway slaves were hiding?

_____

15. What is the meaning of **grim** as it is used in the narrative?

_____

WORDLY WISE

Two nouns are formed from the verb **abolish.** *Abolition* is the act of abolishing or the state of being abolished. (It took a terrible civil war to bring about the *abolition* of slavery in America.) An *abolitionist* is a person who worked to bring about an end to slavery. (William Lloyd Garrison was a famous *abolitionist* who, for thirty-five years, fought to end slavery in America.)

◆ ◆ ◆ ◆ ◆ ◆

Don't confuse the verb **loathe** (with a final -*e*) with the adjective *loath* (without the final -*e*) which means "unwilling." (We were having such a good time that we were *loath* to leave.) The *th* sound in *loathe* is pronounced as in *then*; the *th* sound in *loath* is pronounced as in *thin*.

◆ ◆ ◆ ◆ ◆ ◆

The homophones **meddle** and *medal* sound alike but have different meanings and spellings. A medal is a small, flat piece of metal given as an honor or to reward bravery.

◆ ◆ ◆ ◆ ◆ ◆

The Latin prefix *trans-* means "across" and helps to form many English words. A *transatlantic* voyage is one made across the Atlantic Ocean. A radio or television tower *transmits* signals across the land to be picked up by radio and television sets.

The Latin root *latus* means "to carry" or "to move." It combines with the prefix *trans-* to form **translate.** To translate something is to "move it across" from one language to another.

Lesson 7

Word List

Study the definitions of the words below; then do the exercises for the lesson.

colony
käl´ ə nē

n. 1. A group of people, animals, or plants living close together.
[We found a *colony* of ants in the yard.]
2. A group of people who settle in a new land and have legal ties to the country they came from.
[English people formed a *colony* at Jamestown, Virginia, in 1607.]

compensate
käm´ pən sāt

v. 1. To make up for, to be equivalent to.
[My parents gave me another bike to *compensate* for the one that was stolen.]
2. To pay for.
[Our student council voted to *compensate* the police officer who spoke to our school about illegal drugs.]
compensation *n.* Payment or whatever is given or done to make up for something.
[The pedestrian received ten thousand dollars *compensation* for injuries she suffered when struck by the car.]

deposit
dē päz´ it

v. 1. To lay down.
[The hikers *deposited* their backpacks on the porch.]
2. To put money into a bank account or to give as partial payment.
[Sign your name on the back before you *deposit* the check.]
n. 1. Something laid down.
[The flood left a *deposit* of stones on the river banks.]
2. Money put into a bank account or given as partial payment.
[For a $20 *deposit*, the store will hold the skis.]

fascinate
fas´ ə nāt

v. To attract; to strongly hold the interest of.
[The circus clowns *fascinated* the children in the audience.]
fascinating *adj.* Extremely interesting.
[The museum has a *fascinating* display of Native American crafts.]

feeble
fē´ bəl

adj. 1. Having little strength, weak.
[Lions prey on the most *feeble* zebras in the herd.]
2. Not very believable or satisfying.
[Henry gave the teacher a *feeble* explanation for being late to class: his watch was broken.]

formal
fôr´ məl

adj. 1. Following rules or customs, often in an exact and proper way.
[After the summit meeting, the president gave a *formal* dinner at the White House.]
2. Suitable for events where strict standards of dress and behavior are expected.
[Men's *formal* dress for the evening is white tie and tails.]

frigid
frij´ id

adj. 1. Very cold.
[The morning air was so *frigid* that Sue's car would not start.]
2. Lacking a warm manner; unfriendly.
[The *frigid* greeting we received made it clear that we were not welcome.]

52

harsh
härsh

adj. 1. Rough and unpleasant to the senses.
[In a *harsh* tone of voice, the farmer ordered us to stay away from the cows.]
2. Causing pain; cruel.
[Twelve months in jail was a *harsh* sentence for shoplifting.]
3. Not suitable for living things; extremely uncomfortable.
[Northern Canada's *harsh* climate keeps people from settling there.]

huddle
hud´ əl

v. 1. To crowd together.
[When the downpour began, we all *huddled* under one umbrella.]
2. To curl one's limbs up close to one's body.
[During their first night at Mrs. Brisket's school, Bonnie and Sylvia *huddled* under their thin blankets to keep warm.]
n. A closely packed group.
[The players went into a *huddle* to plan the next play.]

remote
rē mōt´

adj. 1. Far away in time or space.
[The scientists' route took them through a *remote* region of the Amazon rain forest.]
2. Slight or faint.
[There was only a *remote* chance of reaching our destination on time.]
3. Controlled indirectly or from a distance.
[Our garage doors are opened by *remote* control.]
4. Distant in manner.
[The hotel clerk seemed very *remote* and hardly looked at us when we asked for directions.]

resemble
rē zem´ bəl

v. To be like or similar to.
[The markings on the wings of the io moth *resemble* the eyes of a small animal and help to protect it.]

rigid
rij´ id

adj. 1. Stiff and unbending; not flexible.
[The frozen rope was as *rigid* as a stick.]
2. Strict; not easily changed.
[This school has a *rigid* rule that the police will be informed of any student found with a weapon.]

solitary
säl´ ə ter ē

adj. 1. Being alone; lacking the company of others.
[In the nineteenth century, lighthouse keepers often led *solitary* lives.]
2. Being the only one.
[A *solitary* elm grew in the middle of the field.]

substantial
səb stan´ shəl

adj. 1. Strong; solid.
[The chair is not *substantial* enough to support the weight of such a heavy person.]
2. Great in value or size.
[I received a *substantial* pay increase after just one year on the job.]

waddle
wäd´ əl

v. To walk with short steps, swaying from side to side.
[The duck left the pond and *waddled* toward us.]
n. An awkward, clumsy walk.
[The baby smiled excitedly as he ended his *waddle* across the room.]

7A Finding Meanings

Choose two phrases to form a sentence that correctly uses a word from Word List 7. Write each sentence in the space provided.

1. (a) that is operated from a distance.
   (b) that is easy to operate.
   (c) A rigid control is one
   (d) A remote control is one

   _____

2. (a) To waddle is to
   (b) To huddle is to
   (c) hold a person's interest or attention.
   (d) curl one's limbs up close to one's body.

   _____

3. (a) A deposit is
   (b) A colony is
   (c) a group of creatures living close together.
   (d) a payment given to make up for a loss.

   _____

4. (a) To resemble someone
   (b) is to pay that person.
   (c) To compensate someone
   (d) is to apologize to that person.

   _____

5. (a) one that goes on too long.
   (b) A formal apology is
   (c) one that is difficult to believe.
   (d) A feeble apology is

   _____

6. (a) is not changed easily.
   (b) A rigid attitude is one that
   (c) A frigid attitude is one that
   (d) is no longer practiced.

   _____

7. (a) is unpleasantly rough.
   (b) A harsh reply is one that
   (c) is too late to be useful.
   (d) A formal reply is one that

   _____

8. (a) A fascinating place is one
   (b) that is in the tropics.
   (c) A frigid place is one
   (d) that is very interesting.

   _____

9. (a) that is open to the public.
   (b) A solitary building is one
   (c) A substantial building is one
   (d) that has no others close to it.

   _____

10. (a) money given as partial payment.   (c) a path that one follows.
    (b) A deposit is   (d) A waddle is

7B Just the Right Word

Improve each of the following sentences by crossing out the italicized phrase and replacing it with a word (or a form of the word) from Word List 7.

1. From a distance crocodiles *look almost the same as* alligators.

2. Sarita's wind-up toy *swayed from side to side as it took short steps* across the floor.

3. A life that is *lived apart from other people* need not be lonely as long as one has books to read.

4. A *very cold* mass of air from Canada caused this wintry weather.

5. The cast on your broken arm will keep it *in a fixed position and prevent it from bending.*

6. The most *strongly built* of the three pigs' houses was the one made of bricks.

7. These patients recovering from operations are so *lacking in strength* that they cannot walk.

8. Meetings with the emperor are very *carefully arranged so as to follow strict rules.*

9. In the *very distant* past all of the continents were joined together.

10. After skiing all day, we *crowded close together* around the fire to get warm.

7C Applying Meanings

Circle the letter of each correct answer to the questions below. A question may have more than one correct answer.

1. Which of the following can be *compensated?*
   (a) an injured person   (c) a person suffering a loss
   (b) a worker   (d) a victim of a crime

2. Which of the following might be *formal?*
   (a) a joke   (c) a request
   (b) a dance   (d) a bow

3. Which of the following might be *substantial?*
   (a) a meal   (c) a sum of money
   (b) the horizon   (d) a purchase

4. Which of the following can be found in *colonies?*
   (a) settlers   (c) ants
   (b) islands   (d) mountains

5. Which of the following can be *deposited?*
   (a) money in a bank   (c) answers on a test
   (b) eggs in a nest   (d) books on a table

6. Which of the following *resembles* a horse?
   (a) a zebra   (c) a mule
   (b) a giraffe   (d) a donkey

7. Which of the following moves with a *waddle?*
   (a) a snake   (c) a duck
   (b) a frog   (d) an ostrich

8. Which of the following can be *harsh?*
   (a) a climate   (c) a voice
   (b) a punishment   (d) a reward

7D Word Relationships

In each of the groups below, circle the two words that are synonyms.

1. FASCINATING   PUNY   5. REMOTE   LARGE
   BURLY   FEEBLE   SUBSTANTIAL   HARSH

2. PLACE   ABOLISH   6. TERSE   RIGID
   DEPOSIT   COMPENSATE   ALONE   SOLITARY

3. INTEREST   FASCINATE   7. DISTANT   COLONIAL
   QUICKEN   RESEMBLE   REMOTE   MONSTROUS

4. TROPICAL   UNFRIENDLY   8. VERTICAL   STIFF
   FRIGID   FORMAL   RIGID   COLD

7E Narrative   *Read the narrative below; then complete the exercise that follows.*

BIRDS IN TUXEDOES

What is a bird? A creature that flies, of course. And yet, penguins are birds, but they cannot fly. Their wings are too **feeble** to lift them off the ground. This was not always so. Scientists believe that penguins once flew just like other birds. At some time in the **remote** past, they migrated to Antarctica, the land that surrounds the South Pole. The ice sheet there is two miles thick in places, and the temperature varies between zero in summer and minus seventy degrees in winter. It is possible that penguins were the only creatures that could survive in such a **harsh** climate. Without enemies, they would have no need to use their wings, as other birds do, to escape attacks. Gradually, they would have lost the ability to fly.

Over many thousands of years, the wings of penguins became smaller and more **rigid**. To **compensate** for the loss, it seems, they became excellent swimmers. They use their wings as flippers, while their webbed feet help guide them through the water. They can dive to depths of seventy feet and often leap high out of the water for a breath of air. On land, they **waddle** awkwardly or slide along the ice on their stomachs, but under water they glide gracefully and effortlessly. Penguins spend a lot of time in the sea in a never-ending search for fish, lobsters, crabs, and shrimp, which make up a **substantial** part of their diet.

There are several different kinds of penguins. The smallest is no bigger than a duck, while the largest, called the Emperor penguin, is four feet tall and weighs up to ninety pounds. In addition to the shores of Antarctica, penguins make their homes farther north, on the coasts of South Africa, Australia, and New Zealand, or on the Pacific coast of South America.

Each year for several months, penguins come to land to make nests and lay their eggs. Along the shores of Antarctica, where no plants grow, the penguins gather stones for their nests. Females **deposit** the eggs, chalky white in color and usually no more than two, on the nest. Emperor penguins do not build nests. Instead, after an egg is laid, the male penguin holds it on his feet under a fold of stomach skin, which keeps the egg warm. The female Emperor penguin returns to the **frigid** waters to hunt for food for her family.

For two months, while the baby penguins develop in the eggs, the male Emperor penguins **huddle** close together in **colonies** of up to half a million birds so that they can keep warm. A **solitary** penguin would soon lose its body heat and die in the freezing cold of the long Antarctic night. When the baby penguins break out of the shells, they are unable to see and are quite helpless. For several months they have to be fed by their parents before they are ready to take to the water to find their own food.

On land penguins are unlikely to be mistaken for any other kind of bird. With black feathers covering their backs and snowy white feathers running up their fronts, they **resemble** very short men wearing **formal** dress. Their appearance, combined with the way they walk, makes them look slightly comical. Perhaps this explains in part why we humans find them such **fascinating** creatures.

Answer each of the following questions in a sentence. If a question does not contain a vocabulary word, use a vocabulary word in your answer. Use each word only once. Questions and answers will then contain all fifteen words (or forms of the words) from this lesson's word list.

1. Why are penguins a popular feature in aquariums and zoos?

   _____

2. What is the meaning of **deposit** as it is used in the narrative?

   _____

3. In what way do penguins not **resemble** other kinds of birds?

   _____

4. What strikes some people as comical about a penguin's appearance?

   _____

5. Why did penguins' wings become so **feeble**?

   _____

6. How would you describe the summer temperatures of Antarctica?

   _____

7. In what way does the narrative suggest that penguins were **compensated** for losing the ability to fly?

   _____

8. Where do penguins spend much of their time?

   _____

9. According to the narrative, were penguins ever able to fly?

   _____

10. What is the meaning of **rigid** as it is used in the narrative?

    _____

11. What details in the narrative illustrate the **harsh** climate of Antarctica?

    _____

12. Why do Emperor penguins gather in large **colonies**?

    _____

13. Describe the contrast between the way penguins move on land and in water.

    _____

14. What is the meaning of **huddle** as it is used in the narrative?

    _____

15. What would happen to a penguin that wandered off by itself while on land?

    _____

WORDLY WISE

The adjective formed from **colony** is *colonial*. (Virginia was one of the thirteen American *colonies* that declared their independence from British rule in 1776. The town of Williamsburg, Virginia, recreates life in *colonial* America.)

Note that *colony* can also refer to a group of people, especially artists and writers, who come together in a particular place. There they can meet and exchange ideas while working without distractions.

Remote and *distant* are synonyms. Both words mean "far off in distance or time." *Remote*, however, also suggests something cut off and out of the way. Tristan da Cunha, an island in the South Atlantic, and Tokyo, Japan, are each *distant* from New York. But Tokyo is not considered a *remote* city because it is easy to get to by plane. Tristan da Cunha, however, is thought of as a *remote* island because it is difficult to get to.

Solitary is formed from the Latin *solus*, which means "alone." Several other words are formed from the same Latin root. *Solitude* is "the quality or state of being alone." (Henry David Thoreau was seeking *solitude* when he lived alone in the woods near Walden Pond.) *Isolated* means "cut off from the company of others." (We felt *isolated* when the blizzard kept us inside for three days.) *Solitaire* is a card game for just one person.

Lesson 8

Word List

Study the definitions of the words below; then do the exercises for the lesson.

assemble
ə sem′ bəl

v. 1. To bring together into a group; to gather.
[At two o'clock we *assembled* at the door of the museum for a tour.]
2. To put or fit together.
[You need only a screwdriver to *assemble* the bookcase.]
assembly *n.* 1. A group of people gathered for a certain purpose.
[At the *assembly* this morning, the fire chief will talk to us about fire prevention.]
2. The fitting together of various parts.
[The *assembly* of the new gas grill took us less than an hour.]

banquet
baŋ′ kwət

n. A large meal for many people; a feast.
[Six courses were served at the *banquet*, which was given in honor of the teachers who were retiring.]

cargo
kär′ go

n. The load carried by a plane or ship.
[The *cargo* going to Chile was put into containers and loaded onto the boat.]

cask
kask

n. A barrel-shaped container, especially one for holding liquids.
[Wine was imported to colonial New England in large *casks*.]

celebrate
sel′ ə brāt

v. To honor something in a special way.
[Americans *celebrate* the signing of the Declaration of Independence every Fourth of July.]
celebrated *adj.* Famous.
[When Charles Dickens toured America, huge crowds turned out to hear the *celebrated* author.]

decrease
dē krēs′

v. To become smaller or less.
[After June 22 the length of the day gradually *decreases*.]
n. The amount by which something becomes smaller.
[An outbreak of flu caused a *decrease* in school attendance during January.]

desperate
des′ pər ət

adj. 1. Reckless because of feelings of despair.
[People on the upper floors of the burning building jumped from windows in a *desperate* attempt to escape.]
2. So serious as to be almost hopeless.
[The situation of the homeless in our big cities is becoming increasingly *desperate*.]

edible
ed′ ə bəl

adj. Safe or fit to be eaten.
[Are you certain those mushrooms are *edible*?]
n. An item of food; anything that can be eaten.
[We'll serve the beverages at this end of the table and the sandwiches and other *edibles* at the other end.]

frivolous
friv′ ə ləs

adj. Not serious or important; silly.
[Spending money on items like comic books seems *frivolous* to someone who has no money for food.]
frivolity *n.* (fri väl′ə tē) Silly or lighthearted play.
[The giggling children had to be reminded that *frivolity* has no place at a funeral.]

harvest
här´ vəst

n. 1. The gathering of ripe crops for a season.
[In Spain, the grape *harvest* begins in late summer.]
2. The quantity of crops gathered.
[Iowa's corn *harvest* is the largest in years.]
v. To gather in the crops.
[We usually *harvest* the first peas in April.]

hew
hyo͞o

v. 1. To chop down or cut with blows from an ax.
[Let's *hew* these dead branches from the tree before they fall and cause damage.]
2. To cut or shape with blows of an ax or similar tool.
[The Tlingit of the Northwest *hewed* totem poles from tree trunks.]

hostile
häs´ təl

adj. Unfriendly; of or like an enemy.
[The *hostile* audience would not permit the speaker to finish the speech.]
hostility *n.* The expression of unfriendly feelings.
[The governor's plan to close the neighborhood school met with so much *hostility* that it was quickly dropped.]

pledge
plej

v. To make a serious promise.
[A dozen local merchants have *pledged* their support for the new arts program.]
n. A serious promise.
[Before I was hired, I had to sign a *pledge* that I would not give away company secrets.]

prosper
präs´ pər

v. To succeed, especially in terms of money.
[Alaska *prospered* when oil was found there.]
prosperous *adj.* Enjoying growth and success.
[The *prosperous* 1920s ended with the stock market crash of 1929.]

task
task

n. A piece of work that needs to be done.
[Cutting our way through the underbrush was a difficult *task*.]

8A Finding Meanings

Choose two phrases to form a sentence that correctly uses a word from Word List 8. Write each sentence in the space provided.

1. (a) unsure of oneself.
   (b) reckless because of despair.
   (c) To be desperate is to be
   (d) To be prosperous is to be

_____

2. (a) To decrease aid is to
   (b) To pledge aid is to
   (c) abolish it.
   (d) promise it.

_____

3. (a) willingness to make enemies.
   (b) lighthearted play.
   (c) Prosperity is
   (d) Frivolity is

_____

4. (a) To hew something is to   (c) put it together.
   (b) shape it with an ax.   (d) To harvest something is to

_____

5. (a) A celebrated person   (c) is someone who is unfriendly.
   (b) is someone who is careless.   (d) A hostile person

_____

6. (a) A banquet is   (c) a piece of work to be done.
   (b) A task is   (d) payment for work done.

_____

7. (a) A celebrated object   (c) is one that is easily broken.
   (b) An edible object   (d) is one that is famous.

_____

8. (a) is to put it together.   (c) is to shape it by cutting.
   (b) To harvest something   (d) To assemble something

_____

9. (a) A cargo is   (c) the front of a ship.
   (b) A cask is   (d) a barrel used for holding liquids.

_____

10. (a) Banquets are   (c) things that can be eaten.
    (b) seats put around a table.   (d) Edibles are

_____

8B Just the Right Word

Improve each of the following sentences by crossing out the italicized phrase and replacing it with a word (or a form of the word) from Word List 8.

1. My cousin thinks television game shows are *silly and lighthearted* and fun to watch.

2. Our fruit stand is *enjoying a great deal of success* this year compared with previous years.

3. My piano teacher says that formal dress is required for the *large dinner at which many people will be served.*

4. Teachers and students *gathered together in a group* outside the building when the alert sounded.

5. The dock workers will unload the *goods carried by the ship* after the passengers go ashore.

6. In August and September all of us worked many hours to help with the *gathering in of the crops.*

7. A count of tourists coming to South Carolina beaches showed a *drop in their number* for the third year in a row.

8. The bright red berries of the yew tree are not *safe to eat.*

9. The situation of those who survived the earthquake was *so serious as to be almost hopeless.*

10. The *unfriendly feelings expressed* at the meeting made me decide to leave early.

8C Applying Meanings

Circle the letter of each correct answer to the questions below. A question may have more than one correct answer.

1. Which of the following might be found in a *cask?*
   (a) pedestrians
   (b) crevices
   (c) water
   (d) wine

2. Which of the following might be found at a *banquet?*
   (a) blizzards
   (b) edibles
   (c) guests
   (d) beverages

3. Which of the following is a *task?*
   (a) cleaning one's room
   (b) falling asleep
   (c) weeding a garden
   (d) attending college

4. Which of the following can be *assembled?*
   (a) the pieces of a jigsaw puzzle
   (b) the parts of a machine
   (c) a bookcase
   (d) a branch of a tree

5. Which of the following can be *hewed?*
   (a) logs
   (b) trees
   (c) twigs
   (d) paintings

6. Which of the following can be *harvested?*
   (a) apples   (c) mushrooms
   (b) aromas   (d) gales

7. Which of the following do people *celebrate?*
   (a) birthdays   (c) victories
   (b) weddings   (d) retirement

8. Which of the following might be part of a *cargo?*
   (a) grain   (c) oil
   (b) automobiles   (d) nostalgia

8D Word Relationships

In each of the groups below, circle the two words that are synonyms.

1. CELEBRATED   DESPERATE   4. CHALLENGE   PROMISE
   VERTICAL   FAMOUS   PLEDGE   CONQUEST

2. RESEMBLE   PROSPER   5. ARRANGE   HEW
   ASSEMBLE   SUCCEED   GATHER   ASSEMBLE

3. REDUCE   INFLICT
   DEPART   DECREASE

In each of the groups below, circle the two words that are antonyms.

6. OPTIMISTIC   EDIBLE   9. HEW   PLANT
   LIKELY   DESPERATE   CLEAN   HARVEST

7. LONELINESS   FRIENDLINESS   10. BLAND   PROSPEROUS
   HOSTILITY   COMPREHENSION   SERIOUS   FRIVOLOUS

8. POISONOUS   EDIBLE
   SOLITARY   FRIVOLOUS

8E Narrative   *Read the narrative below; then complete the exercise that follows.*

THE FIRST THANKSGIVING

The hundred or so Pilgrims and other passengers who left England in 1620 aboard the *Mayflower* arrived at Plymouth, in what is now Massachusetts. Before going ashore, the forty-one male passengers **assembled** in the ship's main cabin where they wrote the Mayflower Compact. Under this agreement, everyone, Pilgrims and non-Pilgrims alike, would be governed by the same laws. All those present **pledged** to observe the Compact.

Because the Pilgrims came ashore at the end of December, they had to work fast to prepare for winter. Their first **task** was to build shelter to keep themselves safe from animals and bad weather. Soon the sound of axes rang out as trees were chopped down and **hewed** into logs. Next, the *Mayflower*'s **cargo** had to be unloaded. There were root vegetables and lemons in crates, sacks of sugar and flour, beer and cider in **casks**, slabs of salt pork and beef, and seeds for planting in the spring. There were small items of furniture, chests packed with blankets, linens, and clothes. There were family Bibles, tools of all kinds, and guns, but no musical instruments—the Pilgrims considered music and dancing to be **frivolous.**

That first winter was a grim one. Food was scarce, and many people became sick and died. By the time the *Mayflower* sailed back to England in the early spring, the number of people remaining had **decreased** to fewer than sixty, and many of these were too feeble to work. Those who had survived the winter were also worried about the Native Americans, who they feared would be **hostile** toward them as new settlers.

One spring day they were very surprised when a Native American walked into their settlement and greeted them in English. His name was Samoset, and he explained that he had learned English from sea captains who had earlier explored the Atlantic coast. He told them of another man, Squanto, who also spoke English. A week or so later he returned with Squanto and sixty Wampanoags, who lived nearby. The colonists were glad that their visitors were friendly for, with their food almost gone, their situation was **desperate.**

Because of the help of these native people, the colonists quickly learned which berries and other fruits were **edible,** where to catch fish, and the best way to grow corn, beans, and squash. When they needed to talk with other native people, Squanto often acted as their translator.

Later in 1621, after the first **harvest**, the colonists held a **banquet** and invited Massasoit, the leader of the Wampanoags, to bring his people to **celebrate** with them. This was the first Thanksgiving; it lasted three days. The worst was now over for the colonists. When the *Mayflower* returned in 1622, it brought more people to join the colony as well as precious supplies. More ships arrived in the following years, and the Plymouth colony grew in size and began to **prosper**. Its future was no longer in doubt.

Answer each of the following questions in a sentence. If a question does not contain a vocabulary word, use a vocabulary word in your answer. Use each word only once. Questions and answers will then contain all fifteen words (or forms of the words) from this lesson's word list.

1. What do Americans today do to remember the large dinner that took place at Plymouth in 1621?

   _____

2. If the Pilgrims were alive today, what do you suppose they might think of rock concerts?

   _____

3. What did the *Mayflower* carry besides the passengers and crew?

   _____

4. What **task** did the forty-one male passengers complete before going ashore?

   _____

5. What is the meaning of **assembled** as it is used in the narrative?

   _____

6. What valuable information did the Native Americans give the colonists?

   _____

7. What is the meaning of **hewed** as it is used in the narrative?

   _____

8. Why was it likely that the colonists would obey the rules set out in the Mayflower Compact?

   _____

9. What beverages might have been served at the **banquet**?

   _____

10. What would happen to the contents of a **cask** if it got a hole in it?

   _____

11. What might the colonists have **harvested** in 1621?

_____

12. In what way did the Native Americans surprise the colonists?

_____

13. How many colonists survived the first winter?

_____

14. Why might the survivors of the first winter have felt **desperate**?

_____

15. How do you think life in the colony changed as it **prospered**?

_____

WORDLY WISE

The antonym of **edible** is *inedible*. (The food was so overcooked that it was *inedible*.) Another antonym is *poisonous*. (Cultivated mushrooms are *edible*, but some wild mushrooms are *poisonous*.)

Don't confuse **hew** with *hue*, which is a color or shade of color. (Aqua is a blue color with a greenish *hue*.) These two words are homophones; they are pronounced the same, but have different meanings and spellings.

Pledge and *promise* are synonyms, but a pledge is a serious promise, made concerning something important. You might *promise* to meet a friend after school; you *pledge* allegiance to the flag of the United States and to the republic for which it stands.

CROSSWORD PUZZLE

Solve the crossword puzzle below by studying the clues and filling in the answer boxes. Clues followed by a number are definitions of words in Lessons 5 through 8. The number gives the lesson from which the answer to the clue is taken.

Clues Across

1. The highest part (5)
6. To become less or fewer (8)
7. Opposite of strong
9. Lacking strength (7)
10. The largest city in Nebraska
14. To put into a different language (6)
15. Short for "New York City"
18. A cheerful, hopeful person (5)
21. To hate or despise (6)
22. The way to get to a place (5)
23. To promise (8)
24. Safe to eat (8)
25. To gather in crops (8)

Clues Down

2. Used as a temporary replacement (5)
3. To cause to bear something painful (6)
4. Unpleasant; disturbing (6)
5. To chop or cut down with an ax (8)
8. Great pain and suffering (6)
11. Unfriendly (8)
12. Very wicked; terrible (6)
13. To succeed; to do well (8)
16. A deep narrow opening (5)
17. To walk with an awkward, swaying movement (7)
19. A large country in Asia
20. To tempt with a promise of something (5)

Lesson 9

Word List

Study the definitions of the words below; then do the exercises for the lesson.

absurd
ab sʉrd´

adj. So unreasonable as to be laughable; foolish or silly.
[You'd look *absurd* in a suit and tie at the beach.]

accomplish
ə käm´ plish

v. To do something by making an effort; to complete successfully.
[I know I will *accomplish* these errands by noon.]
accomplishment *n.* Something requiring skill and determination that is completed successfully.
[Anne Sullivan's great *accomplishment* was to teach a deaf and blind child to speak and to read.]

ascend
ə send´

v. To rise, usually in a steady way.
[The rocket *ascended* to a height of five hundred feet before falling to earth.]

dense
dens

adj. 1. Tightly packed; crowded close together.
[The tired explorers hacked their way through *dense* vines and bushes to reach the coast.]
2. Thick; hard to see through.
[At the airport there was such *dense* fog that planes couldn't take off.]
3. Stupid, thickheaded.
[I don't want to seem *dense,* but I don't understand your question.]

experiment
ek sper´ ə mənt

n. A test to prove or discover something.
[The *experiment* shows that oxygen and hydrogen combine to form water.]
v. 1. To carry out experiments.
[Benjamin Franklin *experimented* with a kite to show that lightning was a form of electricity.]
2. To try out new ideas or activities.
[A good cook *experiments* with different herbs and spices to create new dishes.]

flimsy
flim´ zē

adj. 1. Easily damaged or broken; not strongly made.
[The cart was too *flimsy* to carry such a heavy load.]
2. Not believable.
[Saying you lost your pen is a *flimsy* excuse for not doing your homework.]

heroic
hi rō´ ik

adj. 1. Very brave; showing great courage.
[The teenager dove into the pond and made a *heroic* rescue of the child who could not swim.]
2. Showing great determination; requiring enormous effort.
[Firefighters made a *heroic* effort to put out the blaze.]

lumber
lum´ bər

n. Wood that has been sawed into boards.
[Have you ordered the *lumber* for the deck you are building?]
v. To move in a clumsy or heavy way.
[The fat old dog *lumbered* toward me.]

mimic
mim´ ik

v. 1. To copy or imitate closely.
[The parrot fascinated us because it could *mimic* human speech so well.]
2. To make fun of by imitating.
[I got upset when you *mimicked* my friend's limp.]

n. One who can imitate sounds, speech, or actions.
[A good *mimic* carefully studies the person being imitated.]

significant
sig nif´ ə kənt

adj. Important; full of meaning.
[July 4, 1776, is a *significant* date in American history.]
significance   *n.* The quality of being important or of giving meaning.
[The *significance* of the Bill of Rights is that it spells out important freedoms enjoyed by all Americans.]

soar
sôr

v. 1. To fly high in the sky.
[We watched the eagles *soar* until they were just specks in the sky.]
2. To rise suddenly and rapidly.
[The cost of a college education is expected to *soar* during the next few years.]

spectator
spek´ tāt ər

n. A person who watches an activity; an onlooker.
[The *spectators* jostled each other as they rushed onto the field at the end of the game.]

suspend
sə spend´

v. 1. To hang while attached to something above.
[The hammock was *suspended* from the porch ceiling.]
2. To stop for a while before going on.
[The inspector *suspended* work on the building until the contractor obtained the proper permits.]
3. To bar from working, attending, or taking part for a while.
[The students caught cheating were *suspended* from school for one week.]

terminate
tʉr´ mə nāt

v. To bring or to come to an end.
[Heavy rain *terminated* the tennis match after only ten minutes of play.]

unwieldy
un wēl´ dē

adj. Hard to handle or control because of large size or heaviness.
[The sofa was so *unwieldy* that getting it up three flights of stairs was a real challenge.]

9A Finding Meanings

Choose two phrases to form a sentence that correctly uses a word from Word List 9. Write each sentence in the space provided.

1. (a) If you suspend something,   (c) you bring it to an end.
   (b) you make a copy of it.   (d) If you terminate something,

_____

2. (a) is easily broken.   (c) Something that is dense
   (b) is tightly packed.   (d) Something that is unwieldy

_____

3. (a) To accomplish something   (c) is to raise it to a higher level.
   (b) is to complete it successfully.   (d) To mimic something

4. (a) that ends quickly.   (c) that shows great determination.
   (b) A heroic effort is one   (d) An absurd effort is one

5. (a) To ascend is to   (c) test or try out an idea.
   (b) To experiment is to   (d) increase in size or amount.

6. (a) A flimsy container is one that   (c) is not strongly made.
   (b) An unwieldy container is one that   (d) is meant to hold liquids.

7. (a) go to a higher level.   (c) fall into a drowsy state.
   (b) To ascend is to   (d) To lumber is to

8. (a) someone who hears.   (c) A spectator is
   (b) someone who watches.   (d) A mimic is

9. (a) move in a clumsy way.   (c) To soar is to
   (b) To lumber is to   (d) feel pain or discomfort.

10. (a) that is meaningful.   (c) An absurd statement is one
    (b) A significant statement is one   (d) that goes on longer than necessary.

9B Just the Right Word

Improve each of the following sentences by crossing out the italicized phrase and replacing it with a word (or a form of the word) from Word List 9.

1. The movie is about the *very brave* women and men who fight forest fires.

2. The bicyclists could not see through the *very thick* fog.

3. The comedian usually gets lots of laughs when he *imitates the sound of* the voices of famous movie stars.

4. Francine's story about seeing a live dinosaur is *too silly to be believed.*

5. The *Mayflower* passengers' spirits *suddenly rose* when they got their first sight of land.

6. Leave the box where it is if you think it is too *large to be picked up and carried easily.*

7. Coach Louis told us that any player who fails the drug test is *not allowed to take part in any games* for the rest of the season.

8. My family's visit to the Vietnam Veterans Memorial in Washington, D.C., was especially *full of meaning* because my uncle's name appears there.

9. Ms. Smith's *carefully controlled attempt to discover if it was possible* to grow orchids indoors year-round was very successful.

10. The *wood that has been sawed into boards* is stacked outside so that it will dry.

9C Applying Meanings

Circle the letter of each correct answer to the questions below. A question may have more than one correct answer.

1. Which of the following can be *dense?*
   (a) a person
   (b) a crowd
   (c) a hole
   (d) a forest

2. Which of the following can *soar?*
   (a) hopes
   (b) elevators
   (c) prices
   (d) birds

3. Which of the following would be an *accomplishment?*
   (a) going to jail
   (b) winning a gold medal
   (c) cheating on a test
   (d) eating a pizza

4. Which of the following can be *suspended?*
   (a) a bird feeder
   (b) a mistake
   (c) work
   (d) a student

5. Which of the following would be *unwieldy?*
   (a) a piano
   (b) a flute
   (c) a 36-inch television set
   (d) a sleep sofa

6. Which of the following could have *significance?*
   (a) a marriage
   (b) a death
   (c) a graduation
   (d) a birth

7. Which of the following might you *experiment* with?
   (a) hair styles
   (b) a chemistry set
   (c) clothing
   (d) food

8. Which of the following can be *flimsy?*
   (a) an aroma
   (b) a task
   (c) a shelter
   (d) an excuse

9D Word Relationships

In each of the groups below, circle the two words that are synonyms.

1. MIMIC   ONLOOKER
   EXPLORER   SPECTATOR

2. DENSE   STUPID
   UNWIELDY   NARROW

3. MIMIC   RISE
   SUSPEND   IMITATE

4. ABSURD   FLIMSY
   ABUNDANT   FOOLISH

5. DROP   SUSPEND
   SOAR   HANG

In each of the groups below, circle the two words that are antonyms.

6. FLIMSY   BLAND
   HARSH   STURDY

9. MEANINGLESS   UNWIELDY
   SIGNIFICANT   AWKWARD

7. SIGNIFICANT   HEROIC
   RELIABLE   COWARDLY

10. LUMBER   BEGIN
    TERMINATE   TEST

8. ASCEND   COMPREHEND
   SUSPEND   FALL

9E Narrative

Read the narrative below; then complete the exercise that follows.

THE SKY'S THE LIMIT

For as long as people have watched birds **soar** far above the earth, they have dreamed of being able to fly. The Montgolfier brothers of France, Jacques and Joseph, thought of a way this might be possible. In 1782, after observing smoke and hot air rising from a fire, they made a small cloth balloon, filled it with hot air, and watched it rise seventy feet. Hot air is less **dense** than cold air and so is lighter. The warmer, lighter air inside the balloon caused it to rise.

The next year they built a balloon with a diameter of thirty-five feet. They filled it with hot air by burning wool and straw on an iron grate that rested in a large basket **suspended** beneath the balloon. After this rose successfully, they built another one, which was even bigger. In September 1783, before a large crowd, which included the French royal family, the Montgolfier brothers placed a sheep, a duck, and a rooster in the balloon's basket and released it. The balloon **ascended** to a height of fifteen hundred feet and stayed in the air for eight minutes.

A hot-air balloon rises because it is lighter than the air around it, but the idea that something heavier than air could ever get off the ground seemed **absurd** to most people. Not everyone thought so, however. By the late 1800s, after the invention of the steam engine and, later on, the much lighter gasoline engine, the first airplanes were being made. Some of these had movable wings to **mimic** the flapping of birds' wings, but they were too **unwieldy** to fly. Some were powered by steam engines, which made them so heavy they couldn't get off the ground. But when the airplane's frame was made lighter, the plane became **flimsy**. Because of this problem, many early flights **terminated** in a crash. Some people believed that to fly in those days was almost a **heroic** act.

It took another pair of brothers, Orville and Wilbur Wright, to figure out how to build a machine that could stay up in the air. The Wright brothers made and repaired bicycles for a living at their shop in Dayton, Ohio. Like many other people at the time, the idea of flying fascinated them. After **experimenting** with kites and gliders, they built a plane with rigid wings that was powered by a small gasoline engine. This was much lighter than a steam engine.

December 17, 1903, is a **significant** date in the history of flying. On that day at Kitty Hawk, North Carolina, the Wright brothers demonstrated that a heavier-than-air machine could successfully fly. Just a handful of **spectators** watched as the plane, with Orville Wright at the controls, began to **lumber** across the grassy field. They cheered as they saw the plane lift off the ground and stay in the air for twelve seconds before landing about 120 feet away. That afternoon the Wright brothers made three more flights—the longest, lasting fifty-nine seconds, covered 852 feet. They had **accomplished** their goal and made it possible for humans to fulfill their dreams of flight. You can see the airplane the Wright brothers built at the National Air and Space Museum in Washington, D.C.

Answer each of the following questions in a sentence. If a question does not contain a vocabulary word, use a vocabulary word in your answer. Use each word only once. Questions and answers will then contain all fifteen words (or forms of the words) from this lesson's word list.

1. Why is a hot-air balloon able to rise?

   _____

2. Why is Kitty Hawk, North Carolina, **significant** in the history of flying?

   _____

3. Describe one **accomplishment** of the Montgolfier brothers.

   _____

4. How high did the first balloon of the Montgolfier brothers rise?

   _____

5. Why were the early airplanes with flapping wings unsuccessful?

   _____

6. What is the meaning of **soar** as it is used in the narrative?

   _____

7. What important family saw the Montgolfiers' hot-air balloon in September 1783?

_____

8. What is the meaning of **suspended** as it is used in the narrative?

_____

9. Why were injuries a common occurrence among the first fliers?

_____

10. Why did some early planes have movable wings?

_____

11. How did the Wright brothers test their ideas before building the first airplane?

_____

12. What is the meaning of **lumber** as it is used in the narrative?

_____

13. What problem developed when airplane frames were made lighter?

_____

14. What might an aircraft designer of today think of the idea of using a steam engine to power an airplane?

_____

15. Why is it not considered **heroic** to fly in today's airplanes?

_____

WORDLY WISE

The noun formed from **ascend** is *ascent*, the act of rising or going higher. (Our *ascent* to the summit took approximately four hours.) The antonyms of these words are *descend* and *descent*. Don't confuse *ascent* with its homophone *assent*. *Assent* means "agreement." (We cannot give our *assent* to the new proposal until the changes we asked for are made.)

❖ ❖ ❖ ❖ ❖ ❖

Soar and *sore* are also homophones. A *sore* is a painful spot on the body, often with the skin broken. *Sore* is also an *adjective* and means "painful."

❖ ❖ ❖ ❖ ❖ ❖

Spectator is formed from the Latin *spectare*, which means "to see" or "to look at." Two other words formed from this root are *inspect* and *spectacles*. When you inspect something, you *look at* it closely; spectacles, another word for eyeglasses, help a person to *see* better.

❖ ❖ ❖ ❖ ❖ ❖

A *pendant* is something that hangs from a chain around a person's neck. This word comes from the Latin *pendere*, which means "to hang." **Suspend** comes from the same Latin root.

❖ ❖ ❖ ❖ ❖ ❖

The Latin *terminus* means "end." It provides the root for the verb **terminate**. Several other words are formed from this root. A *terminus* is the end of a bus or train line. *Terminal* means "of or relating to an end." A *terminal* illness is one that ends in death. Something that is *interminable* seems to go on without an end. (After an *interminable* wait, we finally saw the doctor.)

Lesson 10

Word List

Study the definitions of the words below; then do the exercises for the lesson.

available
ə vāl´ ə bəl

adj. Easy to get; present and ready for use.
[The salesperson said the jacket was *available* in black, brown, and white.]

bondage
bän´ dij

n. The state of being a slave.
[More than two thousand years ago, Moses led the Jewish people out of *bondage* in Egypt.]

donate
dō´ nāt

v. To give to those in need, often through an organization.
[People across the country *donated* food and clothing to the victims of the flood.]
donation *n.* Whatever is donated, as money or goods.
[*Donations* to help rebuild the community center now total sixty thousand dollars.]

establish
e stab´ lish

v. 1. To set up or begin.
[*Established* in 1636, Harvard College, now part of Harvard University, is the oldest college in the United States.]
2. To show to be true.
[Scientists have *established* beyond any doubt that smoking causes cancer and other diseases.]
establishment *n.* Something that has been established, especially a place of business or a public building.
[Many restaurants, stores, and other *establishments* now ban smoking.]

evade
ē vād´

v. 1. To keep away from; to avoid being caught.
[The chipmunk *evaded* the cat by scrambling up a tree.]
2. To avoid doing or answering.
[Persons who *evade* paying income taxes can find themselves in serious trouble.]
evasive *adj.* Carefully avoiding saying too much; not open or direct.
[The captured prisoners were *evasive* when asked who had helped them escape.]

liberate
lib´ ər āt

v. To free.
[A group objecting to experiments on animals opened the monkey cages and *liberated* the animals inside them.]

numerous
noo´ mər əs

adj. A large number; very many.
[The bus makes *numerous* stops before it leaves us at school.]

occasion
ō kā´ zhən

n. 1. A particular time.
[I recognized Marcia at once because we had met on a previous *occasion*.]
2. A special event.
[The presentation in Oslo, Norway, of the 1992 Nobel Peace Prize to Rigoberta Menchu was a great *occasion* for the Guatemalan people.]
occasional *adj.* Happening once in a while.
[We make an *occasional* trip to town to pick up supplies.]

oppose
ə pōz´

v. To be or act against.
[Moin, my best friend, will *oppose* me in the tennis finals.]
opposition *n.* (äp ə zish´ ən) The act or condition of being against.
[There was no *opposition* to the proposal, which passed by a vote of 16 to 0.]

prohibit
prō hib´ it

v. To forbid by law or order.
[The law now *prohibits* smoking in many public places.]

pursue
pər soo´

v. 1. To follow in order to capture; to chase.
[Police *pursued* the stolen car in a high-speed chase across town.]
2. To seek actively; to carry on with.
[Do you intend to *pursue* a career in medicine?]
pursuit   *n.* 1. The act of following after.
[In the early 1930s people desperate for work poured into cities in *pursuit* of jobs.]
2. An activity, as a job or sport, that a person takes part in.
[Jennie and Bruce enjoy canoeing and other outdoor *pursuits* during the summer.]

reassure
rē ə shoor´

v. To make less worried or fearful; to comfort.
[I was nervous before the recital, but my piano teacher *reassured* me.]
reassurance   *n.* The act of giving comfort or the state of receiving comfort.
[Coach Ward's *reassurances* made us more optimistic about our chances of winning.]

reluctant
rē luk´ tənt

adj. Not wanting to do something; unwilling.
[We were *reluctant* to leave our warm beds when we saw the ice on the windows.]
reluctance   *n.* The state of not wanting to do something.
[With great *reluctance,* I agreed to clean my room before my cousins arrived on Saturday.]

superior
sə pir´ ē ər

adj. 1. Excellent of its kind.
[Margot made the team because she is a *superior* runner.]
2. Higher in position or rank.
[A cardinal is *superior* to a bishop in the Catholic church.]
n. A person of higher rank.
[I reported to my *superior* as soon as I returned to work.]

yearn
yʉrn

v. To want very badly; to be filled with longing.
[Dorothy told the Wizard of Oz that she *yearned* to be back in Kansas.]
yearning   *n.* A longing or strong desire.
[As rain leaked slowly through the roof of our tent, I was filled with a *yearning* for my warm, dry bed at home.]

10A Finding Meanings

Choose two phrases to form a sentence that correctly uses a word from Word List 10. Write each sentence in the space provided.

1. (a) a promise to do certain things.
   (b) An establishment is
   (c) a place of business.
   (d) A yearning is

_____

2. (a) have important people calling.
   (b) have many people calling.
   (c) To have numerous visitors is to
   (d) To have occasional visitors is to

3. (a) To liberate someone is to   (c) chase that person.
    (b) To pursue someone is to   (d) put that person in prison.

---

4. (a) To remember an occasion is to   (c) To remember a donation is to
    (b) recall a particular person.   (d) recall a particular time.

---

5. (a) a deep longing.   (c) someone younger than oneself.
    (b) A superior is   (d) A yearning is

---

6. (a) To reassure someone is to   (c) put that person's mind at ease.
    (b) meet that person again.   (d) To oppose someone is to

---

7. (a) To be superior is   (c) To be reluctant is
    (b) to act in a foolhardy way.   (d) to be better than average.

---

8. (a) avoid answering them.   (c) ask them over and over.
    (b) To prohibit questions is to   (d) To evade questions is to

---

9. (a) Liberation is   (c) a state of slavery.
    (b) an unwillingness to act.   (d) Bondage is

---

10. (a) be against it.   (c) To donate something is to
    (b) set it free.   (d) To oppose something is to

10B Just the Right Word

Improve each of the following sentences by crossing out the italicized phrase and replacing it with a word (or a form of the word) from Word List 10.

1. We managed to *get away from* the hornets by running into the house.

2. Tickets for this Saturday's concert are *easy to obtain* from most music stores.

3. The manager was *not very willing* to return my deposit when I cancelled my order for the ski boots.

4. I have to check with a *person of a higher rank* before I can let you in the building on Saturday.

5. My *going in search* of information about lasers led me to spend a lot of time in the library.

6. It has been *shown to be true* that the sun is about five billion years old.

7. Wintergreen Junior High School is seeking *gifts of money to pay* for the sports program.

8. What *special event* are you celebrating with this beautiful cake?

9. The city *does not allow* downtown parking for the duration of the street festival.

10. Paris was *freed from the foreign army that occupied it* on August 25, 1944.

10C Applying Meanings

Circle the letter of each correct answer to the questions below. A question may have more than one correct answer.

1. Which of the following might a person *pursue?*
   (a) an education   (c) an illness
   (b) a runaway horse   (d) a career

2. Which of the following might a person *yearn* for?
   (a) freedom   (c) despair
   (b) agony   (d) prosperity

3. Which of the following statements offers *reassurance?*
   (a) "It'll be okay."   (c) "You'll be sorry."
   (b) "You can do it."   (d) "Don't say I didn't warn you."

4. Which of the following statements shows *reluctance?*
   (a) "Let's go."   (c) "What's the hurry?"
   (b) "I'll have to think about it." (d) "Let's not be too hasty."

5. Which of the following do you *oppose?*
   (a) drunk driving   (c) education
   (b) vacations   (d) crime

6. Which of the following could be *established?*
   (a) a fact   (c) a restaurant
   (b) a hospital (d) a colony

7. Which of the following could be *evasive?*
   (a) a reply (c) an explanation
   (b) a house (d) a demand

8. Which of the following might a person *donate?*
   (a) space (c) time
   (b) money (d) food

10D Word Relationships

In each of the groups below, circle the two words that are synonyms.

1. RELUCTANT   FLIMSY
   NUMEROUS   MANY

2. AVAILABLE   SUPERIOR
   ACCURATE   OBTAINABLE

3. LIBERATE   FREE
   DONATE   TERMINATE

4. ASCEND   PROHIBIT
   BAN   EVADE

5. FRIVOLITY   SLAVERY
   BONDAGE   PURSUIT

In each of the groups below, circle the two words that are antonyms.

6. HEROIC   OCCASIONAL
   WILLING   RELUCTANT

7. POOR   SUPERIOR
   EVASIVE   CLEAN

8. SIGNIFICANT FREQUENT
   FORGOTTEN   OCCASIONAL

9. REASSURE   DISTURB
   REMAIN   YEARN

10. SIGNIFICANCE SUPPORT
    OPPOSITION   DURATION

10E Narrative

Read the narrative below; then complete the exercise that follows.

WITH MOSES TO THE PROMISED LAND

Harriet Tubman was born a slave in Maryland in 1820, but from the time she was a young child, she **yearned** to be free. The hard physical work that she was forced to do made her very strong, and although as a slave she received no education, she was also intelligent and quick-thinking. She put these qualities to good use, first in making her own escape and later in helping others to do the same.

When Harriet was in her late twenties, her owner died. Fearing she would be sold and sent to the deep South, where the work was harder and slave owners more cruel, she decided to escape. She urged her brothers to come with her on the journey North, and they **reluctantly** joined her. Soon after they set out, afraid of being caught, they turned back. So Harriet continued alone, traveling mostly at night, and made it safely to Philadelphia. Although she had found freedom, she couldn't enjoy it because so many others, including her family, were still living in **bondage.**

In 1850 Congress passed a law making it a crime to help runaway slaves. But over the next eleven years Harriet returned **numerous** times to the South to lead other slaves to Canada, where slavery was **prohibited** and escaped slaves were welcome. Altogether during this time she helped to **liberate** over three hundred people, including her parents and brothers and sisters. Along the way she stayed with people who offered food and shelter in their homes, often at great risk to themselves. These houses were called "stations" on what became known as the Underground Railroad.

Between trips Harriet took whatever jobs were **available**—cooking, sewing, or cleaning. She used some of her money to help former slaves start new lives and saved some of it for her next journey south. She had many friends who **opposed** slavery; when she needed money for her work, they would help her by making **donations.**

Slave owners, furious at having their "property" stolen, offered as much as $40,000 for Harriet Tubman's capture. She was often **pursued** by people who wanted the reward. She had many narrow escapes, but she always managed to **evade** being caught. Escaping slaves called her Moses because she led them to freedom just as Moses had led the Jewish people out of slavery in Egypt thousands of years earlier.

During the Civil War, Harriet Tubman worked for the North as a nurse in the Union army. Slaves had been taught by their owners to be afraid of the Union soldiers, but Harriet went behind enemy lines and **reassured** them that they had nothing to fear. On some **occasions** while there, she acted as a spy, reporting to her **superiors** when she returned to the Union side. After the war she worked energetically to start schools in the South for the freed slaves, even though she herself could not read or write. She eventually settled in Auburn, New York, where she **established** a nursing home for elderly African-Americans. When she died in 1913, thousands mourned this courageous woman who had helped so many people.

Answer each of the following questions in a sentence. If a question does not contain a vocabulary word, use a vocabulary word in your answer. Use each word only once. Questions and answers will then contain all fifteen words (or forms of the words) from this lesson's word list.

1. What did the law that Congress passed in 1850 **prohibit**?

   _____

2. What is the meaning of the word **superiors** as it is used in the narrative?

   _____

3. How did Harriet Tubman feel about being a slave?

   _____

4. Why were her brothers **reluctant** to go with Tubman?

   _____

5. How did Harriet Tubman's friends help her?

   _____

6. What is the meaning of **evade** as it is used in the narrative?

   _____

7. Why was Harriet Tubman called Moses by those she helped?

   _____

8. How do you think Tubman might have **reassured** the slaves she was helping?

   _____

9. In what way did the stations on the Underground Railroad help to **liberate** the slaves?

   _____

10. Why do you think some people opened their homes to escaping slaves?

   _____

11. How did the reward for her capture affect Tubman's later trips to the South?

_____

12. What is the meaning of **established** as it is used in the narrative?

_____

13. Why do you think most slaves were unable to read or write?

_____

14. What two activities did Tubman engage in during the Civil War?

_____

15. Why do you think Tubman made **numerous** trips south even though it was very dangerous for her?

_____

WORDLY WISE

The Statue of *Liberty* is a symbol of freedom to people all over the world. To hand out money *liberally* is to hand it out freely, without exercising very much control. Both these words, together with **liberate,** are formed from the Latin *liber,* which means "free." It's interesting to note that the Latin word for "book" is also *liber.* (A *library* is a place where *books* are kept.) There is a clear connection between books and freedom. A person who cannot read a book is in a kind of prison; learning to read sets the mind free to explore the world and everything in it.

The noun formed from the verb **prohibit** is *prohibition,* an order to stop or the act of forbidding. The word is associated with a fascinating period in United States history. In 1919 the Eighteenth Amendment to the Constitution prohibited the sale of alcoholic beverages. The result was that many citizens ignored the law, and gangsters such as Al Capone grew rich by illegally selling alcoholic beverages. Within a few years it was clear that the amendment had failed. Prohibition, as this time was known, ended in 1933 when the Twenty-first Amendment was added to the Constitution. This one abolished the Eighteenth.

Lesson 11

Word List

Study the definitions of the words below; then do the exercises for the lesson.

accelerate
ak sel´ ər āt

v. 1. To go or to cause to go faster.
[The morning train quickly *accelerates* once it leaves the station.]
2. To bring about at an earlier time.
[Increased sunlight *accelerates* the growth of plants.]

altitude
al´ tə tōōd

n. Height above sea level or the earth's surface.
[Mexico City lies at an *altitude* of almost 8,000 feet.]

anxious
aŋk´ shəs

adj. 1. Worried; concerned.
[I am *anxious* about how I did on the Spanish test.]
2. Eager; wishing strongly.
[After writing to each other for over a year, the two penpals are *anxious* to meet.]
anxiety *n.* (aŋ zī´ ə tē) Great uneasiness or concern.
[Our *anxiety* increased as road conditions got steadily worse.]

brace
brās

v. 1. To make stronger by giving support to.
[Mom *braced* the table leg with a metal strip to keep it from wobbling.]
2. To make ready for a shock; to prepare.
[After the pilot's warning, we *braced* ourselves for a bumpy landing.]

n. Something used to support a weak part.
[I wore a *brace* on my leg for four weeks after I injured it doing a high jump.]
bracing *adj.* Giving energy to; refreshing.
[After spending most of the summer in the city, we found the mountain air wonderfully *bracing*.]

confident
kän´ fi dant

adj. Certain; sure.
[We are *confident* we will win Saturday's hockey game.]
confidence *n.* 1. A lack of doubt; a feeling of being certain.
[My parents showed their *confidence* in me by letting me repair the car by myself.]
2. Trust in another to keep a secret.
[Because Felix told me this in *confidence,* I cannot answer your question.]

contact
kän´ takt

n. 1. The touching or joining of two things.
[*Contact* with a live wire will give you an electric shock.]
2. The condition of being in communication with others.
[Before the telephone was invented, people usually stayed in *contact* by writing letters.]
v. To communicate with.
[The Apollo astronauts could not *contact* Earth while their spaceship was traveling behind the moon.]

exult
eg zult´

v. To be joyful; to show great happiness.
[Senator Gray's supporters *exulted* when she easily won reelection.]
exultant *adj.* Very happy.
[Theresa was *exultant* when she crossed the 10K finish line first.]

hangar haŋˊ ər	*n.* A building where aircraft are kept and repaired. [The pilot steered the plane out of the *hangar* and onto the runway.]
maximum maksˊ i məm	*n.* The greatest or highest number or amount. [The largest bus we have for school trips holds a *maximum* of fifty people.] *adj.* Being the greatest or highest number or amount. [The *maximum* speed of this car is 150 miles per hour.]
methodical mə thädˊ i kəl	*adj.* Done in a regular, orderly way. [Our *methodical* search of the house failed to turn up any evidence of a robbery.]
nonchalant nän shə läntˊ	*adj.* Having the appearance of not caring; seeming to show a lack of concern. [Your *nonchalant* attitude to schoolwork worries your parents.]
proceed prō sēdˊ	*v.* To go on, especially after stopping for a while; to continue. [The subway train *proceeded* on its way after I got off at 14th Street.]
saunter sônˊ tər	*v.* To walk without hurrying; to stroll in a relaxed, unhurried manner. [Pedestrians *saunter* along the river bank, enjoying the afternoon sunshine.] *n.* A relaxed, unhurried walk. [Our *saunter* around the park was abruptly terminated by a violent thunderstorm.]
solo sōˊ lō	*n.* A musical piece for one voice or a single instrument. [A jubilant violin *solo* begins the symphony's second movement.] *adj.* Made or done by one person. [Francis Chichester's *solo* voyage around the world made him famous.] *v.* To fly alone, especially for the first time. [Most student pilots *solo* after ten hours of lessons.]
stall stôl	*n.* 1. A place for an animal in a barn. [Each cow in the barn had its own *stall*.] 2. A small stand or booth where things are sold. [I purchased this pottery at one of the *stalls* at the county fair.] *v.* 1. To suddenly lose power. [You will *stall* the engine if you let out the clutch too quickly.] 2. To delay by being evasive. [Tenants sometimes try to *stall* the landlord when they can't pay the rent.]

11A Finding Meanings

Choose two phrases to form a sentence that correctly uses a word from Word List 11. Write each sentence in the space provided.

1. (a) A plane's hangar is
   (b) the amount of cargo it can carry.
   (c) its height above sea level.
   (d) A plane's altitude is

---

2. (a) To accelerate an engine is to
   (b) cause it to lose power suddenly.
   (c) run it at its lowest speed.
   (d) To stall an engine is to

---

3. (a) a performance by one person.   (c) A solo is
   (b) A saunter is   (d) a support for a broken part.

4. (a) a place where goods are sold.   (c) A brace is
   (b) a place where planes are kept.   (d) A hangar is

5. (a) stop suddenly.   (c) go faster.
   (b) To accelerate is to   (d) To exult is to

6. (a) does things in an orderly way.   (c) An anxious person
   (b) is filled with happiness.   (d) A methodical person

7. (a) A contact is   (c) a support for a broken part.
   (b) A brace is   (d) a place where business is done.

8. (a) To be nonchalant about something is   (c) to be concerned about it.
   (b) To be anxious about something is   (d) to be very happy about it.

9. (a) To be confident is to be   (c) reluctant to act or speak.
   (b) sure of oneself.   (d) To be exultant is to be

10. (a) walk in a relaxed, unhurried manner.   (c) To saunter is to
    (b) show a willingness to help.   (d) To proceed is to

11B Just the Right Word

Improve each of the following sentences by crossing out the italicized phrase and replacing it with a word (or a form of the word) from Word List 11.

1. Five striped bass is the *greatest number* you are allowed to catch this month.

2. After checking our coats, we will *make our way* to our seats in the upper balcony.

3. Canadian baseball fans were *filled with happiness* when the Blue Jays won the World Series.

4. I plan to *fly a plane without my instructor* tomorrow.

5. The breeze off the ocean is very *refreshing and gives one renewed energy.*

6. The trainer led the horse back to its *enclosed place in the stable* after her ride.

7. I lost *the possibility to communicate* with my friends after they moved out of state.

8. The skiers were *showing no concern* as they started down the steep slope.

9. Jan was up at dawn, *very eager* to be on his way.

10. I am telling you what the lawyer told me in *the expectation that you will keep it a secret.*

11C Applying Meanings

Circle the letter of each correct answer to the questions below. A question may have more than one correct answer.

1. Which of the following are measurements of *altitude?*
   (a) three tons
   (b) twenty dollars
   (c) six miles
   (d) 10,000 feet

2. Which of the following might you find in a *hangar?*
   (a) airplanes
   (b) spare parts
   (c) tools
   (d) horses

3. Which of the following might cause a person to *exult?*
   (a) receiving a scholarship
   (b) being liberated
   (c) an exceptional harvest
   (d) being thrown into bondage

4. Which of the following remarks shows *confidence?*
   (a) "I give up."   (c) "I'm not sure."
   (b) "I can do it."   (d) "Let me show you how."

5. Which of the following can be *accelerated?*
   (a) plant growth   (c) a route
   (b) an automobile   (d) a crevice

6. Which of the following might cause *anxiety?*
   (a) becoming ill   (c) being denounced
   (b) losing a job   (d) finding a wallet

7. Which of the following can *stall?*
   (a) a horse   (c) an airplane
   (b) an engine   (d) a person

8. Which of the following could be used as a *brace?*
   (a) a steel rod   (c) a length of string
   (b) a broom handle   (d) a handkerchief

11D Word Relationships

In each of the groups below, circle the two words that are synonyms.

1. CONTINUE   LENGTHEN   4. LEAST   NUMEROUS
   ACCELERATE   PROCEED   MAXIMUM   GREATEST

2. STALL   CONTACT   5. JUBILANT   EXULTANT
   TOUCH   PURSUE   FLIMSY   ALERT

3. CONFIDENT   ALONE
   ACTIVE   SOLO

In each of the groups below, circle the two words that are antonyms.

6. TERSE   NONCHALANT   9. CONFIDENCE   DESPAIR
   ANXIOUS   SIGNIFICANT   ALTITUDE   OBEDIENCE

7. SAUNTER   DONATE   10. CARELESS   METHODICAL
   RUN   BRACE   NUMEROUS   OPTIMISTIC

8. STALL   WEAKEN
   TOUCH   BRACE

11E Narrative

Read the narrative below; then complete the exercise that follows.

OFF YOU GO INTO THE WILD BLUE YONDER

After ten weeks of flying lessons, which is about the average instruction period, you are ready to take your first **solo** flight. Today, your instructor will be on the ground instead of sitting beside you. When you arrive at the airfield, you see her standing outside the **hangar**, and she greets you with a friendly wave. As the two of you chat, you try to sound as **nonchalant** as possible, even though your heart is pounding. She must see how nervous you are because she remarks that she has complete **confidence** in you. That makes you feel better, and you begin to relax a little as the two of you **saunter** over to the plane.

After climbing inside and taking a deep breath, you **methodically** complete the checklist of the plane's controls. Then, you wait for a signal from the control tower to **proceed**. As soon as it comes, your feelings of **anxiety** leave you. You start the engine and release the brake. You open the throttle a little, feeding more gasoline to the engine and causing the propeller to whirl faster. The plane starts to move forward. You taxi onto the runway, facing into the wind, and wait.

A voice from the control tower comes through your headphones, giving you permission to take off. You open the throttle wide, and the plane **accelerates** down the runway. Your right hand rests on the "stick," a control that lifts the plane's nose when pulled back and drops the nose when pushed forward. The plane is now traveling so fast that you can feel it trying to leave the ground. You pull back gently on the stick. The ground suddenly drops away beneath you. You are flying!

You have been told to go no faster than eighty-five miles an hour, although the plane has a **maximum** speed of twice that. You reach an **altitude** of five hundred feet and ease back on the throttle, watching your air speed carefully. If it drops below fifty-five miles an hour, the plane will **stall**. To increase speed, you push the stick forward, dropping the nose slightly. Already, it is time to make the first turn. You push the stick gently to the left, and the wing on that side drops, causing the plane to make a turn, or "bank" as you have learned to call it. There are so many things to think about that you hardly notice the view. After making three more left banks, you are on your final approach.

The control tower clears you for landing. You reduce the amount that the throttle is open and can feel the plane dropping. Not too fast. Not too steep an angle. Come in too high and you'll overshoot the runway; come in too low, and you'll fall short. You **brace** yourself as the runway comes rushing toward you.

When the plane is just inches off the ground, you close the throttle and pull back on the stick to raise the nose. Without power from the engine, the wings no longer support the plane, and it drops. You don't want to be too high when this happens or the plane will bounce as it makes **contact** with the ground. But you make a perfect landing. An **exultant** feeling sweeps over you as you roll down the runway and come to a stop. Flying is fun!

Answer each of the following questions in a sentence. If a question does not contain a vocabulary word, use a vocabulary word in your answer. Use each word only once. Questions and answers will then contain all fifteen words (or forms of the words) from this lesson's word list.

1. What large airport building would be easily seen from the air?

   _____

2. What is the **maximum** speed allowed on the flight?

   _____

3. What is the meaning of **stall** as it is used in the narrative?

   _____

4. What might happen if the check of the controls before a flight is less than **methodical**?

   _____

5. How does the pilot receive instructions when in the plane?

   _____

6. What is the meaning of **confidence** as it is used in the narrative?

   _____

7. How does the pilot try to hide a feeling of nervousness before the flight?

   _____

8. How is it made clear that the pilot didn't hurry over to the plane?

   _____

9. What does the pilot need before **proceeding** to take off?

   _____

10. How much instruction is usually necessary before one is allowed to fly alone?

_____

11. What happens to the plane's air speed when the nose drops slightly?

_____

12. What happens to the plane when the pilot closes the throttle?

_____

13. What is the meaning of **brace** as it is used in the narrative?

_____

14. How might the pilot **exult** after landing safely?

_____

15. How might you feel if you were a pilot making your first flight alone?

_____

WORDLY WISE

A plane's **altitude** is measured by an instrument called an *altimeter,* which shows the height above sea level, not the distance to the ground below. It does this by measuring the density of the air outside. It would show the same altitude, say 5,000 feet, over the ocean and over land that was 4,900 feet above sea level. In the second case, the plane actually would be barely skimming the ground.

Don't confuse **hangar,** a large building where aircraft are kept, with *hanger,* a metal, wood, or plastic frame on which clothes are hung.

The opposite of **maximum** is *minimum.* (For many years, most highways in the United States had a *maximum* speed of 55 m.p.h. and a *minimum* speed of 40 m.p.h.)

In Lesson 7 you learned several words formed from the Latin *solus,* which means "alone; without company." **Solo** is another of those words. A *solo* is an activity, musical or otherwise, performed by one person. A piece of music for two people is called a *duet;* for three people, a *trio;* and for four people, a *quartet.*

Lesson 12

Word List

Study the definitions of the words below; then do the exercises for the lesson.

convalesce
kän və les´
    v. To get back health and strength after an illness.
[After the operation on my knee, I will *convalesce* at home.]

dedicate
ded´ i kāt
    v. 1. To set aside for a certain purpose.
[My parents *dedicate* part of their income to saving for my college education.]
2. To devote to a serious purpose.
[Madame Curie *dedicated* her life to science.]
3. To name, address, or set aside as an honor.
[The authors *dedicated* the book to their two children.]

dictate
dik´ tāt
    v. 1. To give orders; to command.
[The law *dictates* that children attend school until they are sixteen.]
2. To say aloud while another writes down the words.
[I *dictated* a letter to the manager of the company.]
dictator   *n.* A person who has complete control over a country; a person who is obeyed without question.
[Hitler ruled Germany as a *dictator* from 1933 to 1945.]

exasperate
eg zas´ pər āt
    v. To make angry; to annoy.
[My brother *exasperates* my parents because he uses the telephone so much.]
exasperating   *adj.* Very annoying.
[Waiting in long lines to enter the stadium, before the game, can be quite *exasperating*.]

notable
nōt´ ə bəl
    adj. Deserving of attention; outstanding.
[Eleanor Roosevelt was one of the most *notable* first ladies to occupy the White House.]

overdue
ō vər dōō´
    adj. 1. Coming later than expected or needed.
[The bus from Boston is *overdue*.]
2. Unpaid when owed.
[My aunt never allows her bills to become *overdue*.]

overthrow
ō vər thrō´
    v. To end the rule of; to defeat, often by using force.
[If we *overthrow* the king, who will take his place?]
overthrew   *past tense.*
[The Polish people finally *overthrew* the Communist government that had been in power for more than forty years.]
n. The action of overthrowing.
[The *overthrow* of Anastasio Somoza, who ruled Nicaragua for many years, came in July 1979.]

penetrate
pen´ ə trāt
    v. 1. To pierce.
[Luckily, the piece of glass Irma stepped on did not *penetrate* her foot.]
2. To pass into or through.
[Very little light *penetrated* the dense forest.]

portrait
pôr´ trit

n. A drawing, painting, or photograph of a person, especially the face.
[The famous *portrait* known as the Mona Lisa is in the Louvre, in Paris.]

rebel
reb´ əl

v. To refuse to accept control by others.
[The Philippine people *rebelled* against the government of Ferdinand Marcos.]
n. A person who refuses to obey orders or the law.
[If the *rebels* continue to gain popular support, they will be a serious threat to the government.]
rebellious *adj.* (rē bel´ yəs) Fighting against another's control; disobedient.
[Grounding is a punishment parents often use for *rebellious* teenagers.]
rebellion *n.* (rē bel´ yən) Open opposition to another's control.
[The Boxer *Rebellion* of 1900 was an attempt by the Chinese to throw foreigners out of the country.]

restrict
rē strikt´

v. To keep within certain limits.
[We *restrict* this pathway to people riding bicycles.]
restriction *n.* A limit.
[Our school has some *restrictions* about what students may wear.]

seldom
sel´ dəm

adv. Not often; rarely.
[Because the sun's rays are so strong, we *seldom* spend the whole day at the beach.]

stimulate
stim´ yoo lāt

v. To make more active.
[The aroma of black bean soup from the kitchen *stimulated* my appetite for lunch.]

tempest
tem´ pəst

n. A violent windstorm usually with snow, rain, or hail.
[A *tempest* at sea is a sailor's greatest fear.]
tempestuous *adj.* Stormy, wild.
[After a *tempestuous* exchange of views on global warming, the two scientists agreed to disagree and ended the discussion.]

upbringing
up´ briŋ iŋ

n. The care and training a child gets while growing up.
[In *Little Women,* Louisa May Alcott describes the *upbringing* of the four March sisters in nineteenth century New England.]

12A Finding Meanings

Choose two phrases to form a sentence that correctly uses a word from Word List 12. Write each sentence in the space provided.

1. (a) end that person's rule by force.
   (b) To overthrow someone is to

   (c) To exasperate someone is to
   (d) serve under that person.

_____

2. (a) is to put limits on it.
   (b) To restrict activity

   (c) To stimulate activity
   (d) is to prohibit it.

_____

3. (a) If an event seldom happens,   (c) If an event is overdue,
   (b) it causes great excitement.   (d) it doesn't happen often.

4. (a) A notable scene   (c) is one that is delayed.
   (b) is one that is stormy.   (d) A tempestuous scene

5. (a) An upbringing is   (c) the time spent recovering.
   (b) A rebellion is   (d) a rising up against those in power.

6. (a) To stimulate someone is to   (c) annoy that person.
   (b) remove that person from power.   (d) To exasperate someone is to

7. (a) One's upbringing is   (c) the care one gets as a patient.
   (b) One's portrait is   (d) the care one gets as a child.

8. (a) is to name it in honor of someone. (c) To dedicate a building
   (b) To penetrate a building   (d) is to tear it down.

9. (a) A dictator is   (c) a fight against control by others.
   (b) A portrait is   (d) a ruler with complete control.

10. (a) is made to oneself.   (c) An overdue pledge is one that
    (b) A notable pledge is one that   (d) should have been made earlier.

12B Just the Right Word

Improve each of the following sentences by crossing out the italicized phrase and replacing it with a word (or a form of the word) from Word List 12.

1. You cannot use the movie pass on Sundays, but that is the only *limit placed upon its use.*

2. The arrow easily *passed through* the target.

3. This *painting which shows the face* of Queen Anne is three hundred years old.

4. While my arm was in a cast, I *had someone write down* what I wanted to say in my letters.

5. The *people who are fighting against their government* appear to be winning.

6. I recently discovered that one of my ancestors was quite *worthy of attention.*

7. After her hip operation, we brought my grandmother to our house to *get back her strength.*

8. Plenty of sunlight has *increased the activity of* my hibiscus plant to develop three new blossoms.

9. The Concord planetarium is *named after her as a way of showing respect* to Christa McAuliffe, who died aboard the *Challenger* space shuttle in January 1986.

10. Trying to teach our dog to obey was an *unpleasant and very annoying* experience.

12C Applying Meanings

Circle the letter of each correct answer to the questions below. A question may have more than one correct answer.

1. Which of the following could be the subject of a *portrait?*
   (a) a hand
   (b) a child
   (c) the mayor of a city
   (d) a tree

2. Which of the following would help a person to *convalesce?*
   (a) quiet surroundings
   (b) fresh air
   (c) feelings of anxiety
   (d) a feeling of optimism

3. Which of the following could *penetrate* the skin?
   (a) a needle   (c) a splinter of wood
   (b) a nail   (d) a snowball

4. Which of the following are part of one's *upbringing*?
   (a) trees   (c) companions
   (b) parents   (d) pets

5. Which of the following might you do during a *tempest*?
   (a) stay home   (c) go sailing
   (b) seek shelter   (d) harvest crops

6. Which of the following can be *restricted*?
   (a) visits   (c) parking
   (b) dreams   (d) speech

7. Which of the following might cause people to *rebel*?
   (a) feelings of nostalgia   (c) feelings of desperation
   (b) harsh rule   (d) a harsh climate

8. Which of the following might be *exasperating*?
   (a) frivolous complaints   (c) airport delays
   (b) meddlesome cousins   (d) free gifts

12D Word Relationships

In each of the groups below, circle the two words that are synonyms.

1. DICTATE   DEFEAT   4. NOTABLE   DELAYED
   OVERTHROW   DONATE   STORMY   OVERDUE

2. RECOVER   LIBERATE   5. BRACE   COMMAND
   CONVALESCE   CONTACT   DICTATE   REBEL

3. EXASPERATE   RESTRICT
   STIMULATE   ROUSE

In each of the groups below, circle the two words that are antonyms.

6. CHALLENGING   PENETRATING   9. TEMPESTUOUS   DENSE
    EXASPERATING   PLEASING   CONFIDENT   CALM

7. NOTABLE   ABSURD   10. EDIBLE   REBELLIOUS
    HARSH   INSIGNIFICANT   NUMEROUS   OBEDIENT

8. RELUCTANTLY   OFTEN
    WISELY   SELDOM

12E Narrative

Read the narrative below; then complete the exercise that follows.

A CHILD OF THE REVOLUTION

When Frida Kahlo was born in Coyoacan, just outside Mexico City, in 1907, her parents probably thought her life would develop much as the lives of other girls of that time. The Mexican **dictator** Porfirio Diaz had been governing for almost thirty years, and under his rule women were **restricted** from taking any part in public life. Furthermore, Frida's parents gave her and her three sisters a strict Catholic **upbringing**. The girls were expected to be obedient daughters and to become good Catholic wives and mothers.

But in 1910, when Frida was three years old, everything changed in Mexico. The people **overthrew** Diaz and established a much more open government, which speedily set about making many changes that were long **overdue**. Education and health care became more widely available. More significantly for Frida Kahlo's future, the new government set out to **stimulate** interest in the arts by supporting the work of Mexican artists.

While her three sisters were largely unaffected by these changes, Frida, who was the **rebellious** one, took part in them. She seemed to enjoy shocking people. One of the ways she did this was to go about wearing men's clothes. Because she was a firm supporter of the 1910 revolution, as an adult she claimed to have been born that year so that she could call herself "a child of the revolution." Her Mexican mother and German father must have despaired of her at times, little knowing that their lively daughter would grow up to become one of Latin America's most **notable** painters.

Frida Kahlo had a difficult childhood. At the age of six she contracted polio, which left her with a weakened right leg. Then, in her late teens, she suffered terrible injuries when she was thrown from a bus onto a metal spike, which **penetrated** her side, almost killing her.

While she **convalesced,** she began to paint. This was a way of taking her mind off the severe pain, from which she was **seldom** free for the rest of her life. Many of her paintings are self-**portraits**; in them she often included the parrots, monkeys, and other pets whose company gave her so much pleasure. Despite their bold, bright colors, however, the paintings clearly express the pain that lies behind them. Kahlo's art was her way of inviting the viewer to share her suffering.

She first met her future husband, the painter Diego Rivera, in 1922, when she was fifteen. They married seven years later. He was twice her age and already a world-famous artist. The marriage was a **tempestuous** one with many separations, a divorce, and later a remarriage. They both had strong personalities and each found the other **exasperating** to live with. Nevertheless, their love was strong and deep; Rivera appears frequently in her paintings.

Toward the end of her life, they lived together in the house where she was born, Casa Azul (the Blue House). After Kahlo's death in 1954, Rivera gave it to the people of Mexico. Now, known as the Frida Kahlo Museum, it is **dedicated** to her life and work.

Answer each of the following questions in a sentence. If a question does not contain a vocabulary word, use a vocabulary word in your answer. Use each word only once. Questions and answers will then contain all fifteen words (or forms of the words) from this lesson's word list.

1. What detail in the narrative suggests that President Diaz was accustomed to being obeyed without question?

   _____

2. How did the Mexican people show their dissatisfaction with President Diaz?

   _____

3. How do you know that Kahlo's parents were not interested in experimenting with different ways of raising children?

   _____

4. Why would Mexican artists have welcomed the 1910 revolution?

   _____

5. Why do you think Kahlo's parents might sometimes have been **exasperated** with Frida?

   _____

6. What is the meaning of **overdue** as it is used in the narrative?

   _____

7. In what way did Kahlo **rebel** against what was considered normal behavior?

_____

8. How do you think Kahlo's weakened right leg affected her life?

_____

9. Why did Kahlo probably lose a lot of blood in her accident?

_____

10. What helped Kahlo to **convalesce?**

_____

11. What is the meaning of **dedicated** as it is used in the narrative?

_____

12. How does the narrative make clear that Kahlo never recovered completely from the accident?

_____

13. Why would it be incorrect to describe Rivera and Kahlo as a compatible couple?

_____

14. What did Frida Kahlo paint?

_____

15. Why are both Diego Rivera and Frida Kahlo honored in the world of art?

_____

WORDLY WISE

Dictate is formed from the Latin verb *dicere*, which means "to say" or "to speak." Other words formed from this root include *diction*, "a person's manner or way of speaking," and *contradict*, "to say the opposite of."

Three nouns are formed from the verb **stimulate**. *Stimulation* is the act of stimulating. (The aroma of freshly baked bread was the only *stimulation* we needed to enter the bakery.) A *stimulant* is a substance, as a drug, that increases bodily activity. (The caffeine in coffee and cola drinks is a *stimulant*.) A *stimulus* is anything that increases activity of any kind. (The reward of $50 was a *stimulus* to the children who were looking for the lost dog.)

CROSSWORD PUZZLE

Solve the crossword puzzle below by studying the clues and filling in the answer boxes. Clues followed by a number are definitions of vocabulary words in Lessons 9 through 12. The number gives the lesson from which the answer to the clue is taken.

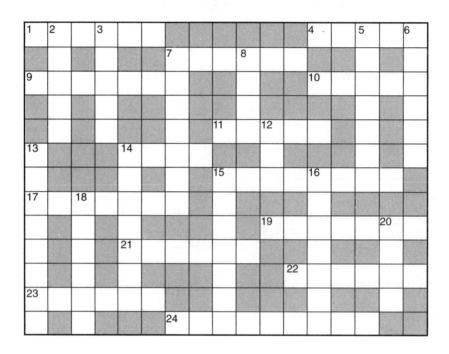

Clues Across

1. Not often (12)
4. A tied ball game goes into _____ innings
7. To chase after (10)
9. To walk in a relaxed, unhurried manner (11)
10. To copy closely (9)
11. To prepare; to make ready for a shock (11)
14. Opposite of "under"
15. To name or address as an honor (12)
17. To stop for a while before going on (9)
19. The state of being a slave (10)
21. To give to a fund or cause (10)
22. A building where aircraft are kept (11)
23. It covers the floor
24. One who watches an activity (9)

Clues Down

2. To keep away from (10)
3. Tightly packed; crowded close together (9)
5. A violent storm (12)
6. To go to a higher level (9)
7. To go on with after stopping for a while (11)
8. To fly high in the sky (9)
12. Opposite of "subtract"
13. To keep within certain limits (12)
14. Past the time set for arrival (12)
15. To give orders (12)
16. To get in touch with (11)
18. Planet known for its rings.
20. Opposite of "sad"

Lesson 13

Word List

Study the definitions of the words below; then do the exercises for the lesson.

accommodate
ə käm´ ə dat

v. 1. To have or to find room for.
[This bus, which *accommodates* thirty adults, will drive to the historic buildings in the center of the city.]
2. To do a favor for.
[Tell me what you want, and I will try to *accommodate* you.]

aggressive
ə gres´ iv

adj. 1. Ready to attack or start fights; acting in a hostile way.
[Many animals become *aggressive* when their young are threatened.]
2. Bold and active.
[Rod Laver, the Australian tennis star, was an *aggressive* player at net.]

bask
bask

v. 1. To relax where it is pleasantly warm.
[At lunch break, several students *basked* in the sunshine flooding the front steps.]
2. To enjoy a warm or pleasant feeling.
[The twins *basked* in the praise heaped on them by their parents.]

carcass
kär´ kəs

n. The dead body of an animal.
[New Zealand exports frozen lamb *carcasses* in refrigerator ships.]

conceal
kən sēl´

v. To keep something or someone from being seen or known; to hide.
[I *concealed* myself behind the curtain just as the thief entered the room.]

flail
flāl

v. To strike out or swing wildly; to thrash about.
[Matt's arms *flailed* desperately as he felt himself sinking into deep water.]

gorge
gôrj

n. A narrow passage between steep cliffs.
[We crossed the *gorge* on a swaying rope bridge.]
v. To stuff with food; to eat greedily.
[The children *gorged* themselves on watermelon at the family picnic.]

morsel
môr´ səl

n. A small amount, especially of something good to eat; a tidbit.
[For appetizers we served stuffed mushrooms and other tasty *morsels*.]

protrude
prō trōōd´

v. To stick out; to project.
[Watch out for the stone ledge that *protrudes* from the wall.]

ripple
rip´ əl

v. To form small waves.
[The breeze *rippled* the surface of the lake.]
n. A movement like a small wave.
[Raindrops made *ripples* in the pond.]

slither
slith´ ər

v. To move with a sliding, side-to-side motion of the body.
[A snake *slithered* through the grass.]

sluggish
slug´ ish

adj. 1. Lacking energy; not active.
[The heat made me *sluggish*.]
2. Slow moving.
[In the dry season, the river becomes little more than a *sluggish* stream.]

snout
snout

n. The nose or jaws that stick out in front of certain animals' heads.
[The *snout* of a ferocious dog may need to be covered with a muzzle.]

taper
tā´ pər

v. 1. To make or become less wide or less thick at one end.
[A boning knife *tapers* to a very sharp point.]
2. *v.* To lessen gradually. (Usually used with *off*.)
[As a loud knock was heard at the door, the speaker's voice *tapered* off, and she fell silent.]
n. A thin candle.
[The only light in the room came from a flickering *taper*.]

visible
viz´ ə bəl

adj. Able to be seen; exposed to view; not hidden.
[On a clear day Mount Shasta is *visible* from fifty miles away.]
visibility *n.* 1. The condition of being easily seen.
[An orange vest increases a cyclist's *visibility* on the road.]
2. The distance within which things can be seen.
[*Visibility* is poor this morning because of the fog.]

13A Finding Meanings

Choose two phrases to form a sentence that correctly uses a word from Word List 13. Write each sentence in the space provided.

1. (a) relax where it is pleasantly warm.
   (b) move by sliding from side to side.
   (c) To taper is to
   (d) To slither is to

   _____

2. (a) An aggressive animal is one
   (b) A sluggish animal is one
   (c) that is a carnivore.
   (d) that is ready to fight.

   _____

3. (a) stuff oneself with food.
   (b) strike out wildly.
   (c) To gorge is to
   (d) To taper is to

   _____

4. (a) a small wave.
   (b) a tasty bit of food.
   (c) A carcass is
   (d) A ripple is

   _____

5. (a) To flail is to
   (b) To bask is to
   (c) hold out one's arms.
   (d) enjoy a pleasant feeling.

   _____

6. (a) within sight.   (c) lacking energy.
   (b) To be visible is to be   (d) To be concealed is to be

   _____

7. (a) keep out of sight.   (c) strike out wildly.
   (b) To protrude is to   (d) To flail is to

   _____

8. (a) an animal's slow movement.   (c) A morsel is
   (b) an animal's projecting nose.   (d) A snout is

   _____

9. (a) speak favorably of that person.   (c) hide that person.
   (b) To conceal someone is to   (d) To accommodate someone is to

   _____

10. (a) the body of a dead animal.   (c) A carcass is
    (b) a narrow passage.   (d) A morsel is

   _____

13B Just the Right Word

Improve each of the following sentences by crossing out the italicized phrase and replacing it with a word (or a form of the word) from Word List 13.

1. The company received an avalanche of mail the first day, but the orders soon *began to arrive in smaller and smaller numbers.*

2. A leaf dropped onto the pond and *made small waves on* the surface.

3. The *narrow passage with cliffs on either side* is two hundred feet deep.

4. Will you be able to *find room for* all five of us in your car?

5. When a *small piece of something good to eat* fell to the floor, we let our dog eat it.

6. Customers who cannot pay their bills are pursued by the company in a very *active and forceful* manner.

7. The Inuit hunters cut up the *dead body of the animal* and shared it among themselves.

8. The twins *wildly swung* their arms and legs as their parents tried to dress them in snowsuits.

9. The tractor engine is *very slow to turn over* on these cold mornings.

10. Watch out! There are several rusty nails *sticking out* from that board lying on the ground in front of you.

13C Applying Meanings

Circle the letter of each correct answer to the questions below. A question may have more than one correct answer.

1. Which of the following would decrease *visibility?*
   (a) fog   (c) a blizzard
   (b) a telescope   (d) darkness

2. Which of the following is an *aggressive* remark?
   (a) "Get out of my way!"   (c) "Forget it!"
   (b) "I'm sorry."   (d) "Would you please repeat that?"

3. Which of the following might make a person *sluggish?*
   (a) a heavy meal   (c) lying in the sun
   (b) bracing air   (d) a stimulant

4. Which of the following animals *slither?*
   (a) snakes   (c) frogs
   (b) lizards   (d) kangaroos

5. Which of the following can *taper?*
   (a) a twelve-inch ruler   (c) a candle
   (b) the blade of a sword   (d) the toe of a shoe

6. Which of the following *protrudes* from the head?
   (a) the neck   (c) the ears
   (b) the nose   (d) the brain

7. In which of the following places might one *bask?*
   (a) on the beach   (c) near a campfire
   (b) beside the pool   (d) on a tropical island

8. Which of the following might *accommodate* your neighbors?
   (a) lending them your tools   (c) denouncing them to your friends
   (b) inviting them to celebrate   (d) watching their house while they're away

13D Word Relationships

In each of the groups below, circle the two words that are synonyms.

1. FLAIL   SAUNTER
   TIDBIT   MORSEL

2. CANDLE   BRACE
   RIPPLE   TAPER

3. PROJECT   BASK
   PROTRUDE   PENETRATE

4. BACK   CARCASS
   NOSE   SNOUT

5. AGGRESSIVE   GORGE
   STUFF   HIDDEN

In each of the groups below, circle the two words that are antonyms.

6. SLUGGISH   RELUCTANT
   ACTIVE   VISIBLE

7. RIPPLE   WIDEN
   EVADE   TAPER

8. HIDDEN   VISIBLE
   CONFIDENT   EDIBLE

9. RESTRICT   REVEAL
   FLAIL   CONCEAL

10. ACCOMMODATE RETIRE
    THWART   SLITHER

13E Narrative

Read the narrative below; then complete the exercise that follows.

BEWARE THE SILENT CROCODILE

Crocodiles are the largest and most ferocious of all reptiles. They live in swampy areas, close to the banks of tropical rivers or lakes. They have been around since the age of the dinosaurs, when they reached lengths of thirty feet or more. The crocodile of today, however, is much smaller than its ancient ancestors, seldom growing longer than fifteen feet from its head to the tip of its long, **tapering** tail.

Crocodiles in the wild are almost unknown in North America. A few can be found in the remaining tidal marshes of the Everglades and the Florida Keys, where they might be mistaken for alligators, their close relatives. Although crocodiles and alligators resemble each other in many ways, there are clear differences between them. The crocodile is the more **aggressive** of the two. It also has a longer and narrower **snout,** and the fourth tooth on each side of its jaw **protrudes,** remaining in view even when its mouth is closed.

A crocodile in the water lies almost entirely **concealed** below the surface, with only its eyes and nostrils **visible**. It can stay like this for hours, its eyes fixed on the water's edge, waiting for a thirsty animal to come to drink. When this happens, the crocodile is careful not to scare away its prey. It disappears beneath the surface, swimming slowly toward the unsuspecting animal, without making the slightest **ripple**.

If the thirsty animal is lucky, it senses the danger in time and escapes. If the crocodile is lucky, it seizes the animal in its jaws, knocks it off balance by **flailing** its powerful tail, and drags it into the water, where the creature drowns. The crocodile then finds a place where it can **gorge** on the dead animal without being disturbed. When it has eaten its fill, it will hide the remains of the **carcass** and return to feed on it later.

When not hunting for food, the crocodile spends much of its time on land. Its belly almost touches the ground as it **slithers** from the water and finds a comfortable spot to **bask** in the sun. Like other reptiles, the crocodile is a cold-blooded animal; therefore, its temperature changes with its surroundings. To escape the extreme heat of midday, it burrows into the soft ground with its sharp claws until it has made a hole large enough to **accommodate** itself. In the cool of the evening, its temperature drops and its movements become **sluggish**.

There are several different kinds of crocodile. The best known is the Nile crocodile of Africa, which has an unusual companion called the crocodile bird. This daring little creature feeds by hopping inside the crocodile's mouth and picking **morsels** of meat from its teeth. The crocodile shows its gratitude for having its teeth cleaned in this way by not eating the bird.

Answer each of the following questions in a sentence. If a question does not contain a vocabulary word, use a vocabulary word in your answer. Use each word only once. Questions and answers will then contain all fifteen words (or forms of the words) from this lesson's word list.

1. Why is it unwise to get too close to a crocodile?

   _____

2. How does the shape of a crocodile's head differ from that of an alligator?

   _____

3. What do crocodiles and snakes have in common?

   _____

4. What is the shape of a crocodile's tail?

   _____

5. Why do crocodiles hide the **carcasses** of animals they have killed?

_____

6. When are crocodiles likely to be slow in their movements?

_____

7. What is the meaning of **bask** as it is used in the narrative?

_____

8. What parts of a swimming crocodile are **visible**?

_____

9. How does a crocodile use its tail to overcome its prey?

_____

10. What is the meaning of **accommodate** as it is used in the narrative?

_____

11. How does the narrative suggest that a crocodile does not toy with its food?

_____

12. Why is the prey of a crocodile unlikely to see it approaching in the water?

_____

13. Why do you think the crocodile's eyes and nostrils **protrude** above the surface when it is in the water?

_____

14. What do crocodile birds eat?

_____

15. Why do crocodiles lie **concealed** in the water for long periods of time?

_____

A *slug* is like a snail but without the shell; it moves just about as fast as a snail, which is very slow indeed. *Slug* comes from an old Scandinavian word *slugje,* which means "a heavy, slow person." Both the noun *slug-gard,* "a lazy, slow-moving person" and the adjective **sluggish** are formed from this word.

◆ ◆ ◆ ◆ ◆ ◆

Don't confuse *tapir,* the name for a large piglike animal that lives in the forests of Central and South America, with **taper.** These two words sound the same but have different meanings and spellings. Can you remember what such pairs of words are called?

Lesson 14

Word List

Study the definitions of the words below; then do the exercises for the lesson.

access
ak´ ses

n. 1. Freedom or permission to enter.
[The students want *access* to the gym this summer.]
2. A way of approach or entry.
[The only *access* to the harbor is this channel.]
accessible *adj.* Able to be used or entered.
[Franklin's Restaurant is *accessible* to people in wheelchairs.]

associate
ə sō´ shē āt

v. 1. To bring together in the mind.
[Many people *associate* lobsters with Maine.]
2. To come or be together as friends or companions.
[Because of her love of racehorses, Anne often *associated* with others who shared that love—jockeys and trainers.]
n. (ə sō´ shē ət) A person with whom one is connected in some way, as in business.
[My father discussed the offer of a job in Chicago with his *associate* at work.]

boisterous
bois´ tər əs

adj. Noisy and uncontrolled.
[The Dixon's party became so *boisterous* that their neighbors complained.]

brilliant
bril´ yənt

adj. 1. Very bright; sparkling.
[My black patent-leather shoes had a *brilliant* shine.]
2. Very clever or smart.
[Einstein's *brilliant* mind was already evident in his youth.]

decade
dek´ ād

n. A ten-year period.
[Some people look back with nostalgia to the *decade* of the nineteen-sixties.]

delicate
del´ i kət

adj. 1. Easily broken or damaged.
[We always wash this *delicate* china by hand.]
2. Needing care and skill.
[Explaining someone's death to a small child is a *delicate* task.]
3. In poor health; weak.
[Although Isabella Bird Bishop was a *delicate* child, as an adult, she traveled through many different parts of the world, sometimes by canoe and other times on horseback.]

employ
em ploi´

v. 1. To hire and put to work for pay.
[Carmen's gift shop *employs* four people.]
2. To use.
[The clown *employed* every trick he knew to make the children laugh.]

idle
ī´ dəl

adj. Doing nothing; not working.
[The workers were *idle* while the power was shut off.]
v. 1. To spend one's time doing nothing.
[Last Sunday, while my brother *idled* for more than an hour in the house, I raked leaves in the yard.]
2. To run (an engine) slowly.
[Let the car *idle* for a few minutes so that the engine can warm up.]

illuminate
il loo´ mə nāt

v. 1. To light up; to supply with light.
[The full moon *illuminated* the path through the woods to our cabin.]
2. To make clear or understandable.
[What you say about Goya's life *illuminates* this painting for me.]

provide
prō vīd´

v. 1. To give what is needed; to supply.
[Two local companies *provided* the money to buy our school band uniforms.]
2. To set forth as a condition.
[Our agreement with the company *provides* for three weeks of vacation time.]

require
rē kwīr´

v. To need or demand.
[Plants *require* light and water in order to grow.]
requirement *n.* Something that is necessary.
[A place to sleep and a simple meal were Johnny Appleseed's only *requirements*.]

taunt
tônt

v. To make fun of in an insulting way; to jeer.
[Don't *taunt* someone just because that person appears different.]
n. An insulting remark.
[An umpire learns to ignore the *taunts* of the crowd and just gets on with the job.]

tolerant
täl´ ər ənt

adj. Willing to let others have their own beliefs and ways, even if different from one's own.
[Traveling is both interesting and enjoyable if you are *tolerant* of customs that seem strange to you.]
tolerate *v.* To accept willingly and without complaining.
[You learn to *tolerate* a certain amount of noise when you live near an airport.]

transform
trans fôrm´

v. To change the form, looks, or nature of.
[A fresh coat of paint will *transform* this room.]
transformation *n.* A complete change.
[The *transformation* of the frog into a prince comes at the end of the story.]

wilderness
wil´ dər nəs

n. An area where there are few people living; an area still in its natural state.
[The Rocky Mountain states contain large areas of *wilderness*.]

14A Finding Meanings

Choose two phrases to form a sentence that correctly uses a word from Word List 14. Write each sentence in the space provided.

1. (a) is unusually smart.
   (b) A delicate child is one who
   (c) A brilliant child is one who
   (d) is noisy and rough.

2. (a) give that person a job.
   (b) give that person a second chance.
   (c) To employ someone is to
   (d) To tolerate someone is to

3. (a) give it up.
   (b) To provide something is to
   (c) To require something is to
   (d) need it.

4. (a) Wilderness is
   (b) remoteness in space or time.
   (c) a way of entering.
   (d) Access is

5. (a) a business partner.
   (b) An associate is
   (c) A decade is
   (d) an insulting remark.

6. (a) to light it up.
   (b) To illuminate a room is
   (c) To transform a room is
   (d) to make it available.

7. (a) An idle person is one who is
   (b) A boisterous person is one who is
   (c) noisy and rough.
   (d) hard to talk to.

8. (a) a reassuring remark.
   (b) A taunt is
   (c) A transformation is
   (d) a complete change.

9. (a) one that runs sluggishly.
   (b) An accessible machine is
   (c) one that is easy to get to.
   (d) An idle machine is

10. (a) is to put up with it.
    (b) To provide something
    (c) To tolerate something
    (d) is to do without it.

14B Just the Right Word

Improve each of the following sentences by crossing out the italicized phrase and replacing it with a word (or a form of the word) from Word List 14.

1. Much of Alaska is *land that is still in its natural state* that needs to be protected.

2. In cold weather, let the engine *run slowly* for a few minutes before you drive any place.

3. Samantha hated school because some of her classmates *made fun of* her for the way she spoke.

4. The *ten-year period* that ended in 1929 was called "the Roaring Twenties."

5. These new curtains will *completely change the appearance of* this bedroom.

6. The matter is *one that needs careful handling*, but I am confident that you can take care of it.

7. This new health insurance will *make sure that you will be covered* for full payment of medical expenses.

8. This book *makes clear and understandable* how the two scientists figured out the structure of DNA.

9. I would be happier if my older sister were more *willing to overlook the faults of others* and less rigid.

10. One *thing that is necessary* to attend the new school is a uniform.

14C Applying Meanings

Circle the letter of each correct answer to the questions below. A question may have more than one correct answer.

1. Which of the following might an *idle* person do?
   (a) watch television
   (b) bask in the sun
   (c) win an Olympic medal
   (d) write a book

2. Which of the following could be a means of *access*?
   (a) a door
   (b) a wall
   (c) an opening
   (d) a window

3. Which of the following are closely *associated?*
   - (a) baseball and summer
   - (b) salt and pepper
   - (c) Hansel and Gretel
   - (d) snowflakes and cornflakes

4. Which of the following can be *brilliant?*
   - (a) a diamond
   - (b) an idea
   - (c) moonlight
   - (d) a student

5. Which of the following can be *delicate?*
   - (a) a china plate
   - (b) a problem
   - (c) a rescue
   - (d) a person's health

6. Which of the following is a *decade?*
   - (a) the 1990s
   - (b) from 1901 to 1999
   - (c) the 1700s
   - (d) 120 months

7. Which of the following might one find in a *wilderness?*
   - (a) schools
   - (b) trees
   - (c) a herd of deer
   - (d) a shopping mall

8. Which of the following would you not *tolerate?*
   - (a) cheating
   - (b) obedience
   - (c) crime
   - (d) prosperity

14D Word Relationships

In each of the groups below, circle the two words that are synonyms.

1. ASSOCIATE   PROVIDE
   CONNECT   CHANGE

2. TAUNT   TRANSFORM
   CHANGE   SHINE

3. CONCEAL   ACCEPT
   JEER   TOLERATE

4. REQUIRE   USE
   EMPLOY   ESTABLISH

5. SUPPLY   IDLE
   PROVIDE   ASK

In each of the groups below, circle the two words that are antonyms.

6. BRILLIANT   DELICATE   9. QUIET   DELICATE
   VISIBLE   DULL   HEROIC   STRONG

7. METHODICAL   RELUCTANT   10. REASSURANCE   TAUNT
   BOISTEROUS   CALM   DECADE   ACCESS

8. REVIVE   WAIT
   OBSCURE   ILLUMINATE

14E Narrative

Read the narrative below; then complete the exercise that follows.

THE WIZARD OF MENLO PARK

Like other cities and towns in the late 1800s, New York City was a gloomy place at night. Streets were lit by flickering gas lights, if at all, and oil lamps or candles were all that people had to **illuminate** their homes. Thomas Edison had a better idea. In 1881 he built the world's first electric power station in Manhattan, helping to change New York into the **brilliantly** lit city we know today.

Edison was born in Ohio in 1847. When he was a small child, his family moved to Port Huron, Michigan. An attack of scarlet fever left him in **delicate** health. This worried his parents enough, so that they did not allow him to join in the **boisterous** games played at his school. The other children were not very **tolerant** of someone who stood apart from the rest, and young Edison had to suffer their **taunts**. His mother, who was a teacher, decided to take him out of school. She taught him at home, where he learned quickly. He asked many questions and liked to experiment on his own to find answers.

At that time much of Michigan was **wilderness,** but the railroad was **transforming** America by making even the most remote places **accessible** to the rest of the country. When the railroad came to Port Huron, it **provided** Edison with his first job. At the age of twelve he was given permission to sell newspapers and candy on the train that ran between his hometown and Detroit. He even printed his own newspaper, which he sold for three cents a copy.

At sixteen he started working full-time on the railroad. For the next four years, he was **employed** as a telegraph operator in different towns. However, there were large portions of the day when he had nothing to do, and Thomas Edison hated to be **idle.** In addition, he **required** only five or six hours of sleep a night. So it was during this time that he began working on inventions along with his experiments.

At twenty-one he invented an electrical vote counter, for which he was given a patent. This meant that the government identified him as the person who thought up the idea and protected it so that it could not be made or sold by others without his permission. When he was thirty, Edison established a research center at Menlo Park, New Jersey, where he and his **associates** ran what was really an inventions factory.

Over the next five **decades**, Edison was granted over a thousand patents by the United States government. Perhaps his most famous invention was the electric light bulb, but others included the record player (which he called a phonograph) and the movie camera. These things seemed like magic to people, so it isn't surprising that he became known as "the Wizard of Menlo Park." The once sickly child outlived most of his schoolmates—when he died in 1931, he was eighty-four years old.

Answer each of the following questions in a sentence. If a question does not contain a vocabulary word, use a vocabulary word in your answer. Use each word only once. Questions and answers will then contain all fifteen words (or forms of the words) from this lesson's word list.

1. How does the narrative make clear that there were few towns in Michigan during Edison's youth?

   _____

2. In what way was the railroad important in Edison's early life?

   _____

3. With what invention do most people **associate** Edison?

   _____

4. What is the meaning of **illuminate** as it is used in the narrative?

   _____

5. Why might Edison have been reluctant to go to school?

   _____

6. What **boisterous** activities might Edison's schoolmates have engaged in?

   _____

7. What details in the narrative show that Edison's mother would not **tolerate** the behavior of Edison's classmates?

   _____

8. What is the meaning of **delicate** as it is used in the narrative?

   _____

9. Why did Edison have **access** to the train from Port Huron to Detroit?

_____

10. As a young man, how did Edison **employ** a lot of his free time?

_____

11. What is the meaning of **idle** as it is used in the narrative?

_____

12. How did Edison change New York City?

_____

13. How would you describe Edison's mind?

_____

14. What must one do to protect a new invention from being copied by others?

_____

15. How long did Edison live?

_____

WORDLY WISE

The Greek word for "ten" is *deka;* it was borrowed by the Romans and became *deca.* Much later it was borrowed once again by the English-speaking people and is found in the word **decade** and also in *December,* which is the *twelfth* month of our year. Why, then, isn't December the tenth month? The answer is that it was the tenth month for the Romans of long ago. When English speakers made it their twelfth month, they still kept the name.

Several nouns are formed from the verb **employ.** An *employee* is a person who works for someone else and is paid for this. An *employer* is a person who gives work to others and pays them. *Employment* is the state or condition of having work or the work itself.

Idle and *idol* are homophones. An *idol* is something, such as a carved figure, that is worshiped as a god. It can also be a person, such as a movie star or sports figure, who is greatly admired.

Illuminate comes from *lumen* the Latin word for "light." Other English words formed from this root include *luminous,* glowing with light, and *luminosity,* the amount of light given off, usually from within a thing itself, for example, a star. (The star with the greatest *luminosity,* apart from our own sun, is Sirius, also known as the Dog Star.)

Lesson 15

Word List

Study the definitions of the words below; then do the exercises for the lesson.

disaster
di zas´ tər

n. Something that causes great damage or harm.
[Hurricane Andrew was the worst *disaster* to hit southern Florida in many years.]
disastrous *adj.* Causing much damage or harm.
[The *disastrous* floods in the Midwest left many people homeless.]

flee
flē

v. To run away from danger or from something frightening.
[I quickly decided to *flee* from the park when I heard a noise behind me.]
fled *past tense.*
[We *fled* from the house when we awoke and smelled gas.]

fracture
frak´ chər

n. A crack or break, as in metal or bone.
[The plane was grounded because of a small *fracture* in the metal tail unit.]
v. To crack or break.
[Ruth *fractured* her arm for the second time this summer when she fell from the swing.]

immense
im mens´

adj. 1. Great in size or extent.
[The Pacific Ocean is an *immense* body of water.]
2. Great in degree.
[To the *immense* relief of his parents, the lost child was soon found.]

intense
in tens´

adj. 1. Very strong; very great.
[The *intense* heat from the fire melted the plastic dishes.]
2. Showing great depth of feeling.
[The scene in the play where the slaves are liberated from bondage is so *intense* that the audience often weeps.]
intensity *n.* Great strength or force.
[The *intensity* of light from the sun is greatest at noon.]

investigate
in ves´ tə gāt

v. To look into closely; to study in great detail.
[The fire marshal will *investigate* the cause of the fire in the old mill.]

lurch
lurch

v. To move forward or to one side suddenly and unexpectedly.
[The car *lurched* to the left to avoid a pothole in the road.]
n. A jerking or swaying movement.
[The bus started with a *lurch*, throwing the standing passengers off balance.]

major
mā´ jər

adj. Great in size, number, or importance.
[Seas and oceans make up the *major* part of the earth's surface.]
n. 1. A military officer just above a captain in rank.
[A colonel is superior in rank to a *major*.]
2. The main subject a student is studying.
[My *major* in college will be Russian.]
v. To study as one's most important subject.
[My cousin Karen *majored* in chemistry and mathematics at Berea College.]

minor
mī´ nər

adj. 1. Small; unimportant.
[Steffi Graf's knee injury was *minor,* so she finished the match.]
n. A person who is not yet an adult; a child.
[*Minors* may attend this movie if an adult goes with them.]

petrify
pe´ tri fī

v. 1. To make rigid with terror; to terrify.
[The director said that he felt his horror movies had failed if they did not *petrify* audiences.]
2. To change into a stonelike substance.
[In Arizona's Painted Desert, we saw examples of wood that had *petrified* over millions of years.]

predict
prē dikt´

v. To say what will happen before it takes place.
[The state office on highway safety *predicts* heavy traffic on the roads this Labor Day weekend.]
prediction   *n.* Something that is predicted.
[The *prediction* of a blizzard by the National Weather Service kept people from traveling last night.]

prone
prōn

adj. 1. Likely to have or do.
[All of us are more *prone* to colds in the winter than in the summer.]
2. Lying face downward.
[I had to lie in a *prone* position because my back was so sunburned.]

sparse
spärs

adj. 1. Thinly grown or spread.
[The grass near the driveway was *sparse,* so we reseeded it.]
2. Not crowded.
[The town meeting had a *sparse* turnout this year.]

topple
täp´ əl

v. 1. To fall or push over.
[The cat *toppled* the pile of books.]
2. To overthrow.
[The student demonstrations helped to *topple* the government.]

urban
ʉr´ bən

adj. Having to do with cities.
[Traffic in *urban* areas is a serious problem during rush hour.]

15A Finding Meanings

Choose two phrases to form a sentence that correctly uses a word from Word List 15. Write each sentence in the space provided.

1. (a) is one that is small and scattered.
   (b) A sparse crowd

   (c) is one that is very boisterous.
   (d) An immense crowd

_____

2. (a) To investigate someone is to
   (b) terrify that person.

   (c) To petrify someone is to
   (d) come to that person's aid.

_____

3. (a) An intense pain is one that
   (b) lasts for a long time.

   (c) A minor pain is one that
   (d) is very great.

_____

4. (a) A prone figure is one
   (b) that is lying face down.

   (c) that stands alone.
   (d) A fleeing figure is one

_____

5. (a) keep it from happening.
   (b) To predict an accident is to

   (c) look into it closely.
   (d) To investigate an accident is to

_____

6. (a) a person who works in a mine.
   (b) a person who is not yet an adult.

   (c) A minor is
   (d) A major is

_____

7. (a) To lurch is to
   (b) To flee is to

   (c) lie in a facedown position.
   (d) move forward suddenly.

_____

8. (a) A prediction is
   (b) A disaster is

   (c) a reminder of a past event.
   (d) a forecast of what will happen.

_____

9. (a) a student's main subject.
   (b) a small wavelike movement.

   (c) A fracture is
   (d) A major is

_____

10. (a) An immense area is one
    (b) An urban area is one

    (c) that is very large.
    (d) that has few people.

_____

15B Just the Right Word

Improve each of the following sentences by crossing out the italicized phrase and replacing it with a word (or a form of the word) from Word List 15.

1. We *ran away* when the dog behind the flimsy gate started growling at us.

2. Much of the eastern United States that was wilderness in the 1700s is now *made up of cities and towns.*

3. The fire was a *terrible event that caused great damage,* but, fortunately, no lives were lost.

4. The car's *sudden movement* to the right told me we had a flat tire.

5. The *crack or break* in my arm took several weeks to heal.

6. The wood is millions of years old and has slowly *turned into a stonelike substance.*

7. The crossing guard's *first and most important* concern is the safety of the children as they are walking to school.

8. The *great force* of the speaker's words brought silence to the large crowd gathered for the memorial service.

9. Premature babies are *very likely* to suffer from lung problems.

10. The Mexican people *ended the rule of* President Diaz in 1910.

15C Applying Meanings

Circle the letter of each correct answer to the questions below. A question may have more than one correct answer.

1. Which of the following would you expect to see in an *urban* area?
   (a) farm animals
   (b) dirt roads
   (c) neon signs
   (d) skyscrapers

2. Which of the following could be *disastrous?*
   (a) an avalanche
   (b) a blizzard
   (c) an accomplishment
   (d) a voyage

3. Which of the following might one *predict*?
   (a) a person's age   (c) the result of an election
   (b) a blizzard   (d) the result of an experiment

4. Which of the following is a *minor* injury?
   (a) a scratched finger   (c) a severed finger
   (b) a pulled muscle   (d) a black eye

5. Which of the following is a *fracture*?
   (a) a broken leg   (c) a broken heart
   (b) a broken promise   (d) a broken arm

6. Which of the following would be visible on a *prone* person?
   (a) the stomach   (c) the back
   (b) the necktie   (d) the knees

7. Which of the following might one *investigate*?
   (a) a decade   (c) a crime
   (b) an explosion   (d) an accident

8. Which of the following can be *toppled*?
   (a) a tower   (c) a stack of books
   (b) a government   (d) a statue

15D Word Relationships

In each of the groups below, circle the two words that are synonyms.

1. MEND   OVERTHROW
   TOPPLE   FRACTURE

2. EXAMINE   PREDICT
   FIND   INVESTIGATE

3. FRACTURE   FLEE
   BREAK   TAUNT

4. TOLERANT   DISASTROUS
   MINOR   TERRIBLE

5. PETRIFY   PREDICT
   FASCINATE   FORETELL

In each of the groups below, circle the two words that are antonyms.

6. TIDY   PRONE
   DENSE   SPARSE

7. IMMENSE   TOLERANT
   TINY   VISIBLE

8. MAJOR   MEAGER
   METHODICAL MINOR

9. FLEE   LURCH
   REMAIN   PETRIFY

10. SLUGGISH   INTENSE
    WEAK   PUNY

15E Narrative

Read the narrative below; then complete the exercise that follows.

WHEN THE EARTH QUAKES

Those who have lived through an earthquake describe it as one of the worst experiences of their lives. When one strikes, often without warning, people are usually too **petrified** to move. The ground, which a few moments before seemed so solid, suddenly **lurches** beneath their feet. Pictures are shaken from the walls, and if the earthquake is severe enough, the walls themselves may **topple.** Water and gas pipes burst, fires flare up, and lives may be lost.

The **intensity** of an earthquake, is determined by a measure called the Richter scale. An earthquake measuring 4.0 is considered **minor,** causing little, if any, harm. One measuring 8.0 is more than one thousand times as powerful and can do **immense** damage. Another measure of the destructive power of an earthquake is the number of lives lost. One of the greatest natural **disasters** in history was the earthquake that struck China in 1556, killing almost a million people.

Earthquakes do the greatest damage in **urban** areas where people are concentrated. Most of the deaths and injuries occur when people are inside collapsing buildings. The San Francisco earthquake of 1906 measured 8.3 and killed 450 people; in 1964, Alaska, which is more **sparsely** settled, also experienced an earthquake measuring 8.3, but there were fewer than 200 deaths.

Scientists who **investigate** the causes of earthquakes are called seismologists. They have learned a great deal about these frightening occurrences. We know that the earth's crust or surface is made of rock five to twenty miles thick, which is **fractured** in many places. The separate pieces, or plates, fit more or less together along the break lines, which are known as "faults." Heat from the earth's interior puts pressure on these plates, causing them to move. Sometimes they rub against each other edge to edge; at other times one plate may ride up over another. These kinds of movements cause earthquakes.

Areas that lie along faults in the earth's crust are especially **prone** to earthquakes, but quakes can occur anywhere in the world. San Francisco lies on the San Andreas Fault, where the Pacific and North American plates meet. It has had two **major** earthquakes in the last century. The Pacific coast regions of Central and South America, where the Nazca and South American plates meet, have also suffered many earthquakes and will continue to do so.

Unfortunately, we still do not know enough about earthquakes to be able to **predict** accurately when one will occur. We do, however, make sure that today's buildings and bridges are strong enough to stand up to them. That is one reason why the 1989 San Francisco earthquake, which measured 6.9 on the Richter scale, took so few lives. But earthquakes are still to be feared. If you should have the misfortune to get caught in one, your first thought might be to **flee** to the nearest open space. Experts tell us, however, that if you are in a modern building, it is probably safer to stay inside. Look for shelter under a sturdy table or in a doorway.

Answer each of the following questions in a sentence. If a question does not contain a vocabulary word, use a vocabulary word in your answer. Use each word only once. Questions and answers will then contain all fifteen words (or forms of the words) from this lesson's word list.

1. What do seismologists do?

   _____

2. What do the instruments used by seismologists measure?

   _____

3. Why did scientists not know the 1989 San Francisco earthquake was coming?

   _____

4. What **urban** area is on the San Andreas Fault?

   _____

5. What is the meaning of **topple** as it is used in the narrative?

   _____

6. What might cause people to fall during an earthquake?

   _____

7. What is the meaning of **minor** as it is used in the narrative?

   _____

8. How might a person describe what it feels like to live through an earthquake?

   _____

9. What would be the result of an earthquake in a city with many flimsy buildings?

   _____

10. How serious would an earthquake measuring 7.8 on the Richter scale be?

   _____

11. In what kind of area is an earthquake likely to do the least damage?

_____

12. Why do you think streets are often flooded after an earthquake?

_____

13. What is the meaning of **prone** as it is used in the narrative?

_____

14. How great was the loss of life in China's 1556 earthquake?

_____

15. During an earthquake, when is it a good idea to **flee** to an open space?

_____

WORDLY WISE

This is an *asterisk* (*). It looks like a star, and in fact the word comes from the Latin word for "star," which is *aster*. **Disaster** comes from the Latin prefix *dis-*, which means "against," and this Latin word for "star." But what does a disaster have to do with the stars? It was once believed (and still is, by some people) that the position of the stars had an effect on people's daily lives. If something bad (a *disaster*) happened to you, it was because the *stars* were *against* you.

Two other words formed from this same root are *astronomy*, the scientific study of planets and stars, and *astrology*, the belief that the stars have an effect on people's daily lives.

✦ ✦ ✦ ✦ ✦ ✦ ✦

If you *break* a leg, you have a **fracture**. If you drop a cup it will *break* into *fragments*. If you *break* down the number 1 into smaller parts, such as halves or quarters, you get *fractions*. Something easily *broken* is *fragile*. All four of these words come from the Latin *frangere* or *fractus*, which means "to break."

✦ ✦ ✦ ✦ ✦ ✦ ✦

The Latin prefix *pre-* means "before." A *premature* baby is one born *before* it is *mature* enough to leave the womb. Knowing this, and keeping in mind the explanation of *dictate* in Wordly Wise 12 (page 101), you should be able to understand how **predict** is formed.

Lesson 16

Word List

Study the definitions of the words below; then do the exercises for the lesson.

abdicate
ab´ di kāt

v. To give up a high office.
[When Edward VIII *abdicated* the throne in 1936, his younger brother became king of England.]

assume
ə so͞om´

v. 1. To take for granted; to suppose.
[We cannot *assume* that Mom and Dad will meet us at the station if the train is two hours late.]
2. To take over; to occupy.
[President Clinton *assumed* office on January 20, 1993.]
3. To pretend to have.
[Edin *assumed* a look of innocence when Vilma asked who had eaten the cookies.]

bungle
buŋ´ gəl

v. To do something badly or without skill.
[Because the shortstop *bungled* the double play, the runner made it safely to first base.]

dominate
däm´ ə nāt

v. 1. To rule or control; to have a very important place or position.
[Rock *dominated* popular music in America for several decades.]
2. To rise high above.
[The Sears Tower *dominates* the Chicago skyline.]

former
fôr´ mər

adj. Coming before in time; having been at an earlier time.
[Three *former* mayors were invited to the dedication of our new city hall.]
n. The first of two just mentioned.
[Both the crocodile and the alligator are dangerous, but the *former* is more aggressive.]

guardian
gär´ dē ən

n. 1. One who protects.
[This ferocious dog acts as *guardian* of the property at night.]
2. One who legally has the care of another person.
[You need the permission of your parent or *guardian* to go on field trips.]

hoist
hoist

v. To lift or raise, especially by using a rope.
[The sailors *hoisted* the sails as we left the harbor.]
n. Something used to lift, as a crane or pulley.
[We cannot raise this unwieldy machine without a *hoist*.]

intercept
in tər sept´

v. To stop or seize something while it is on its way somewhere.
[The Coast Guard can *intercept* boats in United States waters to investigate their cargoes.]

jubilee
jo͞o´ bə lē

n. The celebration of an anniversary, especially a fiftieth anniversary.
[The school marked its *jubilee* with a banquet for graduates from the past fifty years.]

kin
kin

adj. Related by birth or marriage.
[Are you *kin* to the Jordans or are you just a friend of theirs?]
n. pl. (also **kinfolk**) Relatives; family.
[She celebrated her ninetieth birthday with all her *kin* around her.]
next of kin   The person most closely related to someone.
[The hospital requires the name of your *next of kin* when you are admitted.]

pardon
pärd´ n

v. 1. To forgive.
[Alice *pardoned* the Red Queen's rude remark.]
2. To free from legal punishment.
[On taking office, President Ford *pardoned* ex-President Nixon.]
n. The act of forgiving or freeing from legal punishment.
[Many Americans were angered by President Ford's *pardon* of Richard Nixon.]

proclaim
prō klām´

v. To make known publicly; to announce.
[The mayor *proclaimed* May 18 a city holiday.]

provoke
prō vōk´

v. 1. To annoy or make angry.
[Josh said he took Katie's toys away because she *provoked* him with her constant talking.]
2. To call forth; to rouse.
[Senator Biden's comments *provoked* laughter in the audience.]
provocative   *adj.* (prō väk´ ə tiv) Calling forth anger, amusement, or thoughtfulness; trying to cause a response.
[You were being *provocative* when you kept asking the same question over and over.]

reign
rān

v. 1. To rule as a queen or king.
[King Hussein of Jordan *reigned* for over forty years.]
2. To be widespread.
[Terror *reigned* in the streets of Paris during the French Revolution.]
n. 1. The rule of a queen or king; the time during which a person rules.
[The American Revolution occurred during the *reign* of George III.]

riot
rī´ ət

n. 1. Public disorder or violence.
[The 1992 *riots* in Los Angeles continued for several days.]
2. A great and seemingly disordered quantity of something.
[Catherine's rose garden is a *riot* of color in the summer.]
v. To take part in a disorder.
[As the crowd of townspeople *rioted*, the British soldiers opened fire.]

16A Finding Meanings

Choose two phrases to form a sentence that correctly uses a word from Word List 16. Write each sentence in the space provided.

1. (a) To intercept something
   (b) To assume something

   (c) is to deliver it to its destination.
   (d) is to take it for granted.

2. (a) A pardon is   (c) a good deed that goes unrewarded.
    (b) A jubilee is   (d) a celebration to mark an anniversary.

3. (a) To riot is to   (c) give up a position of responsibility.
    (b) To reign is to   (d) take part in a public disorder.

4. (a) To hoist something is to   (c) seize it while it is on its way.
    (b) examine it closely.   (d) To intercept something is to

5. (a) control that person.   (c) forgive that person.
    (b) To pardon someone is to   (d) To provoke someone is to

6. (a) To be someone's guardian is to be   (c) friendly with that person.
    (b) To be someone's kin is to be   (d) related to that person.

7. (a) To reign is to   (c) rise to a higher level.
    (b) give up a high office.   (d) To abdicate is to

8. (a) whose work is in great demand.   (c) who arouses interest or anger.
    (b) A provocative speechwriter is one   (d) A former speechwriter is one

9. (a) lift it by using ropes.   (c) To bungle something is to
    (b) make it widely known.   (d) To hoist something is to

10. (a) To assume a position   (c) is to take it over.
    (b) To proclaim a position   (d) is to lie about it.

16B Just the Right Word

Improve each of the following sentences by crossing out the italicized phrase and replacing it with a word (or a form of the word) from Word List 16.

1. The hospital usually calls your *closest relation* if you are in an accident.

2. Are you trying to *stir things up and cause* a quarrel between your brothers?

3. Cleopatra *occupied the throne and ruled as queen* in Egypt from 51 B.C. to 30 B.C.

4. Singing this solo was my big chance to have a part in the musical, but I'm afraid I *didn't do a very good job of* it.

5. The painting's *seemingly disordered quantity* of color dazzles the eye.

6. Are you the *person legally named to act as parent* of this child?

7. September has been *publicly announced as* "National Seafood Month."

8. After the fall of the Berlin Wall, many feared that Germany might *be much stronger than* the other countries of Europe.

9. Sometimes, Hope will *pretend to have* an Irish accent because she likes the way it sounds.

10. Labradors and collies are both good with children, but I prefer the *first of the two mentioned*.

16C Applying Meanings

Circle the letter of each correct answer to the questions below. A question may have more than one correct answer.

1. Which of the following could be *abdicated?*
   (a) a high office   (c) a school
   (b) an obstacle   (d) a throne

2. Which of the following would be your *kin?*
   (a) your next-door neighbor   (c) your pet rabbit
   (b) your best friend   (d) your uncle's wife

3. Which of the following might be *intercepted?*
   (a) a message   (c) a ball
   (b) a tempest   (d) a disaster

4. Which of the following might be *proclaimed?*
   (a) a result   (c) a pardon
   (b) a portrait   (d) a pledge

5. Which of the following might be *pardoned?*
   (a) a mistake   (c) a drought
   (b) an insult   (d) a rebel

6. Which of the following might *dominate* the skyline?
   (a) a tower   (c) a skyscraper
   (b) a lighthouse   (d) a stop sign

7. After what period of time might a *jubilee* be celebrated?
   (a) one year   (c) sixty years
   (b) fifty years   (d) one hundred days

8. Which of the following can one *assume?*
   (a) a leadership position   (c) a look of surprise
   (b) warm weather in the tropics (d) the presidency

16D Word Relationships

In each of the groups below, circle the two words that are synonyms.

1. KIN   FORMER
   PRONE   RELATED

2. RULE   ABDICATE
   REIGN   SUFFER

3. PROHIBIT   PROCLAIM
   ANNOY   PROVOKE

4. SEIZE   RAISE
   CONTROL   INTERCEPT

5. PORTRAIT   ASSOCIATE
   GUARDIAN   PROTECTOR

In each of the groups below, circle the two words that are antonyms.

6. LOWER   RIOT
   STEAL   HOIST

7. ABDICATE   MISHANDLE
   ASSUME   BUNGLE

8. TERMINATE   ACCOMPLISH
   FORGIVE   BUNGLE

9. MAJOR   FORMER
   CURRENT   SOONER

10. RESENT   PARDON
    RESTRICT   PROCEED

16E Narrative

Read the narrative below; then complete the exercise that follows.

THE LAST QUEEN OF THE ISLANDS

Although she never dreamed it would happen, Liliuokalani grew up to become the queen of the Hawaiian Islands. Born on the island of Oahu in 1838, she was in her teens when her parents died. Her older brother Kalakaua became her **guardian**. They were **kin** to the Hawaiian royal family, but Kalakaua was not expected to succeed to the throne.

When King Lunalilo died in 1874, after ruling for barely one year, many believed that Queen Emma, widow of a **former** king, would be chosen to succeed him. It came as a surprise to Queen Emma's supporters that the elected members of Hawaii's governing body passed her by and **proclaimed** Kalakaua king instead.

King Kalakaua **reigned** for seventeen years. He had no children, so following the death of his younger brother in 1877, he chose Liliuokalani to succeed him to the throne. She ruled in her brother's place when he was absent from the kingdom and represented him at Queen Victoria's Golden **Jubilee** in London in 1887. The islands were **dominated** at that time by powerful planters and businessmen, as well as by Sanford Dole, who was a powerful political leader and lawyer. In 1887, this group forced Kalakaua to sign away almost all of his powers, making him Hawaii's ruler in name only.

Liliuokalani ascended the throne of Hawaii following her brother's death in 1891 and promptly set about regaining real power. The Hawaiian people resented the takeover of their government by the *haoles,* as they called the white-skinned Americans, and supported their queen. When Liliuokalani declared a plan for government that gave more power to native Hawaiians, the *haoles* formed a committee to stop her. On January 16, 1893, the *haole* leaders brought in American sailors and marines, who were stationed on nearby ships, to prevent **riots** from breaking out in support of the queen.

The next day, the committee of *haoles* set up its own government with Sanford Dole as leader. Liliuokalani opposed this and asked the president of the United States for help. After an investigation, President Grover Cleveland ordered that Liliuokalani be returned to the throne. But Dole claimed that the U.S. government had no right to interfere in Hawaii's affairs, and on July 4, 1894, he **assumed** the presidency of the new Republic of Hawaii. Liluokalani remained queen, but with no power to govern.

Early next year, a group of Liliuokalani's supporters rebelled against the new government. The attempt was badly **bungled,** failing miserably. Dole accused Liliuokalani of **provoking** it and arrested her. Although she steadfastly denied being involved, messages between her and her followers had been **intercepted**, and weapons were found in her home. Liliuokalani was told that if she would **abdicate**, her supporters, who were then in jail, would not be put to death. To save their lives, she agreed to step down. She was sentenced to five years imprisonment for her role in the revolt. After eight months Dole **pardoned** her on the condition that she take no further part in politics, and she withdrew to her home, where she continued to fly the Hawaiian flag.

In 1898, Hawaii became part of the United States, with Sanford Dole serving as governor. During World War One, the first Hawaiians died fighting for the United States against Germany. The day she received the news, Liliuokalani lowered the Hawaiian flag and **hoisted** the Stars and Stripes.

Answer each of the following questions in a sentence. If a question does not contain a vocabulary word, use a vocabulary word in your answer. Use each word only once. Questions and answers will then contain all fifteen words (or forms of the words) from this lesson's word list.

1. What do you think was the significance of Liliuokalani's **hoisting** the Stars and Stripes?

    _____

2. What is the meaning of **guardian** as it is used in the narrative?

    _____

3. What did Queen Emma expect to happen when Lunalilo died?

    _____

4. Why didn't Liliuokalani think about becoming queen of the Hawaiian Islands when she was a young girl?

    _____

5. Why was Queen Emma a very strong choice for ruler of Hawaii in 1874?

    _____

6. Why did Liliuokalani visit London in 1887?

    _____

7. Why couldn't President Cleveland **dominate** Sanford Dole?

    _____

8. Why were American sailors and marines brought to land in January 1893?

    _____

9. Why was Liliuokalani's situation so difficult when she was asked to **abdicate**?

    _____

10. What is the meaning of **assumed** as it is used in the narrative?

    _____

11. Why did Dole's government continue to rule after the rebellion of 1895?

    _____

12. Why did the *haoles* claim that Liliuokalani took part in the 1895 uprising?

    _____

13. How did Liliuokalani respond when accused of being responsible for the 1895 rebellion?

    _____

14. What is the meaning of **pardoned** as it is used in the narrative?

    _____

15. How many years was Liliuokalani queen before Hawaii became a republic?

    _____

WORDLY WISE

The antonym of **former** is *latter*. If given a choice between silk and cotton, and you choose the *latter*, you will get cotton. If you choose the *former*, you will get silk.

The Latin prefix *inter-* means "between." *Inter*national affairs are those conducted *between* nations; *inter*state commerce is business conducted *between* states. This prefix is combined with the root from the Latin verb *capere*, "to take," to form the word **intercept**. Something that is *intercepted* is *taken* as it passes *between* the sender and the receiver.

Jubilee has an interesting story behind it. It comes from the Hebrew *yobhel*, which was a ram's horn used as a trumpet. It was blown every fifty years to celebrate the release of the Jews from bondage.

The word applies especially to a fiftieth anniversary but is used to mark other anniversaries as well. In 1897, Queen Victoria celebrated her Diamond Jubilee, by which time she had occupied the British throne for sixty years.

CROSSWORD PUZZLE

Solve the crossword puzzle below by studying the clues and filling in the answer boxes. Clues followed by a number are definitions of vocabulary words in Lessons 13 through 16. The number gives the lesson from which the answer to the clue is taken.

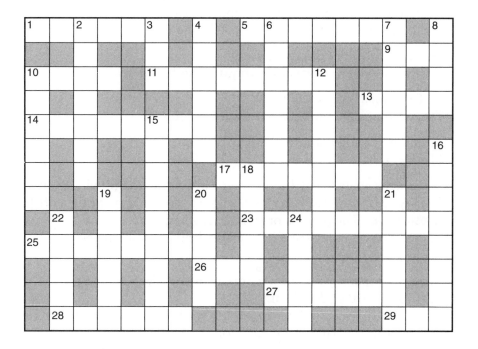

Clues Across

1. To fall over (15)
5. Able to be seen; within view (13)
9. Upset or angry
10. A violent public disorder (16)
11. Something that causes great damage (15)
13. To run from danger (15)
14. To make known publicly (16)
17. To say what will happen before it takes place (15)
23. To seize something while it is on its way (16)
25. One who protects (16)
26. To have
27. Opposite of "in front of"
28. Worn to protect the head
29. Adam and _____

Clues Down

2. To make angry (16)
3. Opposite of "begin"
4. To take for granted (16)
6. Showing great depth of feeling (15)
7. To hire and put to work for pay (14)
8. To do nothing (14)
10. A small wave (13)
12. To need (14)
15. A partner in business (14)
16. To stick out (13)
18. The rule of a queen or king (16)
19. A tasty tidbit (13)
20. A person who is not yet an adult (15)
21. A ten-year period (14)
22. To move suddenly and unexpectedly (15)
24. To become less wide at one end (13)

Lesson 17

Word List

Study the definitions of the words below; then do the exercises for the lesson.

afflict
ə flikt´
v. To bring or cause pain and suffering.
[The patient has been *afflicted* with swollen feet for several months.]
affliction   *n.* A condition of pain, suffering, or trouble.
[Frida Kahlo's *affliction* was the result of a serious accident.]

barren
bar´ ən
adj. Not fruitful; not reproducing.
[When the topsoil is washed away, the land is *barren*.]

consist
kən sist´
v. To be made up; to contain.
[The wedding banquet will *consist* of six courses.]

drought
drout
n. A long period without rain.
[The poor harvest was due to the *drought*.]

erode
ē rōd´
v. To wear away bit by bit; to wear away by action of wind, water, or ice.
[Heavy seas from yesterday's storm have *eroded* parts of the cliff.]
erosion   *n.* The process or state of eroding.
[Cutting down many trees in one area leads to soil *erosion*.]

expand
ek spand´
v. 1. To make or become larger.
[You can *expand* your chest by taking a very deep breath.]
2. To give further details of.
[Mr. da Silva asked me to *expand* on some of the information in my report.]
expansion   *n.* The act, process, or result of enlarging.
[Ten new employees were hired as a result of the company's *expansion*.]

famine
fam´ in
n. A widespread and long-lasting shortage of food that may cause starvation.
[The *famine* in Somalia was the result of several poor harvests in a row.]

fertile
furt´ l
adj. 1. Able to produce good crops.
[The major reason we grow such large tomatoes is the *fertile* soil.]
2. Able to produce offspring.
[A female cat is *fertile* at six months.]
3. Able to produce ideas; inventive.
[Many ideas sprang from Edison's *fertile* brain.]

oasis
ō ā´ sis
n. **oases**   *n. pl.* (ō ā´ sēz) A place where there is water in an otherwise dry area.
[Travelers across the Sahara try to reach the next *oasis* before nightfall.]

pasture
pas´ chər
n. A field of growing grass where animals can eat; a meadow.
[We put the sheep in a different *pasture* to give the grass in this one a chance to grow back.]
v. To put animals out in a field to eat grass.
[We *pasture* our horses on a neighbor's land.]

primitive
prim´ i tiv

adj. 1. From earliest times; ancient.
[The *primitive* cave drawings at Lascaux, France, are over fifteen thousand years old.]
2. Simple or crude.
[The Weinsteins replaced the *primitive* shed behind the house with a modern garage.]

refuge
ref´ yo͞oj

n. 1. Shelter or protection from harm.
[The hikers found *refuge* from the blizzard in a nearby cave.]
2. A place of safety.
[During the hurricane, families living in beach houses found *refuge* in the high school gym.]
refugee *n.* A person forced to leave her or his home or country seeking protection from danger.
[A camp for Kurdish *refugees* was set up between Turkey and Iraq.]

revert
rē vŭrt´

v. To go back to an earlier condition, often one that is not as satisfactory.
[During the week that the electric power lines were being repaired, we *reverted* to eating our meals by candlelight and lantern.]

teem
tēm

v. To be filled; to occur in large numbers.
[The Columbia River once *teemed* with salmon.]

wither
with´ ər

v. To become dried out; to lose freshness.
[The crops will *wither* unless we have rain soon.]

17A Finding Meanings

Choose two phrases to form a sentence that correctly uses a word from Word List 17. Write each sentence in the space provided.

1. (a) go beyond what is permitted.
   (b) To expand is to
   (c) To erode is to
   (d) gradually wear away.

_____

2. (a) a place with water in an otherwise dry area.
   (b) a condition from which one suffers.
   (c) An oasis is
   (d) A pasture is

_____

3. (a) give more details about it.
   (b) To expand on something is to
   (c) To revert to something is to
   (d) mention it for the first time.

_____

4. (a) To consist of something is to
   (b) To teem with something is to
   (c) be made up of it.
   (d) be associated with it.

_____

5. (a) To wither is to   (c) go back to an earlier condition.
    (b) continue to improve.   (d) To revert is to

_____

6. (a) a place of safety in time of danger.   (c) A drought is
    (b) a grassy area where animals feed.   (d) A pasture is

_____

7. (a) To wither is to   (c) dry out from lack of water.
    (b) To teem is to   (d) sink to a lower level.

_____

8. (a) A famine is   (c) a long period without rain.
    (b) A drought is   (d) an area where little can grow.

_____

9. (a) An expansion is   (c) An affliction is
    (b) a place of great danger.   (d) a condition causing suffering.

_____

10. (a) A refuge is   (c) a person in poor health.
    (b) a place of safety.   (d) A famine is

_____

17B Just the Right Word

Improve each of the following sentences by crossing out the italicized phrase and replacing it with a word (or a form of the word) from Word List 17.

1. Al Kufrah is a well-known *place where water is found in an otherwise dry area* in Libya.

2. When children taunted her, it led to the *gradual wearing away* of her confidence.

3. The way the villagers draw water from the river may be *the same as that used in very early times*, but it is quite effective.

4. If the cow you bought is not *capable of producing calves*, the dealer will return the money you paid for it.

5. Our breakfast usually *is made up* of cereal, milk, fruit, and coffee.

6. Because the number of children taking tennis lessons is *growing larger* every year, we now offer three sessions during the summer.

7. Acid rain destroys lakes that once *were filled* with fish.

8. President Roosevelt was *made to suffer when he came down* with polio at the age of thirty-nine.

9. We *provide grass for* our goats in a neighbor's field.

10. Many *persons fleeing for their safety* from Nazi Germany came to the United States in the 1930s.

17C Applying Meanings

Circle the letter of each correct answer to the questions below. A question may have more than one correct answer.

1. Which of the following might *wither?*
   - (a) crops
   - (b) trees
   - (c) leaves
   - (d) beaches

2. Which of the following could one *expand?*
   - (a) one's knowledge
   - (b) one's age
   - (c) one's home
   - (d) one's chest

3. Which of the following can result from *famine?*
   - (a) despair
   - (b) sickness
   - (c) death
   - (d) hunger

4. Which of the following can be *barren?*
   - (a) a goat
   - (b) a valley
   - (c) a pear tree
   - (d) a pasture

5. Which of the following might occur during a *drought?*
   - (a) restrictions on water use
   - (b) forest fires
   - (c) a yearning for rain
   - (d) flooding

6. Which of the following can be *fertile?*
   - (a) a kitten
   - (b) soil
   - (c) a mind
   - (d) a morsel

7. Which of the following might one find in a *pasture?*
   - (a) cargo
   - (b) cows
   - (c) sheep
   - (d) grass

8. Which of the following can be *eroded?*
   (a) soil   (c) cliffs
   (b) confidence   (d) savings

17D Word Relationships

Each group of four words below contains two words that are either synonyms or antonyms. Circle these two words; and then circle the S if they are synonyms, the A if they are antonyms.

1. PASTURE   FAMINE
   SHELTER   REFUGE   S   A

2. TROUBLE   AFFECT
   AFFORD   AFFLICT   S   A

3. HUNGRY   BARREN
   FERTILE   MORSEL   S   A

4. PREDICTION   CONTRACTION
   RIPENESS   EXPANSION   S   A

5. DECIDE   CONTINUE
   REVERT   CONSIST   S   A

6. FLIMSY   WITHERED
   TEEMING   EMPTY   S   A

7. OASIS   REFUGE
   SAFETY   HUNGER   S   A

8. PRIMITIVE   BLOSSOMING
   WITHERED   FRIVOLOUS   S   A

9. DROUGHT   FLOOD
   FIRE   AVALANCHE   S   A

10. CRUDE   PRIMITIVE
    BRIEF   SPARSE   S   A

17E Narrative

Read the narrative below; then complete the exercise that follows.

A HARVEST OF SAND

The ability of the earth to support life depends on the amount of rainfall it receives. The tropical rain forests of Africa, Asia, and Central and South America, which are **teeming** with life, get up to four hundred inches a year. Yet in other parts of the world little or no rain falls, making the land **barren**. Areas where the annual rainfall is less than ten inches a year are called deserts.

The largest of the earth's deserts is the Sahara, in northern Africa, which covers an area almost as big as the United States. Apart from the central portion, which is mountainous, the Sahara **consists** mostly of sand. There is water, but it lies far below the surface in ancient underground lakes. In some places it bubbles to the surface in the form of springs. More often, though, wells have to be dug to get to it. In these places the soil is **fertile**, and people can grow crops and raise animals. **Oases** spring up around these places, often becoming the size of small towns. They are a welcome sight to the travelers who cross this harsh land on the backs of camels, or more commonly today, in four-wheel-drive vehicles.

South of the Sahara are the countries that make up the Sahel, an area that stretches four thousand miles from Senegal in the west to Ethiopia in the east. This part of Africa was once mostly grassland that provided good **pasture** for cattle and made it possible for the people of these countries to be reasonably well fed. In recent years, however, it has been **afflicted** with long dry spells, the worst in nearly two centuries. As the **droughts** continue, rivers and lakes dry up; without water, the grass **withers** and the cattle are left with nothing to feed on. To make matters worse, too many trees that held the soil in place have been cut down for firewood, resulting in widespread soil **erosion**.

Because of changing weather patterns, the Sahara is spreading into the Sahel. As it continues to **expand** southward, the Sahara has taken over more than a quarter of a million square miles since the 1950s. This is equivalent to an area roughly the size of France and Austria combined. Although nothing can be done to change weather patterns, scientists believe that in time conditions will change and the land that is now desert may **revert** to grassland.

The people of the Sahel have suffered greatly, however. Hundreds of thousands have already died as a result of **famine**, and one third of all the children born in the Sahel still die before their fifth birthdays. Millions have left their once prosperous villages and have poured into the overcrowded cities to the south, where they live in **primitive** shelters. Nouakchott, a town on Africa's west coast was home to fewer than twenty thousand people in 1960. In less than thirty years that number had increased to three hundred fifty thousand, most of them **refugees** from the slowly spreading desert to the north.

Answer each of the following questions in a sentence. If a question does not contain a vocabulary word, use a vocabulary word in your answer. Use each word only once. Questions and answers will then contain all fifteen words (or forms of the words) from this lesson's word list.

1. Why are deserts **barren** places?

   _____

2. What happens to the people of the Sahel who are driven from their land?

   _____

3. Where is it possible to grow crops in the Sahara?

   _____

4. How has the Sahara changed in recent years?

   _____

5. What is the meaning of **fertile** as it is used in the narrative?

   _____

6. In what way do tropical rain forests differ from deserts?

   _____

7. What is the main cause of **drought** in the Sahel?

   _____

8. What is the meaning of **primitive** as it is used in the narrative?

   _____

9. How are cattle affected by the worsening conditions in the Sahel?

   _____

10. What happens to plants that don't get enough water?

    _____

11. Why does the cutting down of trees lead to soil **erosion**?

_____

12. Why do scientists think that the Sahel may not remain a desert?

_____

13. How does the present dry spell in the Sahel compare with those in the past?

_____

14. Why would the Sahara have a brownish color when seen from space?

_____

15. How can food shipments from outside help the people of the Sahel?

_____

WORDLY WISE

To **afflict** is to cause pain and suffering. To *inflict* (Word List 6) is to cause something damaging or painful to be felt. If you are confused by the similarity in meaning of these two words, you are not alone. The difference between them is that *afflict* deals with what is *felt,* whereas *inflict* with what is *done.* In the sentence "The judge *inflicted* a severe sentence," the judge *did* something. In the sentence "The prisoner was *afflicted* with guilt," the prisoner *felt* something.

Don't confuse the adjective **barren** with its homophone *baron,* which is a noun and means "a nobleman." The female equivalent is *baroness.*

Primitive tools, which may be tens of thousand of years old, are found buried in many parts of the world. They are among the first tools made by humans, as the word *primitive* suggests. It comes from the Latin *primus,* which means "first." A number of other English words share this root. A *primary* reason is one that comes *first* in importance; a *primer* is a book of *first* instruction in a subject; and a *prime* minister in many countries is the leader who is *first* in importance.

Wither, a verb, should not be confused with the adverb *whither,* meaning "to what place; where." These two words are not homophones because the "h" in *whither* is sounded. *Whither* is a poetic word that is falling out of use. Once when people wished to know where someone was going, they would ask, "Whither are you going?" or "Whither goest thou?"

Lesson 18

Word List

Study the definitions of the words below; then do the exercises for the lesson.

animated
an´ ə māt əd

adj. 1. Alive or seeming to be alive.
[The movie combines *animated* cartoon figures with live actors.]
2. Full of energy; lively.
[The class discussion became quite *animated* when we considered drug tests for student athletes.]

betray
bē trā´

v. 1. To be disloyal to.
[Members of the Underground Railroad could be counted on not to *betray* escaping slaves to their owners.]
2. To show; to reveal.
[Jonas insisted that he wasn't upset, but his tears *betrayed* his true feelings.]

convince
kən vins´

v. To make someone feel sure or certain; to persuade.
[I tried to *convince* my parents that I was old enough to be left alone in the house.]

decline
dē klīn´

v. 1. To slope or pass to a lower level.
[The path *declines* sharply here, then rises.]
2. To refuse to accept.
[Olga *declined* my offer of a ride to school because she wanted to walk.]
3. To become less or weaker.
[Tiny Tim's health could *decline,* the ghost told Scrooge, if no one did anything to help.]
n. 1. A change to a smaller amount or lower level.
[The *decline* in attendance at the ballpark worries the team's owners.]
2. A loss of strength or power.
[The *decline* of the Roman Empire is the subject of a famous book by Edward Gibbon.]

hilarious
hi lar´ ē əs

adj. Very funny.
[The comedian's *hilarious* jokes had us all in stitches.]

likeness
līk´ nəs

n. The state of being similar; something that is similar.
[Your *likeness* to your sister is remarkable.]

meager
mē´ gər

adj. Poor in quality or insufficient in amount.
[A stale crust of bread makes a *meager* meal.]

mischief
mis´ chif

n. 1. Harm or damage.
[Our neighbor's meddling in other people's affairs caused a lot of *mischief*.]
2. Behavior that causes harm or trouble.
[Their *mischief* during class will get them in trouble.]
3. Playfulness; harmless amusement.
[Hiding her mother's hat was just the child's *mischief*.]
mischievous *adj.* (mis´ chə vəs) Playful in a naughty way.
[The *mischievous* cat pawed at the dog's tail.]

144

negotiate
ni gō´ shē āt

v. 1. To arrange by talking over.
[The teachers are meeting with the school board to *negotiate* a new contract.]
2. To travel successfully along or over.
[This slope has some difficult sections that only accomplished skiers can *negotiate*.]

obsolete
äb sə lēt´

adj. No longer sold or in wide use because out-of-date.
[Compact discs made records *obsolete*.]

retain
rē tān´

v. 1. To hold onto; to keep possession of.
[Because of today's victory, we *retained* our position at the top of the girls' hockey league.]
2. To hire the services of.
[The airline *retained* its own safety experts to investigate the wing fractures.]

sensation
sen sā´ shən

n. 1. A feeling that comes from stimulation of the senses.
[Drinking hot cocoa after two hours of sledding gave us a warm *sensation*.]
2. A feeling of great interest or excitement or the cause of such a feeling.
[The appearance at our school of the basketball star caused a *sensation*.]
sensational *adj.* 1. Causing great curiosity and interest.
[The *sensational* headline led me to buy the newspaper I saw at the supermarket.]
2. Very great or excellent.
[With your quick mind, you'll make a *sensational* addition to the debating team.]

somber
säm´ bər

adj. 1. Dark; gloomy.
[We began our hike under a *somber* sky; fortunately, the sun came out in the afternoon.]
2. Sad; serious.
[Grandfather's death put us in a *somber* mood.]

subsequent
sub´ sə kwənt

adj. Coming later; following.
[The first book in the series was a disappointment, but *subsequent* ones have been very enjoyable.]

vow
vou

v. To promise seriously.
[The rescue workers *vowed* to continue working until all those trapped in the building were freed.]
n. A pledge; a promise.
[When my parents became citizens of the United States, they made a *vow* to support this country.]

18A Finding Meanings

Choose two phrases to form a sentence that correctly uses a word from Word List 18. Write each sentence in the space provided.

1. (a) A hilarious story is
   (b) A mischievous story is
   (c) one that could cause trouble.
   (d) one that expresses optimism.

_____

2. (a) An animated speech is
   (b) one that is very lively.
   (c) A somber speech is
   (d) one that is reassuring.

_____

3. (a) To convince someone is to   (c) persuade that person.
   (b) make a promise to that person.   (d) To betray someone is to

---

4. (a) A sensation is   (c) a serious promise.
   (b) A vow is   (d) a serious weakness.

---

5. (a) To betray someone   (c) is to avoid that person.
   (b) To negotiate with someone   (d) is to be disloyal to that person.

---

6. (a) To retain a lawyer's services   (c) To decline a lawyer's services
   (b) is to decide not to use them.   (d) is to terminate them.

---

7. (a) one that is very funny.   (c) An obsolete form of entertainment is
   (b) one that costs a lot of money.   (d) A hilarious form of entertainment is

---

8. (a) To retain a contract is to   (c) arrange it by talking it over.
   (b) To negotiate a contract is to   (d) sign it.

---

9. (a) that causes great excitement.   (c) A meager costume is one
   (b) A sensational costume is one   (d) that is no longer in use.

---

10. (a) A subsequent meeting   (c) A somber meeting
    (b) is one that provokes laughter.   (d) is one that is very serious.

18B Just the Right word

Improve each of the following sentences by crossing out the italicized phrase and replacing it with a word (or a form of the word) from Word List 18.

1. My parents *hired the services of* a tutor to help me with my math.

2. Ten dollars seems a *very small* amount for doing such a lot of work.

3. Dial telephones are now *no longer used very much*.

4. When I met Sara's brother, I immediately noticed his *similarity in appearance* to her.

5. His nervous glances at the clock *gave away* his attempt to hide his anxiety.

6. The Cuddlibear was a *cause of great excitement* at the toy fair.

7. *Traveling successfully over* the icy road during the snowstorm was a challenge for me.

8. Reporting false emergencies to the police and similar *behavior that causes trouble* will result in severe punishment.

9. We discussed the matter at a *meeting that took place after the first* meeting.

10. Angela *made a serious promise* to be more patient with her younger brother.

18C Applying Meanings

Circle the letter of each correct answer to the questions below. A question may have more than one correct answer.

1. Which of the following can one *retain?*
   (a) a lawyer
   (b) one's pride
   (c) one's youth
   (d) one's memories

2. Which of the following can be a *sensation?*
   (a) warmth
   (b) cold
   (c) ice
   (d) fire

3. Which of the following is a *somber* color?
   (a) bright red   (c) pale pink
   (b) dark green   (d) deep brown

4. Which of the following might *decline*?
   (a) a pathway   (c) prices
   (b) one's health   (d) winter

5. Which of the following could one *betray*?
   (a) one's true feelings (c) one's country
   (b) a trust   (d) one's friends

6. Which of the following might one *vow* to do?
   (a) sneeze   (c) protect someone
   (b) love someone   (d) go shopping with someone

7. Which of the following is *animated*?
   (a) a carcass   (c) a cartoon film
   (b) a sleeping child   (d) a comic book

8. Which of the following is likely to cause *mischief*?
   (a) reassuring a classmate   (c) helping a friend
   (b) provoking a quarrel   (d) taunting a companion

18D Word Relationships

Each group of four words below contains two words that are either synonyms or antonyms. Circle these two words; then circle the S if they are synonyms, the A if they are antonyms.

1. REFUSAL   RESEMBLANCE
   MISCHIEF   LIKENESS   S   A

2. SOMBER   INTENSE
   HILARIOUS   TRUE   S   A

3. MISCHIEVOUS   FERTILE
   PLAYFUL   MEAGER   S   A

4. CONVINCE   VOW
   PREDICT   PERSUADE   S   A

5. GENEROUS   MEAGER
   FALSE   OBSOLETE   S   A

6. ACCEPT   BETRAY
   AFFLICT   DECLINE   S   A

| 7. | SPARSE | UP-TO-DATE | | |
| | FERTILE | OBSOLETE | S | A |

| 8. | OLD | PREVIOUS | | |
| | SUBSEQUENT | PROSPEROUS | S | A |

| 9. | OBSCURE | FEARFUL | | |
| | EXCELLENT | SENSATIONAL | S | A |

| 10. | SLUGGISH | ANIMATED | | |
| | PRIMITIVE | FRIVOLOUS | S | A |

18E Narrative

Read the narrative below; then complete the exercise that follows.

A MOUSE IS BORN

In 1927 Walt Disney worked in the movie business, producing short **animated** cartoons. He had started his own film company in Los Angeles four years before, at the age of twenty-one, with five hundred dollars borrowed from a relative. During those four years his business provided him with a **meager** living, and he worked hard on his films, struggling to pay off the debt.

His cartoons were about a character called Oswald, the Lucky Rabbit. A film distributor in New York had been buying his films and renting them to movie houses. The distributor could make a big profit if a film was successful, but Disney was paid a fixed amount for each movie; he got no share of the profits. When the contract with the distributor came to an end, Walt Disney decided to go to New York with his wife, Lilly, to **negotiate** a better deal for himself.

At the meeting, the distributor not only **declined** all of Disney's proposals, but also told the young filmmaker that he would reduce the payments he was making for each cartoon. He knew very well that Disney had no money to pay lawyers to fight him in the courts. Even worse, the distributor boasted that he had secretly hired Disney's own artists to do the drawings for future Oswald movies. Disney was bitter that the distributor had **betrayed** him, but there was nothing he could do about it. He **vowed** never to sell another of his movies to anyone. He would rent them to distributors, but in the future he would **retain** ownership.

Walt Disney was in a **somber** mood when he and Lilly boarded the train for Los Angeles. During the long journey across the country, he decided to create a new character to take the place of Oswald. After making a few marks on paper, he showed

Lilly a sketch of a mouse. Immediately she noticed the **likeness** between her husband and the creature he had drawn; both had a look of harmless **mischief**. She was **convinced** that audiences would love the little mouse with the happy face, but she was dismayed when her husband told her he planned to name it Mortimer. That just didn't sound right to her. "What about Mickey?" she suggested. "Mickey Mouse."

As soon as he arrived in Los Angeles, Walt Disney went to work on the first Mickey Mouse cartoons. He had completed two and was working on *Steamboat Willy*, his third, when sound began to be added to movies. Suddenly silent movies were **obsolete**. Disney promptly added a soundtrack to *Steamboat Willy*. The shrill voice of Mickey was supplied by Walt Disney himself.

When the movie opened in New York in September 1928, it was a **sensation**. Audiences roared with laughter at Mickey's **hilarious** adventures, and **subsequent** movies starring the lovable little mouse were equally successful at the box office. In just three years Walt Disney's company was worth hundreds of thousands of dollars and Mickey Mouse was famous.

Answer each of the following questions in a sentence. If a question does not contain a vocabulary word, use a vocabulary word in your answer. Use each word only once. Questions and answers will then contain all fifteen words (or forms of the words) from this lesson's word list.

1. How would you describe Walt Disney's income in 1927?

   _____

2. What work did Walt Disney do?

   _____

3. What is the meaning of **sensation** as it is used in the narrative?

   _____

4. Why did Disney want to meet with the distributor?

   _____

5. Why didn't Disney get a lawyer and sue the New York distributor?

   _____

6. How did the distributor respond to Disney's proposals for a new contract?

   _____

7. What is the meaning of **betrayed** as it is used in the narrative?

_____

8. What **mischief** did the distributor boast of to Disney?

_____

9. What is the meaning of **somber** as it is used in the narrative?

_____

10. What lesson did Disney learn from his experience with the distributor?

_____

11. What did Lilly notice about the little mouse Walt Disney had drawn?

_____

12. Why do you think silent movies became **obsolete**?

_____

13. What did Lilly do when her husband suggested the name of Mortimer Mouse?

_____

14. Which Disney movies after *Steamboat Willie* had sound?

_____

15. Why did audiences enjoy *Steamboat Willie*?

_____

WORDLY WISE

The Latin word for both "air" and "breath" is *anima*. It provides the root of several English words having to do with being alive, which seems natural since all *animals* must breathe in order to live. **Animated** figures in movie cartoons seem to be alive, while something that is *inanimate* lacks life. Stones, cars, coat hangers, and television sets are all *inanimate* objects.

The adjective **somber** comes from the Latin word for "shade," which is *umbra*. Other words formed from this root include *umbrella*, which not only keeps off the rain but provides shade in bright sunlight, and *sombrero*, a Spanish or Mexican broad-brimmed hat worn to provide shade for the face.

Lesson 19

Word List
Study the definitions of the words below; then do the exercises for the lesson.

dormant
dôr´ mənt

adj. 1. In a sleeplike state.
[Ground hogs remain *dormant* through the winter.]
2. Not active, but able to become active.
[Japan's Mount Fuji is a *dormant* volcano.]

elegant
el´ ə gənt

adj. Graceful or refined in appearance or behavior.
[The tiny curved numbers and the slender hands made the old silver watch an *elegant* timepiece.]

erupt
ē rupt´

v. To burst forth violently.
[The queen *erupted* in anger when told she must abdicate.]
eruption *n.* A violent bursting forth.
[The *eruption* of Mt. St. Helens in 1980 caused immense damage.]

excavate
eks´ kə vāt

v. 1. To dig out.
[The backhoe will *excavate* this spot near the pine tree to create the basement of our new house.]
2. To uncover by digging.
[Heinrich Schliemann began to *excavate* the ancient city of Troy in 1871.]
excavation *n.* The place formed by digging or the process of digging out.
[The *excavation* of Cahuachi, Peru, uncovered many pieces of pottery from the ancient Nazca culture.]

expel
ek spel´

v. 1. To eject; to release, as from a container.
[Electric cars help keep the air clean because they don't *expel* poisonous gases.]
2. To force to leave.
[The school reserves the right to *expel* students for serious offenses.]

fume
fyo͞om

n. (usually *plural*) A disagreeable smoke or gas.
[*Fumes* from passing trucks and buses have damaged the oak trees.]
v. To feel or show anger or resentment.
[My father *fumed* when he discovered that I had left my bicycle out in the rain all night.]

molten
mōlt´ n

adj. Made liquid by heat; melted.
[At colonial Williamsburg, we watched women make tapers by pouring *molten* wax into thin molds.]

painstaking
pānz´ tāk iŋ

adj. Showing or taking great care or effort.
[After a *painstaking* search of the house, we found our missing car keys.]

perish
per´ ish

v. To die; to be killed or destroyed.
[Approximately ten million people *perished* in World War I.]

population
päp yoo lā´ shən

n. 1. The total number of people in a certain place.
[The *population* of the United States is over 250 million.]
2. The total number of plants or animals in a certain area.
[The elm tree *population* decreased greatly after the 1930s because of Dutch elm disease.]
populate *v.* To fill with people.
[The English began to *populate* Australia at the end of the eighteenth century.]

prelude
prel´ yood

n. 1. Something that comes before or introduces the main part.
[The October frost was a *prelude* to a harsh winter.]
2. A short musical piece played as an introduction.
[Suzanne played a piano *prelude* for the spring recital.]

scald
skôld

v. To burn with hot liquid or steam.
[Boiling water from the overturned saucepan *scalded* the child's leg.]
scalding *adj.* Very hot.
[The bath water was *scalding*, so I added some cold water.]

stupendous
stoo pen´ dəs

adj. Amazing because very great or very large.
[It took a *stupendous* effort to return the beached whales to the water.]

suffocate
suf´ ə kāt

v. To kill or die by stopping access to air.
[The trapped miners *suffocated* when their air supply was cut off.]
suffocation *n.* The act or process of suffocating.
[Keep plastic bags away from young children to avoid any chance of *suffocation*.]

tremor
trem´ ər

n. 1. A shaking movement.
[*Tremors* following the 1994 Los Angeles earthquake continued for several weeks.]
2. A nervous or excited feeling.
[When I heard the front door creak open, a *tremor* of fear ran through me.]

19A Finding Meanings

Choose two phrases to form a sentence that correctly uses a word from Word List 19. Write each sentence in the space provided.

1. (a) forbid people to go into it.
   (b) fill it with people.
   (c) To populate an area is to
   (d) To excavate an area is to

_____

2. (a) To perish
   (b) is to tire easily.
   (c) To fume
   (d) is to die.

_____

3. (a) break up into smaller parts.
   (b) burst out violently.
   (c) To suffocate is to
   (d) To erupt is to

_____

4. (a) An excavated building is one
   (b) An elegant building is one
   (c) that is beautifully designed.
   (d) that has been completely rebuilt.

5. (a) that is amazingly large.
   (b) A painstaking job is one
   (c) A stupendous job is one
   (d) that is very boring.

6. (a) To scald is
   (b) To expel is
   (c) to burn with a hot liquid.
   (d) to taunt.

7. (a) To be painstaking is to
   (b) be careless of others' feelings.
   (c) take very great care.
   (d) To be dormant is to

8. (a) prevent that person from breathing.
   (b) permit that person to enter.
   (c) To expel someone is to
   (d) To suffocate someone is to

9. (a) Something that is molten is
   (b) easily damaged.
   (c) made liquid by heat.
   (d) Something that is dormant is

10. (a) Fumes are
    (b) Tremors are
    (c) harmful gases.
    (d) burns caused by hot liquids.

19B Just the Right Word

Improve each of the following sentences by crossing out the italicized phrase and replacing it with a word (or a form of the word) from Word List 19.

1. *His being unable to breathe* was the cause of his death.

2. When the pipe broke, there was a sudden *bursting out* of steam.

3. The *total number of people living in the city* of New York is around seven million.

4. Some of the passengers began to *feel very angry* when told the train would be an hour late.

5. Chopin transformed the *short musical piece played as an introduction* into a form that is complete in itself.

6. The maple trees that line the driveway are *in an inactive state with no signs of life* during the winter.

7. Parkinson's disease causes *rapid back and forth shaking movements* in the hands.

8. The Martian volcano known as Olympus Mons is *amazing because of its great size.*

9. The *process of digging a hole in the ground* revealed the remains of an ancient Chinese temple.

10. The school suspended the minor offenders, but those guilty of major offenses were *forced to leave for good.*

19C Applying Meanings

Circle the letter of each correct answer to the questions below. A question may have more than one correct answer.

1. Which of the following could be *excavated?*
   (a) a hole
   (b) a secret
   (c) soil
   (d) a buried city

2. Which of the following can be *dormant?*
   (a) a volcano
   (b) a rock
   (c) a tree
   (d) an animal

3. Which of the following can *scald* someone?
   (a) a hot beverage
   (b) a hot iron
   (c) a hot temper
   (d) a hot day

4. Which of the following could be *elegant?*
   (a) an aroma
   (b) a restaurant
   (c) a meal
   (d) a dress

5. Which of the following can *perish?*
   (a) people
   (b) time
   (c) hope
   (d) freedom

6. Which of the following can cause *tremors?*
   (a) a sickness
   (b) an earthquake
   (c) excitement
   (d) fear

7. Which of the following can *erupt*?
   (a) an excited crowd   (c) an active volcano
   (b) a burst pipe   (d) an angry character

8. Which of the following can give off *fumes*?
   (a) a faulty oil furnace   (c) an angry person
   (b) a car's exhaust   (d) a lighted cigarette

19D Word Relationships

Each group of four words below contains two words that are either synonyms or antonyms. Circle these two words; then circle the S if they are synonyms, the A if they are antonyms.

1. PERISH   SLEEP
   SCALD   SURVIVE   S   A

2. EJECT   SUFFOCATE
   FRIGHTEN   EXPEL   S   A

3. PAINSTAKING   MOLTEN
   THOROUGH   SHY   S   A

4. VARIED   SCALDING
   FRIGID   ELEGANT   S   A

5. FROZEN   STUPENDOUS
   QUIET   MOLTEN   S   A

6. ELEGANT   METHODICAL
   MEAGER   CRUDE   S   A

7. ENORMOUS   DORMANT
   STUPENDOUS   RIGID   S   A

8. EXCAVATE   ERUPT
   BURY   EXPAND   S   A

9. BARREN   ACTIVE
   SMOOTH   DORMANT   S   A

10. SMOKE   ENDING
    PRELUDE   TREMOR   S   A

19E Narrative

Read the narrative below; then complete the exercise that follows.

THE LOST CITY

Two thousand years ago, Pompeii was a prosperous town with a **population** of perhaps twenty thousand people. It was a busy port located on the Sarnus River, near the Bay of Naples, about a hundred and thirty miles south of Rome. Rich landowners and retired Roman citizens built **elegant** homes in the town and paid for its fine public buildings and temples. The town nestled in the shadow of four-thousand-foot high Mount Vesuvius, and the local farmers cultivated grapes in the mountainside's fertile soil as they had done for centuries.

In A.D. 62, the town was shaken by **tremors** from an earthquake; for the next seventeen years, the people worked to repair the damage. They were not then aware of the danger they were in, but if they had known what we know today, that earthquake would have been a warning to them. **Stupendous** forces were slowly building deep beneath the surface; the earthquake was merely the **prelude** to a far worse disaster.

Vesuvius is a volcano, but it had been **dormant** for eight hundred years. There had been no activity during this time because a thick layer of **molten** rock, called lava, had hardened to form a plug, sealing off the mouth of the volcano like a cork in a bottle. Over the centuries, pressure deep below the earth's surface had been slowly building up inside the volcano. On August 24, A.D. 79, it became so great that the plug of lava was suddenly **expelled** in a tremendous explosion.

So violent was the explosion that the top of the mountain was blown off. Cracks appeared in the earth, and water, heated to boiling by fires beneath the earth's crust, thrust its way to the surface. People and animals were **scalded** as they tried to flee. Smoke, poisonous **fumes**, and ash from the volcano filled the air, **suffocating** many people in their homes. Buildings were crushed by huge rocks hurled from the volcano. Then came a series of avalanches that buried the town, together with everything in it, in twenty feet of stones, cinders, and volcanic ash.

A vivid description of the **eruption** of Vesuvius was given by Pliny the Younger, who later became a famous Roman statesman. He was eighteen years old at the time, and he watched the disaster from twenty miles away on the other side of the bay. His uncle sailed to Pompeii to save the lives of some friends, but died during the attempt. Pliny the Younger described the tragic events of that day in letters he wrote many years later.

For centuries Pompeii lay buried and forgotten. It was not until 1763 that the **excavation** of the ruins first began. **Painstaking** digging revealed streets and buildings filled with the objects of everyday life. Also uncovered were the bodies of the more than two thousand people who **perished** on that terrible day nearly two thousand years ago when the sleeping volcano suddenly woke up.

Answer each of the following questions in a sentence. If a question does not contain a vocabulary word, use a vocabulary word in your answer. Use each word only once. Questions and answers will then contain all fifteen words (or forms of the words) from this lesson's word list.

1. What did the **excavations** at Pompeii reveal?

   _____

2. Why were the citizens of Pompeii unconcerned about Mt. Vesuvius?

   _____

3. What is the meaning of **prelude** as it is used in the narrative?

   _____

4. What evidence is there that some of Pompeii's people were wealthy?

   _____

5. What is the meaning of **tremors** as it is used in the narrative?

   _____

6. What happened when the pressure inside the volcano became too great?

   _____

7. Why did the explosion of Vesuvius have such **stupendous** force?

   _____

8. What materials were thrust from the volcano when it exploded?

   _____

9. What is the meaning of **expelled** as it is used in the narrative?

   _____

10. Why do you think uncovering Pompeii was such **painstaking** work?

    _____

11. Why did the underground water from Vesuvius cause deaths and injuries?

    _____

12. Why was the air at Pompeii dangerous to breathe?

_____

13. What happened to Pliny the Younger's uncle?

_____

14. How large was Pompeii?

_____

15. What were the three major causes of death at Pompeii?

_____

WORDLY WISE

The dormouse is a European animal resembling a small squirrel. It hibernates in winter. This sleeplike state is what gives it its name: the Latin for "sleep" is *dormire*. The first part of this word combines with *mouse* to form *dormouse*. Other English words formed from this Latin word are **dormant** and *dormitory,* a place where people sleep.

The noun and adjective *perishable* are formed from the verb **perish.** *Perishable* foods spoil quickly, and *perishables* are any foods, such as tomatoes and lettuce, that spoil quickly.

What do *premature* (Word List 3), *previous* (Word List 5), *predict* (Word List 15), and **prelude** all have in common? All four are formed from the Latin prefix *pre-,* which means "before." And notice where a *prefix* is found. It comes *before* the rest of the word.

Lesson 20

Word List

Study the definitions of the words below; then do the exercises for the lesson.

ample
am´ pəl

adj. 1. Plenty; more than enough.
[One large turkey will provide *ample* food for eight people.]
2. Large in size.
[A heavy gold watch chain hung across his *ample* stomach.]

burden
bʉrd´ n

n. 1. Something that is carried, especially a heavy load.
[Carrying his frail son on his shoulder was never a *burden*, Bob Cratchit explained.]
2. Anything that is hard to bear.
[The *burden* of caring for four sick children was too much for the baby-sitter.]
v. To add to what one has to bear.
[Don't *burden* your grandparents with this problem.]

compassion
kəm pash´ ən

n. A feeling of sharing the suffering of others and of wanting to help; sympathy; pity.
[Shazia's *compassion* for the homeless led to her working each weekend at the soup kitchen.]
compassionate *adj.* The state of showing compassion.
[The doctor's *compassionate* manner made her loved by all of her patients.]

comply
kəm plī´

v. To act in agreement with a rule or another's wishes.
[Unless you *comply* with the requirement to wear shoes, you cannot enter the restaurant.]

cumbersome
kum´ bər səm

adj. Awkward and hard to handle; unwieldy.
[The crate of oranges was *cumbersome*, but the clerk managed to get it up the stairs.]

distress
di stres´

v. To cause pain or sorrow; to trouble or worry.
[It *distresses* me that no one offered to help when they saw the accident.]
n. Pain, sorrow, or worry.
[The *distress* of a divorce is felt especially hard by the children involved.]

encounter
en koun´ tər

v. 1. To meet unexpectedly.
[Carly Simon *encountered* a crowd of fans in the lobby of her hotel.]
2. To be faced with.
[As the frightened children ran around the corner, they *encountered* a stone wall.]
n. 1. A chance meeting.
[Our *encounter* with our neighbors at the Halloween party was a pleasant surprise.]
2. A battle or fight.
[The first major *encounter* of the Civil War occurred at Fort Sumter on April 12, 1861.]

exert
eg zʉrt´

v. To put forth effort.
[If Jane doesn't *exert* herself more in Spanish class, I'm sure she will not be able to speak the language.]
exertion *n.* The act of tiring oneself; a strong effort.
[The *exertion* of climbing to the top of the ruins left the explorers feeling weak.]

indignant
in dig´ nənt

adj. Angry or resentful about something that seems wrong or unfair.
[Bonnie was *indignant* when Miss Slighcarp, her governess, appeared in the most elegant dress Bonnie's mother owned.]
indignation *n.* Anger that is caused by something mean or unfair.
[My *indignation* was aroused when I was not given a chance to defend myself.]

jest
jest

n. A joke or the act of joking.
[My remark was made in *jest*; I'm sorry you took me seriously.]
v. To joke or say things lightheartedly.
["Surely you *jest*," I said when my aunt suggested throwing out the television set.]

mirth
mᵤrth

n. Laughter; joyfulness expressed through laughter.
[The sight of the three-year-old wearing her mother's hat and shoes provoked much *mirth* among the family.]

moral
môr´ əl

n. A useful lesson about life.
[The play's *moral* was "Look before you leap."]
adj. 1. Having to do with questions of right and wrong.
[The death sentence for murder is a *moral* as well as a legal issue.]
2. Based on what is right and proper.
[You have a *moral* duty to report a crime if you see it.]

outskirts
out´ skᵤrts

n. The parts far from the center, as of a town.
[The plan to build another large shopping mall on the *outskirts* of town was voted down at the meeting.]

resume
re zo͞om´

v. 1. To begin again after a pause.
[The concert will *resume* after a fifteen-minute break.]
2. To occupy again.
[After the station stop, the detective *resumed* his seat for the next part of the journey.]

ridicule
rid´ i kyo͞ol

v. To make fun of; to mock.
[People once *ridiculed* the idea that flight by heavier-than-air machines was possible.]
n. Words or actions intended to make fun of or mock.
[Their *ridicule* of my friend finally provoked me to lose my temper.]
ridiculous *adj.* Laughable; deserving of mockery.
[It is *ridiculous* to suggest that a bridge could be built across the Atlantic Ocean.]

20A Finding Meanings

Choose two phrases to form a sentence that correctly uses a word from Word List 20. Write each sentence in the space provided.

1. (a) is crudely made.
   (b) is awkward to handle.
   (c) A ridiculous object is one that
   (d) A cumbersome object is one that

_____

2. (a) Mirth is
   (b) Distress is
   (c) a calm and untroubled state.
   (d) joy expressed by laughter.

_____

3. (a) An indignant reply   (c) is one that expresses pity.
    (b) A compassionate reply   (d) reveals a deep hatred of others.

4. (a) To encounter someone is to (c) To distress someone is to
    (b) make that person suffer.   (d) feel sorry for that person.

5. (a) Outskirts are   (c) useful lessons about life.
    (b) Morals are   (d) customs that are no longer practiced.

6. (a) anger caused by unfairness. (c) Exertion is
    (b) Indignation is   (d) wrongful behavior.

7. (a) Jests are   (c) parts far from the center.
    (b) Outskirts are   (d) things that are hard to bear.

8. (a) a slow, heavy walk.   (c) A burden is
    (b) An encounter is   (d) a chance meeting.

9. (a) continue it after a pause. (c) To resume a speech is to
    (b) To ridicule a speech is to   (d) bring it to a sudden end.

10. (a) A jest is   (c) something that is hard to bear.
    (b) A burden is   (d) a lesson that teaches right and wrong.

20B Just the Right Word

Improve each of the following sentences by crossing out the italicized phrase and replacing it with a word (or a form of the word) from Word List 20.

1. Caring for Father after he broke his leg *put a load that was hard to bear on* me.

2. The runners were asked to *go back to* their places after the false start.

3. We were *filled with anger over the unfairness of it* when the library had to cut back its hours.

4. I kept my diary secret to avoid my little brother's *making fun of me.*

5. You must have known that I spoke in *a way that was not intended to be taken seriously.*

6. I have *more than enough* spending money for my vacation.

7. In an emergency, if you are ordered to leave the building, you must *do as you are told.*

8. We were panting after our *efforts that left us tired out.*

9. The *lesson that is the main point* of the story is that "haste makes waste."

10. Following their *meeting in battle,* each side proclaimed victory.

20C Applying Meanings

Circle the letter of each correct answer to the questions below. A question may have more than one correct answer.

1. Which of the following would be *cumbersome?*
   (a) a tennis racket
   (b) a small rowboat
   (c) a large envelope
   (d) a picnic table

2. Which of the following might be a *burden?*
   (a) a load of firewood
   (b) a sack of potatoes
   (c) a pardon
   (d) a debt

3. Which of the following can one *resume?*
   (a) a conversation
   (b) one's seat
   (c) a journey
   (d) a destination

4. Which of the following might cause one to feel *compassion*?
   (a) a strange noise   (c) a disaster
   (b) a homeless person   (d) starving people

5. Which of the following might cause *mirth*?
   (a) a bee sting   (c) a tickling in the ribs
   (b) a hilarious story   (d) a plane's sudden loss of power

6. Which of the following might a person *encounter*?
   (a) difficulties   (c) a serious problem
   (b) a school friend   (d) hostility

7. For which of the following must one *exert* oneself?
   (a) watching TV   (c) climbing stairs
   (b) falling asleep   (d) running a marathon

8. Which of the following is the *moral* thing to do?
   (a) to cheat on a test   (c) to choose vanilla over strawberry
   (b) to admit that one lied   (d) to return a lost wallet to its owner

20D Word Relationships

Each group of four words below contains two words that are either synonyms or antonyms. Circle these two words; then circle the S if they are synonyms, the A if they are antonyms.

1. REFUSE   ASSIGN
   COMPLY   JEST   S   A

2. AMPLE   COMPASSIONATE
   KIND   FLIMSY   S   A

3. EXERTION   PATIENCE
   DISTRESS   JOY   S   A

4. LOAD   MIRTH
   BURDEN   SUMMIT   S   A

5. CUMBERSOME   RIDICULOUS
   UNWIELDY   FLIMSY   S   A

6. CREVICE   MEETING
   ENCOUNTER   MORAL   S   A

7. MOCK   CRAVE
   EXERT   RIDICULE   S   A

8. AMPLE   INDIGNANT
   MEAGER   OBSCURE   S   A

9. JEST   MORAL
   RIPPLE   JOKE   S   A

10. OUTSKIRTS   TREMORS
    CENTER   SAUNTER   S   A

20E Narrative

Read the narrative below; then complete the exercise that follows.

A TALE OF TWO DONKEYS

Aesop was a slave who lived in ancient Greece. Although little is known about his life, readers have enjoyed the fables he told for more than twenty-five centuries. Not only are his stories entertaining, but they also teach us something about human behavior, for a fable is a story with a lesson. The characters in them can be animals who talk and behave like humans, or they can be ordinary people, like those in the story that follows.

A farmer and his daughter were on their way to market to sell a donkey, the farmer riding on the animal's back while the daughter plodded along at his side. After they had gone about a mile, they happened to **encounter** a woman drawing water from a well. She was very **indignant** at the sight of the farmer riding in ease while his daughter had to walk. She told the farmer that he should be ashamed of himself. So, to please her, the father and daughter changed places. When the young woman was sitting comfortably on the donkey, they **resumed** their journey.

Just as they reached the **outskirts** of the town, they met a young man who asked the farmer why he was walking when there was **ample** room for both of them on the donkey. To please the young man, the father climbed onto the donkey behind his daughter and they continued on their way.

A little later they passed by two women standing by the side of the road. When they saw the donkey carrying two grown people, the women were filled with **compassion** for the animal. "Have you any idea of the **distress** you are causing that poor donkey?" the older woman called out to the farmer. "The poor creature is half dead from having to carry such a **burden.**" The younger woman loudly remarked that the farmer and his daughter should be carrying the donkey instead of the donkey carrying them. She spoke in **jest,** but the farmer took her seriously and at once set about to **comply** with her suggestion.

First, he tied the donkey's legs to a pole. This took some time, as the donkey had no desire to have its legs tied, but at last the task was accomplished. Such a **cumbersome** load was difficult for the farmer and his daughter to lift. But finally, they managed to hoist the pole onto their shoulders. With the donkey slung upside down between them and struggling to escape, they staggered down the road.

At last, panting from their **exertions**, they reached the market. Their arrival was greeted with considerable **mirth**, so that when the farmer tried to sell the donkey, his attempts were **ridiculed**. For, of course, no one was willing to buy a donkey that had to be carried.

Can you guess the **moral** of this fable? The Hidden Message puzzle in the review section at the end of this lesson will spell it out for you.

Answer each of the following questions in a sentence. If a question does not contain a vocabulary word, use a vocabulary word in your answer. Use each word only once. Questions and answers will then contain all fifteen words (or forms of the words) from this lesson's word list.

1. How do you think people responded when Aesop told this story?

   _____

2. How do you think the ending of the story would have changed if the farmer and his daughter had not **encountered** anyone on the way to town?

   _____

3. What reason do you think Aesop had for telling this story?

   _____

4. Why might one feel **compassion** for the farmer's daughter?

   _____

5. Why do you think the farmer never became **indignant** when people kept telling him what to do?

   _____

6. How did the farmer respond to the various suggestions that were made?

   _____

7. What is the meaning of **burden** as it is used in the narrative?

   _____

8. In what way did the farmer misunderstand the young woman who suggested that he and his daughter should carry the donkey?

_____

9. What do you think probably **distressed** the donkey most?

_____

10. Why would it be difficult for two people to carry a donkey?

_____

11. What is the meaning of **resumed** as it is used in the narrative?

_____

12. How does the narrative make clear that the farmer and his daughter found carrying the donkey hard work?

_____

13. What is the meaning of **ample** as it is used in the narrative?

_____

14. Where were the farmer and his daughter when they met the young man?

_____

15. How do you think the farmer and his daughter must have looked when they reached the market?

_____

WORDLY WISE

The Greek word *pathos,* which means "suffering," has passed unchanged into English via Latin. It means "something that moves a person to feel pity." By combining the Latin root with the prefix *con* (also written *com-* or *col-*), which means "with" or "together," we form the word **compassion.** Several other words are formed from this root. *Sympathy* has the same meaning as *compassion,* although the latter term suggests a greater depth of feeling. *Pathetic* means "arousing feelings of pity." (The *pathetic* cries of the injured animal moved us to tears.)

The language spoken in France from the ninth to the early sixteenth century is called Old French. The Old French verb *encombrer* meant "to put obstacles in the way of."

Cumbersome and several other English words have been formed from this Old French verb. To *encumber* someone is to put a heavy load on that person. (Hikers who are *encumbered* with heavy backpacks are glad of a chance to rest.) An *encumbrance* is anything that is awkward, difficult, or heavy. (Heavy boots are an *encumbrance* when running to catch a school bus.)

◆ ◆ ◆ ◆ ◆ ◆

Resume is a noun meaning "a brief outline or summary, especially of a person's education and work experience." It is sometimes written with a stroke, or accent, over each *e* [résumé]. This is done because it is the French spelling, and *resume* is a French word brought into English. With this meaning, the word is pronounced the French way, *REZ - oo-may.*

HIDDEN MESSAGE

In the spaces provided to the right of each sentence, write the vocabulary words from Lessons 17 through 20 that are missing in each of the sentences below. Be sure that the words you choose fit the meaning of each sentence and have the same number of letters as there are spaces. The number following each sentence gives the lesson from which the missing word comes. If the exercise is done correctly, the shaded boxes will spell out the moral of Aesop's fable on page 165–66.

1. Plants _____ if they are not watered. (17)

2. I warned the child not to get into any _____. (18)

3. _____ meetings went much better than the first one. (18)

4. I will _____ my journey in the morning. (20)

5. The waves are starting to _____ the cliff. (17)

6. It would _____ me to see you hurt in any way. (20)

7. I was filled with _____ for the homeless people. (20)

8. The _____ of China is over one billion. (19)

9. These _____ tools are ten thousand years old. (17)

10. I had an odd _____ as though I were being watched. (18)

11. I made a _____ that I would never smoke. (18)

12. A _____ avalanche almost buried the village. (19)

13. Some plants stay _____ over the winter. (19)

14. I was afraid that the smoke would _____ me. (19)

15. The first crocuses are a _____ to spring. (19)

16. We made a _____ search of the building. (19)

17. Don't _____ yourself if you're feeling tired. (20)

18. I tried not to _____ my true feelings. (18)

19. Will you _____ ownership of the house? (18)

20. Did you _____ any problems with the project? (20)

21. A fan is used to _____ hot air from the kitchen. (19)

22. I must _____ your kind offer. (18)

23. Neglected gardens soon _____ to weeds. (17)

24. The comic's _____ jokes made the crowd roar. (18)

25. Our new house is on the _____ of town. (20)

26. The oak wardrobe was a _____ piece of furniture. (20)

27. The _____ glass glowed a bright cherry red. (19)

28. What will you do with the soil that you _____? (19)

29. The disease causes a _____ in the patient's hands. (19)

30. _____ soil produces good crops. (17)

31. A(n) _____ in the Sahara is a welcome sight. (17)

32. Taking a deep breath will _____ your chest. (17)

33. He began to _____ at the long delay. (19)

34. Will you _____ with my request? (20)

35. We hope to _____ a settlement by tomorrow. (18)

36. You must expect _____ if you dress so oddly. (20)

37. The wedding banquet was in a(n) _____ hotel. (19)

38. When crops fail, the result is often _____. (17)

39. I set down my _____ and rested a while. (20)

40. The long _____ ended with a heavy rainstorm. (17)

41. We have _____ time to make it to the airport. (20)

42. Desert areas are mostly _____ and little grows there. (17)

43. He's liable to _____ in anger without any reason. (19)

44. Blindness did not _____ her until she was 70. (17)

45. They will _____ if they are not rescued soon. (19)

46. I could not live on the _____ wage. (18)

47. This field provides good _____ for the horses. (17)

48. My clown's costume caused a lot of _____. (20)

49. Do you see a _____ between my cousin and me? (18)

50. We found _____ from the storm in an old hut. (17)

51. How can I _____ you I am telling the truth? (18)

52. The coming of the railroad made stage coaches _____. (18)

53. The funeral put us all in a _____ mood. (18)

54. I was most _____ when told I had been left out. (20)

55. Please don't _____ about such a serious matter. (20)

CROSSWORD PUZZLE

Solve the crossword puzzle below by studying the clues and filling in the answer boxes. Clues followed by a number are definitions of vocabulary words in Lessons 17 through 20. The number gives the lesson from which the answer to the clue is taken.

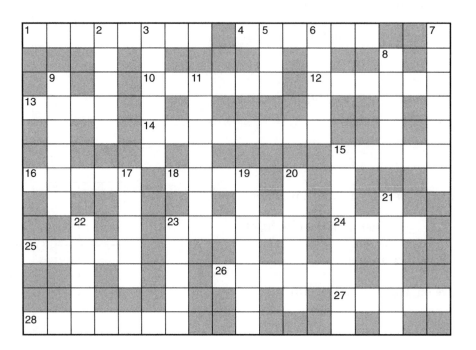

Clues Across

1. Alive or seeming to be alive (18)
4. Dark and gloomy (18)
10. To make or become larger (17)
12. Not able to produce crops (17)
13. A remark made jokingly (20)
14. No longer in use; out-of-date (18)
15. Fruit of the palm tree
16. An area with water in a desert (17)
18. To be angry (19)
23. To go back to an earlier condition (17)
24. To be filled with; to overflow with (17)
25. Good or proper (20)
26. A widespread and longlasting food shortage (17)
27. What noses do
28. Something that comes before the main part (19)

Clues Down

2. Laughter (20)
3. A shaking movement (19)
5. Opposite of "even"
6. Holy book made up of Old and New Testaments
7. To be made up (17)
8. To burst out violently (19)
9. To be disloyal to (18)
11. Grassland where animals can feed (17)
15. Pain, sorrow, or worry (20)
17. To burn with hot liquid (19)
19. Graceful; pleasingly designed (19)
20. To hold onto; to keep (18)
21. Small in amount (18)
22. To wear away bit by bit (17)
23. Opposite of "lower"

ASVAB AFQT

for dummies®

A Wiley Brand

ASVAB AFQT

3rd Edition with Online Practice

**by Angie Papple Johnston
with Rod Powers**

A Wiley Brand

ASVAB AFQT For Dummies®, 3rd Edition with Online Practice

Published by
John Wiley & Sons, Inc.
111 River Street
Hoboken, NJ 07030-5774
www.wiley.com

For general information on our other products and services, please contact our Customer Care Department within the U.S. at 877-762-2974, outside the U.S. at 317-572-3993, or fax 317-572-4002. For technical support, please visit https://hub.wiley.com/community/support/dummies.

Wiley publishes in a variety of print and electronic formats and by print-on-demand. Some material included with standard print versions of this book may not be included in e-books or in print-on-demand. If this book refers to media such as a CD or DVD that is not included in the version you purchased, you may download this material at http://booksupport.wiley.com. For more information about Wiley products, visit www.wiley.com.

Library of Congress Control Number: 2017949051

ISBN 978-1-119-41365-3 (pbk); ISBN 978-1-119-41355-4 (ebk); ISBN 978-1-119-41350-9 (ebk)

Manufactured in the United States of America

10 9 8 7 6 5 4 3 2 1

Contents at a Glance

Table of Contents

Introduction

Because you're reading this book, there's a very good chance that you're interested in joining the U.S. military. I say that because the military recruiting commands are the only people in the entire world who care about the Armed Forces Qualification Test (AFQT) score. The AFQT score is derived from four of the nine Armed Services Vocational Aptitude Battery (ASVAB) subtests. It's used to determine your overall qualification to join the military branch of your choice.

Perhaps you've read the best-selling *ASVAB For Dummies* (Wiley), or some other ASVAB prep book, and you want more practice so you can achieve the highest possible AFQT score. Maybe you've already taken the ASVAB, you want to retest for a higher AFQT score, and you're looking for an advantage. In any case, you've chosen the right book!

The ASVAB has two purposes: First, it's designed to tell the military whether you can cut it within its ranks. It's also designed to show the military where you'll shine as a service member. Four subtests of the ASVAB (Word Knowledge, Paragraph Comprehension, Mathematics Knowledge, and Arithmetic Reasoning) make up the AFQT. The same four subtests, plus the remaining five subtests, are used to determine the fields in which you're eligible to work. (There's no such thing as an Army astronaut. I've checked.)

Long gone are the days when someone could just walk into a recruiter's office and get into the military as long as he had a pulse. Today's all-volunteer military members are the cream of the crop. For example, did you know that under current regulations, you need a minimum of a high school education to join and that no more than 10 percent of all recruits can have a GED or other high-school equivalency certificate?

Something else you may not know: The military services can't just grow to whatever size they want. Like any other government agency, they have a budget, and they have to operate within that budget. Every year, when Congress passes the annual Defense Authorization Act, it tells each military branch how many members it's allowed to have at any given time. By law, the services can't go over the size mandated by congressional leaders (who hold the military purse strings).

Did you also know that of every ten people who walk into a military recruiter's office, only about three are allowed to enlist? Sure, some are disqualified because of medical history or criminal history, but many are turned away because their AFQT scores are too low or because other qualified applicants have higher AFQT scores.

Today's military is high-tech. Even the "common" infantry soldier has to learn how to use and maintain complicated electronic gadgets to survive on the battlefield. The services use the AFQT to determine whether someone is "trainable" in the high-tech military.

About This Book

Full-disclosure doctrine requires me to inform you that much of the information in this book can be found in *ASVAB For Dummies*. The AFQT is, after all, part of the ASVAB, and I wouldn't cheat you by putting part of the information in one book and part of the information in another.

So why should you spend some of your hard-earned money on this book, particularly if you've already bought *ASVAB For Dummies*? Because here you find expanded, more-detailed information about the AFQT and the four subtests that make up the AFQT score. If you're worried about your AFQT score, this book will help you get the highest score you can.

Even if you're not worried about your AFQT score, this book contains four — count 'em, four! — additional practice tests for the four most important subtests of the ASVAB. Extra practice is never a bad thing, as my high-school volleyball coach would say.

As you read through this book, you'll see a couple of special conventions:

>> Whenever I use a new term, I italicize the term and define it nearby, often in parentheses.

>> I put web addresses in mono font so you can easily distinguish them from the surrounding text.

When this book was printed, some web addresses may have needed to break across two lines of text. If that happened, rest assured that I haven't put in any extra characters (such as hyphens) to indicate the break. So when using one of these web addresses, just type in exactly what you see in this book, pretending the line break doesn't exist (or simply click the link if you're reading an e-book).

This book has a few sidebars (shaded boxes) sprinkled throughout. They're full of interesting information about topics described in those chapters, but you don't have to read them if you don't want to; they don't contain anything you must know about the AFQT, so if you're in a hurry, you can skip them. You can also skip anything marked with a Technical Stuff icon. Those tidbits are nonessential, too.

Foolish Assumptions

While writing this book, I made a few assumptions about you — namely, who you are and why you picked up this book. I assume the following:

>> You aren't an idiot. You just want information to help you get the highest AFQT score possible.

>> You're a high-school graduate, you have a high-school equivalency certificate, or you have at least 15 college credits. You just want to brush up on your high-school math and/or English skills as they apply to the AFQT. (If you aren't a high-school graduate or if you don't have a high-school equivalency certificate or at least 15 college credits, you need to get back to school. Very few applicants with a high-school equivalency certificate are allowed to enlist, and then only if they have 15 or more college credits.)

>> You want to join the U.S. military and want to take advantage of all the enlistment goodies that are available, such as enlistment bonuses or additional education benefits. Depending on current recruiting needs, the services often tie enlistment incentives to high AFQT scores. High AFQT scores also help you pick the job you want — and the job you want may be offering a high-dollar enlistment bonus.

Icons Used in This Book

Throughout this book you find icons — little pictures in the margins — that help you use the material in this book to your best advantage. Here's a rundown of what they mean:

The Tip icon alerts you to helpful hints regarding the subject at hand. Tips can help you save time and score higher on the AFQT.

The Remember icon highlights important information you should read carefully.

The Warning icon flags information that may prove hazardous to your plans of acing the AFQT. Often, this icon accompanies common mistakes people make when taking the test or qualifying for enlistment. Pay special attention to the Warning icon so you don't fall into a trap on the test.

The Example icon points out sample questions that appear in the review chapters.

The Technical Stuff icon points out information that's interesting, enlightening, or in-depth but that isn't necessary for you to read. You don't need this information to maximize your AFQT score, but knowing it may make you a better-informed test-taker — or at least help you impress your friends!

Beyond the Book

In addition to the book you're reading right now, be sure to check out the free online Cheat Sheet for details on the AFQT scores you need to enlist in each branch of the military and some pointers on how to achieve a high score on the two math subtests. To get this Cheat Sheet, simply go to www.dummies.com and type "ASVAB AFQT" in the Search box.

The online practice that comes free with this book contains the four AFQT practice tests included in the book, plus four additional AFQT exams. The beauty of the online tests is that you can customize your online practice to focus on the areas that give you the most trouble. So if you need help with Paragraph Comprehension questions or Arithmetic Reasoning problems, just select those question types online and start practicing. Or if you're short on time but want to get a mixed bag of a limited number of questions, you can specify the number of questions you want to practice. Whether you practice a few hundred questions in one sitting or a couple dozen, and whether you focus on a few types of questions or practice every type, the online program keeps track of the questions you get right and wrong so you can monitor your progress and spend time studying exactly what you need.

To gain access to the online practice, all you have to do is register. Just follow these simple steps:

1. **Find your PIN access code.**

   - **Print book users:** If you purchased a hard copy of this book, turn to the inside front cover to find your PIN.

- **E-book users:** If you purchased this book as an e-book, you can get your PIN by registering your e-book at dummies.com/go/getaccess. Go to this website, find your book and click it, and answer the validation questions to verify your purchase. Then you'll receive an email with your PIN.

2. **Go to** Dummies.com **and click** Activate Now.

3. **Find your product** *(ASVAB AFQT For Dummies, 3rd Edition)* **and then follow the on-screen prompts to activate your PIN.**

Now you're ready to go! You can come back to the program as often as you want — simply log in with the username and password you created during your initial login. No need to enter the access code a second time.

Tip: If you have trouble with your PIN or can't find it, contact Wiley Product Technical Support at 877-762-2974 or go to https://hub.wiley.com/community/support/dummies.

Your registration is good for one year from the day you activate your PIN. After that time frame has passed, you can renew your registration for a fee. The website gives you all the details about how to do so.

Where to Go from Here

You don't have to read this book from cover to cover in order to maximize your AFQT score. If you decide to skip around, look over the table of contents and choose which topics you're interested in studying.

You may already know that you'll ace the Paragraph Comprehension subtest, so you want to brush up on word problems. If so, head to Chapters 11 and 12.

You may want to jump straight to Chapter 13 and take the first AFQT practice exam — that way, you can get an idea of which subjects you need to study more. Early on in your reading of the book, check out Chapter 2, which provides invaluable information regarding how the AFQT score is computed and how the score applies to military enlistment.

No matter where you start, I wish you all the best in your future military endeavors. I love every minute of being in the military, and I'm confident that you'll enjoy your time with us, too.

1 Getting Started with the ASVAB AFQT

Get an overview of the ASVAB AFQT, how it's scored, and how to prepare for it.

Check out the differences between the paper and computerized tests, find out what your score means, and get details on the possibility of retaking the test.

Create a study plan to maximize your time between now and test day.

Figure out what study strategy works best for you, take advantage of study tips, and prepare yourself for test day.

Chapter **1**

Examining the AFQT

I f you're thinking about joining the U.S. military, your AFQT score may well be the most important score you achieve on any military test. Sure, it also helps determine which military jobs you're offered or whether you get promoted, but what good are those if you can't get into the military in the first place? You need a qualifying score on the AFQT, or you won't be allowed to enlist. You could be a young Rambo in the making, in perfect health and able to run 3 miles in 3 minutes, and none of that would matter if you didn't have a qualifying AFQT score.

The services have years and years of research to back up their policy of using the AFQT score as an enlistment qualification. Dozens of studies have shown that an individual's AFQT score is one of the most significant factors in determining whether a recruit will make it through basic training and his or her first enlistment period. It costs the military about $55,935 to process a new recruit for enlistment and send that person through basic training (and that's not even including the cost of additional job-specific schooling after you've graduated), so you can see why the services want to maximize their chances of getting their money's worth.

Thankfully, with a little review, there's absolutely no reason that you shouldn't be able to score well on the AFQT. The score is, after all, composed of four areas that you studied intensely during your high-school years: basic math, math word problems, vocabulary, and reading. That's where *ASVAB AFQT For Dummies*, 3rd Edition, comes in. Other test-prep books, such as *ASVAB For Dummies* (Wiley), try to prepare you for the entire Armed Services Vocational Aptitude Battery (ASVAB) and may be a great addition to your review, but this book is specifically designed to help you boost the most important ASVAB score of all: the AFQT score.

Getting a Close-Up View of the AFQT

The AFQT isn't a stand-alone test. You can't just walk into a recruiter's office and say you want to take the AFQT. You have to take the entire ASVAB, which consists of nine separate subtests. Four of those subtests make up the score that's known as the *AFQT score*. The AFQT score determines whether you're qualified to join the service of your choice. (Turn to Chapter 2 for the minimum qualifying scores for each service.)

IN THE BEGINNING, THERE WAS NO AFQT

When you start basic training, you learn about military history. Why not start a little sooner and find out where this whole testing thing came from?

The Army began general testing of draftees during World War I. In order to provide a method for classifying these soldiers, the Army developed the Army Alpha Test, which consisted of 212 multiple-choice and true/false questions, including common-sense questions and vocabulary and arithmetic problems. But many of the draftees couldn't read or write, so the Army developed the Army Beta Test, which required little word knowledge and relied on pictures and diagrams. Nearly 2 million soldiers took one of these tests during World War I.

During World War II, the Army General Classification Test (AGCT) replaced the Alpha and Beta tests. The new test had 150 questions — mostly vocabulary and arithmetic. The AGCT was used by the Army and Marine Corps to assign recruits to military jobs. Of the 9 million soldiers and Marines who took this test during World War II, just over 60 percent could read and write above a third-grade level. During this time, a completely separate aptitude test was given to Navy recruits; it was called the Navy General Classification Test (NGCT). (The Air Force didn't have a test because the United States technically didn't have an Air Force as you know it today; the Air Force was part of the Army back then.)

In 1948, Congress required the Department of Defense to develop a uniform screening test to be used by all the services. In 1950, the Department of Defense came up with the Armed Forces Qualification Test (AFQT). This test consisted of 100 multiple-choice questions in areas such as math, vocabulary, spatial relations, and mechanical ability. The military used this test until the mid-1970s. In addition to the AFQT, service-specific tests classified prospective recruits into jobs. The Army Classification Battery, the Navy Basic Test Battery, and the Airman Qualification Examination (to name a few) were used for classification purposes from the late 1950s to the mid-1970s.

In the 1960s, as military jobs became more diverse and technical, the Department of Defense decided to develop a standardized military selection and classification test and administer it in high schools. That's where the ASVAB entered the picture. The first ASVAB test was given in 1968, but the military didn't use it for recruiting purposes for several years. In 1973, the draft ended and the nation entered the contemporary period, in which all military recruits are volunteers. That year, the Air Force began using the ASVAB; the Marine Corps followed in 1974. From 1973 to 1975, the Navy and Army used their own test batteries for selection and classification. In 1976, the ASVAB became the official military job classification test used by all services, and the AFQT score became the official entry standard.

Here are the four subtests that make up your AFQT score:

>> **Arithmetic Reasoning:** The Arithmetic Reasoning subtest consists of math word problems. The subtest is multiple-choice. On the computerized-adaptive test (the *CAT version* or *CAT-ASVAB*), which most applicants take, you get 39 minutes to correctly solve 16 questions. If you're taking the paper version, you get 36 minutes solve as many of the 30 problems as you can. Chapter 11 leads you step-by-step through solving math word problems. Take a look at Chapter 12 for some tips on doing well on this subtest.

>> **Word Knowledge:** The Word Knowledge subtest is a vocabulary test, plain and simple. You have to find words that are "closest in meaning" or "most opposite in meaning" to underlined words in the question stem. You have to define 16 words in 8 minutes on the CAT-ASVAB or define 35 words in 11 minutes on the paper version. You can boost your vocabulary knowledge by following the advice in Chapter 5 and get an idea of what the subtest is all about in Chapter 6.

» **Paragraph Comprehension:** The Paragraph Comprehension subtest requires you to read a paragraph and then answer one to four questions about information contained in that paragraph. The computerized version has 11 questions in all, and you're expected to complete the subtest in 22 minutes; the paper version has 15 questions you have to power through in 13 minutes. Chapter 7 can help you sharpen your reading comprehension skills, and you can get a little practice with the Paragraph Comprehension subtest in Chapter 8. (**Note:** Many other standardized tests refer to this type of question as "reading comprehension." The military likes to do things its own way, so it refers to them as "paragraph comprehension" questions. Different name, same thing.)

» **Mathematics Knowledge:** This subtest measures your ability to solve high-school level math problems. You have to solve 16 basic math problems in 20 minutes on the CAT-ASVAB or 25 questions in 24 minutes on the paper version. Like the other subtests of the AFQT, all the questions are multiple-choice. To make sure your math skills measure up, see Chapter 9. Chapter 10 gives you an idea about the test format as well as a little extra math practice.

REMEMBER

The AFQT isn't the only qualifying standard the military uses. You have to meet all set standards in order to qualify for enlistment, including age, height and weight, number of dependents, medical history, education level, and criminal history.

Reaping the Benefits of Getting the Highest Possible Score

Chapter 2 gives you the minimum AFQT qualifying scores for each service. But you don't want to be satisfied with making just the minimum. You want to score as high as possible.

The services put great stock in your AFQT score. Not only does a high AFQT score give you a greater chance of enlistment, but it also means you may have access to special incentives, such as the following:

» **Enlistment bonuses and benefits:** Depending on current recruiting needs, individual services often tie the AFQT score to enlistment incentives, such as monetary bonuses or education benefits. For example, the Army often requires a minimum AFQT score of 50 to qualify for a bonus or to qualify for the Student Loan Repayment Program and other programs and benefits.

» **More access to desirable jobs:** Most military jobs are tied to individual line scores derived from the entire ASVAB, but certain enlistment programs sometimes require a minimum AFQT score that is significantly higher than the minimum score needed for a regular enlistment. For example, some Navy jobs (such as those in the nuclear field) require a higher AFQT score.

» **Education level:** You have to have a high school diploma in order to join any of the services. The services can, however, take a limited number of applicants with high school equivalency certificates each year. To qualify with one of these certificates, you must often score higher on the AFQT than a qualified high school diploma holder.

» **Quotas:** When the services are doing well meeting their recruitment goals, they run out of space before they run out of applicants. At these times, the services get to pick and choose whom they let join and whom they don't. Branches commonly raise their AFQT minimum scores temporarily to separate the best-qualified applicants from the rest. Sometimes enlistment gets so competitive that the services require a minimum score of 50 just to consider you. As of this writing, minimum scores for the services tend to rest in the 30s.

>> **Waivers:** One past study indicated that only three out of ten people who walked into a recruiter's office were qualified for enlistment. Certain factors — such as criminal history, age, education level, number of dependents, or medical history — made them ineligible. Some of these eligibility criteria can be waived (sometimes with difficulty and processing delays). However, when the military grants a waiver, it's taking a chance on an otherwise ineligible recruit. For example, if you have criminal misdeeds in your past and require a waiver to enlist, a service is much more likely to grant the waiver if you score 85 on the AFQT than it is if you score 45.

WARNING

Enlistment standards, programs, quotas, and incentives change — sometimes on a week-by-week basis, depending on the service's current recruiting needs. For the latest information, check with a military recruiter.

The AFQT is scored as a percentile. That means, for example, that if you score 70, you've scored as well as or higher than 70 percent of the people whose knowledge yours was measured against. The highest possible score on the AFQT is 99.

TIP

The AFQT isn't a one-shot deal. If you don't achieve a qualifying score, you can retest. After your first test, you have to wait at least 30 days to take a second test. After the second test, in most cases, you have to wait six months before you can test again. Keep in mind the age requirements and needs of the service. Although you can retest, getting a qualifying score upfront is the best way to keep your recruiter happy and your training and placement on schedule.

Establishing a Study Program

If you're not planning to make a study plan, you should plan again. A study plan is essential if you want to score well on the AFQT, so check out the guidelines in Chapter 3. You can adjust the schedule based on how much time you have left before you take the ASVAB.

I can't give you one best way to prepare a study plan. Each person has his or her own learning preferences; what works for you might not work for your best friend. Some people learn better by hearing information, while others like a visual approach — and still others need to put their hands on learning materials to get a good mental grasp on the information.

When you're studying for the ASVAB, you most likely won't put too much emphasis on learning new information. It's more of a review of what you already know, which means you have the freedom to find study techniques that help you remember best — until you've taken the test and left MEPS with your shiny new enlistment contract, that is.

Try to figure out what type of learner you are before developing a plan of study. Chapter 4 can help with this process and give you some tips about what to include in your study plan based on your learning style.

WARNING

Most people don't look forward to sitting down for a study session. Because of that, they try to make studying more enjoyable by spending time on the subjects they already know. After all, studying familiar information is much easier than learning something new. Try not to fall into this trap! If you're already an avid reader, you probably don't need to spend much of your time improving your reading comprehension skills. You're already going to ace that portion of the AFQT, right? Instead, spend most of your time boning up on the areas where you need improvement, such as math and math word problems.

Try to dedicate one to two hours per day to your AFQT studies. Pick a time and place where nobody will interrupt you. Having your dad yell at you to cut the grass probably won't be beneficial to your study session. Also, turn off your cellphone. Is that call as important as your future military career? You won't be allowed to use your phone in basic training anyway, so this is a good time to get into the habit of letting it go for a while.

Guessing Smart

All the questions on the ASVAB are multiple-choice with four possible answers. That means that if you narrow down the possible correct answers by eliminating at least one *incorrect* answer, you'll boost your chances at scoring higher on the test.

Of course, you can increase these odds immensely by studying. But the chances are good that no matter how much time you put into advanced study, you'll come across at least one question on the test that leaves you scratching your head.

You can improve your odds of guessing correctly by guessing smart. Chapter 4 includes tips and techniques about smart guessing in general. Flip to Chapter 6 for tips on intelligent guessing for the Word Knowledge subtest, to Chapter 8 for techniques you can use on the Paragraph Comprehension subtest, to Chapter 10 for Mathematics Knowledge subtest guessing plans, and to Chapter 12 to discover how to make intelligent guesses on the Arithmetic Knowledge subtest.

Using the Practice Exams to Your Advantage

This book includes four full-length AFQT practice exams, with questions that are very similar to the ones you see on the ASVAB subtests that make up the AFQT score. The practice exams included in this book can help increase your confidence and ensure that you're ready to take the actual ASVAB, but you have to use them correctly.

I'll let you in on a little not-so-secret secret: No ASVAB or AFQT preparation book includes the exact same questions as what you'll find on the actual test. Not only would that be unethical, but it would probably also result in several federal law-enforcement agents knocking on the author's door — not my idea of a good time. Actual ASVAB test questions are controlled items; that means that the military keeps them to itself, and people can get into heaps of trouble for sharing them. If you see any questions on the actual ASVAB or AFQT that are the same as the ones you find in this book (or any other preparation guide), it's pure coincidence.

Just because the practice exams don't include the same questions you see on the AFQT doesn't mean that the practice exams aren't valuable — just use them the way they were designed to be used:

>> **Practice Exam 1:** The first practice test is intended as an initial assessment tool. Take this test before you set up your study plan. You can use the results of Practice Exam 1 to determine which areas of the AFQT you need to spend the most time on.

>> **Practice Exam 2:** Use this test as a progress check after a week or two of study. Adjust your study plan accordingly.

>> **Practice Exam 3:** Take this practice exam about a week before you're scheduled to take the actual ASVAB. Use the results to determine which AFQT subjects need a little extra attention.

>> **Practice Exam 4:** Take the final practice exam a day or two before the ASVAB to make sure you're ready and to boost your confidence. If you don't score well, you may want to ask your recruiter to reschedule your ASVAB test for a later date to give you more time to study.

You may find your recruiter trying to rush you to take the ASVAB and medical exam so he can get you signed up quickly. Recruiters live and die off their recruiting goals. Make sure you don't let the recruiter schedule your exam until you're sure you're ready to take the test.

TIP

The mini-AFQT computerized test (see Chapter 2) that recruiters have in their offices is a pretty good indicator of whether you're ready for the real test. Usually, people's AFQT scores are within five or six points of what the mini-AFQT predicts.

REMEMBER

Although you can't equate scores on the practice exam with actual AFQT scores (because of the method of scoring the AFQT; see Chapter 2), shoot for a minimum of 80 percent on each subtest, keeping in mind that the practice exams in this book mimic the paper version of the test. When you're taking the practice tests in this book, here's what you need to make a B grade:

>> **Arithmetic Reasoning:** You need to answer 24 of the 30 Arithmetic Reasoning questions correctly to hit the 80 percent threshold. If you don't, dedicate more study time to solving math word problems.

>> **Word Knowledge:** The Word Knowledge subtest has 35 questions, so focus on this section if you miss more than 7 of them.

>> **Paragraph Comprehension:** If you miss more than 3 of the 15 questions on the Paragraph Comprehension subtest, dedicate more study time to your reading skills.

>> **Mathematics Knowledge:** Missing more than 3 of the 16 Mathematics Knowledge questions puts you below 80 percent, so you'll need further study.

Chapter **2**

Facing the AFQT Head-On

Everyone looking to enlist in the U.S. military has to take the Armed Services Vocational Aptitude Battery (ASVAB). The ASVAB consists of nine separately timed subtests, which the military primarily uses to determine your aptitude to learn various military jobs.

Four of the ASVAB subtests are used to compute the Armed Forces Qualification Test (AFQT) score. This score determines whether you're qualified to join the military service of your choice. Each branch of military service has its own minimum AFQT score standards. Your AFQT score tells the military what your chances are of making it successfully through your enlistment period. The services have conducted countless studies over the years, and the results are clear: The higher your AFQT score, the greater the chances that you'll successfully complete your enlistment contract.

As you can imagine, the AFQT score is very important to the military recruiting commands. If you have a high AFQT score, you can expect your recruiter to be wining and dining you, offering you all kinds of enlistment incentives, and telling all his coworkers that you're his very best friend. On the other hand, if your AFQT score is below the minimum standards set by that service, you can expect your recruiter to say, "Don't call us. We'll call you." If you have a qualifying AFQT score that's mediocre, you can probably still enlist, but you'll most likely miss out on many enlistment goodies, such as enlistment bonuses. (Maybe you'll get a free T-shirt.)

In this chapter, I explain which of the four ASVAB subtests are used to compute your AFQT score and how the military calculates the score. I also tell you the minimum qualifying AFQT scores for each service branch and explain how you can request a retest if your score is too low.

Looking at the Big ASVAB Picture

Depending on where and why you take the test, you may encounter two different versions of the ASVAB: the computerized version and the pencil-and-paper version.

The computerized version of the ASVAB (CAT-ASVAB) contains nine separately timed subtests. On the CAT-ASVAB, Auto Information and Shop Information are separated into two different tests, whereas they're combined on the paper version. In Table 2-1, I outline the nine ASVAB subtests in the order that you take them; the bolded subtests are used to calculate the AFQT score.

TABLE 2-1 **Details about the ASVAB Subtests**

Subtest	Questions/Time (CAT-ASVAB)	Questions/Time (Paper Version)	Content
General Science	16 questions, 8 minutes	25 questions, 11 minutes	General principles of biological and physical sciences
Arithmetic Reasoning	**16 questions, 39 minutes**	**30 questions, 36 minutes**	**Math word problems**
Word Knowledge	**16 questions, 8 minutes**	**35 questions, 11 minutes**	**Correct meaning of a word and best synonym or antonym for a given word**
Paragraph Comprehension	**11 questions, 22 minutes**	**15 questions, 13 minutes**	**Questions based on paragraphs (usually a few hundred words) that you read**
Mathematics Knowledge	**16 questions, 20 minutes**	**25 questions, 24 minutes**	**High school math**
Electronics Information	16 questions, 8 minutes	20 questions, 9 minutes	Electricity and electronic principles and terminology
Mechanical Comprehension	16 questions, 20 minutes	25 questions, 19 minutes	Basic mechanical and physical principles
Auto and Shop Information	11 Auto Information questions, 7 minutes; 11 Shop Information questions, 6 minutes	25 questions, 11 minutes	Knowledge of automobiles, shop terminology, and tool use
Assembling Objects	16 questions, 16 minutes	25 questions, 15 minutes	Spatial orientation

You can't take just the four AFQT subtests of the ASVAB. You have to take all nine subtests in order to get a qualifying AFQT score. The military isn't set up to give *partial* ASVAB tests. For example, if you take the ASVAB and get line scores that qualify you for the military job you want but your AFQT score is too low to join, you have to retake the entire ASVAB — not just the four subtests that make up the AFQT — to get a higher AFQT score.

REMEMBER

During the initial enlistment process, your service branch determines your military job or enlistment program based on the minimum *line scores* it has established. Line scores are computed from the various subtests of the ASVAB. If you get an appropriate score in the appropriate areas, you can get the job you want — as long as that job is available and you meet other qualification factors.

The computerized ASVAB (CAT-ASVAB)

Nobody really cares about the AFQT score except the military — and it cares *a lot!* Because you're reading this book, I'm willing to bet that you're interested in joining the military. And if you're interested in joining the military, you'll most likely take the computerized version of the ASVAB. That's because most people taking the ASVAB for the purpose of joining the military take it at a Military Entrance Processing Station (MEPS), and all these places use the computerized test.

The computerized version of the ASVAB — called the *CAT-ASVAB* (*CAT* stands for Computerized Adaptive Testing) — has the same questions as the paper version. The CAT-ASVAB adapts the questions it offers you based on your level of proficiency. (That's why it's called *adaptive*.) The first test question is of average difficulty. If you answer this question correctly, the next question is more difficult. If you answer the first question incorrectly, the computer gives you an easier question. (By contrast, on the pencil-and-paper ASVAB, easy, medium, and hard questions are presented randomly.) On the ASVAB, harder questions are worth more points than easier questions are, so you want to get to them sooner to maximize your score.

Pros of taking the CAT-ASVAB

Maybe it's because most people are more comfortable in front of a computer than they are with paper and pencil, but military recruiters have noted that among applicants who've taken both the paper-based version and the computerized version of the ASVAB, recruits tend to score slightly higher on the computerized version of the test.

When you take the CAT-ASVAB, the computer automatically calculates and prints your standard scores for each subtest and your line scores for each service branch. (If you're interested in line scores, which are used for military job-classification purposes, you may want to pick up a copy of *ASVAB For Dummies* [Wiley].) This machine is a pretty smart cookie; it also calculates your AFQT score on the spot. With the computerized version, you usually know whether you qualify for military enlistment on the same day you take the test and, if so, which jobs you qualify for.

Cons of taking the CAT-ASVAB

Unlike the pencil-and-paper version, you can't skip questions or change your answers after you enter them on the CAT-ASVAB. This restriction can make taking the test harder for some people. Instead of being able to go through and immediately answer all the questions you're sure of and then come back to the questions that require you to do some head scratching, you have to answer each question as it comes. Also, judging how much time to spend on a difficult question before guessing and moving on can be tough. Finally, if you have a few minutes at the end of the test, you can't go back and check to make sure you marked the correct answer to each question.

The pencil-and-paper test

Most people who take the pencil-and-paper version of the ASVAB do so under the *ASVAB Career Exploration Program*, a cooperative program between the Department of Education and the Department of Defense at high schools all across the United States. Although the results of this version can be used for military enlistment purposes (if taken within two years of enlistment), its primary purpose is to serve as a tool for guidance counselors to use when recommending possible careers to high school students.

You can also take the pencil-and-paper version for purposes of enlistment through a recruiter, but that's not done very often these days. In unusual circumstances, when it's impractical for an applicant to travel to a MEPS location, recruiters can make arrangements for applicants to take the pencil-and-paper version at a Military Entrance Test (MET) site.

TECHNICAL STUFF

Another version of the ASVAB is the Armed Forces Classification Test (AFCT). This version is used by folks already in the military who want to improve their ASVAB scores for the purposes of retraining for a different military job. Except for the name of the exam, the AFCT is exactly the same as the other versions of the ASVAB.

THE MINI-AFQT

You may take a sort of "mini-AFQT" in the recruiter's office. This test is called the Computer Adaptive Screening Test (CAST). Another version in use is called the Enlistment Screening Test (EST).

The CAST and EST aren't qualification tests; they're strictly recruiting tools that recruiters may use at their discretion. The CAST and EST contain questions similar (but not identical) to questions appearing on the ASVAB. They help estimate an applicant's probability of obtaining a qualifying AFQT score. If you take one of these mini-tests and score low, you probably don't want to take the actual ASVAB until you've put in some extensive study time. In fact, many recruiters won't even schedule you for the ASVAB unless you score well on the CAST or EST.

Pros of taking the paper-and-pencil test

The paper-based test allows you to skip questions that you don't know the answer to and come back to them later. You can't do that on the CAT-ASVAB. This option can be a real help when you're racing against the clock and want to get as many answers right as possible. You can change an answer on the subtest you're currently working on, but you can't change an answer on a subtest after the time for that subtest has expired.

You can mark up the exam booklet as much as you want. If you skip a question, you can circle the number of the question in your booklet to remind yourself to go back to it. If you don't know the answer to a question, you can cross off the answers that seem unlikely or wrong to you and then guess based on the remaining answers.

Cons of taking the paper-and-pencil test

On the pencil-and-paper version, harder questions are intermingled with easier questions, so you may find yourself spending too much time trying to figure out the answer to a question that's too hard for you, and you may miss answering some easier questions at the end of the subtest because you ran out of time. The result: Your overall score will be lower.

The paper answer sheets are scored by an optical scanning machine. The machine has a conniption when it comes across an incompletely filled-in answer circle or stray pencil marks and will often stubbornly refuse to give you credit for these questions, even if you answered correctly.

Scoring the AFQT

The military uses some pretty complicated calculations to determine applicants' AFQT scores. Because harder questions carry more weight than easy questions do, the military can't give you a letter grade or a percentage of questions that you answered correctly; that wouldn't tell the armed forces exactly how much you know about each subject.

TECHNICAL
STUFF

Lots of people (mistakenly) call the AFQT score their "ASVAB score." You commonly hear someone say, "I got a 67 on the ASVAB," or "My ASVAB score was 92." That's not correct; it implies that the AFQT is derived from all nine subtests of the ASVAB, and it's not. The AFQT score is computed from just four of the ASVAB subtests — the four subtests of the ASVAB that measure your math and vocabulary and reading skills (see "Looking at the Big ASVAB Picture" earlier in this chapter).

In this section, I explain how the AFQT is scored.

Understanding raw scores

The military scores each subtest of the ASVAB by using a raw score. A *raw score* is the total number of points you receive on each subtest of the ASVAB. You don't see your raw scores on the printout you receive from your recruiter after completing the test. The recruiter walks you back to the waiting area and retrieves two or three copies of your scores on a printout that includes all your line scores for each branch, your AFQT percentile, and some other information.

REMEMBER

You can't use the practice tests in this book (or any other ASVAB or AFQT study guide) to calculate your probable ASVAB scores. ASVAB scores are calculated using raw scores, and raw scores aren't determined simply from the number of right or wrong answers. On the actual ASVAB, harder questions are worth more points than easier questions.

Computing the verbal expression score

The military uses the verbal expression (VE) score to measure your ability to communicate. The score goes toward computing the AFQT score as well as many of the military's line scores. The military brass (or at least their computers) determine your VE score by first adding the value of your Word Knowledge (WK) raw score to your Paragraph Comprehension (PC) raw score. The result is then converted to a scaled score ranging from 20 to 62.

Getting the AFQT score formula

To get your *AFQT raw score*, the computer doubles your VE score and then adds your Arithmetic Reasoning (AR) score and your Mathematics Knowledge (MK) score to it. Here's the formula:

AFQT raw score = 2VE + AR + MK

You don't get to see what your AFQT raw score is on your ASVAB score sheet. Instead, the computer converts it into a percentile that shows you how you stack up against a baseline testing group.

Normalizing the percentile score

Your AFQT raw score is converted to an AFQT *percentile score*, ranging from 1 to 99. How does that work? In 1997, the Department of Defense conducted a "Profile of American Youth" study, which examined the AFQT raw scores of a national sample of 18- to 23-year-olds who took the ASVAB during that year.

Your AFQT percentile score is derived by comparing your AFQT raw score to those of the approximately 14,000 young people who took part in the study. For example, an AFQT percentile score of 50 means that you scored as well as or better than 50 percent of the individuals included in the 1997 study.

Making Sense of Minimum Qualifying Scores

The primary purpose of the AFQT percentile score is to determine whether you qualify for the military service of your choice. Each of the branches has its own priorities, so they all have different minimum qualifying scores.

Considering the AFQT tier categories

AFQT scores are grouped into five categories based on the percentile score ranges shown in Table 2-2. People who score in Categories I and II tend to be above average in trainability; those in Category III, average; those in Category IV, below average; and those in Category V, markedly below average.

TABLE 2-2 ## AFQT Tiers

Category	Percentile Score
I	93–99
II	65–92
III A	50–64
III B	31–49
IV A	21–30
IV B	16–20
IV C	10–15
V	0–9

If your AFQT percentile score falls into Category I, all the military services want you — probably very badly. They also want you if your score falls into Category II or Category IIIA.

If your score falls into Category IIIB, you may or may not be able to enlist, depending in large part on how your chosen branch is currently doing on making its recruiting goals.

REMEMBER

Congress has directed that the military can't accept Category V recruits or more than 4 percent of recruits from Category IV. If you're in Category IV, you must have a high-school diploma to be eligible for enlistment; you can't do it with a high-school equivalency certificate. Even so, if your score falls into Category IV, your chances of enlistment are very small.

Making the military cut

Each of the services has established minimum AFQT qualification scores within its respective recruiting regulations. Keep in mind that minimum scores can change instantly when the needs of the services change, so getting a high score is your best bet in order to remain competitive.

>> **Army (including Army National Guard and Army Reserves):** The Army requires a minimum AFQT score of 31 for those with a high-school diploma and a score of 50 for those with a high-school equivalency certificate. When the Army is experiencing high recruiting and reenlistment rates, it has been known to temporarily increase its qualifying AFQT score minimum to as high as 50.

>> **Air Force (including Air National Guard and Air Force Reserves):** Air Force recruits must score at least 36 points on the AFQT to qualify for enlistment. In actuality, the vast majority (over 70 percent) of those accepted for an Air Force enlistment score 50 or above. For those who have a high-school equivalency certificate rather than a high-school diploma, the minimum is 65.

WARNING

You're more likely to be struck by lightning than to enlist in the Air Force without a high-school diploma. Only about 0.5 percent of all Air Force enlistments each year hold high-school equivalency certificates.

>> **Navy:** Navy recruits must score at least 35 on the AFQT to qualify for enlistment. For those with high-school equivalency certificates, the minimum score is 50. Only between 5 and 10 percent of recruits can actually enlist with a high-school equivalency certificate, and those who do must also be at least 19 years old and show that they have a work history.

>> **Navy Reserves:** The Navy is the only branch for which the requirements for the Navy Reserves are different from the requirements for the branch itself. The Navy Reserves requires a minimum score of 31 on the AFQT for those with a high-school diploma and 50 for those with a high-school equivalency certificate.

>> **Marine Corps (including Marine Corps Reserves):** Marine Corps recruits must score at least 32. Candidates with a high-school equivalency certificate must score a minimum of 50 on the AFQT to be considered. The Marine Corps limits high-school equivalency enlistments to 5 to 10 percent per year.

>> **Coast Guard (including Coast Guard Reserves):** The Coast Guard requires a minimum of 40 points on the AFQT. A waiver is possible for applicants with prior service if their ASVAB line scores qualify them for a specific job and they're willing to enlist in that job. For the very few people (less than 5 percent) who are allowed to enlist with a high-school equivalency certificate, the minimum AFQT score is 50.

REMEMBER

Meeting the minimum qualifying score for the service of your choice is no guarantee of enlistment. During good recruiting times, each branch gets more qualified applicants than it has room for... and that means the military can pick and choose which applicants to accept and which ones to turn away. Usually, rejections are based on ASVAB scores, physical fitness, and what the military calls *medical readiness* (they're not going to pick you if they'll need to patch you up before shipping you out).

Also, enlistment incentives such as enlistment bonuses and college loan repayment deals are often tied to minimum AFQT scores. As with quotas, this situation is subject to change at any time based on each service's current recruiting needs.

Retaking the Test

You can't actually "fail" the AFQT, but you can fail to achieve a high enough score to enlist in the service you want. If your AFQT score is too low, you need to work on one (or more) of four areas: Math Knowledge, Arithmetic Reasoning, Paragraph Comprehension, or Word Knowledge. The military uses your scores in these areas to calculate your AFQT score. Parts 2 and 3 of this book are specifically designed to help you improve your scores on these four subtests. When you're sure you're ready, you can apply (through your recruiter) for a retest.

ASVAB tests are valid for two years, as long as you aren't in the military. In most cases, after you join the military, your ASVAB scores remain valid as long as you're in. In other words, except in a few cases, you can use your enlistment ASVAB scores to qualify for retraining (getting a different job) years later.

After you take an initial ASVAB test (taking the ASVAB in high school doesn't count as an initial test), you can retake the test after 30 days. After the retest, you must wait at least six months before taking the ASVAB again. There's no lifetime limit on how many times you can retest as long as you still meet the other requirements and a recruiter is still willing to work with you.

REMEMBER

When you retake the ASVAB, the score on your *most recent* test is what counts. If you score lower on the retest, that's the score that's used for your military enlistment.

The bad news is that you can't retake the ASVAB on a whim or whenever you feel like it. Each of the services has its own rules.

Army

The Army allows a retest only if

>> Your previous ASVAB test has expired. (**Remember:** Test scores are valid for two years.)

>> You failed to achieve an AFQT score high enough to qualify for enlistment.

>> Unusual circumstances occur. For example, if you're called away from the test because of an emergency, you can retake the test.

Army recruiters aren't allowed to schedule a retest for the sole purpose of increasing scores so applicants can qualify for enlistment incentives, meet line score requirements for specific jobs, or qualify for special enlistment programs.

Air Force

The Air Force doesn't allow you to retest after you've enlisted in the Delayed Entry Program (DEP). Current policy allows retesting of applicants who aren't in the DEP but already have a qualifying AFQT score. Retesting is authorized when the applicant's current line scores limit the service's ability to match an Air Force skill with his or her qualifications.

TECHNICAL STUFF

These days, you can't just take the ASVAB, undergo a medical examination, and head straight out to basic training. You have to wait your turn. The military has only so many basic training slots each month, and it has to reserve a slot for you (often several months in the future). To ensure your commitment, the services enlist you in the DEP. Under this program, you're enlisted in the inactive reserves or in the ready reserves while waiting for your basic training date to arrive.

Navy

The Navy allows you to retake the test if your previous ASVAB test has expired or you've failed to achieve a qualifying AFQT score for enlistment in the Navy.

Recruits in the Navy's DEP can't retest.

Marine Corps

The Marine Corps will authorize a retest if your previous test is expired. Otherwise, recruiters can request a retest as long as the initial scores don't appear to reflect your true capability (considering your education, training, and experience).

Additionally, the retest can't be requested *solely* because your initial test scores didn't meet the standards prescribed for specific military job qualification.

Coast Guard

For Coast Guard enlistments, six months must elapse since your last test before you may retest for the sole purpose of raising scores to qualify for a particular enlistment option. The Coast Guard Recruiting Center may authorize retesting after 30 days have passed since an initial ASVAB test if substantial reason exists to believe that your initial AFQT score or subtest scores don't reflect your education, training, or experience.

Chapter 3

Arming Yourself with a Study Plan

One of the easiest parts of prepping for the ASVAB's Armed Forces Qualification Test is done: You bought this book. Now comes the hard part: studying to get the best possible score.

REMEMBER

What the military really wants to know isn't how much knowledge you already have stashed in your head (although it does use that information). Instead, the military's big question is "Is this person trainable?" Everything in the military is set up to train a beginner, which you'll see if you end up choosing a job that you know nothing about; even if you think you know a bit about it, each branch of the military has its own TTPs (that stands for *tactics, techniques, and procedures*) that you'll have to learn from scratch.

The line scores the military uses to calculate your AFQT score will show them (and you) whether you'll be a good fit for your chosen branch. Combine your AFQT scores with the scores you get on the other subtests, and the military can tell exactly *where* you'll fit in. (You're like a puzzle piece, and the entire test battery shows whether you're part of the kitten's face or the flowers in the top-left corner.) That's why passing the Word Knowledge, Mathematics Knowledge, Arithmetic Reasoning, and Paragraph Comprehension subtests with flying colors is so important.

This chapter gives you a study plan you can customize based on how much time you have before you head to MEPS with your recruiter. After you have a timeline to follow for studying, read Chapter 4, which explains different study strategies that you can use to your advantage.

Do You Have Enough Time?

Your recruiter is going to schedule an appointment for you to take the ASVAB, but if it's too soon, don't be shy. Explain to your recruiter that you don't want to postpone your enlistment by failing the test (or that you'd like to get the best score possible), so you'd like more time to study (see Chapter 2 to find out how long you have to wait to retest if you don't meet the ASVAB's minimum scores for enlistment). You can't settle for an all-night cram session the night before you take the test — that'll leave you frazzled and frustrated, and your scores will probably be lower than they would've been if you hadn't studied at all.

Planning Your Study Strategy

Which areas are most important to you right now? If you often walk around with your nose in a book, you may not need to spend much time on Word Knowledge or Paragraph Comprehension. If you solve complex mathematical formulas for fun, it's probably safe to say that you can do without studying for Mathematics Knowledge and Arithmetic Reasoning.

This study plan assumes that you have about two months to prepare for the ASVAB, but you can adjust it by shaving a week or two off each section so it reflects the right timeline. (Get used to shaving, too — you'll be doing it every day while you're in training. Even when you graduate, you'll have to shave every day before you show up at work.)

TIP

If you're studying for other subtests of the ASVAB, you can blend them into your study plan to replace the AFQT portions of the test where you already have strong skills. If you're struggling with each of the AFQT subtests, it's best to get these down before you move on to other subtests because the AFQT determines whether you're even qualified for enlistment.

8 weeks out: Figure out what you need most

Take the first practice exam in Chapter 13 so you can see exactly where you need to focus your time. You may be a little better at math than you think you are, or you may need some practice figuring out the main idea of passages you've read.

REMEMBER

When you take your first practice exam (and every practice exam after it, for that matter), make sure you're in a quiet place without distractions. Keep some scratch paper handy, and put away your calculator — you won't be able to use it when you take the ASVAB, so using it now will hurt you on test day.

Stick to the time limits given for each subtest — they're printed on each one. The subtests in this book are designed to simulate the real ASVAB test, so the listed times are what you'll be up against on test day. Flip back to Chapter 2 for a refresher on how much time you'll have for each subtest, whether you're taking the standard CAT-ASVAB or you're among the minority taking the pencil-and-paper version. Take the time limits seriously now because the test proctors (and the computers) will take them seriously on test day!

Score each subtest according to the answers in Chapter 14. If you do very well, that's great... but it doesn't mean you can put away this book until the day before the test. Practicing the types of questions you see in Chapters 13, 15, 17, and 19, as well as in the four additional tests online, will help ensure that you score even *better* on test day.

If your scores aren't so hot in one or more areas, now you know where you need to focus. A great way to start: Make flashcards that help you remember important information. Read the sections in this book that explain the areas you need to improve, and then work out the practice questions that show up in the "Subtest" chapters. Review the answer explanations as you check your work to understand how to arrive at the correct answer (even if you got the answer right). Once you join the military, you'll hear more than a few people say, "Even a busted watch is right twice a day," and that applies here, too — it's not enough to land on the right answer. You need to know how to get there.

6 weeks out: Take another test

Take one of the online practice tests rather than one of the tests in the book. The online tests are designed to give you a feel for what you'll experience when you take the computerized ASVAB at MEPS.

The test bank will automatically score your test, and your results will show you which topics you need to spend the next couple of weeks studying. Compare your scores to what you earned on the first practice test to see how far you've come, and see whether you're ready to focus on another area.

Give it a week, and then take the practice test in Chapter 15. Score that based on the answers in Chapter 16, and do the same thing you did after the online test: Choose the subject you want to improve in and focus on it for another week.

If you're struggling in one area, call your recruiter and see whether he or she can set up a study session with you and other recruits. You can also enlist the help of a friend or family member who's stronger in those areas than you are.

4 weeks out: Surprise! Time for another test

The tests in this book serve a few purposes — and one of them is to show you how much progress you've made since the last time you took one. You're only a month out from taking the ASVAB, so now it's time to zero in on the area where you need to make the most improvement. Take the practice test in Chapter 17 and score it with the answers in Chapter 18. In a week, take another online practice test, too.

Which area was the worst? Don't forget to take into account whether you're struggling to find the right answers or spending too much time on one type of question. That's what you need to focus on for the next week.

When you take the next online practice test, you can reevaluate your needs and figure out where to go next (or whether you should keep plugging away at your archenemy on the AFQT, whether it's English or math). If you're working on two subjects, alternate so you don't wear yourself out. There's nothing wrong with taking a break from one and switching to another!

2 weeks out: Five tests down (and three to go)

Take the practice test in Chapter 19 and score it with the answers in Chapter 20. You've been studying pretty intensely, and by now you should have a good idea of how well you'll score on the AFQT portion of the test. If you're looking for a specific job (you can find out what you need to score for your dream job by checking out the appendix in this book), now is the time to hit harder if you don't have a firm grasp on one of the AFQT subjects.

If you haven't already, review the online cheat sheet for this book (go to www.dummies.com and search for "ASVAB AFQT cheat sheet") to check out the qualifying AFQT scores for each branch and to look over some of the basic concepts that'll help you on the test. Information about minimum AFQT qualification scores for each branch is also in Chapter 2.

1 week out: Crunch time

You're a week out from taking the actual ASVAB, so take one of the two remaining online practice tests to simulate what it's really going to be like. Focus all your attention on each question, and keep an eye on the clock. The military always says, "Train as you fight," which means you need to put yourself in a realistic situation while you're practicing for the real deal. By focusing on the online practice tests, you're doing exactly that.

You should see some big improvements at this point (go back and check out your scores from the first practice test you took!). Rank your scores on each section so you can choose which two subjects to focus on this week. Revisit the flashcards you made (or make new ones), call your recruiter or your study buddy, and ask everyone you know to quiz you.

Wait a couple of days, and then take the final online practice test. Try to take it a few days before you go to MEPS — you'll need that time to review everything you need to remember.

The day before the test: Last-minute prep

Before your final study session, gather everything your recruiter has told you to bring to MEPS on test day (see Chapter 4). That way, you can use the afternoon and evening to relax (*yeah, right!*) and mentally prepare yourself for the big day.

When you do settle in to study, review all the notes you've taken and flip through this book to refresh your memory. Don't be hard on yourself, though. You're as prepared as you'll ever be! Also review the last few pages of Chapter 4, which explain what to expect on test day, how to go in prepared, and what to do as you take the ASVAB.

The day before the test is important for more than just studying, too. You'll perform best on the ASVAB if you drink plenty of water, enjoy your day, and get at least eight hours of sleep.

Chapter **4**

Mastering the Art of Studying and Test-Taking

REMEMBER

A military career is all about taking tests. You take tests to enter the military, you take tests in basic training, you take tests when learning your new military job, you take tests when you go to military schools to further your career, and in some branches, you even take tests to earn promotions!

Lots of people think they can't take tests, but realistically, that's just not true. If you couldn't take tests, you never would've made it through high school or gotten a high-school equivalency certificate, and one of the two is required in order to join the military. The truth of the matter is that when people get out of a school environment, they quickly lose the motivation and skills to study properly. Lack of success in test-taking has more to do with ineffective study skills and techniques than it does with intellectual ability.

Effective studying doesn't happen overnight. Studying requires time and patience, so use the plan in Chapter 3 as an outline for your own strategy. Getting the highest possible AFQT score is very much an individual affair; no one path will always produce the best results for everyone. Studying is a process that you learn through trial and error. You have to discover a strategy that works for you.

By incorporating the reading rules, study strategies, and test-taking techniques covered in this chapter, you should increase your chances of achieving the study and test-taking goals you set for yourself.

Reading for Study

I know what you're thinking: "Wait a minute. You talk about reading comprehension in Chapter 7. Why am I reading about reading here?" Reading for the purposes of study is a different kind of reading. *Reading comprehension* just requires you to place information into short-term memory long enough to answer a question about it a few seconds later. To read for the purposes of study, you need to commit important information to your long-term memory — at least long enough to take the ASVAB.

Checking out the survey, question, read, recall, and review method

This method is affectionately known as the SQR³ method by those who make a living teaching students how to study. It helps you separate the important information from the stuff that doesn't matter. Here's how it works:

1. Survey.

The first step is to survey the material to get the big picture. This quick preview allows you to focus your attention on the main ideas and to identify the sections you want to read in detail. The purpose is to determine which portions of the text are most applicable to your task. Read the table of contents, introduction, section headings, subheadings, summaries, and the bibliography. Skim the text in between. Be sure to look at any figures, diagrams, charts, and highlighted areas.

2. Question.

After you've gained a feel for the substance of the material, compose questions about the subject you want answered. First, ask yourself what you already know about the topic and then generate your questions.

3. Read.

Now go back and read those sections you identified during your survey and search for answers to your questions. Look for the ideas behind words. While you're at it, skim the other sections again.

4. Recall.

To help you retain the material, make it a point to summarize the information at appropriate intervals, such as at the ends of paragraphs, sections, and chapters. Your goal isn't to remember *everything* you've read — just the important points. Recite these points silently or aloud. Reciting the points helps you improve your concentration. You can also jot down any important or useful points.

Finally, determine what information you still need to obtain.

5. Review.

This last step involves reviewing the information you've read. Skim a section or chapter immediately after you finish reading it, and take a peek at any notes you made. Go back over all the questions you posed and see whether you can answer them.

Taking and reviewing notes

Reading something once isn't enough to really learn it. That's why note-taking is so important. Clearly written, accurate notes help to capture information for later study and review. Taking notes also helps you to focus and learn during your study time.

TIP

Here are some note-taking and note-studying tips:

>> **Organize the information.** Arrange data or ideas into small groups that make sense to you. Smaller groups make remembering the information easier.

>> **Make the information relevant.** Connect the new information with the information you already know. Recalling the information you already know about a subject helps you recall the new stuff more easily.

>> **Use all your senses during review.** Don't just speak aloud when reviewing your notes; get your entire body into the act. Get up and move around as if you're practicing for a speech.

>> **To commit information to your long-term memory, review the material several times.** Take advantage of your ability to remember best what you read last by changing the order of the information you recite during your review.

>> **Use spaced repetition.** This approach requires you to review information after increasingly long breaks. Review the material again the next day, then again in a week. Keep spacing out the intervals of your reviews to get the most out of the spaced repetition method, which also lets you practice retrieving information from the dustiest corners of your brain.

Putting Study Strategies to Work for You

Knowing how to study is like knowing how to fish: It's a set of learning skills that lasts a lifetime and brings many rewards. Just as there are many ways to fish, there are many ways to study. The key is finding the techniques that work best for you.

Working with your own learning style

Individuals learn best in individual ways. Some people may learn more quickly by hearing something. For others, seeing something may be the way. Still others may learn best by doing something. No one style of learning is better than another. However, by identifying your most effective learning style, you can adjust your study techniques to your individual learning abilities. The point is that it doesn't matter what learning style you're most comfortable with as long as it works for you.

Auditory learners

Auditory learners use hearing to process information. When given a choice, strong auditory learners sit where they can easily hear the speaker and where outside sounds won't interfere. Some auditory learners sit to one side (on the side of their strongest ear). Many times, auditory learners have an easier time understanding the words from songs on the radio and announcements on public address systems than other people do.

Here are some characteristics of auditory learners:

>> They prefer to hear information.

>> They have difficulty following written directions.

>> They have difficulty with reading and writing.

>> They may not look the speaker in the eye; instead, they may turn their eyes away so they can focus more on listening.

TIP

If you're an auditory learner, keep in mind the following study suggestions:

>> Listen to readings and lectures on CDs or online recordings (when available).

>> Participate in discussions, ask questions, and repeat given information.

>> Summarize or paraphrase written material and record the information.

>> Discuss the material with someone else.

Visual learners

Visual learners need to see the big picture. They may choose a seat where they can see the whole stage or screen. They may like the back seat so everything is out in front and they can see it all. Visual learners survey the scene, like to sightsee, and can see the forest despite the trees.

Visual learners share the following characteristics:

>> They need to see it to learn it; they must have a mental picture.

>> They have artistic ability.

>> They have difficulty with spoken directions.

>> They find sounds distracting.

>> They have trouble following lectures.

>> They may misinterpret words.

TIP

If you're a visual learner, follow these suggestions:

>> Use visuals (graphics, films, slides, illustrations, doodles, charts, notes, and flashcards) to reinforce learning.

>> Use multicolored highlighters or pens to organize your notes.

>> Write down directions.

>> Visualize words, phrases, and sentences to be memorized.

>> Write everything down; review often.

Tactile learners

Tactile learners need to touch and feel things. They want to feel or experience the lesson themselves. Given a choice, strong tactile learners are right in the middle of the action. They tear things apart to see how they work and put them back together without the directions. Tactile learners immediately adjust the seat, mirror, radio, and temperature when they get in the car.

Here are some characteristics of tactile learners:

>> They prefer hands-on learning or training.

>> They can often put objects together without the directions.

>> They have difficulty sitting still.

>> They learn better when they can get involved.

>> They may be coordinated and have athletic ability.

TIP

If you're a tactile learner, try the following strategies:

>> Make a model, do lab work, role-play, "be the ball."

>> Take frequent breaks.

>> Copy letters and words to learn how to spell and remember facts.

» Use a computer to study as much as possible.

» Write facts and figures over and over.

» Read and walk, talk and walk, repeat and walk.

Getting the most out of your study time

Whether you're studying for the ASVAB, the AFQT, military promotion tests, or a college course, proper study techniques can help you attain your goals.

Staying motivated

Studying and learning can take you far in life, yet getting down to those tasks can be hard. Whether you're studying for college or to advance your career, studying can be one of the most important things you should be doing. Modern life — whether commercials, the Internet, friends, or TV — continually demands your attention, and all these things can feel easier to attend to than study. So what can you do to stay motivated?

» **Give your study the attention it deserves.** If you were totally isolated, you'd study every last morsel of your subject until you were completely versed in it because nothing else would be there to distract you. Imagine being in a cell with no TV and nothing except *ASVAB AFQT For Dummies*. You'd certainly read it cover to cover — maybe many times! You'd know this book inside out because it's all you'd have to do. Having too much choice over what you pay attention to means you need to exert willpower now more than ever to stay motivated.

» **Think about your goals.** Consider why you're studying and what you're studying for, because presumably it connects to what you want your life to be. All kinds of things may distract you when you're not studying. But ask yourself whether you want your life to be about drinking coffee, playing computer games, watching TV, and chatting with friends. Do you have bigger fish to fry? Your life is about what you do with it, day in and day out.

» **Feed and develop your mind.** In today's culture of entertainment, everything is supposed to be fun and exciting. If you buy into this idea too much, then you stop benefiting from subtle stimuli because they don't immediately excite you. Your mind needs the rigor of study as well as the relaxation of entertainment. When you study well, you find it has its own pleasures and satisfactions above and beyond the good results it can bring into your life.

Managing your time

You may have all the time in the world, but if you don't use it wisely, it won't help you meet your goals. Procrastination is a problem for many people studying for the ASVAB or AFQT. The following tips can help you deal with this issue:

» **Clear your schedule.** Recognize that your obligations and the resulting stress are as important as other people's needs. Set limits around being interrupted or rescheduling your work time to accommodate others. Omit or reschedule some of your other obligations. You want to give full concentration to your studies without feeling guilty about what you're *not* doing.

» **Create a work area that's free from distractions and commit to staying there for at least one to two hours.** If you get sidetracked, remind yourself how this activity will help you meet your goals.

- » **Prioritize.** What has to be done first? What's worth more in terms of your AFQT score? (Chapter 2 can help you with this decision.) What's worth more in terms of your personal, educational, or career goals?

- » **Use a daily to-do list.** This list helps you reach your goals and prioritize your daily tasks. As soon as you've completed a task, check it off your list. There are dozens of apps you can use to keep a to-do list, and your phone probably even came with one. (My favorite is Google Keep: https://keep.google.com.)

- » **Break down your study into chunks.** Estimate how much time you need to complete the task. Don't try to do it all at once. Break it down so it's doable and not so overwhelming. Stay up-to-date to avoid overload.

- » **Recognize that you don't have to be perfect.** Some people are so afraid they won't perform perfectly that they don't do anything at all. Make sure you understand your goals. Then evaluate how important your study is and what level of performance is acceptable to you. Then just do it!

REMEMBER

  If you score better than the 50th percentile on the AFQT, you become a very attractive candidate to the military. You don't need a perfect score to get recruiters to chase you all over town.

- » **Make study enjoyable.** Work on studying first, while you have more energy. Reward yourself when you check tasks off your daily to-do list.

REMEMBER

You're only human, so you probably gravitate toward studying the subject areas that you have an interest in or that you're good at. If you're an avid reader, don't spend too much of your time studying reading comprehension. (You're already likely to sail through that part of the test.) On the other hand, if you had a hard time in math in high school, you'll want to spend extra time brushing up on your arithmetic skills.

Finding the right place to study

After you've found the time to study, commit to a time and place that meets your needs. Ask yourself whether the environment in which you're studying will distract you or allow you to focus. Here are some aspects of the study environment you may need to consider:

- » **Time of day:** Whenever possible, schedule your most challenging courses and most intense study sessions during the time of day when you're most alert. Some people are at their best in the morning; others don't get rolling until late afternoon. You know how you work, so plan to study when you can give it your best.

- » **Posture and mobility:** Recognizing your posture and mobility needs helps you plan where and when you should study. Some people prefer to sit at a table or desk (in a formal posture) in order to concentrate and study effectively. Others are able to learn more easily while sitting comfortably on a sofa or lying on the floor (in an informal posture). Still others need to move about in order to learn; reading while walking on a treadmill may be appropriate for them. Some people can sit and study for long periods of time (they have high persistence), while others need to take frequent breaks (they have low persistence).

- » **Sound:** Contrary to popular belief, not everyone needs to study in a perfectly quiet environment. If you do choose to study to music, choose Baroque classical music, such as compositions by Johann Sebastian Bach and Antonio Vivaldi. The tempo and instrumentation of this music seem to be most compatible with study and learning.

Several studies have shown that Baroque music, with 50 to 80 beats per minute, can lead students into deep concentration — the ideal state for studying vocabulary and memorizing facts. The energizing music of Mozart can help you focus when you're sleepy and helps keep you alert, according to the Johns Hopkins School of Education.

» **Lighting:** Light does make a difference, so study in the environment that best matches your learning preferences. Studies have shown that some people become depressed because of light deprivation during the winter months. If you're one of those people, try to study and spend as much time as possible in highly lit places.

Other studies have shown reading ability can be affected by the light contrast between print and paper color. Black letters printed on white paper create a high contrast. Some people find they have a better time reading black print on blue or gray paper, which has less contrast and is easier on their eyes. (You can't always choose the paper your study material is printed on, but you can choose it for note-taking and reviewing purposes.)

» **Temperature:** You may not be able to control the temperature of the room you're in, but you should be aware of your preference for either a cool or warm environment. Dress in layers so you can adjust to differences in room temperatures. Study in the environments in which you feel most comfortable.

Setting goals

Setting goals is a good way to accomplish a particularly difficult task. Developing study skills is one such task that takes time and effort to master. By setting S.M.A.R.T. goals related to an area of your study skills that needs improvement, you'll be studying like a pro in no time!

S.M.A.R.T. goals are

» **Specific:** After you decide what you want to work on, narrow it down to one thing. Be as specific as possible. Working out one problem at a time makes reaching your goal without spreading yourself too thin much easier. "I want to be a better reader" is too broad. Be more specific; for example, you may say, "I want to improve my reading speed." Write down this specific goal.

» **Measurable:** Goals are only achievable if you can measure them in some way. For example, rather than "I want to improve my reading speed," a measurable goal would be "I want to improve my reading speed by ten words per minute."

» **Actionable:** This step is where you decide how you're going to achieve your goal. Write this part as an "I will" statement. Following the example I give in the preceding bullet, your goal would now look something like "I want to improve my reading speed by ten words a minute. I will do this by skimming over words like *the* and *an.*"

» **Realistic:** Make sure your goals are within reach. "I will improve my reading speed by memorizing every word in the dictionary" isn't reasonable for most people. Everyone has limits due to time, resources, or ability. Don't ignore these restraints, or you'll be setting yourself up to fail.

» **Time sensitive:** Set a date to accomplish the goal. Make sure this date is both specific and realistic for you. "I will meet this goal sometime over the summer" is vague. Try something more like "I will meet this goal by the first day of school next fall." This wording gives you a definite time to shoot for and helps keep you working toward the goal. Goals can take only a few days to achieve; they may take months or years. Just be sure to make the timeline realistic for you and your lifestyle.

Taking the Test: Putting Your Best Foot Forward

Sooner or later, the time for you to actually sit down and take the ASVAB will arrive. It may get here before you think you're ready. Or you may think that test day can't get here fast enough. Regardless of which group you fall into, you can improve your test-taking ability by understanding test-taking techniques, keeping a positive attitude, and overcoming your fears.

TIP

Approach the big test as you'd approach a giant jigsaw puzzle. It may be tough, but you can do it! A positive attitude goes a long way toward success. Use the practice tests in Part 4 and online to familiarize yourself with the test structure and to build your confidence in the subject matter. Although the questions aren't the exact questions you'll see on the ASVAB, they're very, very similar. If you score well on the practice tests, you'll likely score well on the AFQT.

REMEMBER

Some of the tricky problems can knock you off balance. However, if you prepare a plan of attack for what to do if you get stuck, you won't get worried or frustrated. In each of the chapters where I describe the individual tests (Chapters 6, 8, 10, and 12), I give you tips about what to do when things start to look bleak. Go over these individual techniques before the test and make sure you have them down pat.

The day before

On the afternoon or evening before the test, get some exercise. Exercise can help you remain mentally sharp.

Cramming doesn't work. If you've followed the study plan in Chapter 3, the night before the test you should do a quick review and get to bed early. *Remember:* Your brain and body need sleep to function well, so don't stay up late! The night before the test isn't the best time to go out for a few beers with your friends. Headaches and the ASVAB don't work well together.

Test day

The military has a saying: "If you're ten minutes early, you're five minutes late." You hear this tenet more than once in basic training. If you're taking the ASVAB for the purposes of joining the military (and chances of that are pretty good, if you're reading this book), then you're likely taking the test at a Military Entrance Processing Station (MEPS) and your recruiter has probably arranged your transportation.

TIP

At some stations, they conduct the ASVAB test in the afternoon and then set you up with a hotel room (depending on your travel site) to continue processing (medical examination, job selection, security clearance interview, and so on) early the next morning. At others, it's a one-day whirlwind; you stay in a hotel the night before, get up early for the medical exams and the ASVAB, have lunch at MEPS, and pick your job in the afternoon.

Arrive prepared

Your recruiter should brief you about what to expect and, in many cases, will even drive you to MEPS. In other cases, depending on how far you live from the closest MEPS (and whether you have a car), you may be provided with public transportation. In any case, you want to make sure you're on time and ready:

» **Eat a light meal before the test (breakfast or lunch, depending on the test time).** You'll be better able to think when you have some food in your stomach. However, don't eat too much. You don't want to be drowsy during the test. Also, don't drink too much water. The test proctors will allow you to use the restroom if you need to, but with certain rules. If you leave to use the restroom during the paper version of the test, you can't come back until the next subtest begins. You can't leave to use the restroom during the computer version unless you're between subtests, and you can only be absent for up to five minutes.

» **If possible, arrange to arrive at the test site a little early, find a quiet place (such as your recruiter's car), and do a ten-minute power-study to get your brain turned on and tuned up.**

» **Bring only the paperwork your recruiter gave you and a photo ID.** Don't bring a calculator, a backpack, or a sack full of munchies to the testing site. You won't be allowed to have them with you. The same goes for your cellphone, although you can ask your recruiter to hold it for you.

» **Keep in mind that MEPS is owned and operated by the military, so it doesn't have much of a sense of humor when it comes to dress codes.** Dress conservatively. Don't wear clothes with holes in them or profanity written on them. The only people at MEPS who should see your underwear are the doctors during the physical exam. Leave your hat at home because, under the military civilian dress code, you can't wear hats indoors.

Read the directions

Although this instruction may seem obvious, you can sometimes *misread* the directions when you're in a hurry, and that won't help you get the right answer. Each subtest has a paragraph or two describing what the subtest covers and giving instructions on how to answer the questions.

Understand the question

Take special care to read the questions correctly. Most questions ask something like, "Which of the following equals 6?" But sometimes a question may ask, "Which of the following does *not* equal 6?" You can easily skip right over the *not* when you're reading and get the question wrong.

You also have to understand the terms being used. When a math problem asks you to find the product of two numbers, be sure you know what *finding the product* means. (It means you have to multiply the two numbers.) If you add the two numbers together, you arrive at the wrong answer (and that wrong answer, which happens to be the sum in this case, will likely be one of the answer choices).

Review all the answer options

Often, people read a question, decide on the answer, glance at the answer options, choose the option that agrees with their answer, mark the answer, and then move on.

Although this approach usually works, it can lead you astray. On the ASVAB, you're usually supposed to choose the answer that's "most correct." Sometimes several answers are reasonably correct for the question at hand, but only one of them is "most correct." If you don't stop to read and review all the answers, you may not choose the one that's "most correct." Or, after reviewing all the answer options, you may realize that you hastily decided upon an incorrect answer because you misread it.

When in doubt, guess. On the paper ASVAB, guessing is okay. If you choose the correct answer, that's the equivalent of +1 (or more, depending on how the question is weighted). If you don't answer a question, that's the equivalent of 0. If you guess on a question and get the question wrong, that's also the equivalent of 0, not −1. (No penalties here!) But if you guess correctly, that's +1 (or more).

WARNING

If you're taking the CAT-ASVAB, keep in mind that choosing answers randomly toward the end of your subtests increases the likelihood of a penalty. If time is running short, try to read and legitimately answer the questions instead of making random guesses for the remaining items. The CAT-ASVAB applies a relatively large penalty when you provide several incorrect answers toward the end of a subtest.

In each of the chapters on a particular subtest (Chapters 6, 8, 10, and 12), I give you hints for making educated guesses that are specific to that topic. But here are some general rules:

>> Often, an answer that includes *always, all, everyone, never, none,* or *no one* is incorrect.

>> If two choices are very similar in meaning, *neither of them* is probably the correct choice.

>> If two answer options contradict each other, *one of them* is usually correct.

>> The longer the answer, the better the chances that it's the correct answer. The test makers have to get all those qualifiers in there to make sure it's the correct answer and you can't find an example to contradict it. If you see phrases like *in many cases* or *frequently,* that's usually a clue that the test makers are trying to make the answer "most correct."

>> Don't eliminate an answer based on how frequently it appears. For example, if Choice (B) has been the correct answer for the last five questions, don't assume that it must be the wrong answer for the question you're on just because that would make it six in a row.

>> If all else fails, trust your instincts. Often, your first instinct is the correct answer.

TIP

The Air Force Senior NCO Academy conducted an in-depth study of several Air Force multiple-choice test results taken over several years. It found that when students changed answers on their answer sheets, they changed from a right answer to a wrong answer more than 72 percent of the time! The students' first instinct was usually the correct one.

2

Expressing Yourself and Understanding Others

Discover how to build a strong vocabulary. Review prefixes, suffixes, and roots to figure out the meanings of unfamiliar words.

Understand how to find the main point and subpoints of a reading passage, and analyze what you've read.

Test yourself with Word Knowledge and Paragraph Comprehension practice questions.

Chapter 5

Developing a Solid Vocabulary

The military is in love with words. Military personnel write almost everything down in memos, manuals, regulations, standard operating procedures, and policy letters. They should hire a few *For Dummies* authors to write these items, because the current writers seem to love fancy words. A little shovel isn't a shovel in the military; it's an "entrenching tool." The boss of your duty section isn't "the boss" or even "the supervisor"; she's the "noncommissioned officer in charge" (NCOIC for short).

If you're going to be successful in the military, you have to have a solid vocabulary, and that's why the military includes the Word Knowledge subtest as part of the AFQT score. How can you obey a regulation if you don't know what the words mean? And trust me, failure to obey a regulation is a big no-no in the military.

Your score on the Word Knowledge subtest, along with your score on the Paragraph Comprehension subtest (see Chapters 7 and 8), is used to compute what the military calls a *verbal expression* (VE) score. The VE score is then combined with your Arithmetic Reasoning score (see Chapters 11 and 12) and your Mathematics Knowledge score (see Chapters 9 and 10) to compute your AFQT score. (For more information on how these scores combine, turn to Chapter 2.)

The VE score is also used to determine whether you're qualified for many military jobs. If you're interested in which military jobs require a good VE score, you may want to consider picking up a copy of the bestselling book *ASVAB For Dummies,* which is also published by Wiley.

The good news is that anybody can improve his or her vocabulary. You've been learning new words and their meanings since you first learned to talk. In this chapter, I give you some hints, tips, and techniques you can use to speed up the process.

Growing Your Vocabulary

Your vocabulary naturally grows throughout your life. Even professional writers learn a new word once in a while through everyday life experiences. But if the ASVAB is staring you in the face, you may not want to wait for life's natural process. In the following sections, you descry omnifarious contrivances to expedite progression of a comprehensive phraseology. I'm sorry; I got carried away. What I mean is you find some ways to improve your vocabulary.

Reading more to learn more

People who read a lot have larger vocabularies than people who don't read much. That sounds kind of obvious, but I'm sure the government has spent a few thousand dollars funding studies to confirm this.

It doesn't matter much what you read, as long as you make it a regular, daily practice. You don't have to read Homer or Keats. Leave that to the intellectuals in the Berkeley coffee shops. Your reading choices may be action-adventure or romance books for enjoyment, the daily newspaper, magazines, Internet articles and blogs, or even comic books. (If it weren't for Batman and Robin, I wouldn't know what "Zow!" means.)

TIP

When reading online, get into the habit of keeping an extra browser tab open and pointed to an online dictionary site, such as www.dictionary.com. That way, if you run into a word you don't know, you can quickly copy and paste it to the online dictionary. Most browsers let you highlight a word and right-click it to search for it online, too.

Talking to people

Other people have vocabularies that differ from yours. If you speak to a variety of people, and you do it often, you're exposed to a variety of cultures and occupations, all of which expose you to new words.

TIP

Carry a small pocket notebook with you wherever you go. That way, when you come across a new word, you can write it down and look it up in a dictionary later.

Adding words to your vocabulary

Make a goal to learn at least one new word per day. A great way to meet that target is to visit or subscribe to one of the many Internet word-of-the-day websites or download an app. Here are a few suggestions:

>> **Dictionary.com:** You can visit the site daily or subscribe to the word of the day via email. Visit http://dictionary.reference.com/wordoftheday.

>> **Merriam-Webster Online:** A new vocabulary word appears every single day. Point your browser to www.merriam-webster.com/word-of-the-day. You can also download M-W's app to your smartphone; you'll always have a dictionary at your fingertips, and you can check out the word of the day when you have a spare 30 seconds.

>> *The New York Times* **Word of the Day:** *The New York Times* offers a new word every day, along with an example of how the word was used in recent *New York Times* stories. Visit http://learning.blogs.nytimes.com/category/word-of-the-day.

>> *The Oxford English Dictionary:* If you want more than just a word and definition, try the *Oxford English Dictionary* word of the day. In addition to definitions, the page provides pronunciation, spelling, etymology, and a date chart that shows when the word was first used. The word of the day is also available by email subscription and RSS feed. Check out www.oed.com.

A CROSSWORD SUCCESS STORY

My grandma, Emily, never found a crossword puzzle she couldn't solve. She had a tremendous vocabulary . . . but she didn't pick it all up in school. In fact, my grandma dropped out of high school (that wasn't unusual in the 1940s, particularly when kids had to help their families by working) and didn't go back to finish until 1971, after her oldest daughter graduated. Instead, she expanded her vocabulary one crossword clue at a time. She always had a big paperback book of crosswords on her kitchen table, and she could complete difficult puzzles with a pen — something that impresses me to this day!

Try to use your new word in conversation a couple of times to help you remember it. Writing a few example sentences can help you remember the new words in context.

Using puzzles and games to improve your vocabulary

A fun way to increase your word knowledge is to do crossword puzzles or play word games. Scrabble and Mad Libs, for example, are great ways to reinforce new vocabulary words. There are dozens of word game apps, too, such as Word Streak and Words with Friends. You can improve your vocabulary while having fun! It's a win–win.

You're on my list: Working with word lists

Learning a new word doesn't do you much good if you forget it a week later. Learning often requires repetition, and that's especially true when it comes to memorizing new words.

TIP

Keep a list of all the new words you learn and go over that list at least two or three times a week until you're sure the new words have become part of your vocabulary.

Just to get you started, I give you 50 words in Table 5-1.

TABLE 5-1   **Fifty Vocabulary Words**

Word	Part of Speech	Meaning
Abrupt	Adjective	Beginning, ending, or changing suddenly
Acrid	Adjective	Harshly pungent or bitter
Becalm	Verb	To make quiet
Buffoon	Noun	A clown
Chaos	Noun	Utter disorder and confusion
Cognizant	Adjective	Taking notice of something
Defer	Verb	To put off or delay to a later time
Derision	Noun	The act of ridiculing or making fun of something
Effulgence	Noun	Great brightness

(continued)

TABLE 5-1 *(continued)*

Word	Part of Speech	Meaning
Enmity	Noun	Hatred
Famish	Verb	To cause extreme hunger or thirst
Fealty	Noun	Loyalty
Generalize	Verb	To draw general inferences
Grotto	Noun	A small cavern
Habitual	Adjective	According to usual practice
Hideous	Adjective	Extremely ugly or appalling
Ichthyic	Adjective	Fishlike
Icon	Noun	An image or likeness
Illusion	Noun	An unreal image
Irritate	Verb	To excite ill temper or impatience in something
Jovial	Adjective	Merry
Juxtapose	Verb	To place close together
Kernel	Noun	A grain or seed
Kinsfolk	Noun	Relatives
Laggard	Adjective or noun	Falling behind; one who lags behind
Laud	Verb	To praise
Maize	Noun	Corn
Malevolence	Noun	Ill will
Nestle	Verb	To adjust cozily in snug quarters
Novice	Noun	Beginner
Obese	Adjective	Exceedingly fat
Obtrude	Verb	To push or thrust oneself into undue prominence
Pare	Verb	To cut, shave, or remove the outside from anything
Pedagogue	Noun	Teacher; one who is fussily academic
Quadrate	Verb	To make square; to make conform or agree with
Quiescence	Noun	Quietness
Rancor	Noun	Malice
Raucous	Adjective	Loud and rowdy
Sanguine	Adjective	Cheerfully optimistic; having the color of blood
Sepulcher	Noun	A burial place
Teem	Verb	To be full to overflowing
Tenacious	Adjective	Unyielding

Word	Part of Speech	Meaning
Umbrage	Noun	Injury or offense
Vacillate	Verb	To waver
Valid	Adjective	Founded on truth
Velocity	Noun	Speed
Wile	Noun	An act or a means of cunning deception
Wizen	Verb	To become or cause to become withered or dry
Yokel	Noun	Country bumpkin
Zealot	Noun	One who is enthusiastic to an extreme or excessive degree

Getting flashes of memory with flashcards

Flashcards have been around for a long time. They're still in wide use in these days of electronics and computers because they work. And they work especially well for subjects that just require simple memorization.

You can make flashcards from any stiff paper material, like index cards, construction paper, or card stock. Write the words from your list on flashcards — words on the front and a short definition on the back. Use only one word per card.

TIP

As far back as 1885, a psychologist named Hermann Ebbinghaus, who specialized in memory research, published a study that detailed the effective use of flashcards. According to his rules, you should follow these steps:

1. **Review all the cards in the set, looking at each front and back.**

    Go through the set several times.

2. **Test and sort.**

    Read the front of the card. Try to say what's written on the back. If you're wrong, put the card in a "wrong" pile. Do the same for each card until the cards are sorted into "right" and "wrong" piles.

3. **Review the "wrong" pile.**

    Read each card in the "wrong" pile, front and back. Go through the "wrong" pile several times.

4. **Test and sort with the "wrong" pile.**

    Go through the cards of the "wrong" pile, testing yourself with them and sorting them into "right" and "wrong" piles just as you did with all the cards in Step 2. Keep working with the cards of the "wrong" pile until they're all in the "right" pile.

Building a Word from Scratch

Many English words are created from building blocks called roots, prefixes, and suffixes. Not every word has all three, but many have at least one. The *prefix* is the part that comes at the front of a word, the *suffix* is the part that comes at the end of a word, and the *root* is the part that comes in the middle of a word. Think of roots as the base of the word and prefixes and suffixes as word parts that are attached to the base.

If you don't know the meaning of a word, you can often break it down into smaller parts and analyze those parts. For instance, *introspect* is made up from the root *spect*, which means to look, and the prefix *intro*, which means within. Taken together, *introspect* means "to look within." Wasn't that fun?

If you memorize some of these word parts, you'll have a better chance of figuring out the meaning of an unfamiliar word when you see it on the Word Knowledge subtest — and that's a good thing. Figuring out the meaning of unfamiliar words is how people with large vocabularies make them even larger. (They look up words in the dictionary, too.)

Rooting around for roots

A root is a word part that serves as the base of a word. If you recognize a root, you can generally get an idea of what the word means, even if you're not familiar with it. As Mr. Miyagi said in *The Karate Kid*, "Root strong, tree grow strong." All right, Daniel-san, in terms of your vocabulary, think of it this way: If your knowledge of word roots is strong, your vocabulary will be much stronger.

In Table 5-2, I list some common roots. Memorize them. When you sit down to take the ASVAB, you'll be glad you did.

TABLE 5-2 **Roots**

Root	Meaning	Sample Word
anthro or anthrop	relating to humans	anthropology
bibli or biblio	relating to books	bibliography
brev	short	abbreviate
cede or ceed	go, yield	recede
chrom	color	monochrome
circum	around	circumnavigate
cogn or cogno	know	cognizant
corp	body	corporate
dic or dict	speak	diction
domin	rule	dominate
flu or flux	flow	influx
form	shape	formulate
frac or frag	break	fragment
graph	writing	biography
junct	join	juncture
liber	free	liberate
lum	light	illuminate
oper	work	cooperate

Root	Meaning	Sample Word
pat or path	suffer	pathology
port	carry	portable
press	squeeze	repress
scrib or script	write	describe
sens or sent	think, feel	sentient
tract	pull	traction
voc or vok	call	revoke

Attaching prefixes and suffixes

A prefix is a group of letters added before a word or base to alter the base's meaning and form a new word. In contrast, a suffix is a group of letters added after a word or base. Prefixes and suffixes are called *affixes* because they're attached to a root.

Tables 5-3 and 5-4 list some common prefixes and suffixes. Each list has the word part, its meaning, and one word that uses each word part. Writing down additional words that you know for each word part can help you memorize the lists.

TABLE 5-3 Prefixes

Prefix	Meaning	Sample Word
a-	no, not	atheist
ab- or abs-	away, from	absent
anti-	against	antibody
bi-	two	bilateral
contra-	against	contradict
de-	away from	depart
dec-	ten	decathlon
extra-	outside, beyond	extracurricular
fore-	in front of	foreman
geo-	earth	geology
hyper-	excess, over	hyperactive
il-	not	illogical
mal- or male-	wrong, bad	malnutrition
multi-	many	multifamily
non-	not	nonfat
omni-	all	omnivore
ped-	foot	pedestrian

(continued)

TABLE 5-3 *(continued)*

Prefix	Meaning	Sample Word
que-, quer-, or ques-	ask	question
re-	back, again	replay
semi-	half	semisweet
super-	over, more	superior
tele-	far	telephone
trans-	across	transplant
un-	not	uninformed

TABLE 5-4 Suffixes

Suffix	Meaning	Sample Word
-able or -ible	capable of	agreeable
-age	action, result	breakage
-al	characterized by	functional
-ance	instance of an action	performance
-ation	action, process	liberation
-en	made of	silken
-ful	full of	helpful
-ic	consisting of	acidic
-ical	possessing a quality of	statistical
-ion	result of act or process	legislation
-ish	relating to	childish
-ism	act, practice	Buddhism
-ist	characteristic of	elitist
-ity	quality of	specificity
-less	not having	childless
-let	small one	booklet
-man	relating to humans, manlike	gentleman
-ment	action, process	establishment
-ness	possessing a quality	goodness
-or	one who does something	orator
-ous	having	dangerous
-y	quality of	tasty

A Word by Any Other Name: Surveying Synonyms and Antonyms

English is a complicated language. You could probably learn Spanish, German, or even Korean from scratch more easily than you could English. How many other countries do you know that have to teach their own native language throughout all the school grades (and even college!)?

In the English language, you usually have more than one way to say the same thing, even by swapping just one word. These different words with the same meaning are called *synonyms.* Synonyms are different words that have the same or very similar meanings. *Funny, amusing,* and *comical* are synonyms; they all mean the same thing.

In fact, that's what the Word Knowledge subtest on the ASVAB really does: It tests your ability to select synonyms for the underlined words contained in the question stem. Look at the following example.

EXAMPLE

<u>Perform</u> most nearly means

(A) eat.

(B) dance.

(C) execute.

(D) sing.

The correct answer is Choice (C). *Execute* (to carry out something) is a synonym of *perform,* which means the same thing. Although you can perform a dance or perform a song, *dance* and *sing* don't actually mean the same thing as *perform.*

TIP

When you look up a new word in the dictionary (see "Adding words to your vocabulary") and add it to your word list (see "You're on my list: Working with word lists"), you should include synonyms, because you're very likely to see them on the Word Knowledge subtest.

An *antonym* is a word that has the opposite or nearly opposite meaning of another word. *Smile* and *frown* are antonyms of one another. The test makers often use antonyms as wrong answers on the Word Knowledge subtest. Knowing antonyms for words not only improves your chances of narrowing your answer choices. It also beefs up your vocabulary. For example, if you know that *fast* is an antonym of *slow* and you know what *slow* means, you also know what *fast* means.

TIP

How can you find the synonym of a word (or the antonym, for that matter)? A good place to start is the dictionary. Many dictionary entries include the abbreviation *syn.*, which means *synonym.* The words that follow this abbreviation are synonyms of the entry word. You may also see the abbreviation *ant.* in an entry. This abbreviation stands for *antonym,* and the word or words that follow it mean the opposite of the entry word.

Thesauruses are special dictionaries of synonyms and antonyms. We writers use them all the time to make us look smarter. Here are a couple of online thesauruses you can use to look up synonyms for words on your word list:

>> **Thesaurus.com:** www.thesaurus.com

>> **Merriam-Webster Online:** www.merriam-webster.com/thesaurus

Getting Homogeneous with Homonyms

Some words in the English language are spelled the same but have two or more meanings. For example, a *fluke* can mean a fish, the end parts of an anchor, the fins on a whale's tail, or a stroke of luck.

Some words are spelled the same but have different meanings and are often pronounced differently. The word *bow*, meaning a special kind of knot, is pronounced differently from *bow*, meaning to bend at the waist. *Bow*, meaning the front of a boat, is pronounced the same as *bow* (bend at the waist), but *bow*, meaning a weapon, is pronounced the same as *bow* (a special knot). See why foreigners trying to learn English get frustrated?

Other words are pronounced the same but are spelled differently and mean something different. *To, too*, and *two* and *there, their*, and *they're* are examples. All these types of words are collectively known as *homonyms*.

The last type of homonym is especially important when it comes to the Word Knowledge subtest of the ASVAB. The test makers won't try to trick you by having two homonym answers for words that are spelled the same but have multiple meanings, but they will use homonyms that are spelled differently and have different meanings.

EXAMPLE

<u>Flue</u> most nearly means

(A) sickness.

(B) fly.

(C) chimney.

(D) None of the above.

You may be tempted to choose Choice (A), but that would be correct if *flu* were the test word. The past tense of *fly* is *flew*. The word *flue* means a chimney pipe.

Table 5-5 shows you a few more examples of common homonyms.

TIP

You can see an extensive list of homonyms on Enchanted Learning at www.enchantedlearning.com/english/homonyms.

TABLE 5-5 **Common Homonyms**

Word	Definition	Example Sentence
Allowed	Permitted	He <u>allowed</u> the audience to participate.
Aloud	Normal volume of speaking	They couldn't speak <u>aloud</u> in the library.
Cent	A penny	I couldn't believe I got the comic book for just one <u>cent</u>.
Scent	Aroma	The <u>scent</u> coming from the kitchen made my mouth water.
Sent	Past tense of *send*	He <u>sent</u> the letter Monday.
Cue	Stimulus to action	A door slamming was his <u>cue</u> to exit the stage.
Queue	Line	There was a large <u>queue</u> of cars waiting to park.
Die	To cease living	The flowers <u>die</u> when the weather gets cold.
Dye	To color or stain	She wants to <u>dye</u> her hair red.

Word	Definition	Example Sentence
Elicit	To draw or bring out	He vowed to elicit the truth from his friend.
Illicit	Unlawful	He used illicit means to avoid paying taxes.
Fairy	Supernatural being	The fairy was dancing in the night.
Ferry	A boat for crossing rivers or other small bodies of water	The ferry took us quickly across the river.
Gorilla	Large ape	I threw the gorilla a banana.
Guerrilla	Irregular soldier	The band of guerrillas attacked the convoy.
Hangar	Building for airplanes	Jack pulled the aircraft into the hangar.
Hanger	A device for hanging things	Mom said to put the shirt on a hanger.
It's	Contraction of it is	It's a very hot day.
Its	Belonging to it	The bank said its savings accounts were the best.
Know	To possess knowledge	I know you went to the store.
No	Zero or negative	I told John there was no way we would travel together.
Lessen	To make less	We gave him medicine to lessen his pain.
Lesson	Something to be learned	We must never forget the lessons of the past.
Mail	Postal delivery	I expected the check to be in the mail.
Male	A gender	The teacher asked all males to go to one room and all females to go to another.
Naval	Pertaining to ships	He wanted to become a naval officer.
Navel	Belly button	Mom always said not to play with my navel.
Ordinance	Decree or local law	Spitting on the sidewalk was against the town ordinance.
Ordnance	Military ammunition	We were running low, so we asked the sergeant for more ordnance.
Patience	The ability to suppress restlessness	I couldn't believe her patience with the students.
Patients	People under medical care	The nurse treated all her patients with respect.
Reek	Bad smell	The reek of the skunk invaded the living room.
Wreak	Inflict	Jack continued to wreak havoc every time he got upset.
Sleight	Dexterity	The magician's sleight of hand was amazing.
Slight	Small amount	There was only a slight increase in salaries this year.
Threw	Propelled by hand	He threw the ball to first base.
Through	In one side and out the other	Dad drove through the tunnel.
Vary	Change	The interest rate continues to vary up and down.
Very	Extreme	I am very happy with *ASVAB AFQT For Dummies.*
Weak	Not strong	After his illness, Paul was very weak.
Week	Seven days	It'll take at least a week to finish this report.
Your	Belonging to you	Your new car is really cool.
You're	Contraction of you are	You're going to be in trouble when Dad gets home.

Flex Your Lexicon: Vocabulary Exercises

The best way to improve your vocabulary? Practice, practice, and more practice. The vocabulary exercises in this section will give you a little face-time with the nuts and bolts of the questions you'll find in the Word Knowledge subtest of the ASVAB.

Practicing synonyms? It's all the same to me

Activity 1 is a matching game (See? I told you playing word games to grow your vocabulary would be fun!). Match the word on the left with the word that has the most similar meaning — its synonym — on the right; you'll find the correct answers at the end of this chapter.

ACTIVITY 1 Synonym Practice

Answer	Vocabulary Word	Synonym
1.	1. consider	A. uncommon
2.	2. evident	B. capsize
3.	3. scarce	C. fail
4.	4. vain	D. flounder
5.	5. render	E. go-between
6.	6. gadget	F. deliberate
7.	7. backfire	G. give
8.	8. wallow	H. descend
9.	9. habits	I. arrogant
10.	10. fabricate	J. within
11.	11. pressured	K. compelled
12.	12. keel	L. assemble
13.	13. plunge	M. obvious
14.	14. intermediary	N. customs
15.	15. internal	O. apparatus

Antithetic antonyms: The opposite of synonyms

Activity 2 has 15 vocabulary words and their opposites. Your mission, should you choose to accept it, is to match the vocabulary word with the word it is the most opposite of. The correct answers are at the end of this chapter.

Antonym Practice

Answer	Vocabulary Word	Antonym
1.	1. contrary	A. concern
2.	2. disregard	B. innocent
3.	3. protest	C. inept
4.	4. endorse	D. admire
5.	5. guilty	E. freeze
6.	6. ill	F. fabrication
7.	7. melt	G. individual
8.	8. actual	H. clumsiness
9.	9. abstain	I. agreeable
10.	10. despise	J. disapprove
11.	11. faultless	K. imperfect
12.	12. clan	L. counterfeit
13.	13. resourceful	M. continue
14.	14. fact	N. healthy
15.	15. agility	O. concur

Digging around word roots

Activity 3 gives you a word with a common root. It's your job to find the root, guess what the word means, and look it up in the dictionary (or flip to the end of this chapter, where I've written out the definition for you). It's often helpful to think of words you already know that sound similar to words you don't know; that can help you guess the right answers.

ACTIVITY 3 **Word Root Practice**

Word	Root	Your Definition
1. hemorrhage		
2. magnify		
3. alleviate		
4. verbalize		
5. dismal		
6. marine		
7. affirm		
8. admonish		
9. autograph		
10. hydrate		

(continued)

Word	Root	Your Definition
11. convene		
12. relapse		
13. liberate		
14. pathetic		
15. unanimous		

Parsing prefixes: Defining the beginnings of words

Activity 4 has 15 vocabulary words that have prefixes attached. Tap into your existing vocabulary to figure out what each word means based on its prefix. Write the prefix in the column beside the word, and then write what you think the word means. Then, when you're done, check your answers at the end of this chapter.

ACTIVITY 4 **Prefix Practice**

Word	Prefix	Your Definition
1. apolitical		
2. predetermined		
3. devalue		
4. coaxial		
5. extraordinary		
6. miniature		
7. undesirable		
8. forerunner		
9. byproduct		
10. overreact		
11. uplift		
12. midway		
13. intergalactic		
14. omnipotent		
15. substrate		

Suffering through suffixes: The ends of words

Activity 5 contains 15 vocabulary words with suffixes tacked on their back ends. Separate the suffix from the word (and write it down), jot down what the word probably means, and then check your answers in the dictionary or at the end of this chapter.

Suffix Practice

Word	Suffix	Your Definition
1. postage		
2. annoyance		
3. disciplinarian		
4. wisdom		
5. clemency		
6. artful		
7. celestial		
8. zanily		
9. completion		
10. placement		
11. authorship		
12. fascination		
13. fortitude		
14. circular		
15. audible		

Defining words from their context

You find 15 sentences in Activity 6. Try to define the underlined word based on the context of the sentence that it's in and write your definition in the "Your Definition" column. Then look up the word in the dictionary or flip to the end of this chapter to find out whether you were right (or pretty close). Write the official definition in the final column so you can better boost your vocabulary.

ACTIVITY 6 **Context Practice**

Sentence	Your Definition	Dictionary Definition
1. Smoking has <u>deleterious</u> effects on your health.		
2. The topic was too serious for her to be so <u>facetious</u>.		
3. The English <u>lexicon</u> contains hundreds of thousands of words.		
4. She told him not to <u>plagiarize</u>, but he copied the text anyway.		
5. The commander didn't want to <u>capitulate</u>, but the general told him to surrender.		
6. His sunny disposition and <u>sanguine</u> attitude made everyone like him.		
7. Nobody wanted a dictator or a <u>totalitarian</u> regime.		

(continued)

Sentence	Your Definition	Dictionary Definition
8. David vehemently denied the accusations because he was not guilty.		
9. Cheryl never saw a structure as colossal as the Great Pyramid of Giza.		
10. Jesse's bizarre hairstyle often got him attention from the girls at school.		
11. The teens participated in the boycott by refusing to buy coffee.		
12. The embargo on car sales made it impossible to get a new model.		
13. The idea that black cats are unlucky is a fallacy.		
14. The artist made the mosaic with pieces of colored glass.		
15. The dog's constant barking was a nuisance.		

Answers and Explanations

Check your answers for each of the exercises here, and take some time to review the explanations if you're not sure where you went wrong.

Activity 1: Synonyms

Answer	Vocabulary Word	Synonym
1. F	consider	deliberate
2. M	evident	obvious
3. A	scarce	uncommon
4. I	vain	arrogant
5. G	render	give
6. O	gadget	apparatus
7. C	backfire	fail
8. D	wallow	flounder
9. N	habits	customs
10. L	fabricate	assemble
11. K	pressured	compelled
12. B	keel	capsize
13. H	plunge	descend
14. E	intermediary	go-between
15. J	internal	within

Activity 2: Antonyms

Answer	Vocabulary Word	Antonym
1. I	contrary	agreeable
2. A	disregard	concern
3. O	protest	concur
4. J	endorse	disapprove
5. B	guilty	innocent
6. N	ill	healthy
7. E	melt	freeze
8. L	actual	counterfeit
9. M	abstain	continue
10. D	despise	admire
11. K	faultless	imperfect
12. G	clan	individual
13. C	resourceful	inept
14. F	fact	fabrication
15. H	agility	clumsiness

Activity 3: Word Roots

1. *Hemorrhage* is a noun that refers to an escape of blood from a ruptured blood vessel. (It's also a verb that means to bleed profusely.) If you guessed that it had something to do with blood because of the root *hemo*, you were on the right track. Other words using *hemo* include *hemoglobin, hemophilia,* and *hemorrhoids.*

2. *Magnify* is a verb that means to make something appear larger than it is. The root, *magn*, means great or large. Other words that use *magn* include *magnitude* and *magnificent.*

3. *Alleviate* is a verb that means to make suffering or a problem less severe. Its root is *lev*, which means to lift or raise, and you see this root used in the words *levitate, levity,* and *elevate.*

4. *Verbalize* is a verb that means to express ideas or feelings in words. The root of this word, *verb*, literally means word. Other words that contain *verb* include *proverb, reverberate,* and *verbiage.*

5. *Dismal* is an adjective that means depressing or dreary. Its root is *mal*, which means bad or wretched. *Mal* is also part of words such as *malevolent, malfunction,* and *malady.*

6. *Marine* is an adjective that refers something that's of, found in, or produced by the sea. (It's a noun referring to a member of the U.S. Marine Corps, a seascape, and seagoing ships, too.) Its root, *mar*, means sea, and you find it in words such as *marina, maritime,* and *submarine.*

7. *Affirm* is a verb that means to state something as a fact. Its root, *firm*, means firm or strong. You also see *firm* in *confirm*, *firmament*, and *firmly*.

8. *Admonish* is a verb that means to warn or reprimand someone firmly. The root, *mon*, means warn, and it serves as the root in the words *monitor* and *premonition*.

9. *Autograph* is a noun that means a signature (especially that of a celebrity). Its root, *graph*, means to write or draw. You also see *graph* in words such as *biography*, *cartography*, and *graphic*.

10. *Hydrate* is a verb that means to cause to absorb water. *Hydr*, its root, means water. You see it in *hydrant*, *hydroponics*, and *hydrogenated*.

11. *Convene* is a verb that means to come or bring together for a meeting or activity. Its root is *ven*, which means come, just as in the words *event*, *venue*, and *intervene*.

12. *Relapse* is a verb that means to suffer deterioration after a period of improvement. (It's a noun, too, that means the return of a disease or illness after a partial recovery.) Its root is *laps*, which means to slide or slip. Other words that use *laps* include *collapse*, *elapse*, and *prolapse*.

13. *Liberate* is a verb that means to set someone free from a situation, such as imprisonment or slavery, in which their liberty is severely restricted. Its root, *liber*, means free; you also see it in *liberal* and *libertarian*.

14. *Pathetic* is an adjective that means arousing pity, particularly through sadness or vulnerability. Its root is *path*, which means feeling or disease, just like you see in *apathetic*, *pathologist*, and *sociopath*.

15. *Unanimous* is an adjective that refers to two or more people being fully in agreement about something. Its root is *un* (but don't get it confused with the prefix *un-*, which means not). You also see this root in *unity*, *union*, and *reunification*.

Activity 4: Prefixes

1. *Apolitical's* prefix is *a-*, which means not or without. *Apolitical* is an adjective that means not involved or interested in politics. Other words with the prefix *a-* are *atheist*, *asexual*, and *apathy*.

2. *Predetermined*, which is a verb that means established or decided in advance, uses *pre-* as its prefix. *Pre-* means before, and you see it in the words *prefix*, *pregame*, and *prevent*.

3. *Devalue* is a verb that means to reduce the worth or importance of something. Its prefix, *de-*, means off, down, or away from. You see it in words such as *defrost*, *demotivate*, and *devolve*.

4. *Coaxial* is an adjective that means having a common axis (like a coaxial cable). Its prefix, *co-*, means with. *Co-* is also seen in words like *cooperate*, *co-locate*, and *coworker*.

5. *Extraordinary* is an adjective that means very unusual or remarkable. Its prefix is *extra-*, and it means outside or beyond. *Extra-* is also part of the words *extracurricular*, *extraterrestrial*, and *extrajudicial*.

6. *Miniature* is a noun that means a representation or image of something on a reduced or small scale. (It's also an adjective that refers to something that's represented on a small or reduced scale.) As a prefix, *mini-* means small; you also see it in words like *minivan*, *minimal*, and *miniseries*.

7. *Undesirable* is an adjective that means not wanted due to harmfulness or unpleasantness. The prefix, *un-*, means not or against. *Un-* also appears in words such as *unnecessary*, *unhappy*, and *unfazed*.

8. *Forerunner* is a noun that refers to a person or thing that precedes someone or something else. The prefix in this word is *fore-*, and it means before. You also see it in words like *foreman*, *foresee*, and *forego*.

9. *Byproduct* is a noun that refers to an incidental or secondary product made while making something else. Its prefix, *by-*, means near or next to. This prefix also appears in the words *byway* and *bypass*.

10. *Overreact* is a verb that means to respond more emotionally or forcibly than fits the situation. Its prefix is *over-*, which means excessive or above, and you see it in words like *overbearing*, *overjoyed*, and *overuse*.

11. *Uplift* is a verb that means to lift or raise something. It's also a noun that describes the act of raising something. Its prefix, *up-*, means greater, higher, or better, so you see it in *upgrade*, *upright*, and *upsweep*.

12. *Midway* is an adjective and adverb that means in or toward the middle of something. (It's also a noun that refers to the hotspot in an amusement park, carnival, or fair where all the concessions, games, and sideshows are located.) *Mid-* is its prefix, which means middle, so it also shows up in the words *midtown*, *midday*, and *midst*.

13. *Intergalactic* is an adjective that refers to something relating to or situated between two or more galaxies. Its prefix, *inter-*, means among or between. You find it in *international*, *Internet*, and *interim*.

14. *Omnipotent* is an adjective that means having unlimited power or able to do anything. *Omni-* is its prefix, and it means all. You also see it in *omnivore*, *omnibus*, and *omniscient*.

15. *Substrate* is a noun that means a substance or layer that underlies something. *Sub-*, its prefix, means under, so you also see it in *subway*, *submarine*, and *subsystem*.

Activity 5: Suffixes

1. *Postage* is a noun that refers to the charge for sending a letter or other matter by mail. Its suffix is *-age*, which means action or process. It also appears in *passage*, *pilgrimage*, and *voyage*.

2. *Annoyance* is a noun that means nuisance or a person or thing that annoys. Its suffix, *-ance*, means state or quality of, so you see it in words like *defiance*, *brilliance*, and *compliance*.

3. *Disciplinarian* is a noun that means a person who enforces or advocates discipline, and its suffix is *-arian*, which means a person who does something. This suffix appears in *vegetarian*, *librarian*, and *egalitarian*.

4. *Wisdom* is a noun that means scholarly knowledge or learning, or the state of being wise. Its suffix is *-dom*, which means condition of, state, or realm, so it also shows up in words like *boredom*, *freedom*, and *kingdom*.

5. *Clemency* is a noun that means a disposition to show compassion or forgiveness, leniency, or mercy. Its suffix is *-ency*, which means condition or quality. You find it in *dependency*, *efficiency*, and *complacency*.

6. *Artful* is an adjective that means crafty, cunning, skillful, or clever. Its suffix, *-ful*, means full of, so you see it in words like *helpful*, *cheerful*, and *thankful* as well.

7. *Celestial* is an adjective that means pertaining to the sky or to the universe beyond the atmosphere. Its suffix is *-ial*, which means relating to. It also makes an appearance in words like *editorial*, *martial*, and *racial*.

8. *Zanily* is an adverb that means comically or clownishly, and its suffix is *-ily*, which means in a certain manner. You see it in *sloppily*, *steadily*, and *breezily*.

9. *Completion* is a noun that means conclusion or fulfillment. Its suffix is *-ion*, which means action or process, and it appears in *celebration*, *navigation*, and *abduction*.

10. *Placement* is a noun that means location or arrangement or that indicates the act of placing. Its suffix is *-ent*, which means action or result. You see *-ent* in words like *movement*, *shipment*, and *abolishment*.

11. *Authorship* is a noun that means origin with reference to an author, creator, or producer of a work. Its suffix is *-ship*, which means skill of or state or condition of, and it shows up in words like *citizenship*, *friendship*, and *governorship*.

12. *Fascination* is a noun that means the state or instance of being fascinated, and its suffix is *-tion*. The suffix *-tion* means state or quality, so you also see it in *frustration*, *attention*, and *dejection*.

13. *Fortitude* is a noun that means mental and emotional strength during difficulty, adversity, or danger. Its suffix, *-tude*, means state, condition, or quality, and it shows up in words like *gratitude*, *magnitude*, and *servitude*.

14. *Circular* is an adjective that means having the form of a circle or being roundabout or indirect. Its suffix is *-ular*, which means relating to or resembling. You find it in *cellular*, *muscular*, and *regular*, too.

15. *Audible* is an adjective that means capable of being heard, and its suffix is *-ible*, which means able to be. You see it in words like *plausible*, *legible*, and *visible*.

Activity 6: Context

1. *Deleterious* is an adjective that means causing harm or damage.

2. *Facetious* is an adjective that means treating serious issues with deliberately inappropriate humor.

3. *Lexicon* is a noun that means the vocabulary of a person, language, or branch of knowledge.

4. *Plagiarize* is a verb that means to take someone else's work or idea and pass it off as one's own.

5. *Capitulate* is a verb that means to cease to resist or to surrender.

6. *Sanguine* is an adjective that means optimistic or positive, especially in a difficult or bad situation.

7. *Totalitarian* is an adjective that means relating to a system of centralized, dictatorial government that requires complete subservience to the state.

8. *Vehemently* is an adverb that means in a forceful, passionate, or intense manner.

9. *Colossal* is an adjective that means extremely large.

10. *Bizarre* is an adjective that means very strange or unusual, especially in a way that causes interest or amusement.

11. *Boycott* is a verb that means to withdraw from commercial or social relations as a punishment or protest.

12. *Embargo* is a noun that means an official ban on trade or other commercial activity with a particular country.

13. *Fallacy* is a noun that refers to a mistaken belief, especially if it's based on an unsound argument.

14. *Mosaic* is a noun that refers to a picture or pattern made by arranging small colored pieces of a hard material.

15. *Nuisance* is a noun that means a person, thing, or circumstance causing inconvenience or annoyance.

Chapter 6

The Word Knowledge Subtest

A decent vocabulary is essential in the military if you want to get ahead. The military operates on paperwork, and whether you're trying to get more supplies (submit necessary logistical requisitions) or get the assignment you want (application for personnel career-enhancement programs), you need to develop a good vocabulary.

Word Knowledge is what the military calls the vocabulary subtest on the ASVAB. Because a strong vocabulary is essential to success in the military, the Department of Defense has made this vocabulary test a part of the all-important AFQT score — the score that determines whether you're qualified to join the military service of your choice (see Chapter 2). The military considers clear communication so important that this skill is taught and graded at all levels of leadership training and is often required for promotion.

REMEMBER

Word knowledge isn't part of the AFQT score just because the military likes to use big words. It's included because words stand for ideas, and the more words you understand, the more ideas you can understand (and the better you can communicate with others). Society (including people in the military) often equates a large vocabulary with intelligence and success.

Getting Acquainted with the Test Format

The Word Knowledge portion of the ASVAB measures your vocabulary knowledge. It consists of 16 questions on the version most people take: the CAT-ASVAB. (There are 35 questions on the paper version, but most people don't take that one.) The questions come in three styles: synonyms, context, and antonyms. Your task is to choose the answer closest in meaning to the underlined word unless the test specifically tells you to choose the answer *most opposite* in meaning. Look at the following examples:

EXAMPLE

<u>Abatement</u> most nearly means

(A) encourage.

(B) relax.

(C) obstruct.

(D) terminate.

In this case, the correct answer is Choice (D) because *abatement* means putting an end to something or subsiding.

In the second type of question, you see an underlined word used in the context of a sentence. Again, your goal is to choose the answer closest in meaning to the underlined word as it's used in the sentence. For example:

EXAMPLE

His painting was <u>garish</u>.

(A) offensive

(B) tacky

(C) pretty

(D) expensive

REMEMBER

"Closest in meaning" doesn't mean "the exact same thing." You're looking for words most similar in meaning.

In case you're wondering, the answer is Choice (B).

Finally, you'll encounter a handful of questions about antonyms. You'll know you're facing an antonym question when you see the words *most opposite in meaning*. Consider the following question:

EXAMPLE

The word most opposite in meaning to <u>achieve</u> is

(A) win.

(B) junction.

(C) fail.

(D) championship.

The correct answer is Choice (C) because *achieve* means to successfully bring something about by effort, skill, or courage — and the opposite of that is to fail.

Bumping Up Your Test Score

Sometimes on the Word Knowledge subtest, you either know the answer at first glance, or you don't. Even with that restriction, however, you can pick up a few tricks to help you get the best score possible.

Keeping an eye on the clock

Like all the ASVAB subtests, the Word Knowledge subtest is timed. On the CAT-ASVAB, you get 8 minutes to answer 16 questions, meaning you get to spend about 30 seconds on each one. If you're one of the few people taking the paper version, you have 11 minutes to answer the 35 questions, which translates into slightly less than 20 seconds to answer each question. For most people, that's plenty of time (as long as you're not thinking more about what you're missing on Facebook than you are about the test).

If you're taking the computerized version of the ASVAB, your remaining time appears on the computer screen. If you're taking the paper version of the test, a clock is clearly visible in the room, and the test proctor posts the start and stop time for the subtest on a blackboard or whiteboard.

Watching out for the evil homonym

A *homonym* is a word with multiple unrelated meanings (see Chapter 5). The word may be spelled the same for both or all meanings, or it may be spelled differently. If it's spelled the same, it may have a different pronunciation. Some homonyms spelled differently can have the same pronunciation.

The ASVAB doesn't contain any trick questions. In other words, the test doesn't present you with two legitimate answers and ask you to try to decide which one is the "best." However, homonyms can still trip you up if you don't pay attention. Look at the following example:

EXAMPLE

Isle most nearly means

(A) walkway.

(B) island.

(C) intention.

(D) description.

Isle and *aisle* are homonyms. *Isle* means island, and *aisle* means walkway (like in the grocery store). They're two words that sound the same, but they're spelled differently and mean different things. In this case, the correct answer is Choice (B).

Some homonyms are spelled the same but have different meanings. Just for the record, these are called *heteronyms* (one new word for your vocabulary: check!). You won't see multiple correct definitions on the Word Knowledge subtest when you're doing a direct definition problem, but you may see such multiple correct definitions when the word is used in the context of a sentence. For example:

EXAMPLE

Jack tied a bow around his neck.

(A) knot

(B) weapon

(C) ship front

(D) triangle

All the answer choices are proper definitions for the word *bow*. However, only one choice, Choice (A), makes sense for *bow* in the context of the sentence. It just wouldn't make sense for Jack to tie a weapon, the front of a ship, or a triangle around his neck.

Considering guessing

Sometimes on the Word Knowledge subtest, you just don't know the answer. In that case, don't leave it blank. (You can't leave answers blank on the computerized version of the test anyway.) The paper version of the ASVAB doesn't penalize you for wrong answers. If you leave the answer blank, you have a 0 percent chance of getting it right. But if you make a wild guess, you have a 25 percent chance of stumbling upon the right answer.

WARNING

On the CAT-ASVAB, make sure your guesses are educated and that you don't click random answer buttons quickly just to get through. The test's creators designed the grading software to issue a pretty hefty penalty for multiple wrong answers toward the end of your subtests. They figure this scenario implies you were running out of time and didn't read the questions; to do well on the ASVAB and AFQT, you need to be prepared with adequate time for each question.

TIP

Keep in mind that although you may know the word in the question, you may not know one or more of the words in the multiple-choice answers. In that case, use the process of elimination to narrow down your choices. Eliminate the words you know *aren't* correct and guess which of the remaining words is most *likely* correct.

Before making a wild guess, take a few seconds to look at the word from a different perspective. You may find that you know the word after all — just in a different form. In English, one root word can be changed slightly to perform all sorts of roles; it might be able to act as a noun, a verb, an adjective, or an adverb with just a little modification. So if you know what the root word *attach* means, you can figure out what the word *attachment* means. If you know *adherent,* you can deduce what *adherence* means. (You can find much more information on this topic in Chapter 5.)

You can use root word clues to identify unfamiliar words on the ASVAB. Say you run across the word *memento* on the Word Knowledge test:

EXAMPLE

<u>Memento</u> most nearly means

(A) souvenir.

(B) beauty.

(C) speed.

(D) trouble.

If you don't have a clue what the word *memento* means, all is not lost. Take a closer look. What other word starting with the letters *mem-* do you know? How about the word *memory*? *Memory* is a noun that means something you remember, so the word *memento* is likely related to memories. Other words you might know are *memoir, memorable,* and even the word *memo*. So when you look over the possible choices, you can choose the one that has something to do with memory.

But wait. None of the answers actually says "memory." Now what? Just use the process of elimination. One of the answers has a lot to do with memory: Choice (A), *souvenir.*

Trying On Some Sample Questions

Now you're ready to pit your skills against the Word Knowledge subtest of the ASVAB. Try these sample questions to see how you do. They're similar to what you'll see on the ASVAB.

1. <u>Bestial</u> most nearly means
   - (A) playful.
   - (B) animal-like.
   - (C) tantalizing.
   - (D) pregnant.

2. The enemy was <u>relentless</u> with negotiations.
   - (A) overwhelmed
   - (B) happy
   - (C) strict
   - (D) peaceful

3. <u>Malignant</u> most nearly means
   - (A) tumor.
   - (B) angry.
   - (C) kind.
   - (D) evil.

4. Bernard wanted to ask a lawyer whether his friend's investment idea was <u>licit</u>.
   - (A) legal
   - (B) profitable
   - (C) illegal
   - (D) sensible

5. <u>Achromatic</u> most nearly means
   - (A) automatic.
   - (B) tasty.
   - (C) colorless.
   - (D) manual.

6. The legal team was impressed with her <u>dynamic</u> ideas.
   - (A) offensive
   - (B) fun
   - (C) powerful
   - (D) cowering

7. <u>Wry</u> most nearly means
   - (A) smile.
   - (B) distorted.
   - (C) angry.
   - (D) happy.

8. Melissa was justifiably proud of her recent <u>abstinence</u>.
   - (A) grades
   - (B) sobriety
   - (C) trustworthiness
   - (D) awards

9. <u>Tolerate</u> most nearly means
   - (A) accept.
   - (B) conserve.
   - (C) annoy.
   - (D) rush.

10. Lyle's landlord instructed him to <u>vacate</u> the apartment.
    - (A) paint
    - (B) leave
    - (C) clean
    - (D) sell

Answers and Explanations

Use this answer key to score the practice Word Knowledge questions.

1. **B.** *Bestial* is an adjective that means having animal characteristics. Noting the similarity between the words *bestial* and *beast* can lead you in the right direction with this question.

2. **C.** Used as an adjective, *relentless* means unyieldingly severe, strict, or harsh. The other words don't fit the context of the sentence.

3. **D.** *Malignant* is an adjective that means evil or harmful. You may have been tempted to select Choice (A) because you've heard of a malignant tumor, but *tumor* and *malignant* don't mean the same thing.

4. **A.** *Licit* is an adjective that means lawful. Although you may not have been familiar with the word *licit*, chances are good that you've come across the opposite-meaning word, *illicit*, and you probably know that it means illegal. So you can deduce that *licit* means the opposite of illegal, or legal.

5. **C.** *Achromatic* is an adjective that means having no color. If you knew that the word root *chrom* refers to color and that the prefix *a-* means without, you could figure out that *achromatic* means without color.

6. **C.** Used as an adjective, *dynamic* refers to a process or system that's characterized by constant progress, activity, or change. You can use clues in the sentence to rule out Choices (A) and (D) because if the legal team is impressed, she's probably not offensive or cowering. Although *dynamic* can mean fun, the word closest in meaning to what's in the sentence is *powerful*.

7. **B.** *Wry* is an adjective that means crooked or twisted.

8. **B.** *Abstinence* is a noun that means the willful avoidance of something — for example, a substance such as alcohol or drugs.

9. **A.** *Tolerate* is a verb meaning to allow or accept without hindrance.

10. **B.** *Vacate* is a verb that means to give up occupancy of a location. The word root, *vac*, is key here. A *vacation* involves leaving your normal place of residence. When people *evacuate* an area, they leave that area. A *vacuum* is created when matter leaves a given area.

Chapter 7
Reading for Comprehension

The military services want their members to understand what they're reading. This skill is known as *reading comprehension,* but on the ASVAB, it's called *paragraph comprehension,* and it makes up part of your AFQT score.

Why does the military place so much importance on reading comprehension? Quite simple: Miscommunication has been the leading cause of almost every major military accident or battlefield disaster in history.

The military runs on paperwork. A former Air Force vice chief of staff once commented that he had looked at 13,000 pieces of paper in a five-day period. Granted, you won't see quite so much correspondence as a newly enlisted member, but you'll have to read and understand your share of memos, policy letters, regulations, manuals, and forms. In some branches, your promotions are based, in part, on how well you can read, comprehend, and retain information from written material. And the higher rank you earn, the more paperwork you'll see.

Reading comprehension involves several skills that anyone can develop with practice. To thoroughly understand what you read, you must develop the abilities to recognize the main idea, recall details, and make inferences. The information in this chapter helps you improve your reading comprehension skills, making it possible for you to nail the Paragraph Comprehension subtest of the ASVAB.

Taking Pointers about Points

When someone writes something, he's almost always trying to make a point. This message is called the *main point* or *principal idea* of the writing. The paragraph or passage may also contain information that supports or reinforces the main point; these little gems are called *subpoints.*

Picking out the main point

The main point is the most important part of a paragraph or passage. It's the primary theme that the writer wants you to understand. In many cases, the writer states the main point simply. In other cases, the writer may imply the main point rather than state it directly.

Quite often, the main point of a paragraph or passage is contained in the first sentence. You may recall from school that your English teacher referred to this sentence as the *topic sentence.* Sometimes a writer also rephrases or summarizes the main point in the passage's last sentence.

In the following passage, the main idea is stated in the first sentence:

> U.S. military forces will increasingly be called upon in the immediate future for peaceful military-to military contacts, humanitarian intervention, peace support, and other nontraditional roles. The end of the Cold War transformed U.S. national security. The United States entered the 21st century with unprecedented prosperity and opportunities threatened by complex dangers. Problems associated with fostering a stable global system require the U.S. military to play an essential role in building coalitions and shaping the international environment in ways that protect and promote U.S. interests.

The main point is stated clearly in the very first sentence: "U.S. military forces will increasingly be called upon in the immediate future for peaceful military-to–military contacts, humanitarian intervention, peace support, and other nontraditional roles." The sentences that follow are subpoints that help clarify and emphasize the paragraph's main point.

Sometimes the main point isn't in the first sentence. Look at the passage again, slightly reworded:

> The end of the Cold War transformed U.S. national security. The United States entered the 21st century with unprecedented prosperity and opportunities threatened by complex dangers. Problems associated with fostering a stable global system require the U.S. military to play an essential role in building coalitions and shaping the international environment in ways that protect and promote U.S. interests. A key assumption is that U.S. military forces will increasingly be called upon for peaceful military-to-military contacts, humanitarian intervention, peace support, and other nontraditional roles.

The paragraph's main point remains the same, but it isn't stated until the last sentence.

Sometimes the main point isn't clearly stated but is rather implied. Take a look at the following paragraph:

> The plane landed at 9 p.m. The children were disappointed that new security rules prevented them from meeting their father at the gate. They waited with their mother in the car outside the airport doors, amidst dozens of other people in vehicles, there for similar purposes. With each passing moment, their excitement grew. Finally, the automatic doors opened, and he walked out. "Dad! Hey, Dad!" the excited children yelled.

Though it's not directly stated, the main point of this paragraph is obviously that the children's father is coming home.

Take another look at the preceding passage. When trying to determine the main point of a paragraph, ask yourself the following:

>> **Who or what is this paragraph about?** A father returning to his family.

>> **What aspect of this subject is the author talking about?** The moments before and the moment of the father's appearing at the airport doors.

>> **What is the author trying to get across about this aspect of the subject?** The drama of the father's reunion with his family.

Simplifying subpoints

Most writers don't stick to just one point. If they did, most paragraphs could be reduced to just one sentence. But it doesn't work that way. Writers usually try to reinforce their main points by providing details. These subpoints may include facts, statistics, or descriptions that support the passage's main point. Subpoints help you see what the author is saying. Take, for instance, the following passage:

> For the purposes of drill, Air Force organizations are divided into elements, flights, squadrons, groups, and wings. The "rule of two" applies (that is, an element must consist of at least two people, a flight must consist of at least two elements, and so on). Usually, an element consists of between eight and ten people, and a flight has six or eight elements. Drill consists of certain movements by which the flight or squadron is moved in an orderly manner from one formation to another or from one place to another.

Notice how the writer uses the second, third, and fourth sentences to explain in detail how Air Force organizations are divided for the purposes of drill. These supporting details are subpoints.

TIP

Look for signal words in the passage — words like *again, also, as well as, furthermore, moreover,* and *significantly.* These signal words may call your attention to supporting facts.

Analyzing What You've Read

Understanding what you read involves more than just picking out main points and subpoints. To analyze a paragraph, you need to examine the passage carefully to identify causes, key factors, and possible results. Analyzing a passage requires you to draw conclusions from what you've read and understand relationships among the ideas in the text.

Say what? What does that passage mean?

By drawing conclusions about a passage's meaning, you reach new ideas that the author implies but doesn't come right out and state. You must analyze the information the author presents to make inferences from what you've read. What conclusions can you infer from the following paragraph?

> The local school district is facing a serious budgetary crisis. The state, suffering a revenue shortfall of more than $600 million, has cut funding to the district by $18.7 million. Already, 65 teachers have been laid off, and more layoffs are expected.

Can you conclude that the local school district really stinks? Possibly, but that's not the point the author is trying to make. Although the author doesn't come straight out and say so, you can draw the conclusion that if the state revenue shortfall could somehow be corrected — by increasing state sales tax or income tax, for example — the local school district's budgetary crisis could be resolved. The author never actually makes this point, but you can draw this conclusion from the facts presented by using reason and logic.

WARNING

When analyzing a passage, leave your baggage at the door. For example, you may not like the current governor, but nothing in the passage suggests that the writer supports electing a new governor to solve the budget problem.

Say it again, Sam: Paraphrasing

Paraphrasing means to rewrite a passage using your own words. This strategy is often useful when you're trying to understand a complex idea. Putting the passage in your own words can help you understand the main idea, which can in turn help you discover information that may not be stated directly. Paraphrasing can also be helpful in making inferences and drawing conclusions from the information provided. Look at the following short passage:

> On-the-job training (OJT) is often the most effective method of training because the employer tailors the training to meet the specific job requirements. OJT can be as casual as giving a few pointers to a new worker or as formal as a fully structured training program with timetables and specified subjects.

How would you paraphrase this passage? If you wrote something like the following, you'd be on the right track:

> Some OJT programs involve a formal lesson plan, while others simply tell a new employee what to do and how to do it. OJT works well because new employees can be taught what they need to do the specific job.

REMEMBER

Paraphrasing is just saying the same thing using different words. In basic training, your drill instructor may say, "You really need to work on your running time," or he may say, "Get the %$@* lead out of your pants and run faster!" Both mean the same thing.

Improving Your Reading Comprehension Skills

Some people read and comprehend better than others, but one thing is for certain: You're not born with the ability to read. It's something you learn. Like almost anything that is learned, you can use proven techniques to help you do it better:

>> Read more and watch TV less.

>> Practice skimming and scanning.

>> Learn to identify the main ideas and the all-important subpoints.

>> Work on the meanings of strange or difficult words.

>> Practice paraphrasing.

>> Reflect on what you've read.

Taking the time to read

Joseph Addison once noted that "Reading is to the mind what exercise is to the body." My dad has been painting walls to look like stone, precious metals, and all kinds of other materials — anything other than drywall — for more than 30 years. As a result, you wouldn't be able to tell the difference between one of his walls and the real deal. My brother's been wielding a tattoo gun for more than 20 years. He practiced on grapefruits and oranges (and a few brave volunteers). With more practice, he got better (thankfully!), and he gets better each time he creates a new tattoo.

The point is that you can improve any skill with practice. If you don't read well, the chances are good that you don't read much. You don't need a $4 million government-funded study (although I'm sure there are a few) to know that people who read a lot are more likely to be better readers than people who don't read so much.

If you learn to read for fun, you'll automatically read more, and I guarantee that your reading skills will improve immeasurably after a relatively short time. So how do you learn to read for fun? Simple: Choose reading material in subject areas that interest you.

You don't have to pick up *A Tale of Two Cities* or *War and Peace.* You can start with the newspaper, a biography of a person you admire, or magazines you find at the library. Personally, I like *For Dummies* books. If you devote at least one hour a day to improving your reading comprehension, you'll see results fast — maybe within a month or so.

Skimming and scanning

Different situations call for different styles of reading. The technique you choose depends on your purpose for reading. For example, you may be reading for enjoyment, to find information, or to complete a task. If you're reading for enjoyment, you usually read and savor every word. However, in other situations — such as when you're just trying to find the main ideas or look up specific information — you may not want to read every single word.

Skimming

You can skim to quickly identify the main ideas of a text. For example, most people don't read a newspaper word for word. Instead, they skim through the text to see whether they want to read an article in more depth. Most people can skim three to four times faster than normal reading. Skimming is especially useful if you have lots of material to read in a limited amount of time.

Here are some points to keep in mind when you practice skimming:

> » If the article or passage has a title, read it. It's often the shortest possible summary of the content.

> » Read the first sentence or paragraph. This introductory text often consists of the main point(s).

> » If the text has subheadings, read each one, looking for relationships among them.

> » Look for clue words that answer who, what, where, how, why, and when.

> » Pay attention to qualifying adjectives, such as *best, worst, most,* and so on.

> » Look for typographical clues such as boldface, italics, underlining, or asterisks.

Scanning

Scanning involves moving your eyes quickly down the page seeking specific words and phrases. When you scan, you must be willing to skip over several lines of text without actually reading and understanding them.

Scanning is a useful technique when you're looking for keywords or specific ideas. For example, when you look up a word in the dictionary, you probably use the scanning technique. In most cases, you know what you're looking for, so you concentrate on finding a particular answer.

When scanning a document:

>> Keep in mind what you're scanning for. If you keep a picture in your mind, the information is more likely to jump out at you from among all the other printed words.

>> Anticipate what form the information is likely to appear in. Will it be numbers? Proper nouns?

>> Let your eyes run over several lines of print at a time.

>> When you find the information you're looking for, read the entire sentence.

Skimming and scanning are useful techniques for many of the Paragraph Comprehension problems. I talk more about this subtest in Chapter 8.

Looking for the main ideas and subpoints

Reading wouldn't have much purpose if you just let your eyes wander over the words without walking away with some sense of what the author is talking about. The author's ideas are included in the main point and subpoints of the writing. You need to practice extracting this information from your reading material. See the "Taking Pointers about Points" section earlier in this chapter.

Building your vocabulary

It's hard to understand what you're reading if you don't understand the individual words. Effective reading comprehension involves developing a solid vocabulary. Use the techniques in Chapter 5 to strengthen your vocabulary, and you'll simultaneously improve your reading comprehension skills. The two skills go hand in hand.

When practicing reading, try not to look up new words in a dictionary right away. Stopping to look up words often impairs your concentration and lessens your ability to comprehend what you've read.

Instead, start by trying to puzzle out the meaning of a new word by looking at the context in which the word is used in the sentence or phrase. For example, take the following passage:

> It had been three days since the shipwreck, and Tammy was unable to find food or much drinkable water. At that point, she would have done anything to get off that wretched island.

You can derive several important clues about the meaning of the word *wretched* based on its context in the passage. Obviously, Tammy isn't having a very good time, nor does she find the island to be a pleasant environment. Therefore, you can surmise that *wretched* has something to do with unpleasantness.

Paraphrasing

Putting the text in your own words can help you understand what the writer is talking about. I talk more extensively about this in the "Say it again, Sam: Paraphrasing" section earlier in this chapter.

You probably won't have time on the Paragraph Comprehension subtest to rewrite passages on your scratch paper. But by practicing the technique while you hone your reading comprehension skills, you'll develop the ability to paraphrase in your mind.

Remembering by reflecting

Reflecting simply means thinking about what you've read. If you take a few minutes to think about it, you're more likely to remember it. Did you enjoy the passage or article? Did you find it interesting? Do you agree or disagree with the author's views? *Warning:* Thinking about what you've read may cause you to learn something!

Speaking about Speed

Dozens of speed-reading courses, software, and online programs absolutely guarantee, without qualification, to turn you into a speed-reading wizard. However, if your goal is to score well on the Paragraph Comprehension subtest, I recommend you save your money.

The Paragraph Comprehension subtest isn't a speed-reading test. You'll get 22 minutes to answer 11 questions on the computerized version of the test; if you're one of the few people who takes it on paper, you'll have 13 minutes to answer 15 questions. Either way, this is plenty of time for most people. The best part is that in many cases, you'll answer multiple questions about the same passage. That means by the time you get to the second (or, in rare cases, the third) question, you've already gained a good understanding of what the passage is about.

If you're still worried about your reading speed, just remember: The more you read, the better (and faster) you'll get at it. Read to comprehend by using the information in this chapter, and your speed will automatically get faster as you practice.

Diving for Facts: Paragraph Comprehension Practice

The Paragraph Comprehension subtest of the ASVAB is designed to keep you on your toes. You'll have to dig for the main idea, pull out facts, draw conclusions about what you've read, and find out what the author of the passage is implying. Each of these exercises is designed to help you do those things — and to gauge where you need a little more practice.

Finding the main idea

Read each of the following passages and underline (or circle — it's your book!) the clues that help you figure out the main idea; then put it into your own words in the space below the passage. Refer back to "Taking Pointers about Points" if you need a refresher. Check your answers by flipping to the "Answers and Explanations" section at the end of this chapter.

Passage 1

About 70 percent of people are eligible for a home office deduction on their taxes, but many are afraid to claim it because they think it'll get them audited. The truth is that the law allows you to claim a home office deduction if you use some space in your house exclusively for work (so guest bedrooms with a computer don't count). If you're eligible, you probably should claim it — but you should talk to a tax professional to be sure.

Main idea: _____

_____

Passage 2

The sliding boundary between the Pacific Plate and the North American Plate is called the San Andreas Fault. It effectively divides California into two parts, with San Diego and Los Angeles on the Pacific Plate; San Francisco and Sacramento are on the North American Plate. When the two plates build up enough pressure, one finally gives way and causes earthquakes. It's a common myth that the San Andreas Fault will eventually crack and send California into the ocean. One thing remains certain, though: The fault isn't going away, and neither are the earthquakes it causes.

Main idea: _____

_____

Passage 3

Currently serving or honorably discharged veterans may be eligible for the Post-9/11 G.I. Bill, which is an education benefit from the Veterans Administration. The Post-9/11 G.I. Bill pays for you to go to college or a trade school, and if you enroll full-time, you'll also get a monthly stipend to help pay for your housing. In some cases, a parent can transfer the benefit to his or her children or to a spouse.

Main idea: _____

_____

Passage 4

In 1990, the U.S. Supreme Court ruled that it's unconstitutional to ban people from burning the American flag, saying that preventing people from doing so would violate their First Amendment rights. As you know, the First Amendment to the U.S. Constitution guarantees us freedom of speech and a number of other freedoms, such as the freedom to exercise our religious beliefs, the freedom to peaceably assemble, and the freedom to petition the government when we disagree with elected officials. In the Supreme Court case *United States v. Eichman*, the Court upheld the right to burn the flag in this context. The U.S. Flag Code actually prescribes burning the flag when it becomes "so tattered that it no longer fits to serve as a symbol of the United States." Several organizations, including the Veterans of Foreign Wars, the American Legion, and the Boy and Girl Scouts of America, conduct dignified flag-burning ceremonies when necessary.

Main idea: _____

_____

Going on a fact-finding mission

Some of the Paragraph Comprehension questions on the ASVAB require you to hunt for specific facts in written passages. The questions you encounter may ask you to find out who, what, when, where, why, or how, and you'll most likely have to return to the passage to find the correct answers. Use the following exercises to test your fact-hunting skills; then flip to the "Answers and Explanations" section at the end of this chapter to see how accurate you were.

When it comes to voting rights (and the responsibilities that come with them), Americans are very clear about what they want. Four out of five Americans support early voting, and 63 percent support automatic voter registration. As many as 19 percent of all citizens are completely against requiring some form of voter identification at the polls. No matter what people prefer, though, that doesn't change the fact that just over half of all eligible voters turn out for general elections and even fewer show up for midterm elections.

How many Americans support early voting? _____

How many Americans support automatic voter registration? _____ _____

How many Americans are against requiring voter identification at the polls? _____

How many eligible voters vote in general elections? _____

Passage 6

Nice is a beautiful city on the coast of France, less than an hour's drive from Cannes (the city famous for its film festival) and about 932 kilometers from Paris. The city is known for its natural beauty, and painters — including Marc Chagall, Henri Matisse, and Niki de Saint Phalle — have been trying to capture its essence for centuries. After a tumultuous history, the city itself was annexed by France in 1860, and it has remained part of the country ever since.

What artists have created famous paintings of Nice? _____ _____

How far is Nice from Paris? _____ _____

When was Nice annexed by France? _____ _____

Passage 7

The National Museum of Natural History, run by the Smithsonian Institution, is located in the heart of Washington, D.C., between the White House and Capitol Hill. It offers free admission, although some of the attractions inside (most notably the butterfly exhibit and the IMAX theater) do charge a fee. The three-story museum has only two floors of exhibits; the ground floor contains shops and a few cafés offering drinks and prepackaged foods. On the first floor, you'll find the Ocean Hall, a modern mammal exhibit, and the Human Origins Exhibit. You can take stairs or an elevator to the second floor, where you'll find a remarkable dinosaur exhibit that includes a full T-Rex skeleton, the Hope Diamond, and the Live Insect Zoo.

Where is the National Museum of Natural History located? _____ _____

How many stories is the museum? _____ _____

Where would you go to learn about human evolution? _____

Passage 8

The "terrible twos," according to most parents, are very real and very difficult. Dr. Vanessa LoBue says that this tough time actually begins when toddlers are about 18 months old, and it's because little ones aren't good at emotion regulation or self-control. . . and that those two factors combine to create the perfect storm. Dr. Jeremy Friedman, who wrote a book about dealing with toddlers, says that you can minimize tantrums and defuse meltdown situations by staying calm, being loving, and providing reassurance to your toddler.

Who said that the "terrible twos" start when kids are 18 months old? _____ _____

What is Dr. Jeremy Friedman's book about? _____ _____

According to the passage, why do toddlers go through such difficulty? _____ _____ _____

Drawing conclusions on your own

In some cases, the ASVAB's Paragraph Comprehension questions want you to figure out what the passage is telling you when it doesn't actually say what you need to know. You'll have to draw conclusions based on what the passage does contain and choose the best answer from the four choices the test makers created for you. Use these passages to draw your own conclusions, and when you're done, head to the "Answers and Explanations" section to find out how you did.

Passage 9

Simón could smell the sweet scent of man-tecada baking in the house when he dropped his bike near the porch stairs after school. He burst through the door, hoping they were done and ready to eat. Mom was standing in the kitchen, laughing at Paloma, whose tiny hands were covered in flour, and Dad was snapping pictures with his phone as the little girl toddled across the floor. Simón said, "Mom, may I have a piece of mantecada?" Mom smiled and said, "Yes, as soon as you've had your dinner."

What is mantecada? _____

_____

How old is Paloma likely to be? _____

_____

What time of day is it? _____

_____

Passage 10

The twins were both surprised when their mother took them to the mall on Sunday afternoon — the Sunday right before the big day — but the festive music, snowy seasonal décor, and throng of shoppers were distracting. . . and exciting. A long line of people trailed into the food court; young parents with strollers, grandparents peering over boxes and bags to smile at their grandkids, and everyone in between were slowly inching forward. The occasional flash of a camera brightened the space toward the front of the line, and both girls squealed happily when they figured out why they were there.

When does this story take place? _____

_____

Why are so many people waiting in line? _____

_____

Passage 11

The littlest one tumbled over the pile of his playful littermates. He made his way to Cheryl, his tail wagging as he panted. She bent down to scratch his pointed ears, and when he looked up into her eyes, she made her decision. "I'm going to call you Jack," she whispered.

What is Jack? _____

_____

What was Cheryl's decision? _____

_____

Passage 12

Heather watched the lizard dart up the tree, took a huge gulp of water, and wiped the sweat from her face with a towel. As her breathing slowed, she knew she could've been faster. She knew that she'd *have* to be faster if she wanted to stand a chance against the other competitors. The problem: she didn't really want to compete. Even if she did, she wasn't sure she had the skill to keep up. She pushed aside her negative thoughts, bent down to tie her shoe, and thought she could still see a handful of competitors near the bend in the road ahead. "Twenty-three miles down and three more to go," she thought, the dread ebbing away as she took off again at a comfortable pace.

Why is Heather sweating? _____

_____

What is Heather participating in? _____

_____

Answers and Explanations

Check your answers against these and see how close you were to finding the correct ones.

Passage 1: The main idea of this passage is that some people can claim a home office deduction on their taxes. It's mentioned in the first and second sentences, and it's alluded to (hinted at) in the final sentence.

Passage 2: The main idea of this passage is the San Andreas Fault and why it causes earthquakes.

Passage 3: The main idea of this passage is the Post–9/11 G.I. Bill — what it is and who can use it.

Passage 4: This passage is about burning the American flag. It mentions why it's legal to do so as freedom of speech and when the U.S. Flag Code prescribes (calls for) it.

Passage 5: Four out of five Americans support early voting; 63 percent of Americans support automatic voter registration; 19 percent of Americans oppose voter identification requirements; and just over half of all eligible voters vote in general elections.

Passage 6: Marc Chagall, Henri Matisse, and Niki de Saint Phalle have painted Nice; the city is 932 kilometers from Paris; and France annexed it in 1860.

Passage 7: The National Museum of Natural History is located in Washington, D.C., between the White House and Capitol Hill; the museum is three stories high; you'll find the exhibit about evolution on the first floor, in the Human Origins section.

Passage 8: Dr. Vanessa LoBue said that the "terrible twos" begin around 18 months; Dr. Jeremy Friedman's book is about dealing with toddlers; and 18-month-old kids aren't good at emotion regulation or self-control.

Passage 9: Mantecada is most likely a dessert; Paloma is most likely a toddler; and the story takes place in the afternoon.

Passage 10: The story takes place the Sunday before Christmas; the girls are excited because they're waiting to have their pictures taken with Santa Claus.

Passage 11: Jack is a dog; Cheryl decided she was going to keep him.

Passage 12: Heather is sweating because she's run 23 miles; she's competing in a marathon.

Chapter **8**

The Paragraph Comprehension Subtest

The Paragraph Comprehension subtest has the fewest questions of any of the ASVAB subtests. However, it's one of the most important subtests of the ASVAB. The military uses this test (along with the Word Knowledge subtest; see Chapters 5 and 6) to compute your verbal expression (VE) score, which in turn is an important part of your AFQT score. (If you want to see how these scores combine, turn to Chapter 2.)

This subtest is nothing more than a reading comprehension test, much like many of the reading tests you took in school. You're asked to read a short passage (a paragraph) and then answer one to four questions about information contained in that paragraph. Unfortunately, you probably won't find the reading to be very interesting. No passages from *Harry Potter* or about spacemen shooting ray guns here. You're more likely to read about the corn crop harvest rates in Nebraska or the principles of time management. The key is to stay focused. After all, you have to answer only 11 or 15 questions, depending on your version of the test, and the paragraphs aren't that long.

REMEMBER

A large percentage of military jobs require a solid score on this subtest. If you're interested in which military jobs require you to score well on the Paragraph Comprehension subtest, I humbly recommend you head to your favorite book retailer and buy a copy of the best-selling *ASVAB For Dummies* (Wiley). You'll be glad you did.

Tackling the Test Format: Types of Questions

The Paragraph Comprehension subtest requires you to read a short paragraph and then answer one or more multiple-choice questions about what you've read. These questions can generally be broken down into one of four types, which I like to call the treasure hunt, getting the point, dictionary, and deep thinking.

The treasure hunt

Treasure hunt questions require you to find specific information within the paragraph. The good thing about this type of question is that by employing the scanning techniques in Chapter 7, you can often find the answer without having to read the entire paragraph. Try the following example:

EXAMPLE

A new study has found that 21 percent of people arrested in the United States for driving under the influence were arrested again for the same crime within five years. The study, commissioned by the U.S. Department of Justice, analyzed recidivism rates for DUI between 2002 and 2007. During this period, there were more than 930,000 arrests for DUI. Of these, 195,300 — or 21 percent — were arrested again for violating DUI laws a second time within the established time frame. The study found that 34 percent of the repeat offenses occurred within six months of the original arrest.

How many people were arrested for DUI more than once between 2002 and 2007?

(A) 930,000

(B) 195,300

(C) 210,000

(D) None of the above

By letting your eyes quickly scan the paragraph, you notice that all the large numbers are contained in the middle. If you stop and read the two sentences that include large numbers, you find the answer to the question: Choice (B).

Sometimes the answer isn't so obvious, and you have to dig a little deeper to find the treasure. Take the following question, for example:

EXAMPLE

George Armstrong Custer (December 5, 1839–June 25, 1876) was a U.S. Army officer and cavalry commander in the Civil War and the American Indian Wars. At the start of the Civil War, Custer was a cadet at the U.S. Military Academy at West Point, and his class's graduation was accelerated so that they could enter the war. Early in the Gettysburg Campaign, Custer's association with cavalry commander Major General Alfred Pleasonton earned him a promotion at the age of 23 from first lieutenant to brigadier general of volunteers. By the end of the Civil War (April 9, 1865), Custer had achieved the rank of major general of volunteers but was reduced to his permanent grade of captain in the regular army when the troops were sent home.

How old was George Custer at the end of the Civil War?

(A) 24

(B) 25

(C) 26

(D) 34

The answer is still right there in the paragraph, but you have to use a little judgment (and math) to find it. General Custer was born on December 5, 1839 (which you can find in the first sentence) and the Civil War ended on April 9, 1865 (which the last sentence tells you). Therefore, Custer was 25 years old, Choice (B), at the end of the war. (He didn't turn 26 until December of that year.)

Getting the point

This type of question asks you to discern the main topic, point, or idea of the paragraph (see Chapter 7 for more information). When you look for the main point, skimming the paragraph rather than reading it in its entirety is often helpful (see Chapter 7). Try this one on for size:

The farmers' market reopened the second weekend of May. Amid the asparagus and flowers, shoppers chatted about the return of temperatures in the seventies. Across the street, children (and their dogs) were playing Frisbee in the park. Finally, spring had come to town.

What is the main point of the passage?

(A) The farmers' market has reopened.

(B) Children like playing Frisbee.

(C) Spring had come to town.

(D) Shoppers were chatting.

In this paragraph, you may think that the farmers' market reopening is the main point, but the other information about the temperature and the kids playing Frisbee tells you that the main idea is something a bit broader than the market opening. The main idea is stated in the last sentence: "Finally, spring had come to town." Therefore, Choice (C) is the correct answer.

When skimming for the main point of a paragraph, start with the first sentence, and then read the last sentence. The main idea is often contained in one of these sentences.

Dictionary

Much like the Word Knowledge subtest (covered in Chapters 5 and 6), this type of question requires you to define a word as used in the context of the passage. The correct definition that the question is looking for can be the most common meaning of the word, or it can be a less well-known meaning of the word.

In either case, you have to read the passage, make sure you understand how the word is being used, and select the answer option that is closest in meaning to the word as it's used in the passage. Consider this example:

In the 18th century, it was common for sailors to be pressed into service in Britain. Young men found near seaports could be kidnapped, drugged, or otherwise hauled aboard a ship and made to work doing menial chores. They were not paid for their service, and they were given just enough food to keep them alive.

In this passage, <u>pressed</u> means

(A) hired.

(B) ironed.

(C) enticed.

(D) forced.

The correct answer is Choice (D). The descriptions of the conditions these sailors found themselves in should help you decide that they weren't hired or enticed; ironed is one meaning of the word *pressed*, but it isn't correct in this context.

Deep thinking

If the Paragraph Comprehension questions on the ASVAB simply asked you to scan a passage and find the main point or supporting details, it would be a pretty simple test. But the subtest goes beyond that. In order to properly answer some of the questions on the test, you have to analyze what you've read and draw conclusions.

REMEMBER

The *conclusion* — which may be called an *inference* or *implication* — must be reasonably based on what the passage says. You have to use good judgment when deciding what conclusions you can logically draw from what you've read. Be careful not to confuse passage content with your opinion.

Try this example:

EXAMPLE

One of the main reasons motorcyclists are killed in crashes is that the motorcycle itself provides virtually no protection in a crash. For example, approximately 80 percent of reported motorcycle crashes result in injury or death; a comparable figure for automobiles is about 20 percent.

Safe motorcycle riding means

(A) always wearing a helmet.

(B) using premium gas.

(C) selecting the most expensive motorcycle.

(D) always riding with a buddy.

The correct answer is Choice (A). The author didn't specifically state in the passage that wearing a helmet is important, but you can infer the correct answer because the author gives the reason for fatalities: Motorcycles themselves offer virtually no protection in a crash. Based on the information provided in the passage, you can logically conclude that even the small degree of protection offered by a helmet increases the safety of riding motorcycles. None of the other choices is as closely connected to the idea of safety.

Planning Your Attack

The best way to score well on the Paragraph Comprehension subtest is to improve your reading comprehension skills by following the advice I give in Chapter 7. However, you can also do a few things on test day to make sure you score as high as possible:

>> **Watch the time.** As with all the ASVAB subtests, this test is timed. You have 22 minutes to read through and answer 11 questions on the CAT-ASVAB or 13 minutes for 15 questions on the paper version. This period is plenty of time, so you shouldn't feel rushed. Don't relax *too* much, though; you don't have time for daydreaming, either.

>> **If you don't know the answer, you may take an educated guess by using the process of elimination.** On the paper version, you may guess freely at your discretion (hopefully, you won't have to after reading this book). However, on the computerized test, you risk receiving a penalty for too many wrong answers at the end of the subtest. (Those clever test graders have figured out that means you've run out of time and have become desperate to finish.) If you need to guess, make sure to eliminate as many choices as possible before choosing your answer.

>> **Question first, read later.** Your first instinct may be to read the entire paragraph before looking at the questions. However, many reading comprehension test experts recommend the opposite. If the question asks you to find specific information or discern the main idea of the paragraph, skimming or scanning (see Chapter 7) can save loads of time. Read the question first so you can best decide what reading technique to use.

>> **Take it one question at a time.** Some passages have more than one question associated with them, but you should look at only one question at a time. If you're taking the CAT-ASVAB, you don't have a choice — and you can't skip ahead and come back. You must answer a question to move on to the next.

>> **Understand each question.** What is the question asking you to do? Are you supposed to find the main point? Draw a conclusion? Find a word that is nearest in meaning? Make sure you know what the question is asking before you choose among the answer options. This tip may seem obvious, but when you're in a hurry, you can make mistakes by misunderstanding the questions.

>> **Read each answer option carefully.** Don't just select the first answer that seems right. *Remember:* On the Paragraph Comprehension subtest, one answer is often "most correct," while others are "almost right." You want to choose the "most correct" answer, not the "almost right" answer. And to do that, you have to read *all* the answers.

>> **Check your baggage at the door.** Answer each question based on the passage, not your own opinions or views on the topic.

>> **Don't choose ambiguous answer options.** They're incorrect 99.99 times out of 100. (Oh, heck, call it 100 times out of 100.) If an answer strikes you as not quite true but not totally false, that answer is incorrect. The people who wrote the questions put that choice there to throw you off. Don't give them the satisfaction of falling for their trap!

>> **Always be cautious about *never*.** For the most part, answer options that are absolutes are incorrect. *Never, always,* and related words are often a sign that you should select a different answer. Words like *generally* and *usually* are more likely to be part of the correct answer.

Surveying Sample Test Questions

Time for you to put all the great advice I provide in this chapter and Chapter 7 to good use. (You can see that I'm not usually accused of being too modest.) Quiz yourself on the following sample test questions to see whether your reading comprehension is up to speed. Read each short paragraph, which is followed by one or more questions regarding information contained in that passage. Make sure to read the paragraph carefully before selecting the choice that most correctly answers the question.

First, stick to one excuse. Thus, if a tradesman, with whom your social relations are slight, should chance to find you taking coppers from his till, you may possibly explain that you are interested in Numismatics and are a Collector of Coins; and he may possibly believe you. But if you tell him afterwards that you pitied him for being overloaded with unwieldy copper discs, and were in the act of replacing them by a silver sixpence of your own, this further explanation, so far from increasing his confidence in your motives, will (strangely enough) actually decrease it. And if you are so unwise as to be struck by yet another brilliant idea, and tell him that the pennies were all bad pennies, which you were concealing to save him from a police prosecution for coining, the tradesman may even be so wayward as to institute a police prosecution himself.

—G. K. Chesterton

1. The author is giving the reader advice about

(A) collecting coins.

(B) stealing.

(C) dealing with tradesmen.

(D) becoming a police officer.

Ethics are standards by which one should act based on values. Values are core beliefs such as duty, honor, and integrity that motivate attitudes and actions. Not all values are ethical values (integrity is — happiness is not). Ethical values relate to what is right and wrong and thus take precedence over nonethical values when making ethical decisions.

2. According to the paragraph, values can best be defined as

(A) ethics.

(B) stealing.

(C) core beliefs.

(D) right and wrong.

Questions 3 and 4 refer to the following passage.

Although the average consumer replaces the tires on his or her automobile every 50,000 miles, steel-belted radials can last for 60,000 miles. However, they must be properly maintained. The tires must be inflated to the correct air pressure at all times, and tires must be rotated and balanced according to a routine maintenance schedule. The tread should be checked for correct depth regularly.

3. How long can steel-belted radials last?

(A) 25,000 miles

(B) 50,000 miles

(C) 60,000 miles

(D) No one knows.

4. Proper tire maintenance, as described in the passage, does *not* include

(A) keeping tires properly inflated.

(B) balancing and rotating tires.

(C) checking the tread.

(D) checking the lug nuts.

Questions 5 and 6 refer to the following passage.

Some people argue that baking is an art, but Chef Debra Dearborn says that baking is a science. She says that if you follow a recipe carefully, assembling the ingredients accurately, cooking at the specified temperature for the specified period of time, your cookies will always turn out right. Chef Dearborn says the best baking is like the best experiment; anyone can duplicate it.

5. In this passage, the word *assembling* most nearly means

(A) measuring.

(B) putting together.

(C) buying.

(D) storing.

6. According to the passage, a person who can't make a decent batch of cookies

(A) should get out of the kitchen.

(B) is an artist.

(C) isn't following the recipe carefully.

(D) is Chef Dearborn.

Boiler technicians operate main and auxiliary boilers. They maintain and repair all parts, including pressure fittings, valves, pumps, and forced-air blowers. Technicians may have to lift or move heavy equipment. They may have to stoop and kneel and work in awkward positions.

7. According to this job description, a good candidate for this job would be

(A) a person with management experience.

(B) an individual with keen eyesight.

(C) a person who isn't mechanically minded.

(D) a person who is physically fit.

In June 2004, the city council passed a resolution requiring all residents to paint their address numbers on their homes using a bright color. This was done to assist firemen, police, and paramedics in finding an address during an emergency. In August, 300 residences were randomly sampled, and it was found that 150 had complied with the new ordinance.

8. According to the passage, what percentage of the randomly sampled residences had complied with the new ordinance?

    (A) 10 percent

    (B) 20 percent

    (C) 50 percent

    (D) 60 percent

Questions 9 and 10 refer to the following passage.

The younger the child, the trickier using medicine is. Children under 2 years shouldn't be given any over-the-counter (OTC) drug without a doctor's approval. Your pediatrician can tell you how much of a common drug, like acetaminophen (Tylenol), is safe for babies. Prescription drugs also can work differently in children than adults. Some barbiturates, for example, which make adults feel sluggish, will make a child hyperactive. Amphetamines, which stimulate adults, can calm children. When giving any drug to a child, watch closely for side effects. If you're not happy with what's happening with your child, don't assume that everything's okay. Always be suspicious. It's better to make the extra calls to the doctor or nurse practitioner than to see a child have a bad reaction to a drug. And before parents dole out OTC drugs, they should consider whether they're truly necessary. Americans love to medicate — perhaps too much.

A study published in the October 1994 issue of the *Journal of the American Medical Association* found that more than half of all mothers surveyed had given their 3-year-olds an OTC medication in the previous month. Not every cold needs medicine. Common viruses run their course in seven to ten days with or without medication. Although some OTC medications can make children more comfortable and help them eat and rest better, others may trigger allergic reactions or changes for the worse in sleeping, eating, and behavior. Antibiotics, available by prescription, don't work at all on cold viruses.

9. A common problem in America is

    (A) over-medication.

    (B) parents not heeding the advice of their doctors.

    (C) OTC drugs not requiring a prescription.

    (D) the cost of prescription medication.

10. When a parent is in doubt about giving a child medication, it's best to

    (A) speak with a pharmacist.

    (B) call a doctor or nurse practitioner.

    (C) read the label closely.

    (D) research the side effects.

Answers and Explanations

Use this answer key to score the practice Paragraph Comprehension questions.

1. **B.** Mr. Chesterton is expounding on how sticking to one excuse may help you if you're caught taking coins from the tradesman's till.

2. **C.** The second sentence defines the word *values*.

3. **C.** If you used the scanning technique explained in Chapter 6, you would've found this answer quickly.

4. **D.** This example is a negative question that requires extra care in answering. A negative question asks you for something that is not true or not included in the paragraph. If you're rushed or in a hurry, you can easily misread the question.

5. **B.** Although measuring is something you do when baking, it doesn't "most nearly" mean the same thing as assembling. *Putting together* does.

6. **C.** The passage states that if you follow a recipe carefully, your cookies will always turn out right.

7. **D.** Although the passage doesn't say, "This job requires a physically fit person," the duties listed imply that it does. A person with management experience or keen eyesight may make a good candidate, but the passage doesn't list these traits as requirements for the job. A person who isn't mechanically minded may not have the knowledge necessary to maintain and repair boilers and all their parts. This leaves Choice (D), and it's true that a person who is physically fit would be a good choice for the job.

8. **C.** The author didn't specifically say that 50 percent hadn't complied, but she included enough information in the passage that you can calculate it on your own.

9. **A.** The 11th and 12th sentences in the passage suggest that Americans probably medicate too much.

10. **B.** The passage states that making the extra calls to a doctor or nurse practitioner is better than giving the child a drug that causes a bad reaction. Although the other choices may be good advice, they aren't stated or implied in the paragraph.

3

Calculating Better Math Knowledge

Chapter **9**

Knowing Your Math

L azarus Long, a fictional character created by Robert A. Heinlein, once said, "Anyone who cannot cope with mathematics isn't fully human. At best, he is a tolerable subhuman who has learned to wear shoes, bathe, and not make messes in the house."

Perhaps Mr. Long's observation is a little harsh. Some people seem to be born mathematicians, while others struggle with many of its concepts. The fact remains, however, that the military seems to agree with Mr. Long. You can't join the military without proving that you know the fundamentals of math. Fully 50 percent of your AFQT score is based on your ability to solve math problems. And as I indicate in Chapter 2, your AFQT score determines whether you can join the military.

The good news is that although the military wants you well-grounded in math, it's not looking for rocket scientists. That's NASA's job. The two math subtests of the AFQT test your math ability only at the high school level, so you don't have to break out any advanced calculus or plot the orbit of subatomic particles.

While I was deciding what to cover in this chapter, I quickly realized that I can't give you an entire high school math education in one chapter. Heck, I couldn't do that in one whole book. Then I realized that I don't have to try to cram all the math you learned in 13 years of school into one chapter. If you're reading this book, you're obviously interested in joining the military. And to join the military, you must be either a high school graduate or have a high school equivalency certificate, or you must have at least 15 college credits. That means you've already learned this stuff. All I need to do is provide you a bit of a refresher to remind you of all those math rules you may have forgotten or stashed away in the back of your mind. And that's what you find here: a refresher course, designed to draw out all the math you should already know!

So look at it this way: You already know what you need to know in order to ace the AFQT. Your job is just to remind yourself of what you know. In this chapter, I help you do exactly that.

Making the Most of Math Terminology

Some people are intimidated by math in part because it has its own language. In Chapter 11, I explain how to use keywords in math word problems to translate English into mathematical equations. But that's not enough. You need to know basic math terminology to solve many of the problems you see on the two math subtests that make up the AFQT.

I just looked in my handy-dandy pocket math dictionary. There are more than 700 mathematical terms listed there. Wait a minute! Sit back down. You don't need to memorize 700 terms. You won't see the math term *brachistochrone* on any of the subtests, for example.

TECHNICAL STUFF

Brachistochrone is a term from Greek meaning "shortest time." The special property of a brachistochrone is the fact that a bead sliding down a brachistochrone-shaped, frictionless wire will take a shorter time to reach the bottom than it would on a wire curved into any other shape. Just in case you were curious.

Although you don't need to know 700 math terms, you should memorize the most common terms because you're likely to see them used in one way or another on the Mathematics Knowledge subtest or the Arithmetic Reasoning subtest. Here's some of what you need to know:

>> **Average:** The *average* usually refers to the *arithmetic mean* or just the *mean average*. To find the mean of a set of n numbers, add the numbers in the set and divide the sum by n. For example, the average (or arithmetic mean) of 3, 7, 10, and 12 is $\frac{3+7+10+12}{4}$, or 8.

>> **Coefficient:** The *coefficient* is a number multiplied by a variable or by a product of variables or by powers of variables in a term. For example, 123 is the coefficient in the term $123x^3y$.

>> **Evaluate:** *Evaluate* means to figure out or calculate. If you're asked to evaluate $5 + 3$, that means to simplify the expression to 8.

>> **Integer:** An *integer* is a whole number that can be expressed without a decimal or fraction component. Examples of integers include 1, 70, and –583.

>> **Pi:** In math equations and terms, pi is usually expressed by its Greek letter, π. *Pi* represents the ratio of the circumference of a circle to its diameter, and it's used in several formulas, especially formulas involving geometry. Pi's value is 3.141592653589793. . . (on and on forever), but using the value 3.14 or $\frac{22}{7}$ is traditional in common math problems.

>> **Prime/composite numbers:** A *prime number* is a positive integer that can be divided evenly only by itself and 1. For example, 2, 3, 5, 7, 11, 13 are the first six primes. One afternoon, all the famous mathematicians got together over a beer and agreed among themselves that 1 isn't a prime number.

   Positive numbers that have factors other than themselves and 1 as factors are called *composite numbers*. Again, by convention, 1 isn't considered a composite number.

>> **Product:** The *product* is the result of multiplication. The product of 2 and 9 is 18.

>> **Quotient/remainder:** The *quotient* is the result of division. 40 divided by 5 has a quotient of 8.

   But what if one number doesn't divide evenly into the other? The *remainder* is what's left over in that scenario. 43 divided by 5 has a quotient of 8 and a remainder of 3.

>> **Reciprocal:** A *reciprocal* is a fraction flipped upside down. The reciprocal of x is $\frac{1}{x}$. The reciprocal of $\frac{1}{x}$ is x, and $x \neq 0$.

>> **Sum:** The *sum* is the result of addition. The sum of 3 and 6 is 9.

You're not done with math vocabulary yet. You still need to know many more math words and terms. I explain them throughout the rest of the chapter.

The Heart of Math: Exploring Expressions and Equations

Math without expressions and equations is like a fire hydrant without a dog; they just go together. So what's the difference between a mathematical *expression* and an *equation*?

> » An *expression* is any mathematical calculation or formula combining numbers and/or variables. Expressions don't include equal signs (=). For example, $3 + 2$ is an expression, and so is $x(x+2)-3$.
>
> » An *equation,* on the other hand, is a mathematical sentence built from expressions connected by an equal sign (=). For example, $3 + 2 = 5$ is an equation, and $x(x+2)-3 = 30$ is also an equation.

This section gives you the lowdown on keeping equations balanced and simplifying expressions.

Keeping equations balanced

One of the coolest things about equations is that you can do almost anything you want to them as long as you remember to do the exact same thing to both sides of the equation. This rule is called keeping the equation *balanced.* For example, if you have the equation $4 + 1 = 3 + 2$, you can add 3 to both sides of the equation, and it still balances out: $4 + 1 + 3 = 3 + 2 + 3$. You can divide both sides by 3, and it still balances: $(4+1) \div 3 = (3+2) \div 3$.

TIP

Equation balancing becomes especially handy in algebra (see the later section "Alphabet Soup: Tackling Algebra Review").

Obeying the order of operations

In math, you must solve equations by following steps in a proper order. If you don't, you won't get the right answer. Many of the most frequent math errors occur when people don't follow the *order of operations* when solving mathematical problems.

REMEMBER

Keep in mind the following order of operations:

1. **Start with any calculations in brackets or parentheses.**

When you have *nested* parentheses or brackets (parentheses or brackets inside other parentheses or brackets), do the inner ones first and work your way outward.

Groupings where parentheses are implied, such as numerators or denominators (like $\frac{1}{2+3}$) or the numbers under a radical (like $\sqrt{1+2}$), are performed first, just as they would be if there were official parentheses around them.

2. **Do any terms with exponents and roots.**

3. **Complete any multiplication and division, in order from left to right.**

4. **Do any addition and subtraction, in order from left to right.**

TIP

An easy way to remember this order is to think of the phrase "Please Excuse My Dear Aunt Sally" (Parentheses, Exponents, Multiply and Divide, Add and Subtract). The order of operations isn't absolute, though, because you can simplify *different parts* of an expression in the same step — as long as you're simplifying and not combining terms that don't belong together. (The more you can simplify an equation, the better. You'll save precious time on the ASVAB and reduce the possibility of copying errors, too.)

Take the following expression out for a ride.

EXAMPLE

Solve: $3 \times (5 + 2) + 5^2 \div 2$.

Do the calculations in the parentheses first:

$3 \times 7 + 5^2 \div 2$

Next, simplify the exponents:

$3 \times 7 + 25 \div 2$

Do multiplication and division from left to right:

$21 + 12.5$

Finally, perform addition and subtraction from left to right:

33.5

Mental math: Mixing it up with the commutative, associative, and distributive properties

TIP

Although the order of operations tells you to do steps in a certain order (see the preceding section), some mathematical properties let you choose a different path. Using the commutative, associative, and distributive properties can make numbers smaller and easier to work with — sometimes easy enough that you can do calculations in your head instead of relying on your scratch paper. Anything that saves you time and brain power on the ASVAB is great, because you're working on a limited time budget . . . and you can't use a calculator.

The commutative and associative properties: Moving numbers in your head

The commutative and associative properties let you break the rules about adding or multiplying from left to right. The *commutative property of addition* says you can rearrange the numbers you're adding without changing the result:

$$28 + 27 + 2 = 28 + 2 + 27$$
$$= 30 + 27$$
$$= 57$$

Similarly, the *associative property of addition* lets you decide how to group the numbers you're adding:

$$19 + 46 + 4 = 19 + (46 + 4)$$
$$= 19 + (50)$$
$$= 69$$

Together, these properties let you add a string of numbers in whatever order you like. For example, you can make calculations easier by pairing up numbers whose ones digits add up to 10 before adding other numbers in the list.

Because subtracting is essentially the same thing as adding a negative number, you can extend these addition properties to subtraction problems, too — just be careful to keep track of the negative signs (see the later section "Playing with Positive and Negative Numbers" for details). The following example shows how smart groupings can let you add and subtract figures faster. Notice which calculations are easier to do in your head.

Left to Right	Reordered and Regrouped
$27 - 98 - 27 + 8$	$27 - 98 - 27 + 8$
$= -71 - 27 + 8$	$= (27 - 27) + (-98 + 8)$
$= -98 + 8$	$= 0 + (-90)$
$= -90$	$= -90$

Similarly, the *commutative and associative properties of multiplication* let you multiply numbers in any order you like. Check out how switching the numbers around can make mental math easier:

Left to Right	Reordered and Regrouped
$5 \times 13 \times 2$	$(5 \times 2) \times 13$
$= 65 \times 2$	$= 10 \times 13$
$= 130$	$= 130$

You can even use these multiplication properties with division, as long as you remember that division is the same thing as multiplying by a fraction (see the later section "Multiplying fractions"):

Left to Right	Reordered and Regrouped
$35 \times 23 \div 7$	$35 \times 23 \times \frac{1}{7}$
$= 805 \div 7$	$= \frac{35}{7} \times 23$
$= 115$	$= 5 \times 23$
	$= 115$

The distributive property: Breaking up large numbers

Have you ever envied those people who can perform calculations on large numbers in their heads? What if I told you that you can be one of those people? That's right. All you have to do is practice the distributive property of math.

The *distributive property,* often referred to as the *distributive law of math,* lets you separate or break larger numbers into parts for simpler arithmetic. It basically says that $a(b + c)$ is the same as $(a \times b) + (a \times c)$.

Suppose you want to mentally multiply 4 by 53; 4×53 is the same as $(4 \times 50) + (4 \times 3)$. Four times 50 is easy; it's 200. Four times 3 is also easy. It's 12. Two hundred plus 12 is 212.

Try another one with a bit of a twist.

EXAMPLE

Mentally perform the calculation 12×19.

12×19 is equivalent to $12(20 - 1) = (12 \times 20) - (12 \times 1)$.

You can quickly mentally calculate that 12 times 20 is 240 and that 12 times 1 is 12. Subtract 12 from 240, and you have 228.

Figure 9-1 illustrates how this process works.

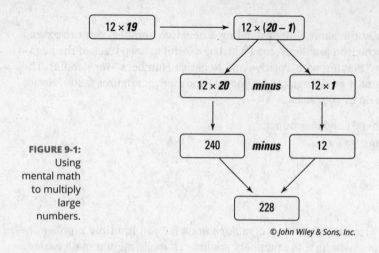

FIGURE 9-1:
Using mental math to multiply large numbers.

© John Wiley & Sons, Inc.

If 12×20 is still too large for mental calculation, you can break it down as $(12 \times 10) + (12 \times 10)$, or $120 + 120$.

You can also use the distributive property for division, although that takes a bit more practice: $340 \div 4$ is the same as $(340 \div 2) \div 2$. You can quickly calculate that 340 divided by 2 is 170, and 170 divided by 2 is 85.

Or you can express $340 \div 4$ as $(100 \div 4) + (100 \div 4) + (100 \div 4) + (40 \div 4)$. You can mentally calculate 100 divided by 4 as 25. Forty divided by 4 is also easy — it's 10. So $25 + 25 + 25 + 10 = 85$. Keep practicing, and you'll be known as the neighborhood lightning calculator.

Having Fun with Factors

A *factor* is simply a number that is multiplied to get a product. *Factoring* a number means taking the number apart. It's kind of like multiplying in reverse. For example, the factors of 12 are 1, 2, 3, 4, 6, and 12 because all these numbers can be divided evenly into 12.

Here are some other factors:

>> **2:** 1, 2

>> **3:** 1, 3

>> **4:** 1, 2, 4

>> **5:** 1, 5

>> **6:** 1, 2, 3, 6

>> **16:** 1, 2, 4, 8, 16

>> **20:** 1, 2, 4, 5, 10, 20

>> **45:** 1, 3, 5, 9, 15, 45

Understanding types of factors

A factor can be either a prime number or a composite number (except 1 and 0 are neither prime nor composite). As I mention in the section "Making the Most of Math Terminology" earlier in this chapter, prime numbers have only themselves and 1 as factors, while composite numbers can be divided evenly by other numbers.

The prime numbers up to 100 are 2, 3, 5, 7, 11, 13, 17, 19, 23, 29, 31, 37, 41, 43, 47, 53, 59, 61, 67, 71, 73, 79, 83, 89, and 97.

Finding prime factors

Any composite number can be written as a product of prime factors. Mathematicians call this process *prime factorization*. To find the prime factors of a number, you divide the number by the smallest possible prime number and work up the list of prime numbers until the result is itself a prime number.

Say you want to find the prime factors of 240. Because 240 is even, start by dividing it by the smallest prime number, which is 2: $240 \div 2 = 120$. The number 120 is also even, so it can be divided by 2: $120 \div 2 = 60$. Then $60 \div 2 = 30$ and $30 \div 2 = 15$. Now, 15 isn't even, so check to see whether you can divide it by 3 (the next highest prime number); $15 \div 3 = 5$, which itself is a prime number, so 240 is now fully factored.

$$240 \div 2 = 120$$
$$120 \div 2 = 60$$
$$60 \div 2 = 30$$
$$30 \div 2 = 15$$
$$15 \div 3 = 5$$

Now, simply list what you divided by to write the prime factors of 240. The prime factors of 240 are $2 \times 2 \times 2 \times 2 \times 3 \times 5$.

Looking at Least Common Multiples

A *common multiple* is a number that is a multiple of two or more numbers. For example, 20, 30, and 40 are common multiples of the numbers 5 and 10. The *least common multiple* (LCM) of two or more numbers is the smallest number (not zero) that's a multiple of both or all the numbers. The LCM is useful in solving many math problems — especially those involving fractions (check out the following section for info on working with fractions).

One way to find the LCM is to list the multiples of each number, one at a time, until you find the smallest multiple that's common to all the numbers.

Find the LCM of 45 and 50.

>> **Multiples of 45:** 45, 90, 135, 180, 225, 270, 315, 360, 405, 450

>> **Multiples of 50:** 50, 100, 150, 200, 250, 300, 350, 400, 450

The LCM of 45 and 50 is 450.

That's rather cumbersome, isn't it? Wouldn't it be great if you had an easier way? You do, and I'm here to let you in on the secret: An easier way to find the LCM is first to list the prime factors of each number (as explained in the preceding section):

>> The prime factors for 45 are $3 \times 3 \times 5$.

>> The prime factors for 50 are $2 \times 5 \times 5$.

Then multiply each factor the greatest number of times it occurs in either number. If the same factor occurs more than once in both numbers, you multiply the factor the greatest number of times it occurs. For example, 5 occurs as a prime factor of both 45 (where it occurs once) and 50 (where it occurs twice); the two occurrences in the factorization of 50 beat the single occurrence in the factorization of 45. The number 3 occurs two times, 5 occurs two times, and 2 occurs once, so you have $3 \times 3 \times 5 \times 5 \times 2 = 450$.

REMEMBER

Checking your answer to see whether the original numbers divide evenly into the LCM you calculate is always a great idea. You can in fact divide 45 and 50 evenly into 450, so you're good to go in this example.

Now that you're getting the hang of it, try another one:

EXAMPLE

What is the least common multiple of 5, 27, and 30?

List the prime factors of each number:

>> **Prime factors of 5:** 5

>> **Prime factors of 27:** $3 \times 3 \times 3$

>> **Prime factors of 30:** $2 \times 3 \times 5$

The number 3 occurs a maximum of three times, 5 occurs a maximum of one time, and 2 occurs a maximum of one time: $3 \times 3 \times 3 \times 5 \times 2 = 270$. Check your answer by seeing whether 5, 27, and 30 can all divide evenly into 270.

Conquering the Fear of Fractions

I don't know why, but most people I've talked to don't like to do math with fractions. Maybe it's because teachers always used pies as examples, and that just makes people hungry. The pies were all imaginary, too, so you didn't even get a piece after all the figuring was done. I'm going to break convention and use squares of cardboard instead. Sure, they're harder to cut than pies, but they don't smell as enticing.

A *fraction* is nothing more than part of a whole. Take a look at Figure 9-2.

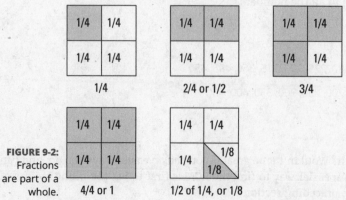

FIGURE 9-2: Fractions are part of a whole.

© John Wiley & Sons, Inc.

Each shaded area represents part of a whole, or a fraction of the whole. It doesn't have to be fourths. If I had divided the cardboard into two equal pieces, each shaded area would represent one-half. If the cardboard were cut into three equal pieces, each piece would be one-third of the whole.

Fractions aren't difficult to work into your mathematical skills as long as you remember a few rules and techniques.

Defining parts and types of fractions

The top number of a fraction is called the *numerator*. The bottom number is known as the *denominator*. For example, in the fraction $\frac{7}{16}$, 7 is the numerator and 16 is the denominator.

TIP

You may also see numerators and denominators separated by a / sign rather than one on top of the other; 1/4 is the same as $\frac{1}{4}$.

If the numerator is smaller than the denominator, the fraction is less than a whole (smaller than 1). This kind of fraction is called a *proper fraction.* The fraction $\frac{3}{16}$ is a proper fraction, as is $\frac{1}{3}$.

If the numerator is larger than the denominator, the fraction is larger than a whole (larger than 1), and the fraction is called an *improper fraction.* The fraction $\frac{17}{16}$ is an improper fraction.

REMEMBER

Converting improper fractions to mixed numbers is customary in math, especially after all mathematical operations are complete. A *mixed number* is a whole number plus a fraction. The easiest way to convert an improper fraction to a mixed number is to divide the numerator by the denominator. You convert $\frac{17}{16}$ to a mixed number by dividing 17 by 16: $17 \div 16 = 1$, with a remainder of 1, so the improper fraction converts to $1\frac{1}{16}$.

Simplifying fractions

Simplifying (or *reducing*) fractions means to make the fraction as simple as possible. You're usually required to simplify fractions on the ASVAB math subtests before you can select the correct answer. For example, if you worked out a problem and the answer was $\frac{4}{8}$, the correct answer choice on the math subtest would probably be $\frac{1}{2}$, which is the simplest equivalent to $\frac{4}{8}$.

Many methods of simplifying fractions are available. In this section, I give you the two that I think are the easiest; you can decide which is best for you.

Method 1: Dividing by the lowest prime numbers

Try dividing the numerator and denominator by the lowest prime numbers until you can't go any further. (The earlier section "Understanding types of factors" has details on this process.)

EXAMPLE

Simplify $\frac{24}{108}$.

Both the numerator and denominator are even numbers, so they can be divided by the lowest prime number, which is 2. Then $24 \div 2 = 12$, and $108 \div 2 = 54$. The result is $\frac{12}{54}$.

The numerator and denominator are both still even numbers, so divide by 2 again: $12 \div 2 = 6$, and $54 \div 2 = 27$. The result is $\frac{6}{27}$.

This time the denominator is an odd number, so you know it isn't divisible by 2. Try the next highest prime number, which is 3: $6 \div 3 = 2$, and $27 \div 3 = 9$. The result is $\frac{2}{9}$.

Because no common prime numbers divide evenly into both 2 and 9, the fraction is fully simplified.

Method 2: Listing prime factors

This method of simplification is my favorite. Simply list the prime factors of both the numerator and the denominator as explained in the earlier section "Finding prime factors" and then see whether any cancel out (are the same).

EXAMPLE

Simplify $\frac{24}{108}$.

The prime factors of 24 are $2 \times 2 \times 2 \times 3$.

The prime factors of 108 are $2 \times 2 \times 3 \times 3 \times 3$.

You can now write the fraction as $\frac{2 \times 2 \times 2 \times 3}{2 \times 2 \times 3 \times 3 \times 3}$.

Two of the 2s and one of the 3s cancel out, so you can remove them from both the numerator and the denominator. What's left is $\frac{2}{3 \times 3}$, or $\frac{2}{9}$.

Multiplying fractions

Multiplying fractions is very easy. All you have to do is multiply the numerators by each other, multiply the denominators by each other, and then simplify the result, as shown in the following equation:

$$\frac{4}{5} \times \frac{3}{7} \times \frac{9}{15} = \frac{4 \times 3 \times 9}{5 \times 7 \times 15} = \frac{108}{525}$$

The fraction $\frac{108}{525}$ can be simplified to $\frac{36}{175}$ (see the earlier section "Simplifying fractions").

If you can cross-cancel before you multiply, multiplying fractions is even easier. Here's the same problem. The 3 in the numerator and the 15 in the denominator have a common factor: They're both divisible by 3. If you divide both by 3 before multiplying, you don't have to reduce the fraction at the end:

$$\frac{4}{5} \times \frac{\overset{1}{\cancel{3}}}{7} \times \frac{9}{\underset{5}{\cancel{15}}} = \frac{36}{175}$$

TIP

Before multiplying mixed numbers, change them to improper fractions by multiplying the denominator by the integer and adding it to the numerator. For example, $2\frac{5}{8}$ is a mixed number. To convert it to an improper fraction, multiply 8 by 2 and add 5 to the result:

$$2 \times 8 = 16$$
$$16 + 5 = 21$$

The end result is $\frac{21}{8}$.

Dividing fractions

Dividing fractions is almost the same as multiplying, with one important difference: You have to convert the second fraction (the *divisor*) to the reciprocal and then multiply. As I explain in the earlier "Making the Most of Math Terminology" section, the reciprocal is simply a fraction flipped over.

EXAMPLE

Solve: $\frac{3}{5} \div \frac{2}{5}$.

Take the reciprocal of the second fraction and multiply it by the other fraction:

$$\frac{3}{5} \div \frac{2}{5} = \frac{3}{5} \times \frac{5}{2} = \frac{3 \times 5}{2 \times 5} = \frac{15}{10}$$

The fraction $\frac{15}{10}$ is an improper fraction, which you can convert to $1\frac{5}{10}$ (see the earlier section "Defining parts and types of fractions"). Then you can simplify $1\frac{5}{10}$ to $1\frac{1}{2}$ (see the earlier section "Simplifying fractions").

Adding and subtracting fractions

Adding and subtracting fractions can be as simple as multiplying and dividing them, or it can be more difficult. As the following sections show, it all depends on whether the fractions have the same denominator.

Adding and subtracting fractions with like denominators

To add or subtract two fractions with the same denominator, add (or subtract) the numerators and place that sum (or difference) over the common denominator:

$$\frac{2}{9} + \frac{3}{9} = \frac{2+3}{9} = \frac{5}{9}$$

$$\frac{3}{9} - \frac{2}{9} = \frac{3-2}{9} = \frac{1}{9}$$

Adding and subtracting fractions with different denominators

You can't add or subtract fractions with different denominators. You have to convert the fractions so they all have the same denominator, and then you perform addition or subtraction as I explain in the preceding section.

Converting fractions so they share the same denominator involves finding a *common denominator*. A common denominator is nothing more than a common multiple of all the denominators, as I describe in the earlier section "Looking at Least Common Multiples."

EXAMPLE

Find a common denominator for the fractions $\frac{3}{5}$ and $\frac{1}{8}$.

The multiples of 5 are 5, 10, 15, 20, 25, 30, 35, and 40.

The multiples of 8 are 8, 16, 24, 32, and 40.

A common denominator for the fractions $\frac{3}{5}$ and $\frac{1}{8}$ is 40.

The next step in the addition/subtraction process is to convert the fractions so they share the common denominator. To do this, divide the original denominator into the new common denominator and then multiply the result by the original numerator.

Start with $\frac{3}{5}$. Divide the original denominator (5) into the new common denominator (40): $40 \div 5 = 8$. Next, multiply the result (8) by the original numerator (3): $8 \times 3 = 24$. The equivalent fraction is $\frac{24}{40}$.

Perform the same operation with the second fraction, $\frac{1}{8}$. Divide the original denominator (8) into the new common denominator (40): $40 \div 8 = 5$. Next, multiply this (5) by the original numerator (1): $5 \times 1 = 5$. The equivalent fraction is $\frac{5}{40}$.

Now that the fractions have the same denominator, you can add or subtract them as shown in the preceding section:

$$\frac{3}{5} + \frac{1}{8} = \frac{24}{40} + \frac{5}{40} = \frac{29}{40}$$

Performing multiple operations

Sometimes you have to work through more than one operation on a set of fractions. Give this one a try:

EXAMPLE

$$\frac{\frac{1}{8} + \frac{3}{4}}{\frac{3}{5} - \frac{2}{10}} \times \frac{4}{5}$$

On the surface, this problem looks complicated. But if you remember the *order of operations* (see the earlier section "Obeying the order of operations") and take the problem one step at a time, it's really easy.

Under the order of operations, you do the work in the implied sets of parentheses (the top and bottom of the big fraction) first:

$$\frac{1}{8} + \frac{3}{4} = \frac{1}{8} + \frac{6}{8} = \frac{7}{8}$$

and

$$\frac{3}{5} - \frac{2}{10} = \frac{6}{10} - \frac{2}{10} = \frac{4}{10} = \frac{2}{5}$$

If you write the big fraction bar as a division sign, the problem now reads $\left(\frac{7}{8} \div \frac{2}{5}\right) \times \frac{4}{5}$.

Continue by performing the next operation in the parentheses:

$$\frac{7}{8} \div \frac{2}{5} = \frac{7}{8} \times \frac{5}{2} = \frac{35}{16}$$

The problem is now much simpler: $\frac{35}{16} \times \frac{4}{5}$.

$$\frac{35}{16} \times \frac{4}{5} = \frac{35 \times 4}{16 \times 5} = \frac{140}{80} = \frac{70}{40} = \frac{35}{20} = 1\frac{15}{20} = 1\frac{3}{4}$$

Converting fractions to decimals

Some math problems require you to perform operations on both decimal numbers (see the later section "Dealing with Decimals") and fractions. To properly perform such calculations, you must either convert the fraction to a decimal number or convert the decimal to a fraction.

Converting a fraction to a decimal number is easy. You simply divide the numerator by the denominator. For example $\frac{3}{4}$ is

$$\begin{array}{r} 0.75 \\ 4\overline{)3.00} \\ \underline{-2\ 8} \\ 20 \\ \underline{-20} \\ 0 \end{array}$$

EXAMPLE

Try the following:

Solve: $\frac{1}{2} + 0.34$.

Convert the fraction to a decimal by dividing the numerator by the denominator:

$$\begin{array}{r} 0.5 \\ 2\overline{)1.0} \\ \underline{-1\ 0} \\ 0 \end{array}$$

Now you can easily perform the operation: $0.5 + 0.34 = 0.84$.

Comparing fractions

The two math subtests of the ASVAB often ask you to compare fractions to determine which one is the largest or smallest. If the fractions all have the same denominator, it's easy. The fraction with the largest numerator is the largest, and the one with the smallest numerator is the smallest.

But how do you compare fractions that have different denominators? I'll leave it up to you to determine which of the following proven methods you like the best.

Method 1: Finding a common denominator

The first method is to convert the fractions so they all have a common denominator (see the earlier section "Adding and subtracting fractions with different denominators"). After conversion, the fraction with the largest numerator is the largest fraction, and the one with the smallest numerator is the smallest. This method is what you probably learned in school.

EXAMPLE

Which of the following fractions is the largest: $\frac{5}{12}$, $\frac{3}{4}$, $\frac{9}{15}$, or $\frac{13}{16}$?

First, find a common multiple for the denominators:

>> **The multiples of 12:** 12, 24, 36, 48, 60, 72, 84, 96, 108, 120, 132, 144, 156, 168, 180, 192, 204, 216, 228, 240.

>> **The multiples of 4:** 4, 8, 12, 16, 20, 24, 28, 32, 36, 40, 44, 48, 52, 56, 60, 64, 68, 72, 76, 80, 84, 88, 92, 100, 104, 108, 112, 116, 122, . . . , 240.

>> **The multiples of 15:** 15, 30, 45, 60, 75, 90, 105, 120, 135, 150, 165, 180, 195, 210, 225, 240.

>> **The multiples of 16:** 16, 32, 48, 64, 80, 96, 112, 128, 144, 160, 176, 192, 208, 224, 240.

The lowest common denominator for all four fractions is 240.

Next, convert all the fractions so they have a denominator of 240 by dividing the new common denominator by the original denominator of the fraction and then multiplying the result by the original numerator:

>> $\frac{5}{12} = \frac{100}{240}$

>> $\frac{3}{4} = \frac{180}{240}$

>> $\frac{9}{15} = \frac{144}{240}$

>> $\frac{13}{16} = \frac{195}{240}$

The largest fraction is the one with the largest numerator: $\frac{195}{240}$, or $\frac{13}{16}$.

Method 2: The cross-product method

You may find Method 1 to be a bit time-consuming. If so, I think you'll enjoy this method. I certainly wish my teachers had heard of it when I was in high school. Maybe they explained it and I was sleeping that day.

The second method is called the *cross-product method*. To use it, you compare the cross-products of two fractions. The first cross-product is the product of the first numerator and the second denominator. The second cross-product is the product of the second numerator and the first denominator. If the cross-products are equal, the fractions are equivalent. If the first cross-product is larger, the first fraction is larger. If the second cross-product is larger, the second fraction is larger.

EXAMPLE

Which of the following fractions is the largest: $\frac{5}{12}$, $\frac{3}{4}$, $\frac{9}{15}$, or $\frac{13}{16}$?

Compare the first two fractions, $\frac{5}{12}$ and $\frac{3}{4}$: $5 \times 4 = 20$ and $12 \times 3 = 36$. The second fraction is larger.

Compare the larger fraction, $\frac{3}{4}$, with the third fraction, $\frac{9}{15}$: $3 \times 15 = 45$ and $4 \times 9 = 36$, so $\frac{3}{4}$ is still the largest fraction.

Now compare $\frac{3}{4}$ to the final fraction, $\frac{13}{16}$: $3 \times 16 = 48$ and $4 \times 13 = 52$.

The final fraction, $\frac{13}{16}$, is the largest.

Getting rational about ratios

Ratios represent how one quantity is related to another quantity. A ratio may be written as *A:B* or $\frac{A}{B}$ or using the phrase "*A* to *B*."

A ratio of 1:3 says that the second quantity is three times as large as the first. A ratio of 2:3 means that the second quantity is three times as large as one-half of the first quantity. A ratio of 5:4 means the second quantity is four times as large as one-fifth of the first quantity.

A ratio is actually a fraction. For example, the fraction $\frac{3}{4}$ is also a ratio of 3 to 4. Solve problems including ratios the same way you solve problems that include fractions.

Dealing with Decimals

Decimals are a method of writing fractional numbers without using a numerator and denominator. You can write the fraction $\frac{7}{10}$ as the decimal 0.7; you pronounce it "seven-tenths" or "zero point seven." The period or decimal point indicates that the number is a decimal.

Other decimals exist, such as hundredths or thousandths. They're all based on the number ten:

» **0.7:** Seven-tenths $\left(\dfrac{7}{10}\right)$

» **0.07:** Seven-hundredths $\left(\dfrac{7}{100}\right)$

» **0.007:** Seven-thousandths $\left(\dfrac{7}{1,000}\right)$

» **0.0007:** Seven-ten-thousandths $\left(\dfrac{7}{10,000}\right)$

» **0.00007:** Seven-hundred-thousandths $\left(\dfrac{7}{100,000}\right)$.

If a decimal is less than 1, it's traditional in mathematics to place a zero before the decimal point. Write "0.7," not ".7."

A decimal may be greater than 1. The decimal 3.7 would be pronounced as "three and seven-tenths" $\left(3\dfrac{7}{10}\right)$.

Converting decimals to fractions

To convert a decimal to a fraction, write all the digits following the decimal point in the numerator. If you see zeros before any nonzero digits, you can ignore them.

The denominator is always a one followed by zeros. The number of zeros in the denominator is determined by the total number of digits to the right of the decimal point (including the leading zeros):

» **One digit:** Denominator = 10. Example: $0.7 = \dfrac{7}{10}$

» **Two digits:** Denominator = 100. Example: $0.25 = \dfrac{25}{100}$

» **Three digits:** Denominator = 1,000. Example: $0.351 = \dfrac{351}{1,000}$

» **Four digits:** Denominator = 10,000. Example: $0.0041 = \dfrac{41}{10,000}$

If necessary, reduce the fraction (see the earlier section "Simplifying fractions").

Of course, you can also convert fractions to decimals (see the "Converting fractions to decimals" section earlier in this chapter).

Adding and subtracting decimals

You add and subtract decimals just as you do regular numbers (integers), except that before you perform your operation, you arrange the numbers in a column with the decimal points lined up one over the other.

EXAMPLE

Add the numbers 3.147, 148.392, and 0.074.

Put the numbers in an addition column with the decimal points lined up and perform the addition:

$$
\begin{array}{r}
3.147 \\
148.392 \\
+\ \ 0.074 \\
\hline
151.613
\end{array}
$$

Multiplying decimals

Multiplying decimals requires three steps:

1. Convert the decimals to whole numbers by moving the decimal points to the right, remembering to count how many spaces you move each decimal point.

2. Multiply the whole numbers just as you'd perform any other multiplication.

3. Place the decimal point in the product by moving the decimal point to the left the same number of total spaces you moved the decimal points to the right at the beginning.

EXAMPLE

Multiply: $3.724 \times 0.0004 \times 9.42$.

First, convert the decimals to whole numbers by moving the decimal points to the right (remember to count).

> 3.724 becomes 3,724 (decimal moved three spaces).
>
> 0.0004 becomes 4 (decimal moved four spaces).
>
> 9.42 becomes 942 (decimal moved two spaces).

Next, perform the multiplication on the whole numbers:

> $3,724 \times 4 \times 942 = 14,032,032$

Finally, put the decimal point in the correct position by moving it to the left the same number of places you moved the points to the right. You moved the decimal points a total of nine spaces to the right at the beginning, so now place the decimal point nine spaces to the left:

> 14,032,032 becomes 0.014032032

REMEMBER

If you run out of numbers before you're finished counting spaces to the left, add zeros (as shown in the example) until you've finished counting.

Dividing decimals

Dividing decimals can be a challenge. You have to use both subtraction and multiplication. You also need to be pretty good at rounding (see the later "Rounding" section) and estimating numbers.

REMEMBER

You're not allowed to use a calculator on the ASVAB math subtests.

You can divide decimals in two ways: long division and conversion.

Method 1: Long division

To do long division with decimals, follow these steps:

1. If the divisor isn't a whole number, move the decimal point in the divisor all the way to the right (to make it a whole number), and move the decimal point in the dividend the same number of places to the right.

2. Position the decimal point in the result directly above the decimal point in the dividend.

3. Divide as usual.

If the divisor doesn't go into the dividend evenly, add zeros to the right of the last digit in the dividend and keep dividing until it comes out evenly or a repeating pattern shows up.

Try the following division problem:

7.42 ÷ 0.7

EXAMPLE

Write the problem on your scratch paper in long-division form:

$0.7\overline{)7.42}$

Now move the decimal point one place to the right, which makes the divisor a whole number. Also move the decimal point in the dividend one place to the right:

$7\overline{)74.2}$

Position the decimal point in the result directly above the decimal point in the dividend:

$7\overline{)74.\overset{\cdot}{2}}$

Divide as usual. Seven goes into 70 ten times with 4 left over; then drop the 2 down:

$$\begin{array}{r} 10. \\ 7\overline{)74.2} \\ \underline{70} \\ 042 \end{array}$$

Seven goes into 42 six times:

$$\begin{array}{r} 10.6 \\ 7\overline{)74.2} \\ \underline{70} \\ 042 \\ \underline{42} \\ 0 \end{array}$$

When you're finished dividing decimals, you're finished. You don't have to move the decimal point around like you do after you've multiplied decimals.

REMEMBER

Method 2: Conversion

The other way to divide decimals is to convert the decimals to fractions and then divide the fractions (see the earlier sections "Converting decimals to fractions" and "Dividing fractions," respectively).

REMEMBER

Try the problem from the preceding section, using the conversion method.

7.42 ÷ 0.7

EXAMPLE

First, convert the decimals to fractions:

$$7.42 = 7\frac{42}{100} = \frac{742}{100}$$

$$0.7 = \frac{7}{10}$$

$$7.42 \div 0.7 = \frac{742}{100} \div \frac{7}{10}$$

Take the reciprocal of the divisor (flip the second fraction upside down) and then multiply:

$$\frac{742}{100} \times \frac{10}{7} = \frac{742 \times 10}{100 \times 7} = \frac{7,420}{700}$$

The fraction $\frac{7,420}{700}$ can be simplified (see "Simplifying fractions") to $10\frac{3}{5}$. Convert $\frac{3}{5}$ to a decimal (see "Converting fractions to decimals"), and the answer is 10.6.

Rounding

Rounding a number means limiting a number to a few (or no) decimal places. For example, if you have a $1.97 in change in your pocket, you may say, "I have about $2." The rounding process simplifies mathematical operations.

To round a number, you first determine what place you're rounding to. For example, the math subtests that make up the AFQT may ask you to round to the nearest tenth. Then look at the number immediately to the right of that place. If the number is 5 or greater, round the digit to the left up; for any number under 5, round the digit to the left down. Thus, you'd round 1.55 up to 1.6 and 1.34 down to 1.3.

TIP

You can also round other numbers, such as whole numbers. For example, 1,427 becomes 1,400 when you round to the nearest 100. However, most of the rounding operations you encounter on the Mathematics Knowledge subtest involve rounding decimals to the nearest tenth or nearest hundredth.

Perusing percents

Percent literally means "part of 100." That means, for example, that 25 percent (25%) is equal to $\frac{25}{100}$, which is equal to 0.25.

If a problem asks you to find 25 percent of 250, it's asking you to multiply 250 by 0.25.

TIP

To convert a percent to a decimal number, remove the percent sign and move the decimal point two places to the left: 15 percent is 0.15, and 15.32 percent is 0.1532. Conversely, to change a decimal number to percent, add the percent sign and move the decimal point two places to the right: 4.321 is equal to 432.1 percent.

Playing with Positive and Negative Numbers

Numbers can be positive or negative. A *positive* number is any number greater than zero. So 4; 3.2; 793; $\frac{3}{4}$; $\frac{1}{2}$; and 430,932,843,784 are all positive numbers.

Numbers smaller than zero are *negative* numbers. Every positive number has a negative number equivalent. You express negative numbers by putting a negative (minus) sign (−) in front of the number: −7, −18, −$\frac{3}{4}$, and −743.42 are all negative numbers.

In the math subtests of the ASVAB, you'll often be asked to perform mathematical operations on positive and negative numbers. Just remember the following rules:

>> Adding two positive numbers always results in a positive number: $3 + 3 = 6$

>> Adding two negative numbers always results in a negative number: $-3 + -3 = -6$

>> Adding a negative number is the same as subtracting a positive number:
$-3 + (-3) = 3 - 3 = 0$

>> **Subtracting a negative number is the same as adding a positive number:**
$$3 - (-3) = 3 + 3 = 6$$

>> **Multiplying or dividing two positive numbers always results in a positive number:**
$$3 \div 3 = 1$$

>> **Multiplying or dividing two negative numbers always results in a positive number:**
$$-3 \times -3 = 9$$

>> **Multiplying or dividing a negative number by a positive number always results in a negative number:** $-3 \times 3 = -9$

TIP

When you multiply a series of positive and negative numbers, count the number of negative numbers. If the number is even, the result will be positive. If the number is odd, the result will be negative.

Everyone knows that 10 is larger than 5 and that 20 is larger than 15. With negative numbers, however, it works just the opposite: −10 is smaller than −5, and −20 is smaller than −15.

REMEMBER

As you'll recall from your math in school, any number multiplied by zero is zero.

Rooting for Roots and Powers

Many of the problems you see on the ASVAB math subtests require you to perform calculations involving roots, such as square roots and cube roots, and numbers raised to exponents. If that sounds confusing, don't worry; it's really not. Read on.

Advice about exponents

Exponents are an easy way to show that a number is to be multiplied by itself a certain number of times. For example, 5^2 is the same as 5×5, and 4^3 is the same as $4 \times 4 \times 4$. The number or variable that is to be multiplied by itself is called the *base*, and the number or variable showing how many times it's to be multiplied by itself is called the *exponent*.

Here are important rules when working with exponents:

>> **Any base raised to the power of 1 equals itself.** For example, $6^1 = 6$.

>> **Any base raised to the zero power (except 0) equals 1.** For example, $3^0 = 1$.

TECHNICAL STUFF

In case you were wondering, according to most calculus textbooks, 0^0 is an "indeterminate form." What mathematicians mean by "indeterminate form" is that in some cases it has one value, and in other cases it has another. This stuff is advanced calculus, however, and you don't have to worry about it on the ASVAB math subtests.

>> **To multiply terms with the same base, you add the exponents.** For example, $7^2 \times 7^3 = 7^5$.

>> **To divide terms with the same base, you subtract the exponents.** For example,
$$4^5 \div 4^3 = 4^2.$$

>> **If a base has a negative exponent, it's equal to its reciprocal with a positive exponent.** For example, $3^{-4} = \dfrac{1}{3^4}$.

>> **When a product has an exponent, each factor is raised to that power.** For example,
$$(5 \times 3)^3 = 5^3 \times 3^3.$$

Roots

A root is the opposite of a power or an exponent. There are infinite kinds of roots. You have the *square root,* which means "undoing" a base to the second power; the cube root, which means "undoing" a base raised to the third power; a fourth root, for numbers raised to the fourth power; and so on. However, on the ASVAB math subtests, the only questions you're likely to see will involve square roots and possibly a couple of cube roots.

Square roots

A math operation requiring you to find a square root is designated by the *radical symbol* $\left(\sqrt{\ }\right)$. The number underneath the radical line is called the *radicand.* For example, in the operation $\sqrt{36}$, the number 36 is the radicand.

A square root is a number that, when multiplied by itself, produces the radicand. Take the square root of 36 $\left(\sqrt{36}\right)$, for example. If you multiply 6 by itself $\left(6\times6\right)$, you come up with 36, so 6 is the square root of 36.

However, as I mention in the earlier section "Playing with Positive and Negative Numbers," when you multiply two negative numbers together, you get a positive number. For example, -6×-6 also equals 36, so -6 is also the square root of 36.

That brings me to an important rule: When you take a square root, the results include two square roots — one positive and one negative.

TECHNICAL STUFF

Computing the square roots of negative numbers, such as $\sqrt{-36}$, is also possible, but it involves concepts such as imaginary numbers, which are more advanced than what you're asked to do on the ASVAB.

There are two types of square roots:

>> **Perfect squares:** Only some numbers, called *perfect squares,* have exact square roots.

>> **Irrational numbers:** All the rest of the numbers have square roots that include decimals that go on forever and have no pattern that repeats (non-repeating, non-terminating decimals), so they're called *irrational numbers.*

PERFECT SQUARES

Finding a square root can be difficult without a calculator, but because you can't use a calculator during the test, you're going to have to use your mind and some guessing methods. To find the square root of a number without a calculator, make an educated guess and then verify your results.

The radical symbol indicates that you're to find the principal square root of the number under the radical. The principal square root is a positive number. But if you're solving an equation such as $x^2=36$, then you give both the positive and negative roots: 6 and -6.

To use the educated-guess method, you have to know the square roots of a few perfect squares. One good way to do so is to study the squares of the numbers 1 through 12:

>> 1 and -1 are both square roots of 1.

>> 2 and -2 are both square roots of 4.

- » 3 and –3 are both square roots of 9.
- » 4 and –4 are both square roots of 16.
- » 5 and –5 are both square roots of 25.
- » 6 and –6 are both square roots of 36.
- » 7 and –7 are both square roots of 49.
- » 8 and –8 are both square roots of 64.
- » 9 and –9 are both square roots of 81.
- » 10 and –10 are both square roots of 100.
- » 11 and –11 are both square roots of 121.
- » 12 and –12 are both square roots of 144.

IRRATIONAL NUMBERS

When the ASVAB asks you to figure square roots of numbers that don't have perfect squares, the task gets a bit more difficult. If you have to find the square root of a number that isn't a perfect square, the ASVAB usually asks you to find the square root to the nearest tenth.

Suppose you run across this problem:

EXAMPLE

$\sqrt{54} =$

Think about what you know:

- » The square root of 49 is 7, and 54 is slightly greater than 49. You also know that the square root of 64 is 8, and 54 is slightly less than 64. (If you didn't know that, check out the preceding section.)
- » If the number 54 is somewhere between 49 and 64, the square root of 54 is somewhere between 7 and 8.
- » Because 54 is closer to 49 than to 64, the square root will be closer to 7 than to 8, so you can try 7.3 as the square root of 54:

  1. **Multiply 7.3 by itself.**

     $7.3 \times 7.3 = 53.29$, which is very close to 54.

  2. **Try multiplying 7.4 by itself to see whether it's any closer to 54.**

     $7.4 \times 7.4 = 54.76$, which isn't as close to 54 as 53.29.

  3. **7.3 is the square root of 54 to the nearest tenth.**

Cube roots

A *cube root* is a number that when multiplied by itself three times equals the number under the radical. For example, the cube root of 27 is 3 because $3 \times 3 \times 3 = 27$. A cube root is expressed by the radical sign with a 3 written on the left of the radical. For example, the cube root of 27 would be expressed as $\sqrt[3]{27}$.

REMEMBER

You may see one or two cube-root problems on the math subtests of the ASVAB but probably not more than that. Plus, the problems you encounter will probably be perfect cubes and won't involve irrational numbers.

Each number has only one cube root (unlike square roots). If the radicand is positive, the cube root will be a positive number.

Also, unlike with square roots, finding the cube root of a negative number without involving advanced mathematics is possible. If the radicand is negative, the cube root will also be negative. For example, $\sqrt[3]{-27} = -3$.

Just like square roots, you should memorize a few common cube roots:

>> 1 is the cube root of 1, and –1 is the cube root of –1.

>> 2 is the cube root of 8, and –2 is the cube root of –8.

>> 3 is the cube root of 27, and –3 is the cube root of –27.

>> 4 is the cube root of 64, and –4 is the cube root of –64.

>> 5 is the cube root of 125, and –5 is the cube root of –125.

>> 6 is the cube root of 216, and –6 is the cube root of –216.

>> 7 is the cube root of 343, and –7 is the cube root of –343.

>> 8 is the cube root of 512, and –8 is the cube root of –512.

>> 9 is the cube root of 729, and –9 is the cube root of –729.

>> 10 is the cube root of 1,000, and –10 is the cube root of –1,000.

Scientific notation

Scientific notation is a compact format for writing very large or very small numbers. Although it's most often used in scientific fields, you may find a question or two on the Mathematics Knowledge subtest of the ASVAB asking you to convert a number to scientific notation, or vice versa.

Scientific notation separates a number into two parts: a *characteristic*, which is always greater than or equal to 1 and less than 10, and a *power of ten*. Thus, 1.25×10^4 means 1.25 times 10 to the fourth power, or 12,500; 5.79×10^{-8} means 5.79 times 10 to the negative eighth power. (Remember that a negative exponent is equal to its reciprocal with a positive exponent, so 10^{-8} means $\frac{1}{100,000,000}$). In this case, the scientific notation comes out to 0.0000000579.

Alphabet Soup: Tackling Algebra Review

Algebra problems are equations, which means that the quantities on both sides of the equal sign are equal — they're the same: $2 = 2$, $1 + 1 = 2$, and $3 - 1 = 2$. In all these cases, the quantities are the same on both sides of the equal sign. So, if $x = 2$, then x is 2 because the equal sign says so.

Visiting variables

Most algebraic equations involve using one or more variables. A *variable* is a symbol that represents a number. Usually, algebra problems use letters such as n, t, or x for variables. In most algebra problems, your goal is to find the value of the variable. For example, in the equation $x + 4 = 60$, you'd try to find the value of x by using the rules of algebra.

Following the rules of algebra

Algebra has several rules or properties that — when combined — allow you to simplify equations. Some (but not all) equations can be simplified to a complete solution:

>> **You may combine like terms.** This rule means adding or subtracting terms with variables of the same kind. The expression $4x + 4x$ simplifies to $8x$. $2y + y$ is equal to $3y$. The expression $13 - 7 + 3$ simplifies to 9.

>> **You may use the distributive property to remove parentheses around unlike terms** (see "The distributive property: Breaking up large numbers" earlier in this chapter).

>> **You may add or subtract any value as long as you do it to both sides of the equation.**

>> **You may multiply or divide by any number (except 0) as long as you do it to both sides of the equation.**

Combining like terms

One of the most common ways to simplify an expression is to combine like terms. Numeric terms may be combined, and any terms with the same variable part may be combined.

Take, for instance, the expression $5x + 3 + 3x - 6y + 4 + 7y$.

TIP

In algebra, when two or more variables are multiplied, it's traditional to place the variables next to each other and omit the multiplication sign ($\times$): $a \times b = ab$. The same rule applies to variables multiplied by numbers: $4 \times y = 4y$.

$5x$ and $3x$ are like terms. So are $-6y$ and $7y$. 3 and 4 are also like terms because they're numbers without variables. By combining the like terms, you get

$$5x + 3x = 8x$$

$$-6y + 7y = 1y \text{ (or just } y)$$

$$3 + 4 = 7$$

By combining the like terms, the expression $5x + 3 + 3x - 6y + 4 + 7y$ simplifies to $8x + y + 7$.

Using the distributive property

I know what you're thinking: Combining like terms is pretty cool, but what if you have unlike terms contained within parentheses? Doesn't the order of operations require you to deal with terms in parentheses first? Indeed, it does, and that's where the distributive property comes in.

As I explain earlier in the chapter, $a(b + c) = ab + ac$. For example, $6(4 + 3)$ is mathematically the same as $(6 \times 4) + (6 \times 3)$.

Applying the same principle to algebra, the distributive property can be very useful in getting rid of those pesky parentheses:

$$4(x + y) = 4x + 4y$$

Using addition and subtraction

You can use addition and subtraction to get all the terms with variables on one side of an equation and all the numeric terms on the other. That's an important step in finding the value of the variable.

The equation $3x = 21$ has only the variable term on one side and only a number on the other. The equation $3x + 4 = 25$ doesn't.

REMEMBER

You can add and subtract any number as long as you do it to both sides of the equation. In this case, you want to get rid of the number 4 on the left side of the equation. How do you make the 4 disappear? Simply subtract 4 from it:

$$3x + 4 - 4 = 25 - 4$$

The equation simplifies to $3x = 21$.

Using multiplication and division

The rules of algebra also allow you to multiply and divide both sides of an equation by any number except zero. Say you have an equation that reads $3x = 21$, or 3 times x equals 21. You want to find the value of x, not three times x.

What happens if you divide a number by itself? The result is 1. Therefore, to change $3x$ to $1x$ (or x), divide both sides of the equation by 3:

$$3x = 21$$
$$\frac{3x}{3} = \frac{21}{3}$$
$$1x = 7$$
$$x = 7$$

But what if the equation were $\frac{2}{3}b = 21$? What would you do then?

I'll give you a hint: If you multiply any fraction by its reciprocal, the result is 1. Remember, a reciprocal is a fraction flipped upside down.

$$\frac{2}{3}b = 21$$
$$\frac{3}{2} \cdot \frac{2}{3}b = 21 \cdot \frac{3}{2}$$

Remember to multiply both sides of the equation by $\frac{3}{2}$.

$$1b = \frac{21}{1} \cdot \frac{3}{2}$$
$$b = \frac{21 \cdot 3}{1 \cdot 2}$$
$$b = \frac{63}{2}$$
$$b = 31\frac{1}{2}$$

All Is Not Equal: Examining Inequalities

Earlier in the chapter, I say that all equations include equal signs (=), and I stand by that statement. After all, I wouldn't lie to you. However, some math problems look very much like equations, but they use signs other than the equal sign.

These problems are called *inequalities.* An equation states that each side of the equation separated by the equal sign is equal to the other. An inequality, on the other hand, says that the two sides separated by an inequality sign are *not* equal to each other.

Just as with equations, the solution to an inequality is all the values that make the inequality true. For the most part, you solve inequalities the same as you'd solve a normal equation. You need to keep some facts of inequality life in mind, however. Short and sweet, here they are:

>> **Negative numbers** are less than zero and less than positive numbers.

>> **Zero** is less than positive numbers but greater than negative numbers.

>> **Positive numbers** are greater than negative numbers and greater than zero.

Although there's only one equal sign (=), several signs are associated with inequalities:

>> $\neq$ means *does not equal* in the way that 3 does not equal 4, or $3 \neq 4$.

>> $>$ means *greater than* in the way that 4 is greater than 3, or $4 > 3$.

>> $<$ means *less than* in the way the 3 is less than 4, or $3 < 4$.

>> $\leq$ means *less than or equal to* in the way that x may be less than or equal to 4, or $x \leq 4$.

>> $\geq$ means *greater than or equal to* in the way that x may be greater than or equal to 3, or $x \geq 3$.

You solve inequalities by using the same principles of algebra used to solve equations, with the exception of multiplying or dividing each side by a negative number (check out the earlier "Following the rules of algebra" section). Take the following example:

EXAMPLE

Solve: $3x + 4 < 25$.

The inequality says that $3x$ plus 4 is less than 25. You solve it in the same way as you would the equation $3x + 4 = 25$:

$$3x + 4 < 25$$
$$3x + 4 - 4 < 25 - 4$$
$$3x < 21$$
$$\frac{3x}{3} < \frac{21}{3}$$
$$x < 7$$

REMEMBER

Although you solve inequalities the same way you solve equations, keep two important rules in mind when working with inequalities:

>> In algebra, if $a = b$, then $b = a$. In other words, you can swap the data on each side of the equal sign, and the equation means the same thing. So $2x + 4 = 18$ and $18 = 2x + 4$ are the same thing. This interchangeability doesn't work with inequalities. In other words, $2x + 4 > 18$ isn't the same as $18 > 2x + 4$. When you swap the data in an inequality, you have to change the inequality sign to balance the inequality (keep the inequity true). So $2x + 4 > 18$ is the same as $18 < 2x + 4$.

>> When you multiply or divide both sides of the inequality by a negative number, the inequality sign is reversed. That means if you multiply both sides of the inequality $3 < 4$ by -4, your answer is $-12 > -16$.

Solving Quadratics

A *quadratic equation* is an algebraic equation in which the unknown is raised to an exponent of 2 (and no higher), as in x^2. Quadratic equations can be very simple or very complex (or several degrees of difficulty in between). Here are some examples:

» $x^2 = 36$

» $x^2 + 4 = 72$

» $x^2 + 3x - 33 = 0$

REMEMBER

The exponent in a quadratic is never higher than 2 (because it would then no longer be the *square* of an unknown but a cube or something else). An equation that includes the variable x^3 or x^4 is *not* a quadratic.

You can solve quadratics in three primary ways: the square-root method, factoring, or the quadratic formula. Which method you choose depends on the difficulty of the equation.

Method 1: The square-root method

Simple quadratic equations (those that consist of just one squared term and a number) can be solved by using the *square-root rule*:

If $x^2 = k$, then $x = \pm\sqrt{k}$, as long as k isn't a negative number.

Remember to include the $\pm$ sign, which indicates that the answer is a positive or negative number. Take the following simple quadratic equation:

EXAMPLE

Solve: $3x^2 + 4 = 31$.

1. **First, isolate the variable by subtracting 4 from each side.**

The result is $3x^2 = 27$.

2. **Next, get rid of the 3 by dividing both sides of the equation by 3.**

The result is $x^2 = 9$.

3. **You can now solve by using the square root rule.**

$x^2 = 9$

$x = \pm\sqrt{9}$

$x = 3$ and $x = -3$

Method 2: The factoring method

Most quadratic equations you encounter on the ASVAB math subtests can be solved by putting the equation into the quadratic form and then factoring.

The *quadratic form* is $ax^2 + bx + c = 0$, where a, b, and c are just numbers. All quadratic equations can be expressed in this form. Want to see some examples?

» **$2x^2 - 4x = 32$:** This equation can be expressed in the quadratic form as $2x^2 + (-4x) + (-32) = 0$. In this case, $a = 2$, $b = -4$, and $c = -32$.

» $x^2 = 36$: You can express this equation as $1x^2 + 0x + (-36) = 0$. So $a = 1$, $b = 0$, and $c = -36$.

» $3x^2 + 6x + 4 = -33$: Expressed in quadratic form, this equation reads $3x^2 + 6x + 37 = 0$. So $a = 3$, $b = 6$, and $c = 37$.

Ready to factor? How about trying the following equation?

EXAMPLE

Solve: $x^2 + 5x + 6 = 0$.

Because I like you, I've already expressed the equation in quadratic form (the expression on the left is equal to zero), saving you a little time.

TIP

You can use the factoring method for most quadratic equations where $a = 1$ and c is a positive number.

The first step in factoring a quadratic equation is to draw two sets of parentheses on your scratch paper, and then place an x at the front of each, leaving some extra space after it. As with the original quadratic, the equation should equal zero:

$$(x \quad)(x \quad) = 0$$

The next step is to find two numbers that equal c when multiplied together and equal b when added together. In the example equation, $b = 5$ and $c = 6$, so you need to hunt for two numbers that multiply to 6 and add up to 5. For example, $2 \times 3 = 6$ and $2 + 3 = 5$. In this case, the two numbers you're seeking are positive 2 and positive 3.

Finally, put these two numbers into your set of parentheses:

$$(x + 2)(x + 3) = 0$$

Any number multiplied by zero equals zero, which means that $x + 2 = 0$ and/or $x + 3 = 0$. The solution to this quadratic equation is $x = -2$ and/or $x = -3$.

REMEMBER

When choosing your factors, remember that they can be either positive or negative numbers. You can use clues from the signs of b and c to help you find the numbers (factors) you need:

» If c is positive, then the factors you're looking for are either both positive or both negative:

- If b is positive, then the factors are positive.
- If b is negative, then the factors are negative.
- b is the sum of the two factors that give you c.

» If c is negative, then the factors you're looking for are of alternating signs; that is, one is negative and one is positive:

- If b is positive, then the larger factor is positive.
- If b is negative, then the larger factor is negative.
- b is the difference between the two factors that gives you c.

Try another one, just for giggles:

EXAMPLE

Solve: $x^2 - 7x + 6 = 0$.

Start by writing your parentheses:

$$(x \quad)(x \quad) = 0$$

In this equation, $b = -7$ and $c = +6$. Because b is negative and c is positive, both factors will be negative.

You're looking for two negative numbers that multiply to 6 and add to -7. Those numbers are -1 and -6. Plugging the numbers into your parentheses, you get $(x - 1)(x - 6) = 0$. That means $x = 1$ and/or $x = 6$.

Method 3: The quadratic formula

The square-root method can be used for simple quadratics, and the factoring method can easily be used for many other quadratics, as long as $a = 1$. (See the two preceding sections.) But what if a doesn't equal 1, or you can't easily find two numbers that multiply to c and add up to b?

You can use the quadratic formula to solve any quadratic equation. So why not just use the quadratic formula and forget about the square-root and factoring methods? Because the quadratic formula is kind of complex:

$$x = \frac{-b \pm \sqrt{b^2 - 4ac}}{2a}$$

The quadratic formula uses the a, b, and c from $ax^2 + bx + c = 0$, just like the factoring method.

Armed with this knowledge, you can apply your skills to a complex quadratic equation:

Solve: $2x^2 - 4x - 3 = 0$.

EXAMPLE

In this equation, $a = 2$, $b = -4$, and $c = -3$. Plug the known values into the quadratic formula and simplify:

$$x = \frac{-b \pm \sqrt{b^2 - 4ac}}{2a}$$

$$x = \frac{-(-4) \pm \sqrt{(-4)^2 - 4(2)(-3)}}{2(2)}$$

$$x = \frac{4 \pm \sqrt{16 + 24}}{4}$$

$$x = \frac{4 \pm \sqrt{40}}{4}$$

$$x = \frac{4 \pm 6.3}{4}$$

$$x = \frac{4 + 6.3}{4} \text{ and } x = \frac{4 - 6.3}{4}$$

$$x = 2.58 \text{ and } x = -0.58$$

Rounded to the nearest tenth, $x = 2.6$ and $x = -0.6$.

Knowing All the Angles: Geometry Review

According to my handy pocket dictionary, *geometry* is "the branch of mathematics that deals with the deduction of the properties, measurement, and relationships of points, lines, angles, and figures in space from their defining conditions by means of certain assumed properties of space." Sounds interesting!

Really, geometry is simply the branch of mathematics that's concerned with shapes, lines, and angles. From the perspective of the ASVAB math subtests, you should be able to identify basic geometric shapes and know certain properties about them so you can determine their angles and measurements. You see a lot of geometry-related questions on both the Mathematics Knowledge and the Arithmetic Reasoning subtests of the ASVAB.

Knowing all the angles

Angles are formed when two lines intersect at a point. Many geometric shapes are formed by intersecting lines, which form angles. Angles can be measured in degrees. The greater the number of degrees, the wider the angle is:

>> A straight line is exactly 180°.

>> A *right angle* is exactly 90°.

>> An *acute angle* is more than 0° and less than 90°.

>> An *obtuse angle* is more than 90° but less than 180°.

>> *Complementary angles* are two angles that equal 90° when added together.

>> *Supplementary angles* are two angles that equal 180° when added together.

Take a look at the different types of angles in Figure 9-3.

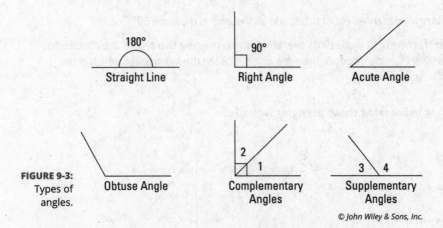

FIGURE 9-3: Types of angles.

© John Wiley & Sons, Inc.

Common geometric shapes

I'm not going to explain all the possible geometric shapes for two reasons: Doing so would take this entire book, and you don't need to know them all to solve the math problems you find on the ASVAB. However, you should recognize the most common shapes associated with geometry.

Getting square with quadrilaterals

A *quadrilateral* is a geometric shape with four sides. All quadrilaterals contain interior angles totaling 360°. Here are the five most common types of quadrilaterals:

>> **Squares** have four sides of equal length, and all the angles are right angles.

>> **Rectangles** have all right angles.

>> **Rhombuses** have four sides of equal length, but the angles don't have to be right angles.

>> **Trapezoids** have at least two sides that are parallel.

>> **Parallelograms** have opposite sides that are parallel, and their opposite sides and angles are equal.

Figure 9-4 gives you an idea of what these five quadrilaterals look like.

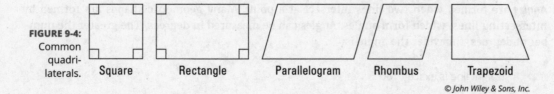

FIGURE 9-4: Common quadrilaterals.

Square   Rectangle   Parallelogram   Rhombus   Trapezoid

© John Wiley & Sons, Inc.

Trying out triangles

A *triangle* consists of three straight lines whose three interior angles always add up to 180°. The sides of a triangle are called *legs*. Triangles can be classified according to the relationship among their angles, the relationship among their sides, or some combination of these relationships. You should know the three most common types of triangles:

>> **Isosceles triangle:** Has two equal sides, and the angles opposite the equal sides are also equal.

>> **Equilateral triangle:** Has three equal sides, and all the angles measure 60°.

>> **Right triangle:** Has one right angle (90°); therefore, the remaining two angles are *complementary* (add up to 90°). The side opposite the right angle is called the *hypotenuse*, which is the longest side of a right triangle.

Check out Figure 9-5 to see what these triangles look like.

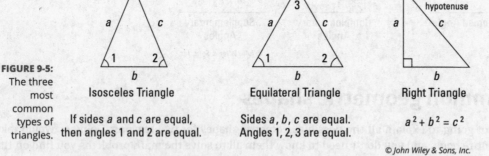

FIGURE 9-5: The three most common types of triangles.

Isosceles Triangle
If sides *a* and *c* are equal, then angles 1 and 2 are equal.

Equilateral Triangle
Sides *a*, *b*, *c* are equal. Angles 1, 2, 3 are equal.

Right Triangle
$a^2 + b^2 = c^2$

© John Wiley & Sons, Inc.

Settling on circles

A *circle* is formed when the points of a closed line are all located equal distances from a point called the *center* of the circle. A circle always has 360°. The closed line of a circle is called its *circumference*. The *radius* of a circle is the measurement from the center of the circle to any point on the circumference of the circle. The *diameter* of the circle is measured as a line passing through the center of the circle, from a point on one side of the circle to a point on the other side of the circle. The diameter of a circle is always twice as long as the radius. Figure 9-6 shows these relationships.

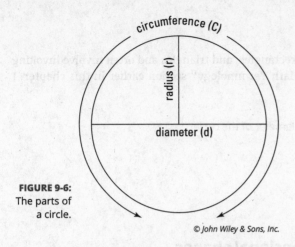

FIGURE 9-6:
The parts of
a circle.

circumference (C)

radius (r)

diameter (d)

© John Wiley & Sons, Inc.

Famous geometry formulas

The math subtests of the ASVAB often ask you to use basic geometry formulas to calculate geometric measurements. You should commit these simple formulas to memory.

Quadrilateral formulas you should know

You may be asked to calculate the perimeter (distance around), the area, or the diagonal of a square or rectangle. Use the following formulas:

>> **Perimeter of a square:** $P = 4s$, where s = one side of the square

>> **Area of a square:** $A = s^2$

>> **Diagonal of a square:** $d = s\sqrt{2}$

>> **Perimeter of a rectangle:** $P = 2l + 2w$, where l = the length and w = the width of the rectangle; you can also write this formula as $P = 2(l + w)$

>> **Area of a rectangle:** $A = lw$

>> **Diagonal of a rectangle:** $d = \sqrt{l^2 + w^2}$

Good-to-know triangle formulas

Some math problems on the ASVAB may ask you to calculate the perimeter or area of a triangle. The following formulas are used for these two purposes:

>> **Perimeter of a triangle:** $P = s_1 + s_2 + s_3$, where s = the length of each side of the triangle

>> **Area of a triangle:** $A = \frac{1}{2}bh$, where b = the length of the triangle's base (bottom) and h = the height of the triangle

TIP

A special formula called the *Pythagorean theorem* says that if you know the length of any two sides of a right triangle, you can find the length of the third side. It works only on right triangles, however. The formula is $a^2 + b^2 = c^2$, where c equals the length of the triangle's hypotenuse and a and b equal the lengths of the remaining two sides.

Circle formulas

Circles are a bit more complex than squares, rectangles, and triangles and often involve invoking the value of π. In the "Making the Most of Math Terminology" section earlier in this chapter, I tell you that π is approximately equal to 3.14.

>> **Radius of a circle:** $r = \frac{1}{2}d$, where d = the diameter of the circle

>> **Diameter of a circle:** $d = 2r$

>> **Circumference of a circle:** $C = 2\pi r$

>> **Area of a circle:** $A = \pi r^2$

Handy formulas for three-dimensional shapes

Sometimes the math subtests require you to calculate measurements for solid (three-dimensional) shapes. These types of questions generally come in two flavors: calculating volume or calculating surface area.

Volume is the space a shape takes up. You can think of volume as how much a shape would hold if you poured water into it. *Surface area* is the area of the outside of the shape — for example, the amount of area you'd have to cover if you were to paint the outside of the solid shape.

>> **Volume of a cube:** $V = s^3$, where s = the length of one side of the cube

>> **Volume of a box (also called a rectangular prism):** $V = lwh$, where l = the length, w = the width, and h = the height of the box

>> **Volume of a cylinder:** $V = \pi r^2 h$, where r = the radius of the cylinder and h = the height of the cylinder

>> **Surface area of a cube:** $SA = 6s^2$

>> **Surface area of a box (rectangular prism):** $SA = 2lw + 2wh + 2lh$

You Got a Problem? Math Knowledge Exercises

The best way to get better at math is to practice, and I couldn't let you leave this chapter without giving you a few run-throughs on the material you just read. These exercises are designed to help you flex your math muscles. You'll practice terminology (I promise not to quiz you on the word *brachistochrone*), run around with Dear Aunt Sally, and convert fractions. You'll also keep equations balanced and identify which formulas you should use to solve problems on the ASVAB.

Math terminology practice

Remember when your mother said, "It's not *what* you say; it's *how* you say it"? She wasn't talking about math. In mathematics, it's exactly what you say that matters. Use Activity 1 to match the signal words to the correct mathematical operations (addition, subtraction, multiplication, or division), and then check the "Answers and Explanations" section at the end of this chapter to make sure you're right.

Math Terminology

Signal Word	Operation (addition, subtraction, multiplication, or division)
1. Increase	
2. Deduct	
3. Product	
4. Quotient	
5. Sum	
6. Of	
7. Difference	
8. Total	
9. Less	
10. By	

Order of operations practice

Math is a lot like the military: There are right ways and wrong ways to do everything. In mathematics, it's all about the order of operations. Remember that Aunt Sally — although we always have to apologize for her (Please Excuse My Dear Aunt Sally) — can show you how to solve any math problem in the right order (refer back to "Obeying the order of operations," earlier in this chapter). In Activity 2, look at the problem and determine which operations you'll do first, then which you'll do second. You don't need to perform the calculations. When you're done, see whether you're right in the "Answers and Explanations" section at the end of this chapter. When you're only simplifying things, it's often okay to switch the first and second operations you perform.

ACTIVITY 2 **Order of Operations**

Problem	First	Second
Example: $5 + 6 + (17 \cdot 2)$	$(17 \cdot 2)$	Add 5, 6, and the product of 17 and 2
1. $(4-3)(3+19)$		
2. $12^2 - (13+22)$		
3. $\frac{18}{3} + 27$		
4. $14 + x(18^2)$		
5. $7^3 \div 4$		
6. $6 \div 3 + 12$		
7. $\frac{3}{4} + 38.6 + 24.2$		
8. $\frac{0.3^{17}}{2}$		
9. $(4^3 + 17) + y$		
10. $4 + 4 + 8 - \left(\frac{18^2}{2}\right)$		

Converting fractions and decimals

When you run into an ASVAB question that contains fractions and decimals, you'll most likely need to convert one or the other to solve the problem (see "Dealing with Decimals" earlier in this chapter). Use Activity 3 to practice switching between fractions and decimals, and then check the "Answers and Explanations" section at the end of this chapter to see how well you did.

ACTIVITY 3 **Fractions and Decimals**

Problem	Your Conversion
1. 0.17	
2. $\frac{2}{5}$	
3. $1\frac{3}{10}$	
4. 4.75	
5. 18.925	
6. $\frac{21}{8}$	
7. $7\frac{21}{5}$	
8. 9.217	
9. –37.2	
10. $8\frac{81}{8}$	

Solving equations and inequalities

When you take the ASVAB, you'll do plenty of mental math — but you'll also use some of the unlimited supply of scratch paper the test proctor gives you to write equations. Simple errors in an equation can throw off your entire game, though, so use Activity 4 to practice solving each equation or inequality. When you're finished, check your work in the "Answers and Explanations" section at the end of this chapter. (If you need to brush up on balancing equations, see the "Following the rules of algebra" section earlier in this chapter.)

ACTIVITY 4 **Solving Equations and Inequalities**

Problem	Your Work
1. $3x + 7 = 25$	
2. $20x - 3 < 57$	
3. $x - 3 = 17$	
4. $4x + 5 = 1 + 5x$	
5. $9y - 7 = 7y - 11$	

Identifying formulas

Many of the algebra and geometry questions on the ASVAB require you to plumb the depths of your memory for a specific mathematical formula. If you can't remember it, you're going to have a tough time coming up with the right answer. Use Activity 5 to match each type of problem with the appropriate formula to solve it. (*Note:* Not all of these formulas appear in this chapter.) Make sure you connected the right pairs by checking your answers in the "Answers and Explanations" section at the end of this chapter.

ACTIVITY 5 Identifying Formulas

Answer	Formula Type	Formula
1.	1. Quadratic equation	A. $A = lw$
2.	2. Pythagorean theorem	B. $d = rt$
3.	3. Area of a triangle	C. $A = \pi r^2$
4.	4. Area of a rectangle	D. $ax^2 + bx + c = 0$
5.	5. Circumference of a circle	E. $C = 2\pi r$
6.	6. Slope-intercept form	F. $A = \frac{1}{2}bh$
7.	7. Distance traveled	G. $a^2 + b^2 = c^2$
8.	8. Simple interest	H. $V = lwh$
9.	9. Area of a circle	I. $I = prt$
10.	10. Volume of a rectangular prism	J. $y = mx + b$

Answers and Explanations

Check your answers for each of the exercises here, and take some time to review the explanations if you're not sure where you went wrong.

Activity 1: Math Terminology

1. Increase: addition

2. Deduct: subtraction

3. Product: multiplication

4. Quotient: division

5. Sum: addition

6. Of: multiplication

7. Difference: subtraction

8. Total: addition

9. Less: subtraction

10. By: multiplication

Activity 2: Order of Operations

Problem	First	Second
1. $(4-3)(3+19)$	$(4-3)$	$(3+19)$
2. $12^2 - (13+22)$	12^2	$(13+22)$
3. $\frac{18}{3}+27$	$18 \div 3$	add 27
4. $14 + x(18^2)$	18^2	multiply 18^2 by x
5. $7^3 \div 4$	7^3	divide by 4
6. $6 \div 3 + 12$	$6 \div 3$	add 12
7. $\frac{3}{4}+38.6+24.2$	$3 \div 4$	add the remaining numbers
8. $\frac{0.3^{17}}{2}$	0.3^{17}	divide by 2
9. $(4^3+17)+y$	4^3	add 17
10. $4+4+8-\left(\frac{18^2}{2}\right)$	18^2	divide by 2

Activity 3: Fractions and Decimals

Problem	Your Conversion
1. 0.17	$\frac{17}{100}$
2. $\frac{2}{5}$	0.4
3. $1\frac{3}{10}$	1.3
4. 4.75	$4\frac{3}{4}$
5. 18.925	$18\frac{37}{40}$
6. $\frac{21}{8}$	2.625
7. $7\frac{21}{5}$	11.2
8. 9.217	$9\frac{217}{1,000}$
9. −37.2	$-37\frac{1}{5}$
10. $8\frac{81}{8}$	18.125

Activity 4: Solving Equations and Inequalities

1.
$$3x + 7 = 25$$
$$3x + 7 - 7 = 25 - 7$$
$$3x = 18$$
$$\frac{3x}{3} = \frac{18}{3}$$
$$x = 6$$

2.
$$20x - 3 < 57$$
$$20x - 3 + 3 < 57 + 3$$
$$20x < 60$$
$$\frac{20x}{20} < \frac{60}{20}$$
$$x < 3$$

3.
$$x - 3 = 17$$
$$x - 3 + 3 = 17 + 3$$
$$x = 20$$

4.
$$4x + 5 = 1 + 5x$$
$$4x + 5 = 5x + 1$$
$$4x + 5 - 5x = 5x + 1 - 5x$$
$$-x + 5 = 1$$
$$-x + 5 - 5 = 1 - 5$$
$$-x = -4$$
$$x = 4$$

5.
$$9y - 7 = 7y - 11$$
$$9y - 7 - 7y = 7y - 11 - 7y$$
$$2y - 7 = -11$$
$$2y - 7 + 7 = -11 + 7$$
$$2y = -4$$
$$\frac{2y}{2} = \frac{-4}{2}$$
$$y = -2$$

Activity 5: Identifying Formulas

1. D. The quadratic equation is $ax^2 + bx + c = 0$.

2. G. The Pythagorean theorem is $a^2 + b^2 = c^2$.

3. F. The formula to find the area of a triangle is $A = \frac{1}{2}bh$, where A represents area, b represents the length of the base, and h represents the triangle's height.

4. A. The formula to find the area of a rectangle is $A = lw$, where A represents area, l represents the rectangle's length, and w represents the rectangle's width.

5. **E.** The formula to find the circumference (the distance around) a circle is $C = 2\pi r$, where C represents circumference and r represents the circle's radius (the distance from the center of the circle to its outer edge).

6. **J.** The formula for slope-intercept form of a line is $y = mx + b$, where m is the slope and b is the y-intercept. In this formula, x and y represent coordinate points.

7. **B.** The formula to find distance traveled is $d = rt$, where d represents distance, r represents rate (speed), and t represents time.

8. **I.** The formula to figure out simple interest is $I = prt$, where I represents interest, p represents principal, r represents the rate of interest per year expressed as a decimal, and t represents the time periods involved.

9. **C.** The formula to find the area of a circle is $A = \pi r^2$, where A represents area and r represents the circle's radius (the distance, in a straight line, from the circle's center to its outer edge).

10. **H.** The formula to find the volume of a rectangular prism is $V = lwh$, where V represents volume, l represents length, w represents width, and h represents height.

Chapter **10**

The Mathematics Knowledge Subtest

The Mathematics Knowledge subtest is one of two math subtests given to help determine your AFQT score. This chapter and Chapter 9 prepare you for the types of questions and knowledge you need in order to feel confident and score competitively on the Mathematics Knowledge portion of the ASVAB. Chapters 11 and 12 review your ability to correctly answer word problems for the Arithmetic Reasoning subtests.

Most of the time, the Mathematics Knowledge subtest contains only one or two questions testing each specific mathematical concept. For example, one question may ask you to multiply fractions, the next question may ask you to solve a mathematical inequality, and the question after that may ask you to find the value of an exponent. (If you've suddenly become nervous after reading the preceding sentence, don't worry. I cover all this stuff in Chapter 9.)

All this variety forces you to constantly shift your mental gears to quickly deal with different concepts. You can look at this situation from two perspectives: These mental gymnastics can be difficult and frustrating, especially if you know everything about solving for *x* but nothing about deriving a square root. But variety can also be the spice of life, as your grandma may have said. If you don't know how to solve a specific type of problem, this oversight may cause you to get only one question wrong (or maybe two — but think positively). On the flip side, having trouble in a specific area helps you zero in on what you need to focus your study on so you can improve your weaker areas.

Taking Stock of the Test Structure

On the CAT-ASVAB, the Mathematics Knowledge subtest consists of 16 questions covering the entire array of high-school math, and you have 20 minutes to complete the subtest. (If you're taking the paper version of the ASVAB, you have to answer 25 questions in 24 minutes.) You don't necessarily have to rush through each calculation, but the pace you need to set (about a minute per question) doesn't exactly give you time to daydream about what you're having for dinner. You have to concentrate to solve each problem quickly and accurately.

The lovely people who made up the rules have dictated you can't use a calculator for any of the math questions on the ASVAB. When you enter the testing room, you get a pencil and a sheet of scratch paper. (I guess their thinking is that if you're in the middle of a combat zone and find a sudden need to solve for *x*, you may find your calculator full of sand and worthless.) The good news is that all the questions on the math subtests of the ASVAB are designed so you can solve them without electronic calculation.

The Mathematics Knowledge subtest features three types of questions:

» **Direct math:** This type of question presents you with a mathematical equation and asks you to solve it.

» **Math law:** This type of question asks you about a mathematical law, rule, term, or concept.

» **Combined:** This type of question asks you to use a mathematical law, rule, term, or concept to solve a problem.

Direct math questions

The direct math question is the most common type of question on the Mathematics Knowledge subtest. In a direct math question, you're presented with an equation and asked to solve it. You see a lot of these.

EXAMPLE

Solve for x: $2x + 4(2x + 7) = 3(2x + 4)$.

(A) 0.75

(B) −4

(C) 1.25

(D) −1.25

The correct answer is Choice (B), −4. This is an algebraic equation that you can solve using the rules of algebra (see Chapter 9):

$$2x + 4(2x + 7) = 3(2x + 4)$$
$$2x + 8x + 28 = 6x + 12$$
$$10x + 28 = 6x + 12$$
$$10x + 28 - 6x = 6x + 12 - 6x$$
$$4x + 28 = 12$$
$$4x = -16$$
$$x = -4$$

Math law questions

Sometimes the Mathematics Knowledge subtest asks you a question that doesn't involve solving a mathematical problem. Instead, you're expected to answer a question concerning a mathematical concept, math term, rule, or law. You're not likely to see more than two or three of these kinds of questions on the test, however.

EXAMPLE

In the expression $432xy + 124xy$, the "432" is called the

(A) multiplier.

(B) coefficient.

(C) matrix.

(D) prime.

The correct answer is Choice (B), coefficient. A *coefficient* is the number multiplied by a variable or by a product of variables or by powers of variables in a term. (You can find more useful math terms in Chapter 9.)

Combined questions

You may see several combined questions on the Mathematics Knowledge subtest. These questions require you to use a particular math term, rule, or concept to solve a mathematical problem.

EXAMPLE

What is the quotient of 4 and 4?

(A) 8

(B) 16

(C) 0

(D) 1

The right answer is Choice (D), 1. To solve this problem, you need to know that a *quotient* is the result of a division operation. When you've figured that out, you have to perform the operation:

$$4 \div 4 = 1$$

Planning Your Test Attack

For most people, scoring well on the Mathematics Knowledge subtest requires more than just showing up on time and borrowing a No. 2 pencil and piece of scratch paper. Maybe everything on the test will go perfectly, and you'll breeze through without a problem. On the other hand, maybe you'll get stuck on a question or run into other roadblocks. When this happens, having a plan of attack is helpful.

Keeping an eye on the all-important clock

Like all subtests of the ASVAB, the Mathematics Knowledge subtest is timed. If you're taking the computerized version of the ASVAB, you get 16 questions in 20 minutes, and your remaining time will be shown in the corner of your computer screen.

If you're taking the paper version of the test, you have just 24 minutes to try to correctly answer 25 questions. That's 57.6 seconds per question. (Do you like the way I used math to figure that out?) The room will have a clock in it, and the start time and stop time will be posted somewhere in the room, easily visible to you and the other test takers.

TIP

Keep an eye on the clock. You want to try to finish the test before time runs out. Try to average about 45 or 50 seconds per question. If you get stuck on a question, try the "Playing the guessing game" techniques later in this chapter.

Doubling your chances by double-checking

REMEMBER

If you have time, double-check your answers. Those crafty test makers often provide wrong answer choices that work if you made a common error, so don't assume that your answer is the right one just because it matches one of the possible answer choices. Look at the following example:

EXAMPLE

Solve: $\frac{1}{4} \div \frac{1}{2} =$

(A) $\frac{1}{8}$

(B) 2

(C) 17

(D) $\frac{1}{2}$

To correctly solve this problem, you multiply the first fraction by the *reciprocal* (flipped over) value of the second fraction:

$$\frac{1}{4} \div \frac{1}{2} = \frac{1}{4} \times \frac{2}{1} = \frac{2}{4} = \frac{1}{2}$$

The correct answer is Choice (D), $\frac{1}{2}$. If you multiplied the fractions instead of dividing, you would've gotten Choice (A). If you took the reciprocal of the first fraction rather than the second, you would've gotten Choice (B). If you took a wild guess, you might've gotten Choice (C).

WARNING

Although double-checking your answers is always a good idea, remember to watch the time. You don't want to run out of time with only half the questions answered because you've spent too much time double-checking all your answers.

Using the answer choices to your advantage

If you're stuck on a particular problem, sometimes plugging the possible answer choices into the equation can help you find the right answer.

EXAMPLE

Solve: $\frac{1}{2}x - 45 = 5$.

(A) 25

(B) 50

(C) 100

(D) 75

The right answer is Choice (C), 100. Suppose you experience a complete brain freeze and can't remember how to handle a variable multiplied by a fraction. You don't have to jump straight to random guessing at this point. You can replace x in the equation with the known possible answer choices and see whether any of them work.

First, recognize that you can simplify the equation to $\frac{1}{2}x = 50$ by adding 45 to both sides. Now start substituting the answer choices for x:

» $x = 25$: $\frac{1}{2} \times 25 = 50 \rightarrow 12.5 = 50$. That doesn't work.

» $x = 50$: $\frac{1}{2} \times 50 = 50 \rightarrow 25 = 50$. That certainly doesn't work.

» $x = 100$: $\frac{1}{2} \times 100 = 50 \rightarrow 50 = 50$. You can stop here because Choice (C) is the correct answer.

WARNING

Don't forget that plugging in all the answers is time-consuming, so save this procedure until you've answered all the problems you can answer. If you're taking the computer version, you can't skip a question, so budget your time wisely; if you don't have much time, just make a guess and move on. You may be able to solve the next question easily.

Playing the guessing game

If time is running short on the CAT-ASVAB, try to read and legitimately answer the questions instead of filling in random guesses for the remaining items. The CAT-ASVAB applies a relatively large penalty when you provide several incorrect answers toward the end of the subtest.

If you're taking the paper version of the ASVAB, you can always skip the tough questions and come back to them after you've finished the easier ones. If you're taking the computerized version of the ASVAB, the software doesn't let you skip questions.

Guessing incorrectly on any of the paper ASVAB subtests doesn't count against you. It's okay to fill in an answer — any answer — on your answer sheet because if you don't, your chances of getting that answer right are zero. But if you take a shot at it, your chances increase to 25 percent, or one in four.

WARNING

If you're taking the paper version of the test and elect to skip questions until later, make sure you mark the next answer in the correct space on the answer sheet. Otherwise, you may wind up wearing out the eraser on your pencil when you discover your error at the end of the test. Or, even worse, you may not notice the error and wind up getting several answers wrong because you mismarked your answer sheet.

The process of elimination

Guessing doesn't always mean "pick an answer, any answer." You can increase your chances of picking the right answer by eliminating answers that can't be right.

EXAMPLE

Solve: $\frac{1}{8} \times \frac{4}{5} =$

(A) $1\frac{1}{8}$

(B) $1\frac{1}{4}$

(C) $\frac{1}{10}$

(D) $\frac{1}{5}$

Any fraction that is less than 1 that is multiplied by another fraction that is less than 1 is going to result in an answer that is less than 1. That means Choices (A) and (B) can't be correct. Your odds of guessing the right answer have just improved from one in four to one in two, or a 50/50 chance. (By the way, the correct answer is Choice (C).)

Solving what you can and guessing the rest

Sometimes you may know how to solve part of a problem but not all of it. If you don't know how to do all the operations, don't give up. You can still narrow your choices by doing what you can. Suppose this question confronts you:

EXAMPLE

What is the value of $(-0.4)^3$?

(A) −0.0027

(B) −0.000064

(C) 0.000064

(D) 0.0009

What if you don't remember how to multiply decimals? All is not lost! If you remember how to use exponents, you'll remember that you have to multiply $-0.04 \times -0.04 \times -0.04$. If you simplify the problem and just multiply $-4 \times -4 \times -4$ without worrying about those pesky zeros, you know that your answer will be negative and will end in the digits 64. With this pearl of wisdom in mind, you can see that Choices (A), (C), and (D) are all wrong. You logically guessed your way to the correct answer, Choice (B)!

Practice Makes Perfect: Sampling Some Practice Questions

How about putting all the knowledge you've gained about the Mathematics Knowledge subtest to the test? Here are ten questions that are very similar to those you're likely to see when you take the actual test.

1. Which of the following fractions is the smallest?

(A) $\frac{3}{4}$

(B) $\frac{14}{17}$

(C) $\frac{4}{7}$

(D) $\frac{5}{8}$

2. What is the product of $\sqrt{36}$ and $\sqrt{49}$?

(A) 1,764

(B) 42

(C) 13

(D) 6

3. Solve: $2x - 3 = x + 7$

(A) 10

(B) 6

(C) 21

(D) −10

4. A circle has a radius of 15 feet. What is most nearly its circumference?

(A) 30 feet

(B) 225 feet

(C) 94 feet

(D) 150 feet

5. At 3 p.m., the angle between the hands of the clock is

(A) 90 degrees.

(B) 180 degrees.

(C) 120 degrees.

(D) 360 degrees.

6. If $3 + y \geq 13$, what is the value of y?

(A) Greater than or equal to 10

(B) Less than or equal to 10

(C) 10

(D) 6

7. $y^3 \times y^2 \times y^{-3} =$

(A) y^2

(B) y^{-13}

(C) y^8

(D) x^{23}

8. 14 yards + 14 feet =

(A) 16 yards

(B) 15 yards

(C) 28 feet

(D) 56 feet

9. What is 35 percent of 85?

(A) 33.2

(B) 65.32

(C) 21.3

(D) 29.75

10. What is most nearly the average of 37, 22, 72, and 44?

(A) 43.8

(B) 55.2

(C) 175

(D) 77.1

Answers and Explanations

Use this answer key to score the practice Mathematics Knowledge questions.

1. C. One method of comparing fractions is called the *cross-product method* (see Chapter 8).

The cross-products of the first fraction and the second fraction are $3 \times 17 = 51$ and $14 \times 4 = 56$. The first fraction is smaller.

The cross-products of the first fraction and the third fraction are $3 \times 7 = 21$ and $4 \times 4 = 16$. The third fraction is smaller.

The cross-products of the third fraction and the fourth fraction are $4 \times 8 = 32$ and $5 \times 7 = 35$. The third fraction, Choice (C), is still smaller, so it's the smallest of all the fractions.

2. B. The square root of 36 is 6, and the square root of 49 is 7. The product of those two numbers is $6 \times 7 = 42$.

3. A. Rearrange the equation and solve as follows:

$$2x - 3 = x + 7$$
$$2x - x = 7 + 3$$
$$x = 10$$

4. C. The circumference of a circle is $\pi \times$ diameter, the diameter equals two times the radius, and π is approximately 3.14. Therefore, $30 \times 3.14 \approx 94$.

TIP

The $\approx$ sign means *approximately equals.* It's used here because the answer, 94, is a rounded number.

5. A. At 3 p.m., one hand is on the 12, and the other is on the 3. This setup creates a *right angle* — a 90-degree angle.

6. A. Solve the inequality the same way you'd solve an algebraic equation:

$$3 + y \geq 13$$
$$y \geq 13 - 3$$
$$y \geq 10$$

7. A. When you multiply powers with the same base, add the exponents:
$y^3 \times y^2 \times y^{-3} = y^{3+2+(-3)} = y^2$.

8. D. Convert the yards to feet by multiplying by 3: $14 \times 3 = 42$ feet. Add this to 14 feet: $42 + 14 = 56$ feet.

9. D. Multiply 85 by the decimal equivalent of 35 percent, or 0.35: $0.35 \times 85 = 29.75$.

10. A. Add the numbers and then divide by the number of terms: $37 + 22 + 72 + 44 = 175$, and $175 \div 4 = 43.75$. Round this number up to 43.8.

Chapter **11**

Working with Word Problems

Two types of mathematics tests are part of the AFQT. The first type is the Mathematics Knowledge subtest that I discuss in Chapters 9 and 10. The second type is the Arithmetic Reasoning subtest, which is the topic of this chapter and Chapter 12.

In the Mathematics Knowledge subtest, you have it pretty easy. You see a mathematical equation, and you do your best to solve it. The Arithmetic Reasoning subtest is more involved. You have to set up your own equations to solve the problem. That doesn't seem fair! Those crafty test makers are asking you not only to solve the problem but also to write the equation in the first place... It's almost as if they want to see how much you know so they can find you the right job!

Lots of people have difficulty with translating a word problem into a mathematical equation. If you're starting to sweat at the mere thought of math word problems, you're not alone. Just take a deep breath, relax, and don't worry. I'm here to guide you through the process.

Making Sense of Word Problems

The purpose of math word problems is to test your ability to use general mathematics to solve everyday, real-world problems. That's what all the textbooks say. However, in my "real world," I've never once wondered how old Anna is if she's three years older than Chuck, and in five years, her age and Chuck's age would equal 54. I'd just ask Anna how old she is. If she didn't answer, I wouldn't buy her a birthday present.

In all fairness, arithmetic reasoning can actually be quite helpful in sharpening your ability to figure out dimensions of spaces, construction information, travel time, and the probability of being late if you decide to go shopping at the Post Exchange before your important meeting with your First Sergeant. You may even want to understand how much interest you've acquired in your bank account, how much cash you have left over after lunch, and how much that badminton set really costs after you take 20 percent off.

When you realize that math word problems are designed to measure your ability to use basic math to solve *fictional* problems, they can be kind of fun — sort of like solving a puzzle.

Setting Up the Problem

Word problems are nothing more than a series of expressions that fit into an equation. An equation is a combination of math expressions. (If that sounds like Greek to you, check out Chapter 9.) The expressions in math word problems are generally stated in English. Your job is to dig out the relevant facts and state them in mathematical terms. You do so by

>> Getting organized

>> Understanding the problem

>> Identifying the information you need

>> Translating the problem into one or more solvable mathematic equations

I cover all these tasks in greater detail in the following sections.

Getting organized

Getting organized isn't really a step as much as it is a method. You need to be organized throughout the problem-solving process. Being organized helps you think clearly and ensures you don't get lost while trying to define and solve the problem.

TIP

When using your scratch paper, draw and label your pictures and graphs clearly. And be sure to mark your calculations with the question number. If you go back to your notes and can't remember what you were thinking about when you drew that picture, you'll be frustrated and will waste valuable time — and you don't have any time to waste on the Arithmetic Reasoning subtest. (For more on pictures, see the sidebar "A picture can be worth a thousand equations.")

Understanding the problem

Make sure you read the entire problem, but be careful: Don't try too hard to understand the problem on the first read-through. I know that doesn't seem to make any sense, but bear with me.

Math word problems can be broken down into two parts:

WARNING

>> **The problem statement:** The problem statement isn't really an object to be understood. It's simply a source of information you can use, as needed, to solve the equation.

The information included in the problem statement is often confusing or disorganized. Sometimes *distracters* (information that has nothing to do with solving the problem) are mixed in, leading to confusion and making the problem difficult to solve. (See the "Dealing with distracters" sidebar for more information.)

>> **The problem question:** The problem question is the meat of the matter. Exactly what is the questioner asking you to find? This part of the problem is the one you really need to understand.

A PICTURE CAN BE WORTH A THOUSAND EQUATIONS

When you walk in to take the ASVAB, the kindly test proctors are going to give you a piece of blank scratch paper. If you want more, they'll gladly give you more; they'll even give you more if you run out during the exam. Sure, the scratch sheet is handy for figuring out equations, but it's also useful for drawing diagrams and pictures to help you clarify the problem in your mind.

Sometimes, drawing a simple diagram can save you loads of time when you're trying to get a quick grasp on how to solve a math word problem. Here's one of my favorite examples:

A ladybug walks 5 inches directly south. She then turns and walks 10 inches directly east. If she then sprouts her wings and flies directly back to her starting point, how far will she have to fly?

This problem becomes instantly clear with a quick diagram on your scratch paper, like the sketch shown here.

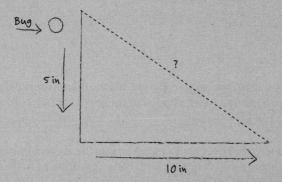

The crudely drawn diagram on your scratch paper makes it instantly clear that you need to find the length of the hypotenuse of a right triangle. If you read Chapter 9, you know that you can use the Pythagorean theorem $\left(a^2 + b^2 = c^2\right)$ to figure out this problem. Without that sketch, you may not realize how simple this problem really is.

Identifying the information you need

After you've separated the question from the statement (see the preceding section), list the facts in a clear, concise list. Identify exactly what the question is asking of you. Figure out what you need but don't have, and name things. Pick variables (a, b, x, and so on) to stand for the unknowns, clearly labeling these variables with what they stand for.

REMEMBER

Be as clear as possible when you identify the information you need. You don't want to spend five minutes on a word problem solving for x, only to reach the end and forget what x is supposed to stand for.

TIP

Pay particular attention to include units of measure, such as feet, miles, inches, pounds, dollars, and so on. One of the fastest ways to mess up on a math word problem is by forgetting the apples-and-oranges rule. You generally can't perform mathematical operations on different units of measurement. Ten apples plus ten oranges equals 20 pieces of fruit; it does *not* equal 20 apples, nor does it equal 20 oranges. Look at the following example:

A carpenter buys 44 feet of wood. If she adds the wood to the 720 inches of wood she already owns, how many feet of wood will she have?

DEALING WITH DISTRACTERS

If math word problems were all straightforward questions, such as "What is 10 multiplied by 10?" you could skip this chapter. However, the people on the Department of Defense's payroll who write the questions stay awake at night to think up ways to complicate things. The use of distracters is one such way.

A *distracter* is any piece of information included in the problem statement that has absolutely nothing to do with solving the problem. Consider the following example:

> In November, the National Weather Service recorded 1 inch of snow and 3 inches of rain in Grand Forks, North Dakota. In December, these numbers were reversed, with 3 inches of snow and only 1 inch of rain. How much snow did Grand Forks receive in total?

You don't need to know how much rain fell in Grand Forks to solve this problem. The amount of rain has absolutely nothing to do with the problem question. It's a distracter; its purpose is to distract you from focusing on the real question. The problem mentions rain, so it has to figure into the problem in some way, doesn't it? Wrong! Be sure to read the question carefully and ignore any information that's just there to trip you up.

If you add 44 to 720, you're going to get the wrong answer. Before you can add the numbers, you have to either convert 44 feet of wood to inches ($44 \cdot 12 = 528$ inches) or convert 720 inches to feet ($720 \div 12 = 60$ feet).

Make sure when you select your answer, it has the correct unit of measurement. Those tricky test writers often give several options with different units to make sure you're paying attention and can correctly identify what unit to use.

Translating the problem

Now you're at the tough part. The hardest thing about doing word problems is taking the English words and translating them into mathematics. Luckily, math word problems often contain certain *keywords* that can help.

Although the following keywords *often* indicate a mathematical operation in a word problem, that's not always the case. You have to use a little common sense. "A man was walking down the street" doesn't mean a division operation. "Matt and Paul were working *together*" doesn't necessarily mean you're going to perform addition regarding Matt and Paul.

Addition keywords

Several words and phrases used in math word problems indicate an addition operation:

>> Increased by

>> More than

>> Combined

>> Together

>> Total of

>> Sum

>> Added to

"The drill sergeant can do 100 pushups more than Private Jones can" is equivalent to Private Jones + 100 = drill sergeant. "Together, they can do 300 pushups" can be mathematically stated as drill sergeant + Private Jones = 300.

Try the following example, just to see if you're getting the hang of things:

EXAMPLE

The drill sergeant can do 100 pushups more than Private Jones. Together, they can do 300 pushups. How many pushups can Private Jones do?

The question is asking you how many pushups Private Jones can do. You're not really interested in how many the drill sergeant can do, and the problem statement tells you that they can do 300 pushups together. You also know that the drill sergeant can do 100 more than Private Jones.

List the important information:

>> Let j = the number of pushups that Private Jones can do. This figure is what you really want to find out, so you need to define it first.

>> Let d = the number of pushups that the drill sergeant can do. You don't really want to know this information, but it's a necessary fact in order to solve the problem.

>> You know another definition of d. The problem statement tells you that the drill sergeant can do 100 more pushups than Private Jones, which means that $d = j + 100$, which is the same (mathematically) as saying $j = d - 100$.

>> You know that together they can do 300 pushups, which tells you that $d + j = 300$.

All you need to do now is to solve that final equation in terms of j. First, subtract d from both sides to express the equation in terms of j: $d + j = 300$ is the same as $j = 300 - d$. (I cover algebraic properties in Chapter 9.)

You already have a definition for d from above $(d = j + 100)$. Substitute this value for d in the equation you're now working to solve:

$$j = 300 - d$$
$$j = 300 - (j + 100)$$
$$j = 300 - j - 100$$
$$2j = 200$$
$$j = 100$$

Private Jones can do 100 pushups.

TIP

As an alternative, you can also substitute "$j + 100$" for d in the equation $d + j = 100$. The answer will be the same.

Even if you can do this particular problem in your head (300 total – 100 more = 200, divide by two to get 100), try to avoid doing so. You want to get in the practice of setting up and solving equations for each question. Often, you'll stumble on a word problem that can be solved only by using an equation, and you want to be an expert at the proper procedures.

REMEMBER

Because math can be a tricky thing (I've been known to believe $2 + 2 = 3$ before my morning coffee), it's always a good idea to check your answer to make sure it makes sense. Plug your answer into the original problem and see whether it works out: The drill sergeant can do 100 pushups more than Private Jones: $100 + 100 = 200$. The drill sergeant can do 200 pushups. Together, they can do 300 pushups: $100 + 200 = 300$. Makes sense.

Subtraction keywords

If you see any of the following words and phrases in a math word problem, it generally indicates a subtraction operation:

» Decreased by

» Minus

» Less

» Difference between/of

» Less than

» Fewer than

"Becky's pay decreased by $10" can be stated mathematically as Becky – 10. This phrasing is also the same as "Becky's pay minus $10," or "Becky's pay, less $10."

"The difference between Bob's pay and Becky's pay" can be expressed as Bob – Becky.

WARNING

The *less than* and *fewer than* terms work backward in English from what they are in the math. Although "Becky's pay minus $10" is Becky – 10, "Becky's pay less than x" is *not* Becky – x; it's x – Becky.

Multiplication keywords

The following words and phrases usually mean a multiplication operation when included in a math word problem:

» Of

» Times

» Multiplied by

» Product of

» Increased/decreased by a factor of

"15 percent of x" is mathematically expressed as $x \cdot 0.15$. "x times y" and "x multiplied by y" mean $x \cdot y$. "The product of x and y" is the same as $x \cdot y$.

REMEMBER

Increased by a factor of and *decreased by a factor of* can involve addition and subtraction in combination with multiplication. "x increased by a factor of 10 percent" is expressed as $x + (x \cdot 0.10)$.

Division keywords

If you see the following words/phrases in a math word problem, "division operation" should pop into your mind:

» A

» Per

» Average

>> Ratio of

>> Quotient of

The first two terms in this list mean "divided by" — for example, "I bought 2 gallons of milk at the grocery store and paid $3, so milk was $1.50 a gallon," or "Milk was $1.50 per gallon."

To find the average of a group of numbers, you add the numbers and then divide by the number of terms. "The average of a, b, and c" is $(a+b+c) \div 3$.

Mathematically, *ratios* are expressed as fractions. A ratio of five to three is written as $\frac{5}{3}$, which is the same as saying $5 \div 3$. Chapter 9 has more detail about how to work with ratios.

The "quotient of x and y" is the same as $x \div y$.

Practicing keywords

Learning how to recognize keywords is essential in translating English into mathematical expressions. Try a few examples, just to see if you're getting the hang of it:

>> **Translate "the sum of 13 and y" into a math expression.** This phrase translates to $13 + y$. The keyword *sum* indicates an addition operation.

>> **How do you write "the quotient of a and 6" as an expression?** The keyword *quotient* means division, so this example translates to $a \div 6$.

>> **How do you write "7 less than y" as a mathematical expression?** It's $y - 7$. If you answered $7 - y$, you forgot that "less than" is backward in math from how it's used in English.

>> **Translate "the ratio of x plus 6 to 8" into an expression.** "x plus 6" is an addition operation, while the keyword *ratio* indicates division. This problem translates to $\frac{x+6}{8}$.

Are you ready to try a couple of longer ones? I knew you were!

>> **The length of a rectangle is 45 inches more than its width. Let the width = w; express the length in mathematical terms.** *More than* is a keyword that means addition. Because the width = w, you write the length mathematically as $w + 45$.

>> **Paul is three years older than Marsha, who is four times the age of Brian. Express Marsha's age as an algebraic expression.** You can express Paul's age, Marsha's age, and Brian's age with any variables you choose, but using the first letters of their names just makes sense. That way, you have less chance of forgetting what variable stands for what. "Four *times*" indicates multiplication. Marsha's age can be written as $4 \cdot b$, or $4b$. Paul's age can be expressed as $m + 3$, so Marsha's age can also be written as $p - 3$.

Confused? Check out Chapter 9 for the properties of algebraic equations.

Trying Out Typical Word Problems

When you can recognize common keywords and translate them into mathematical expressions as I describe earlier in the chapter, you're ready to take on a few math word problems.

Because math word problems generally represent fictional real-life situations, the test writers can theoretically come up with an infinite number of possible problems. However, math word problem test writers must have limited imaginations because certain types of questions seem to pop up more often than others. This observation is true whether you're taking the SAT or the Arithmetic Reasoning subtest of the ASVAB.

Age problems

Age problems involve figuring out how old someone is, was, or will be. You generally solve them by comparing someone's age to the ages of other people.

Sometimes you can solve an age problem by using a one-variable solution, and sometimes it takes several variables. In the following sections, I show you how to solve the same problem by using either a one-variable solution or a two-variable solution.

One-variable solution

EXAMPLE

Sid is twice as old as Mary. In three years, the sum of their ages will be 66. How old are they now?

Let Mary's age = x. Because Sid is twice as old as Mary, his age can be represented as $2x$.

In three years, Mary's age will be $x + 3$, and Sid's age will be $2x + 3$. The sum of their ages will be 66.

You now have an equation you can work with:

$$(x+3)+(2x+3)=66$$
$$3x+6=66$$
$$3x=60$$
$$x=\frac{60}{3}$$
$$x=20$$

REMEMBER

What did x stand for again? Was it Mary's age or Sid's age? Be sure to clearly label variables on your scratch paper so you don't get frustrated and tear your hair out in front of everyone else. That causes talk.

The x represents Mary's age, so Mary is 20 years old. Because Sid is twice Mary's age, Sid is 40 $(2 \cdot 20 = 40)$.

REMEMBER

If you have time, check your answer to see that it makes sense: Sid (age 40) is twice as old as Mary (age 20). In three years, the sum of their ages will be $(40+3)+(20+3)=43+23=66$. It fits! Isn't math fun?

Two-variable solution

EXAMPLE

Sid is twice as old as Mary. In three years, the sum of their ages will be 66. How old are they now?

Let m = Mary's age and s = Sid's age. You know that Sid is twice as old as Mary, so $s = 2m$. That gives you your first equation.

You also know that in three years, the sum of their ages will be 66. Stated mathematically:

$$(m+3)+(s+3)=66$$

You can simplify this equation:

$$m + s + 6 = 66$$
$$m + s = 60$$

You now have two equations with two variables that you can use to solve the problem:

$$s = 2m$$
$$m + s = 60$$

Replace s in the second equation with the definition of s in the first equation:

$$m + 2m = 60$$
$$3m = 60$$
$$m = \frac{60}{3}$$
$$m = 20$$

Mary is 20 years old. That's the same answer you get when you use the one-variable solution in the preceding section.

Geometric problems

These problems require you to compute the volume, perimeter, area, circumference, diameter, and so on of various geometric shapes.

EXAMPLE

You're painting a fence that is 20 feet long and 6 feet high. How much square footage of fence are you covering with paint?

The area formula for a rectangle is $A = lw$, where l is length and w is width, so the answer to this simple problem is $A = 6 \cdot 20 = 120$ square feet.

Generally, the Arithmetic Reasoning test makers don't let you off so easy, though. The problem is more likely to be written something like the following.

EXAMPLE

You're painting a fence that is 20 feet long and 6 feet high. Paint costs $20 per gallon, and 1 gallon of paint covers 60 square feet of fence. How much do you need to spend on paint to complete the project?

The problem now requires a couple of extra steps to answer. First, you have to compute the area of the fence. You already did that: 120 square feet.

Now you have to determine how many gallons of paint you need to buy to cover 120 square feet. Because 1 gallon of paint covers 60 square feet, you need $120 \div 60 = 2$ gallons of paint.

Finally, you need to figure how much 2 gallons of paint cost. Paint is $20 per gallon, and you need 2 gallons, so $20 \cdot 2 = \$40$.

TIP

You get quite a few geometric problems on the Arithmetic Reasoning subtest. To make sure you're ready for them, memorize the basic geometric formulas in Table 11-1.

TABLE 11-1 **Basic Geometric Formulas**

Shape	Function	Formula
Square	Area	$A = s^2$
	Perimeter	$P = 4s$
	Diagonal	$d = s\sqrt{2}$
Rectangle	Area	$A = lw$
	Perimeter	$P = 2l + 2w$
	Diagonal	$d = \sqrt{l^2 + w^2}$
Triangle	Perimeter	$P = s_1 + s_2 + s_3$
	Area	$A = \frac{1}{2}bh$
Right Triangle	Pythagorean theorem	$a^2 + b^2 = c^2$
Circle	Radius	$r = \frac{d}{2}$
	Diameter	$d = 2r$
	Circumference	$C = 2\pi r$
	Area	$A = \pi r^2$
Cube	Volume	$V = s^3$
	Surface Area	$SA = 6s^2$
Rectangular Box	Volume	$V = lwh$
	Surface Area	$SA = 2lw + 2wh + 2lh$
Cylinder	Volume	$V = \pi r^2 h$

TIP

Because many of these formulas relate to each other, remembering (or re-creating) them might be easier if you connect them. Remember:

» Drawing a diagonal through a square or rectangle creates two right triangles, which means the diagonal formulas are just the Pythagorean theorem solved for the hypotenuse.

» The volume formulas are the area of a base shape (a rectangle or circle) times the height.

» Surface area formulas for boxes and cubes are based on the area of a rectangle — it's just that you're working with six rectangles instead of one.

You can find more information about using all these formulas in Chapter 9.

Coin problems

I think mathematicians must have big piggy banks. Many math word problems ask you to figure out how many coins of various types a person has.

EXAMPLE

Jeremy has 12 more nickels than quarters. How many coins does he have if the total value of his coins is $2.70?

Let q = quarters. Because Jeremy has 12 more nickels than quarters, you can represent the number of nickels as $q + 12$. Jeremy has \$2.70 worth of coins, which is equal to 270¢. A quarter is 25¢, and a nickel is 5¢. Jeremy's total coins together must equal 270¢. Therefore,

$$(25¢ \cdot \text{number of quarters}) + (5¢ \cdot \text{number of nickels}) = 270¢$$

Or, writing it another way:

$$25q + 5(q + 12) = 270$$
$$25q + 5q + 60 = 270$$
$$30q = 210$$
$$q = \frac{210}{30}$$
$$q = 7$$

Jeremy has 7 quarters. Because he has 12 more nickels than quarters, he has $7 + 12 = 19$ nickels, for a total of $19 + 7 = 26$ coins.

Does this answer make sense? Always remember to check your answer. Jeremy has 12 more nickels (19 nickels) than quarters (7 quarters). How much money does he have? 19 nickels = 95¢ and 7 quarters = 175¢, so 95¢ + 175¢ = 270¢ = \$2.70. It looks good to me.

Travel problems

I wish I could travel as much as word problem test writers seem to. They come up with a lot of travel problems. They especially seem to like trains and planes.

Travel problems involve using the distance formula, $d = rt$, where d is the distance, r is the rate, and t is the time. Generally, the problems come in three basic types: traveling away from each other, traveling in the same direction, and traveling at 90-degree angles.

Traveling away from each other

When two planes (or trains, cars, people, or even bugs) travel in opposite directions, they increase the distance between them in direct proportion. To solve these types of problems, you compute the distance traveled from the starting point for each plane (or train, car, person, or bug).

EXAMPLE

Train A travels north at 60 mph. Train B travels south at 70 mph. If both trains leave the station at the same time, how far apart will they be at the end of two hours?

To solve this problem, you compute the distance traveled by train A and then the distance traveled by train B and add the results together.

The distance formula is $d = rt$. The rate of travel for train A is 60 mph, and it travels for two hours:

$$d = 60 \times 2$$
$$d = 120$$

Train A travels 120 miles during the two-hour period.

WARNING

When using the distance formula, you have to pay attention to the units of measurement. Remember the apples-and-oranges rule (see "Identifying the information you need" earlier in this chapter). If rate (r) is expressed in kilometers per hour, your result (d) will be kilometers. If rate (r) is expressed as miles per second, you must either convert it to mph or convert time (t) to seconds.

YOU KNOW WHAT THEY SAY ABOUT ASSUMING . . .

Math word problems require you to make basic assumptions. In the train problem in the section "Traveling away from each other," you're to assume that both trains travel at a constant rate of speed. You're supposed to ignore the fact that they may slow down for a curve, or that they'll probably need a little time to get up to cruising speed.

If a question gives you the average daily output of a factory and asks you what the output will be in a year, you're supposed to assume that the year is 365 days long.

If you're asked how high the kite is flying 300 feet away from you, you must assume that the ground is perfectly level.

If . . . well, you get the point.

The rate of travel for train B is 70 mph, and it also travels for two hours:

$$d = 70 \times 2$$
$$d = 140$$

Train B travels 140 miles during the two-hour period.

Train A is 120 miles from the station and train B is 140 miles from the station, in the opposite direction. The two trains are $120 + 140 = 260$ miles apart.

Traveling in the same direction

If two trains are traveling in the same direction but at different rates of speed, one train travels farther in the same time than the other travels. The distance between the two trains is the difference between the distance traveled by train A and the distance traveled by train B.

EXAMPLE

Train A travels north at 60 mph. Train B also travels north, on a parallel track, at 70 mph. If both trains leave the station at the same time, how far apart will they be at the end of two hours?

Train A traveled 120 miles, and train B traveled 140 miles. (If you're wondering why I didn't show my work here, check out the calculations in the preceding section.) Because they're traveling in the same direction, you subtract to find the distance between them: $140 - 120 = 20$. The two trains are 20 miles apart.

Traveling at 90-degree angles

Some travel problems involve two people or things moving at 90-degree angles and then stopping; the problem then asks you what the distance is (as the crow flies) between the two people or things, which means you need to use the distance formula and a little basic geometry.

EXAMPLE

Train A travels north at 60 mph. Train B travels east at 70 mph. Both trains travel for two hours. Then a bee flies from Train A and lands on Train B. Assuming the bee flew in a straight line, how far did the bee travel between the two trains?

Train A travels 120 miles, and Train B travels a distance of 140 miles. (Head to the earlier section "Traveling away from each other" for the math that gets you those distances.)

Because the trains are traveling at 90-degree angles (one north and one east), the lines of travel form two sides of a right triangle. Figure 11-1 should make this setup easy to visualize.

The Pythagorean theorem says that if you know the length of two sides of a right triangle, you can find the length of the third side by using the formula $a^2 + b^2 = c^2$, where c is the longest side:

$$120^2 + 140^2 = c^2$$
$$14,400 + 19,600 = c^2$$
$$c = \sqrt{34,000}$$
$$c = 184.39$$

The bee flies 184.39 miles.

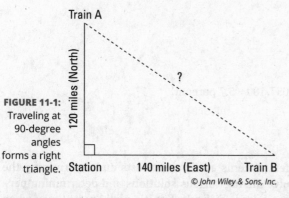

FIGURE 11-1: Traveling at 90-degree angles forms a right triangle.

TIP

Finding the square root of a very large number can be a daunting task, especially because you don't have a calculator available during the ASVAB. When you reach this point of the equation, just squaring the possible answers to see which one works is often easier.

Investment/loan problems

These problems are primarily focused on simple interest rates for investments and loans, using the formula $I = prt$, where I is the interest, p is the principal, r is the rate of interest, and t is the time.

The investment/loan problems you see on the Arithmetic Reasoning subtest are pretty simple. They're nowhere near as difficult as similar situations in real life, where interest is compounded.

To solve these problems, replace what's known in the interest formula and then solve for anything else.

EXAMPLE

John invests $1,500 for three years at an annual interest rate of 7 percent. How much will John have at the end of the three-year period?

Plug the known information into the interest formula, $I = prt$:

$$I = \$1,500 \times 0.07 \times 3$$
$$I = \$315$$

REMEMBER

Percent means "part of 100." To convert percentage into a decimal, divide the percentage by 100. That means 7 percent equals $\frac{7}{100}$ and 0.07. To convert a decimal into percentage, multiply by 100. You get $0.07 = 0.07 \cdot 100 = 7$ percent. (Flip to Chapter 9 for more information about working with percentages and decimals.)

John will make $315 in interest. Adding this amount to his original investment of $1,500 tells you that John will have a total of $1,500 + $315 = $1,815.

That was pretty easy, so let me throw another one at you.

EXAMPLE

You invest $700, and after five years you receive a total of $900. What was the annual interest rate?

On the surface, this one looks a bit more complicated, but you solve it the same way: Plug what's known into the interest formula, $I = prt$, and solve for the rest.

You invested $700 and received $900. Therefore, you made $900 − $700 = $200 in interest.

$$\$200 = \$700 \times r \times 5$$
$$\$200 = \$3,500r$$
$$r = \frac{\$200}{\$3,500}$$
$$r = 0.057$$

Expressed as a percentage, this amount is $0.057 \cdot 100 = 5.7$ percent.

Mixture problems

Mixture problems often involve mixing different items at different costs and determining the final cost of the mixture. They can also involve mixing various solutions and determining percentages of the solution mixture. This concept sounds difficult, but it's really pretty easy when you know how. Are you ready to try a couple of problems?

EXAMPLE

How many quarts of a 70-percent alcohol solution must be added to 50 quarts of a 40-percent alcohol solution to produce a 50-percent alcohol solution?

Let $x =$ the number of quarts of 70-percent solution needed. The amount of alcohol contained in x quarts of the 70-percent solution is represented by $0.7x$. (I explain how to convert a percentage into a decimal in the preceding section.)

You have 50 quarts of the 40-percent solution, so the amount of alcohol contained in those 50 quarts is represented by $50 \cdot 0.4 = 20$ quarts.

The total number of quarts of solution can be represented as $50 + x$ (the number of quarts of 40-percent solution plus the unknown number of quarts of 70-percent solution). Half (50 percent) of that solution will be alcohol, so $0.5(50 + x)$.

Maybe Table 11-2 can make this scenario a bit clearer:

TABLE 11-2 **Alcohol Mixtures**

	Quarts of Solution	Percent Alcohol (as Decimal)	Total Quarts of Alcohol
70% solution	x	0.7	$0.7x$
40% solution	50	0.4	$0.4(50) = 20$
50% solution	$50 + x$	0.5	$0.5(50 + x)$

The fourth column of the table gives you your equation: $0.7x + 20 = 0.5(50 + x)$. First, distribute the 0.5 to the terms in parentheses. Then work the equation as follows:

$$0.7x + 20 = 25 + 0.5x$$
$$0.7x = 5 + 0.5x$$
$$0.7x - 0.5x = 5$$
$$0.2x = 5$$
$$x = \frac{5}{0.2}$$
$$x = 25$$

The final mixture will require 25 quarts of 70-percent solution.

EXAMPLE

A grocery store wants to offer a mixture of green and red grapes to sell for $4.20 per pound. If green grapes cost $3 per pound and red grapes retail for $6 per pound, how many pounds of red grapes should the grocer add to 12 pounds of green grapes to produce the desired mixture?

Let x = the pounds of red grapes. The total amount of grapes will be the pounds of green grapes (12) plus the unknown pounds of red grapes (x), or $12 + x$. The total cost of green grapes at $3 per pound is $12 \cdot \$3 = \$36$.

Red grapes sell for $6 per pound, so their total cost is represented as $6x$.

The total cost of the mixture is to be $4.20 per pound, so you can represent it as $4.2(12 + x)$.

Table 11-2 worked so well for the last problem that I want to use one again. Check out Table 11-3.

TABLE 11-3 **Grape Mixtures**

Type	Cost per Pound	Pounds	Total Cost
Green	$3	12	$3·12 = $36
Red	$6	x	$6x$
Mixture	$4.20	$12 + x$	$4.20(12 + x)$

Again, the last column gives you your equation: $36 + 6x = 4.2(12 + x)$. First, distribute the 4.2 to the terms in parentheses. Then work the equation as follows:

$$36 + 6x = 50.4 + 4.2x$$
$$6x - 4.2x = 50.4 - 36$$
$$1.8x = 14.4$$
$$x = \frac{14.4}{1.8}$$
$$x = 8$$

The mixture will require 8 pounds of red grapes.

Percent problems

Percent problems involve working with percentages, such as discount savings, pay raises, and so on. You often see them on the Arithmetic Reasoning subtest. They're relatively simple to solve.

EXAMPLE

Leroy makes $8.95 per hour. He's such a good worker that his boss gives him a 25 percent raise. How much per hour does Leroy make now?

To find the dollar amount of the raise, multiply Leroy's previous salary by the decimal equivalent of 25 percent: $8.95 \cdot 0.25 = 2.237$. Round this number up to $2.24, just to make Leroy smile. (You can read about rounding decimals in Chapter 9.) Now add the raise to Leroy's original salary: $8.95 + $2.24 = $11.19.

EXAMPLE

Katie is very excited. For only $45, she bought a set of towels that usually sells for $60. What was the percentage of her discount?

Divide the new price by the original price: $45 \div 60 = 0.75$. The new price is 75 percent of the original price, which means Katie's discount was 25 percent.

Work problems

These problems involve two or more people or things working together. You're expected to figure out how long they'll take to complete a task together.

EXAMPLE

Patrick can build a wall in five hours. Dennis can build the same wall in seven hours. How long will they take to build the wall together?

TIP

You can use a general formula to solve such work problems. It's $\frac{a \times b}{a + b}$, where a is the time the first person or thing takes to do the job and b is the time it takes the second person or thing to do the job.

Patrick needs five hours to build the wall, and Dennis seven hours. Plugging the data into the work formula gets you the following:

$$\frac{5 \times 7}{5 + 7} = \frac{35}{12} = 2\frac{11}{12}$$

It will take them $2\frac{11}{12}$ hours to build the wall together.

Wasn't that fun? I bet you're eager to try another one.

EXAMPLE

One hose can fill an aboveground pool in three hours. Another hose will fill it in six hours. How long will filling the pool take using both hoses?

Just plug the numbers into your handy-dandy work equation:

$$\frac{3 \times 6}{3 + 6} = \frac{18}{9} = 2$$

It will take two hours to fill the pool when using both hoses.

Number problems

Number problems are pretty straightforward. The questions ask you to manipulate numbers with basic addition, subtraction, multiplication, or division. Most people find these types of word problems to be pretty easy.

Do you want to try a few, just to get your feet wet? Sure you do.

EXAMPLE

Jesse is a bartender at a local pub. On Friday, he made $27.40 in tips; on Saturday, he made $34.70 in tips; and on Sunday, he made $7 less than he made on Friday. How much did Jesse earn in tips during the three days?

See what I mean? Pretty straightforward. Jesse made $27.40 + $34.70 + ($27.40 − $7) = $82.50 in tips.

EXAMPLE

Rob "Speedy Gonzalez" Barton ran 1.5 miles in 9:57. The next day, he ran it in 10:02. On the third day, he ran it in 10:07. What is his average time for the 1.5-mile run?

First, convert all the times into seconds, just to make the math a little easier:

$$9:57 = (9 \cdot 60) + 57 = 597 \text{ seconds}$$
$$10:02 = (10 \cdot 60) + 2 = 602 \text{ seconds}$$
$$10:07 = (10 \cdot 60) + 7 = 607 \text{ seconds}$$

Add the seconds together: $597 + 602 + 607 = 1,806$ seconds. Now, divide by the number of times Rob ran the 1.5-mile run (three times) to discover that his average speed is $1,806 \div 3 = 602$ seconds. Finally, convert the seconds to minutes by dividing by 60: $602 \div 60 = 10$ minutes, with 2 seconds left over. Rob's average time for the 1.5-mile run is 10:02.

EXAMPLE

The sum of two consecutive odd positive numbers is 112. What are the numbers?

As I note in the "Addition keywords" section earlier in this chapter, *sum* means addition. Let $n =$ the first number. That means that $n + 2 =$ the second number (because they're consecutive *odd* numbers). Here's your equation:

$$n + (n + 2) = 112$$

Solve for *n*:

$$2n + 2 = 112$$
$$2n = 110$$
$$n = \frac{110}{2}$$
$$n = 55$$

The first number is 55. The second number is $55 + 2 = 57$.

Practical Mathematicals: Arithmetic Reasoning Exercises

Just like your physical fitness level will inch up the more you conduct PT (that's short for *physical training*) with your fellow service members, you'll get better at solving word problems with more practice. Use these exercises to gauge your performance and figure out where you need to break more of a mental sweat. The answers to each practice exercise are at the end of this chapter, so head there when you're finished with each activity to check your work.

Fact-finding to figure out which formulas to use

Way back in Chapter 7, I mention that some of the ASVAB's Paragraph Comprehension questions require you to go into a passage and pull out facts. Just add math, and you have Arithmetic Reasoning questions. You'll have to figure out what problem the question is asking you to solve and then determine which formula you need to solve it. (There's more on specific formulas in Chapter 9.) Read the sentences in Activity 1 and, in the column next to the problem, write which formula(s) you'll need to solve a problem with that type of sentence in it. When you're done, check out the "Answers and Explanations" section at the end of this chapter to see how many you got right.

ACTIVITY 1 **Fact-Finding**

Problem	Required Formula
1. Two people are traveling in opposite directions.	
2. Find the area of a rectangle with dimensions of *x* by *y*.	
3. The diameter of a circle is *x*. Find its area.	
4. Someone invested *x* for *y* years and receives *z* percent in interest.	
5. Two people worked together to do something.	
6. Find the area of a triangle with sides measuring *x* and *y*.	
7. Find the circumference of a circle with a radius of *x*.	
8. Find the length of a side of a right triangle.	
9. Find the volume of a swimming pool with sides of *x* and *y* and a depth of *z*.	
10. Find the perimeter of a yard that is *x* feet long and *y* feet wide.	

Real-world formula problems

In Activity 1, you determined which formulas to use for specific types of problems. In Activity 2, you do something similar — but this time, you match the appropriate formula to the word problem provided. (Save your actual problem–solving for Chapter 13, where you'll take your first ASVAB practice test.) When you're finished, check the "Answers and Explanations" section at the end of this chapter.

ACTIVITY 2 **Applying Formulas to Problems**

Answer	Question	Formula
1.	A circular swimming pool measures 15 feet across. What is its circumference?	A. $I = prt$
2.	Mary and Shelley are filling the swimming pool for Frank. It takes Shelley 5 hours to fill the pool alone, and it takes Mary 8 hours. How long will it take them together?	B. $t = \dfrac{d}{r}$
3.	Two dogs, Tonka and Cujo, are running north and east, respectively. Cujo runs 15 miles, while Tonka runs 13 miles. When they're done, another dog, Achilles, runs in a straight line from Cujo to Tonka. How far did Achilles travel between the two dogs?	C. $V = s^3$
4.	Abigail and Matthew invest $2,500 for four years at an annual interest rate of 3.5 percent. How much will they have at the end of four years?	D. $\dfrac{a \times b}{a + b}$
5.	A gift box measures 12 inches across on each side, and it's 14 inches deep. What is the gift box's volume?	E. $A = \frac{1}{2}bh$
6.	You're painting a wall that's 11 feet high and 13 feet long. How many square feet will you paint?	F. $P = 2l + 2w$
7.	A man traveled 86 miles at a speed of 7 miles per hour. How long did it take him?	G. $C = 2\pi r$
8.	A woman is ordering prefabricated fencing for her yard, which is 45 feet long and 38 feet wide. How many feet of fencing should she order?	H. $A = lw$
9.	Three people put their money together and bought a square safe. One side of the safe is 13 inches long, and it's an inch thick all around. How much room is left inside the safe?	I. $V = lwh$
10.	You want to pass a triangle-shaped note in math class, but you know your eagle-eyed teacher can see notes that have an area of more than 4 square inches. Is a triangle-shaped piece of paper with a 3.5-inch base and a height of 2.5 inches small enough to pass in class?	J. $a^2 + b^2 = c^2$

Putting together tables to make calculations easier

In many cases, sketching a table to help you solve a problem can be a huge help — especially when you're pressed for time (check out "Mixture problems" earlier in this chapter for a little more guidance). Creating a table can give you the equation you need to solve the problem, so use Activity 3 to practice drawing your own table and coming up with an equation that solves the problem. When you're done (or if you're not sure what to do next), flip to the "Answers and Explanations" section at the end of this chapter.

ACTIVITY 3 Creating Tables

Question	Your Table	Your Equation
1. A man needs to add a 70-percent alcohol solution to 30 gallons of a 20-percent alcohol solution to create a 50-percent alcohol solution. How many quarts of the 70 percent alcohol solution does he need?		
2. A candy shop is selling a combination of caramels and chocolate-covered pretzels for $5 per pound. Caramels cost $4 per pound, and chocolate-covered pretzels cost $6 per pound. How many pounds of pretzels should the shopkeeper add to 10 pounds of caramel to produce the right mixture?		
3. A pilot in the D.C. National Guard flew 600 nautical miles. For the first part of the 7-hour trip, he flew at 150 knots. For the last part of the trip, he flew at 130 knots. How long did he fly the helicopter at each speed?		
4. How many pounds of carrots that cost $0.80 per pound must be mixed with 8 pounds of celery, which costs $1.25 per pound, to create a mixture that costs $1 per pound?		
5. A river flows at about 2 miles per hour. A motorboat can travel 15 miles down the river (with the current) in the same amount of time it takes to travel 10 miles up the river (against the current). How fast is the boat in still water?		

Answers and Explanations

After you've completed the exercises, check your answers here. If you don't quite grasp the concepts you need for the Arithmetic Reasoning subtest, go back to the appropriate sections earlier in this chapter to brush up on them.

Activity 1: Fact-Finding

1. Travel problems require you to use the distance formula, which is $d = rt$, where d represents distance, r represents rate (speed), and t represents time. You can also use variations of the formula to find speed and time; just isolate the variable you need. (For example, you can find speed if you know distance and time by using the formula $r = \frac{d}{t}$, and you can find time when you know distance and speed by using the formula $t = \frac{d}{r}$.)

2. The formula for the area of a rectangle is $A = lw$, where A represents area, l represents length, and w represents width.

3. The formula for the area of a circle is $A = \pi r^2$, where A represents area and r represents radius. (Remember, a circle's radius is half its diameter, and pi is about equal to 3.14.)

4. You can figure out this type of simple-interest problem using the formula $I = prt$, where I represents interest, p represents principal, r represents the interest rate, and t represents time. (You can figure out principal with the formula $p = \frac{I}{rt}$, the interest rate with the formula $r = \frac{I}{pt}$, and the amount of time for the investment with the formula $t = \frac{I}{pr}$.)

5. Work problems are best solved with the formula $\frac{a \times b}{a + b}$, where a represents one person's work and b represents the other person's work.

6. The formula to find the area of a triangle is $A = \frac{1}{2}bh$, where A represents area, b represents the length of the base, and h represents the triangle's height.

7. If you know a circle's radius or diameter (radius is half of the diameter), you can find a circle's circumference (the distance all the way around the outside) using the formula $C = 2\pi r$, where C represents circumference and r represents the circle's radius.

8. You have to find the length of a side of a right triangle in problems that ask you to determine the distance between two objects traveling at a 90-degree angle, which means you need the Pythagorean theorem. It's $a^2 + b^2 = c^2$. In the Pythagorean theorem, a and b represent the lengths of the triangle's legs (the two sides that form a right angle), and c represents its hypotenuse.

9. The formula to find the volume of a box (or rectangular prism) is $V = lwh$, where V represents volume, l represents length, and h represents height. You can also find the volume of a cube, in which all the sides are equal, by using the formula $V = s^3$, where V still represents volume and s represents the length of one side.

10. The formula to find the perimeter of a rectangle is $P = 2l + 2w$, where P represents perimeter, l represents length, and w represents width. If you're dealing with a square, the formula is just $P = 4s$, where P represents perimeter and s represents the length of one of its sides.

Activity 2: Applying Formulas to Problems

1. **G.** The problem asks you to find the circumference of a circle, and the formula for that is $C = 2\pi r$, where C represents circumference and r represents the circle's radius. Remember, the radius of a circle is half its diameter.

2. **D.** The formula to solve a work problem that asks you how long it will take two people together to accomplish a task is $\frac{a \times b}{a + b}$.

3. **J.** Because this problem deals with a right triangle (the two dogs are running north and east, which forms a right angle, and the third dog travels from one dog to the other), you can use the Pythagorean theorem, which is $a^2 + b^2 = c^2$, to solve it. First, you have to figure out how far each dog got while running for 30 minutes. When you've done that, you can use the Pythagorean theorem to get an answer (and tell the dogs' owners to start using leashes). In this formula, a and b represent Tonka's and Cujo's distances.

4. **A.** Investment and loan problems can typically be solved with the interest formula, which is $I = prt$. I stands for interest, p represents the principal, r represents the interest rate, and t represents the amount of time you're evaluating.

5. **I.** You need to find the volume of a rectangular prism (or box), and the formula for that is $V = lwh$, where V represents volume, l represents length, w represents width, and h represents height.

6. **H.** When a problem asks you, "How many square feet...," it's looking for an area. The formula for the area of a rectangle is $A = lw$, where A represents area, l represents length, and w represents width.

7. **B.** Modify the distance formula so you can figure out how long it took the man to travel 86 miles at 7 miles per hour; you use $t = \frac{d}{r}$, where t represents time, d represents distance, and r represents rate (or speed).

8. **F.** The problem asks you to find the perimeter of a rectangle, and the formula for that is $P = 2l + 2w$, where P represents perimeter, l represents length, and w represents width.

9. **C.** In this problem, you need to use the formula for the volume of a cube, which is $V = s^3$, where V represents volume and s represents the length of a side.

10. **E.** If you want to sneak the note past the teacher, you need to figure out the area of a triangle. The formula for that is $A = \frac{1}{2}bh$, where A represents area, b represents the length of the base, and h represents the triangle's height. (For the record, the triangle-shaped note in the problem would've gotten you detention.)

Activity 3: Creating Tables

1. Your table should look like this:

	Gallons of Solution	Percent of Alcohol	Total Gallons of Alcohol Solution
70% solution	x	0.7	$0.7x$
20% solution	30	0.3	$0.3(50) = 15$
50% solution	$50 + x$	0.5	$0.5(50 + x)$

The table tells you that your equation will be $0.7x + 15 = 0.5(50 + x)$.

2. Your table should look like this:

Candy Type	Cost per Pound	Pounds	Total Cost
Caramels	$4	10	$4 \times 10 = 40$
Pretzels	$6	x	$6x$
Mixture	$5	$10 + x$	$5(10 + x)$

Your table tells you your equation should be $40 + 6x = 5(10 + x)$.

3. Your table should look like this:

	Distance	Rate	Time
First part of trip	d	150	t
Last part of trip	$600 - d$	130	$7 - t$
Total	600		7

The table tells you that, using the distance formula $(d = rt)$ — where d represents distance, r represents rate (speed), and t represents time — your equation will look like this: $600 - d = 130(7 - t)$.

4. Your table should look like this:

	Total Cost	Price per Pound	Amount in Pounds
Carrots	$0.8x$	$0.80	x
Celery	10	$1.25	8
Mixture	$x + 8$	$1.00	$x + 8$

Based on what's in the table, your equation should be $0.8x + 10 = x + 8$.

5. Your table should look like this:

	Distance	Rate	Time
Downriver	15	$x + 2$	$\dfrac{15}{x + 2}$
Upriver	10	$x - 2$	$\dfrac{9}{x - 2}$

The table shows you that your equation to find the boat's speed should be $\dfrac{15}{x + 2} = \dfrac{9}{x - 2}$.

Chapter **12**

The Arithmetic Reasoning Subtest

The ASVAB has two math subtests — Mathematics Knowledge and Arithmetic Reasoning — and both are used for computing your AFQT score. Of the two, the Arithmetic Reasoning subtest may be considered the more difficult for most people (probably because you first have to decide what the problem is before you can solve it).

Among other things, math word problems measure your reasoning skills. That's why the military services put so much emphasis on this particular subtest. They want recruits who can figure things out — recruits who can solve problems.

REMEMBER

If you're starting to get nervous, don't. You've been doing arithmetic word problems since the third grade. Sure, they're a little more difficult now than when Mrs. Grundy was telling you that you had three apples and gave one to Tammy, but the fact is, this material isn't new for you. You've done it before. The military is just asking you to do it again, that's all.

I'm here to help you get ready. In this chapter, I tell you what you can expect on the Arithmetic Reasoning subtest, give you a few methods that may help improve your score and get you through those rough spots, and then — just for fun — toss a few practice questions at you. For help on the Mathematics Knowledge subtest, check out Chapters 9 and 10.

Looking at the Test Structure

The Arithmetic Reasoning subtest is the second subtest on the ASVAB, right after the General Science subtest. Therefore, it's the first subtest you encounter on the ASVAB that affects your AFQT score.

The Arithmetic Reasoning subtest asks you to read a word problem, determine what the question is asking, solve the problem with mathematics, and select the correct answer. (Then you have to repeat the process numerous times.) Most of the problems look like this:

EXAMPLE

Jane walks 5 miles to work each morning and 5 miles home each evening. How many miles does Jane walk in a day?

(A) 6 miles

(B) 8 miles

(C) 7 miles

(D) 10 miles

I hope you picked Choice (D), 10 miles! That was an easy question just to get you warmed up. Unfortunately, the questions the military writes are a bit tougher.

You have 39 minutes to answer 16 questions for the CAT-ASVAB (computerized version); if you happen to take the paper test, you must answer 30 questions in 36 minutes (makes sense, doesn't it?).

You see a mixture of hard questions, medium questions, and easy questions on this subtest. The hard ones are worth more points than the medium ones, which are worth more points than the easy ones. If you're taking the CAT-ASVAB (see Chapter 2), the computer automatically selects the question difficulty based on how you answered the preceding question. If you're really good at math word problems, you may only see hard questions!

The test administrator supplies you with scratch paper so you can work out some of the problems on paper, if necessary. The people who make up the rules don't allow recruits (or anyone else) to use calculators on the ASVAB. All you're allowed is your brain, your trusty No. 2 pencil, and a piece of scratch paper. If you're lucky, they may let you sneak in your thinking cap.

Developing a Test Strategy

The U.S. military doesn't win wars without a strategy, and you should have a set strategy for conquering the Arithmetic Reasoning subtest. A strategy is more than "I'll try to solve all the problems quickly and correctly." That works fine if everything goes right and you know how to solve the questions instantly when you see them, but the test probably won't go that way. Your strategy needs to include plans to keep things going smoothly, as well as ideas of what to do if things start going wrong.

Keeping track of the time

This chapter is supposed to be about the Arithmetic Reasoning subtest, so I think it's time for a practice question. Ready?

EXAMPLE

You have to take a math test consisting of 30 multiple-choice questions. You have 36 minutes to complete the test. How much time do you have for each question?

(A) 1 minute, 12 seconds

(B) 90 seconds

(C) 1 minute

(D) 1 minute, 20 seconds

First, convert the minutes to seconds so you don't have to deal with fractions or decimals: $36 \times 60 = 2,160$ seconds. Now, divide the total number of seconds by the number of test questions: $2,160 \div 30 = 72$ seconds. You have 72 seconds, or Choice (A), 1 minute and 12 seconds, to complete each question.

You can take a different approach by simplifying the problem before you start to solve it, too. Look at it this way: You know you have more than a minute for each question, because there are more minutes than there are questions (if you had less than a minute, there would be more questions than there are minutes). If 30 questions take at least 30 minutes, you can divide the remaining 6 minutes you have (remember, you get 36 minutes to complete the test) among the 30 questions:

$$\frac{360 \text{ seconds}}{30 \text{ questions}} = \frac{36 \text{ seconds}}{3 \text{ questions}} = 12 \text{ seconds per question}$$

Add the 12 seconds per question to the 1 minute you knew you had when you started. You still have 1 minute, 12 seconds to answer each question.

You can also leave the time in minutes until the end of the problem by creating a ratio and reducing it:

$$\frac{36 \text{ minutes}}{30 \text{ questions}} = \frac{6 \text{ minutes}}{5 \text{ questions}} = 1.2 \text{ minutes per question}$$

Now convert the 0.2 minutes to seconds:

$$0.2 \text{ minutes} = (0.2)(60 \text{ seconds}) = 12 \text{ seconds}$$

No matter which way you solve it, you still get a minute and 12 seconds to solve each problem.

That's not much time, considering that you have to read the question, determine what it's asking, translate the problem into mathematical equations, solve those equations, and then answer the question — and, if you have time, check your answer. But that's how Arithmetic Reasoning goes, at least on the paper test.

If you're taking the computerized version of the ASVAB, the time remaining for the subtest ticks down right there on your computer screen. If you're taking the paper version of the ASVAB, you'll see a large clock clearly visible somewhere on the wall. The test proctor also posts the start time and end time of the subtest where you can easily see it.

Don't spend too much time on any one question. If a question is stumping you, admit defeat, choose an answer (see the "Logical guessing" section later in this chapter), and move on. You don't want to find yourself in a position where you only have 15 minutes left and you're on question 3.

Choosing an answer and checking it twice

Checking your answer to ensure it makes sense in relation to the question is always a good idea if you have time. You don't always have time on the Arithmetic Reasoning subtest, but if you find yourself running ahead of the clock, take a few seconds to check your answer by running through the calculations again, trying a different method to solve the problem, or simply making sure the answer seems reasonable.

Don't assume that the answer you got is correct just because it's one of the answer choices. Those crafty test makers often use common mistakes as possible answer choices.

If you're taking the paper version of the ASVAB, you should also leave enough time at the end of the subtest to check and make sure you've marked your answer sheet correctly. Make sure the answer blocks are completely filled in, and make sure you didn't make the rookie mistake of answering the wrong question with the right answer.

Using the answer choices: There's more than one way to skin an equation

If you're stumped and just can't seem to write equations to solve a problem, you can often answer the question by seeing which of the answer choices works. Look at the following example:

EXAMPLE

The product of two consecutive negative even integers is 24. Find the lower number.

(A) −2

(B) −4

(C) −6

(D) −7

Say you set up an algebra problem; you decide that if you let the lower integer be *n*, then $n(n+2) = 24$. Correctly solving this problem involves factoring a quadratic equation (see the end of this section if that sentence scares you). Perhaps quadratic equations aren't your cup of tea, and you get stuck at $n^2 + 2n - 24 = 0$. (If so, Chapter 9 may be of some help.) But before giving up and making a wild guess, try seeing which of the answer choices works:

» **−2:** No negative even integer is larger than −2, so Choice (A) doesn't work.

» **−4:** $-4 \times -2 = 8$, so Choice (B) doesn't work.

» **−6:** $-6 \times -4 = 24$. Choice (C) works!

WARNING

Don't test all the answer choices unless you're absolutely stuck. It can use up a lot of time. In essence, you're computing the problem (up to) four times.

There are other ways to settle on the right answer, too. Maybe you automatically thought of factors of 24, noted that 4 and 6 are consecutive even numbers, and turned them into negative numbers. Or maybe you recognized that 24 is very near the square number 25, which equals 5×5, so you knew that consecutive even factors of 24 would probably be 4 and 6, the even numbers just above and below 5. No matter which way you look at it, knowing there are usually a handful of ways to solve a problem can help you get over hurdles meant to trip you up on the ASVAB.

Thought I forgot about the original problem? Here's the "proper" (algebraic) way to solve it. Let the first integer equal *n*. Then the next consecutive even integer is $n+2$.

$$n(n+2) = 24$$
$$n^2 + 2n = 24$$
$$n^2 + 2n - 24 = 0$$
$$(n+6)(n-4) = 0$$
$$n = -6 \text{ and } n = 4$$

The answer can't be 4, because the problem asks for a negative number. The first number (the smallest, *n*) is −6, which means the second number $(n+2)$ is −4.

Logical guessing

Sometimes nothing else works, and you just have to guess. If you're taking the paper version of the ASVAB, you can always skip the hard questions and go back to them when you finish the other questions. If you choose to do so, remember to leave enough time to go back and answer, even if your method is "eeny-meeny-miny-mo." There is no penalty for wrong answers on the paper version of the ASVAB. If you get the question wrong, you get zero points. If you leave the answer blank, you also get zero points. If you make a wild guess, you have at least a one in four chance of getting the answer right and getting points. Be careful, however, of guessing on a series of questions at the end of the test if you're taking the computer version. If you give a lot of wrong answers toward the end of the CAT-ASVAB, the computer dings you in the score department because it's programmed to believe you mismanaged your time.

You can't skip questions on the CAT-ASVAB. The computer doesn't present you with the next question until you answer the current one. Unfortunately, you don't have the option of going back and giving the question another try when you finish the rest of the subtest. You have to decide whether to use more of your precious time to figure it out or guess and move on.

Guessing doesn't have to be wild, however. Sometimes you can improve your chances by eliminating obviously wrong answers. Consider the brain stumper from the preceding section:

EXAMPLE

The product of two consecutive negative even integers is 24. Find the lower number.

(A) −2

(B) −4

(C) −6

(D) −7

Choice (A) is obviously incorrect because no number larger than −2 can be both negative and even. You can quickly see that Choice (D) is wrong because it's an odd number, and the question is asking for a negative even number. Now, if you have to guess, you've just changed the odds from a one in four chance to a 50/50 chance.

Taking Arithmetic Reasoning out for a Spin

I promised you a chance to practice, and here it is. In this section, I give you ten fairly simple math word problems, similar to what you see on the Arithmetic Reasoning subtest.

Don't worry about time here; use these questions to get used to the general test structure and to practice some of the concepts from this chapter and Chapter 11. When you're ready, you can move on to the full-blown AFQT practice tests that start in Chapter 13.

1. If apples are on sale at 15 for $3, what is the cost of each apple?

(A) 50¢

(B) 25¢

(C) 20¢

(D) 30¢

2. A noncommissioned officer challenged her platoon of 11 enlisted women to beat her record of performing a 26-mile training run in four hours. If all the enlisted women match her record, how many miles will they have run?

(A) 71.5 miles

(B) 6.5 miles

(C) 286 miles

(D) 312 miles

3. Margaret gets her hair cut and colored at an expensive salon in town. She is expected to leave a 15 percent tip for services. If a haircut is $45 and a color treatment is $150, how much of a tip should Margaret leave?

(A) $22.50

(B) $29.25

(C) $20.00

(D) $195.00

4. A bag of sand holds 1 cubic foot of sand. How many bags of sand are needed to fill a square sandbox measuring 5 feet long and 1 foot high?

(A) 5 bags

(B) 10 bags

(C) 15 bags

(D) 25 bags

5. The day Samantha arrived at boot camp, the temperature reached a high of 90 degrees in the shade and a low of −20 degrees at night in the barracks. What is the average between the high and low temperatures for the day?

(A) 35 degrees

(B) 45 degrees

(C) 70 degrees

(D) 62 degrees

6. Farmer Beth has received an offer to sell her 320-acre farm for $3,000 per acre. She agrees to give the buyer $96,000 worth of land. What fraction of Farmer Beth's land is the buyer getting?

(A) $\frac{1}{4}$

(B) $\frac{1}{10}$

(C) $\frac{1}{5}$

(D) $\frac{2}{3}$

7. A map is drawn so that 1 inch equals 3 miles. On the map, the distance from Kansas City to Denver is 192.5 inches. How far is the round trip from Kansas City to Denver in miles?

(A) 192.5 miles

(B) 577.5 miles

(C) 385 miles

(D) 1,155 miles

8. Margaret and Julie can sell their store for $150,000. They plan to divide the proceeds according to the ratio of the money they each invested in the business. Margaret put in the most money, at a 3:2 ratio to Julie. How much money should Julie get from the sale?

(A) $50,000

(B) $30,000

(C) $60,000

(D) $90,000

9. In the military, $\frac{1}{4}$ of an enlisted person's time is spent sleeping and eating, $\frac{1}{12}$ is spent standing at attention, $\frac{1}{6}$ is spent staying fit, and $\frac{2}{5}$ is spent working. The rest of the time is spent at the enlisted person's own discretion. How many hours per day does this discretionary time amount to?

(A) 6 hours

(B) 1.6 hours

(C) 2.4 hours

(D) 3.2 hours

10. Train A is headed east at 55 mph. Train B is also heading east on an adjacent track at 70 mph. At the end of four hours, how much farther will train B have traveled than train A?

(A) 40 miles

(B) 50 miles

(C) 60 miles

(D) 70 miles

Answers and Explanations

Use this answer key to score the practice Arithmetic Reasoning questions.

1. **C.** Divide $3 by 15.

2. **C.** Multiply 26×11. The other information in the question is irrelevant; it's there to throw you off.

3. **B.** Add $45 and $150 and multiply the answer by 15 percent, or 0.15. A shortcut: Find 15 percent of the original $150, which is $22.50. The only choice possible is Choice (B) because it's the only one that's a little higher than $22.50. You can estimate to solve this problem, too, because $150 + $45 is about $200, and 15 percent of $200 is $30; Choice (B) is the closest answer.

4. **D.** The volume formula for a square or rectangular box is $V = lwh$, so $V = 5 \times 5 \times 1 = 25$ cubic feet. Each bag holds 1 cubic foot of sand.

5. **A.** Add the two temperatures given and then divide by the number of terms, 2: $(90 + -20) \div 2 = 70 \div 2 = 35$.

6. **B.** $96,000 divided by $3,000 (the price per acre) equals 32 acres, and 32 acres divided by 320 acres (the total size of the farm) equals 10 percent, or $\frac{1}{10}$ of the land. *Tip:* You may find the division easier if you write this problem out as a fraction and reduce it, like this:

$$\frac{96,000}{3,000} = \frac{96,\cancel{000}}{3,\cancel{000}} = \frac{96}{3} = 32$$

7. **D.** Multiply 192.5×3 to get the distance in miles, and then double the answer to account for both legs of the trip.

8. **C.** According to the ratio, Margaret should get $\frac{3}{5}$ of the money, and Julie should get $\frac{2}{5}$ of the money. You calculate these fractions by adding both sides of the ratio together $(3 + 2 = 5)$ to determine the denominator. Each side of the ratio then becomes a numerator, so Margaret's investment is $\frac{3}{5}$ of the total investment, and Julie's is $\frac{2}{5}$ of the total investment. (You can check these fractions by adding $\frac{3}{5}$ and $\frac{2}{5}$ to get $\frac{5}{5}$ or 1, which is all the money.) Divide $150,000 by 5, and then multiply the answer by 2 to determine Julie's share of the money.

9. **C.** Calculate this answer by first assigning a common denominator of 60 to all the fractions and adjusting the numerators accordingly: $\frac{15}{60}, \frac{5}{60}, \frac{10}{60}, \frac{24}{60}$. Add the fractions to find out how much time is allotted to all these tasks. The total is $\frac{54}{60}$, which leaves $\frac{6}{60}$ or $\frac{1}{10}$ of the day to the enlisted person's discretion. $\frac{1}{10}$ of 24 hours is 2.4 hours.

10. **C.** The distance formula is $d = rt$. Plug in the known values:

    - Train A: $d = 55 \times 4 = 220$ miles

    - Train B: $d = 70 \times 4 = 280$ miles

    Train B traveled $280 - 220 = 60$ miles farther than train A.

    You can also find the difference in speed, and then multiply by 4:

    $70 - 55 = 15$ and $15 \times 4 = 60$.

4 AFQT Practice Exams

Chapter **13**

Practice Exam 1

The Armed Forces Qualification Test (AFQT) consists of four of the nine subtests given on the Armed Services Vocational Aptitude Battery (ASVAB). The four subtests used to determine your AFQT score are Arithmetic Reasoning, Word Knowledge, Paragraph Comprehension, and Mathematics Knowledge.

Your AFQT score is very important. Although all the ASVAB subtests are used to determine which military jobs you may qualify for, the AFQT score determines whether you're even qualified to join the military. All the military service branches have established minimum AFQT scores, according to their needs (see Chapter 2 for more information).

The AFQT is not a stand-alone test (it's part of the ASVAB), but in this chapter, I present the subtests applicable to the AFQT in the same order in which you'll encounter them when you take the actual ASVAB.

After you complete the entire practice test, check your answers against the answer key in Chapter 14.

REMEMBER

The test is scored by comparing your raw score to the scores of other people, which produces a scaled score. So just because you missed a total of 20 questions doesn't mean that your score is 80. (That would be too simple.) Turn to Chapter 2 to find out how the AFQT score is derived from these four subtests.

Your goal in taking this practice test is to determine which areas you may still need to study. If you miss only one question on the Word Knowledge subtest, but you miss 15 questions on Arithmetic Reasoning, you probably want to devote some extra study time to developing your math skills before you take the ASVAB.

Answer Sheet for Practice Exam 1

Part 1: Arithmetic Reasoning

1. Ⓐ Ⓑ Ⓒ Ⓓ	7. Ⓐ Ⓑ Ⓒ Ⓓ	13. Ⓐ Ⓑ Ⓒ Ⓓ	19. Ⓐ Ⓑ Ⓒ Ⓓ	25. Ⓐ Ⓑ Ⓒ Ⓓ
2. Ⓐ Ⓑ Ⓒ Ⓓ	8. Ⓐ Ⓑ Ⓒ Ⓓ	14. Ⓐ Ⓑ Ⓒ Ⓓ	20. Ⓐ Ⓑ Ⓒ Ⓓ	26. Ⓐ Ⓑ Ⓒ Ⓓ
3. Ⓐ Ⓑ Ⓒ Ⓓ	9. Ⓐ Ⓑ Ⓒ Ⓓ	15. Ⓐ Ⓑ Ⓒ Ⓓ	21. Ⓐ Ⓑ Ⓒ Ⓓ	27. Ⓐ Ⓑ Ⓒ Ⓓ
4. Ⓐ Ⓑ Ⓒ Ⓓ	10. Ⓐ Ⓑ Ⓒ Ⓓ	16. Ⓐ Ⓑ Ⓒ Ⓓ	22. Ⓐ Ⓑ Ⓒ Ⓓ	28. Ⓐ Ⓑ Ⓒ Ⓓ
5. Ⓐ Ⓑ Ⓒ Ⓓ	11. Ⓐ Ⓑ Ⓒ Ⓓ	17. Ⓐ Ⓑ Ⓒ Ⓓ	23. Ⓐ Ⓑ Ⓒ Ⓓ	29. Ⓐ Ⓑ Ⓒ Ⓓ
6. Ⓐ Ⓑ Ⓒ Ⓓ	12. Ⓐ Ⓑ Ⓒ Ⓓ	18. Ⓐ Ⓑ Ⓒ Ⓓ	24. Ⓐ Ⓑ Ⓒ Ⓓ	30. Ⓐ Ⓑ Ⓒ Ⓓ

Part 2: Word Knowledge

1. Ⓐ Ⓑ Ⓒ Ⓓ	8. Ⓐ Ⓑ Ⓒ Ⓓ	15. Ⓐ Ⓑ Ⓒ Ⓓ	22. Ⓐ Ⓑ Ⓒ Ⓓ	29. Ⓐ Ⓑ Ⓒ Ⓓ
2. Ⓐ Ⓑ Ⓒ Ⓓ	9. Ⓐ Ⓑ Ⓒ Ⓓ	16. Ⓐ Ⓑ Ⓒ Ⓓ	23. Ⓐ Ⓑ Ⓒ Ⓓ	30. Ⓐ Ⓑ Ⓒ Ⓓ
3. Ⓐ Ⓑ Ⓒ Ⓓ	10. Ⓐ Ⓑ Ⓒ Ⓓ	17. Ⓐ Ⓑ Ⓒ Ⓓ	24. Ⓐ Ⓑ Ⓒ Ⓓ	31. Ⓐ Ⓑ Ⓒ Ⓓ
4. Ⓐ Ⓑ Ⓒ Ⓓ	11. Ⓐ Ⓑ Ⓒ Ⓓ	18. Ⓐ Ⓑ Ⓒ Ⓓ	25. Ⓐ Ⓑ Ⓒ Ⓓ	32. Ⓐ Ⓑ Ⓒ Ⓓ
5. Ⓐ Ⓑ Ⓒ Ⓓ	12. Ⓐ Ⓑ Ⓒ Ⓓ	19. Ⓐ Ⓑ Ⓒ Ⓓ	26. Ⓐ Ⓑ Ⓒ Ⓓ	33. Ⓐ Ⓑ Ⓒ Ⓓ
6. Ⓐ Ⓑ Ⓒ Ⓓ	13. Ⓐ Ⓑ Ⓒ Ⓓ	20. Ⓐ Ⓑ Ⓒ Ⓓ	27. Ⓐ Ⓑ Ⓒ Ⓓ	34. Ⓐ Ⓑ Ⓒ Ⓓ
7. Ⓐ Ⓑ Ⓒ Ⓓ	14. Ⓐ Ⓑ Ⓒ Ⓓ	21. Ⓐ Ⓑ Ⓒ Ⓓ	28. Ⓐ Ⓑ Ⓒ Ⓓ	35. Ⓐ Ⓑ Ⓒ Ⓓ

Part 3: Paragraph Comprehension

1. Ⓐ Ⓑ Ⓒ Ⓓ   4. Ⓐ Ⓑ Ⓒ Ⓓ   7. Ⓐ Ⓑ Ⓒ Ⓓ   10. Ⓐ Ⓑ Ⓒ Ⓓ   13. Ⓐ Ⓑ Ⓒ Ⓓ
2. Ⓐ Ⓑ Ⓒ Ⓓ   5. Ⓐ Ⓑ Ⓒ Ⓓ   8. Ⓐ Ⓑ Ⓒ Ⓓ   11. Ⓐ Ⓑ Ⓒ Ⓓ   14. Ⓐ Ⓑ Ⓒ Ⓓ
3. Ⓐ Ⓑ Ⓒ Ⓓ   6. Ⓐ Ⓑ Ⓒ Ⓓ   9. Ⓐ Ⓑ Ⓒ Ⓓ   12. Ⓐ Ⓑ Ⓒ Ⓓ   15. Ⓐ Ⓑ Ⓒ Ⓓ

Part 4: Mathematics Knowledge

1. Ⓐ Ⓑ Ⓒ Ⓓ   6. Ⓐ Ⓑ Ⓒ Ⓓ   11. Ⓐ Ⓑ Ⓒ Ⓓ   16. Ⓐ Ⓑ Ⓒ Ⓓ   21. Ⓐ Ⓑ Ⓒ Ⓓ
2. Ⓐ Ⓑ Ⓒ Ⓓ   7. Ⓐ Ⓑ Ⓒ Ⓓ   12. Ⓐ Ⓑ Ⓒ Ⓓ   17. Ⓐ Ⓑ Ⓒ Ⓓ   22. Ⓐ Ⓑ Ⓒ Ⓓ
3. Ⓐ Ⓑ Ⓒ Ⓓ   8. Ⓐ Ⓑ Ⓒ Ⓓ   13. Ⓐ Ⓑ Ⓒ Ⓓ   18. Ⓐ Ⓑ Ⓒ Ⓓ   23. Ⓐ Ⓑ Ⓒ Ⓓ
4. Ⓐ Ⓑ Ⓒ Ⓓ   9. Ⓐ Ⓑ Ⓒ Ⓓ   14. Ⓐ Ⓑ Ⓒ Ⓓ   19. Ⓐ Ⓑ Ⓒ Ⓓ   24. Ⓐ Ⓑ Ⓒ Ⓓ
5. Ⓐ Ⓑ Ⓒ Ⓓ   10. Ⓐ Ⓑ Ⓒ Ⓓ   15. Ⓐ Ⓑ Ⓒ Ⓓ   20. Ⓐ Ⓑ Ⓒ Ⓓ   25. Ⓐ Ⓑ Ⓒ Ⓓ

Part 1: Arithmetic Reasoning

TIME: 36 minutes for 30 questions

DIRECTIONS: Arithmetic Reasoning is the second subtest of the ASVAB. These questions are designed to test your ability to use mathematics to solve various problems that may be found in real life — in other words, math word problems.

Each question is followed by four possible answers. Decide which answer is correct, and then mark the corresponding space on your answer sheet. Use your scratch paper for any figuring you want to do. You may *not* use a calculator.

1. Amy and Dan bought each of their four kids an ice cream cone and one iced coffee for themselves to share. Each ice cream cone cost $1.25, and their total bill was $7.50. How much did the iced coffee cost?

   (A) $2.75
   (B) $2.50
   (C) $1.25
   (D) $1.75

2. Sergeant Major Stanley is drawing a map in the sand for his troops. He draws the Tuz Mayor's Compound as a square measuring 18 inches on one side. What is the area of the square?

   (A) 36 square inches
   (B) 72 square inches
   (C) 324 square inches
   (D) 583 square inches

3. Currently, Danielle is twice as old as Abigail. In three years, the sum of their ages will be 30. What is Danielle's current age?

   (A) 16
   (B) 14
   (C) 10
   (D) 8

4. Tammy bought a set of rims for her truck for $500. She spent some money on window tint and twice as much on a new radio. Her total bill for all of these modifications was $950. How much did she spend on the radio?

   (A) $300
   (B) $325
   (C) $150
   (D) $450

5. Half a number plus 17 is 57. What is the number?

   (A) 20
   (B) 90
   (C) 80
   (D) 40

6. A recipe to make 10 pancakes requires 3 cups of flour and 2 tablespoons of baking powder. If you only need to make six pancakes, how many cups of flour do you need?

   (A) $1\frac{8}{5}$ cups
   (B) $1\frac{1}{8}$ cups
   (C) $1\frac{4}{5}$ cups
   (D) $1\frac{1}{4}$ cups

7. Tim and Jason are painting a room. It takes Tim 10 hours to paint a room of that size alone, but Jason can get it done in 8 hours. Approximately how long will it take them to paint the room together?

   (A) 4.2 hours
   (B) 4.4 hours
   (C) 9 hours
   (D) 9.4 hours

8. Ebony is building a rectangular garden in her backyard. To fit in everything she wants to grow, she needs a garden with an area of 156 square feet. If her garden is 12 feet long, how wide should it be?

   (A) 10 feet
   (B) 15.6 feet
   (C) 13 feet
   (D) 12 feet

GO ON TO NEXT PAGE →

9. Two consecutive odd numbers have a sum of 92. What are the numbers?

(A) 41 and 51

(B) 44 and 48

(C) 43 and 45

(D) 45 and 47

10. Davy gets $17 per month in allowance. He saved two months' worth of allowance and then spent $\frac{3}{5}$ of it on apps for his phone. He spent $\frac{1}{8}$ of the remaining money on a bumper sticker. Of the money left after purchasing the sticker, Davy spent $\frac{1}{2}$ of it on candy. How much did Davy spend on the candy?

(A) $5.95

(B) $2.85

(C) $1.70

(D) $13.60

11. Three baristas, Pilar, Maria, and Tatiana, made $187 in tips on Saturday. Pilar made $12 more than Maria, and Maria made twice as much as Tatiana. How much did Tatiana make in tips?

(A) $70

(B) $35

(C) $25

(D) $65.50

12. Mr. Brown confiscated a triangle-shaped note from a student during his fourth-period math class. The note's base was 8 centimeters and its height was 12 centimeters. What was the note's area?

(A) 48 square inches

(B) 96 square inches

(C) 52 square inches

(D) 32 square inches

13. A car travels at a speed of 7^2 miles per hour. If the car travels at that speed for 2^4 hours, how many miles has the car gone?

(A) 112 miles

(B) 392 miles

(C) 594 miles

(D) 784 miles

14. Two runners are racing on a 2-mile course. The start gun fires at 1:15 p.m. The first runner speeds along at an average pace of 10.3 miles per hour, while the second runner travels at a pace of 10 miles per hour. How long does it take for the second runner to reach the finish line?

(A) 12 minutes

(B) 13.3 minutes

(C) 14 minutes

(D) 14.8 minutes

15. A man in a boat travels downstream for three hours. The current averages 4 miles per hour. The man then turns around and travels the same distance upstream, against the current. It takes him four hours to return to his starting point. The boat's speed is constant the entire trip. How far did the man travel round-trip?

(A) 96 miles

(B) 112 miles

(C) 192 miles

(D) 216 miles

16. Sadie spent $447 shopping for school clothes. Sweatshirts cost $27.50 each, and jeans cost $33.25 per pair. Sadie purchased 15 items of clothing, so how many pairs of jeans did she buy?

(A) 5

(B) 6

(C) 8

(D) 9

17. Luke's microscope has an objective lens that can magnify something 11^8 times. Its eyepiece can further magnify something 11^2 times. What is Luke's microscope's maximum magnification?

(A) 11^6

(B) 11^{10}

(C) 121^{16}

(D) 11^{16}

18. Michael spends $27 on chocolate that costs $4.50 per pound. How many pounds of chocolate did he buy?

(A) 4.5 pounds

(B) 5 pounds

(C) 6 pounds

(D) 6.8 pounds

19. A kite has one diagonal length of 18.5 cm and another diagonal length of twice that. What is the kite's area?

(A) 111 cm²

(B) 256.75 cm²

(C) 342.25 cm²

(D) 684.5 cm²

20. If the height-to-width ratio of an American flag is 1:1.5, how wide is the flag if it is 60 inches high?

(A) 40 inches

(B) 60 inches

(C) 90 inches

(D) 120 inches

21. The price of a car has increased by 5 percent. It was originally listed for $23,550. What is the current price of the car?

(A) $23,950

(B) $24,323.50

(C) $24,727.50

(D) $31,975

22. If you walk around the outside edge of a field that measures 300 feet by 160 feet and end where you started, how many feet did you walk?

(A) 460 feet

(B) 800 feet

(C) 920 feet

(D) 1,100 feet

23. Carter used all of his quarters at the car wash, but he still has 23 coins in his pocket. Some of them are nickels, and some are dimes, but the total in his pocket is $1.50. How many of the coins are dimes?

(A) 7

(B) 8

(C) 9

(D) 10

24. Tim is building a toy UFO for his daughter. He cuts a circle from a piece of tin with a diameter of 12.5 inches. What is the approximate area of the shape Tim cut?

(A) 78.5 square inches

(B) 115.3 square inches

(C) 122.7 square inches

(D) 490.7 square inches

25. Vicki is packing a suitcase for her vacation. She knows she'll be picking up a music box as a gift for her friend Danielle. The hand-carved music box measures 8 inches wide, 8 inches high, and 8 inches long. Vicki's suitcase measures 19 inches wide, 30 inches high, and 10 inches long. How much space will Vicki have left for her clothes if she plans to pack the music box when she comes home?

(A) 5,188 cubic inches

(B) 3,894 cubic inches

(C) 5,700 cubic inches

(D) 6,212 cubic inches

26. How many legs do six horses, four dogs, and two kangaroos have?

(A) 36

(B) 38

(C) 41

(D) 44

GO ON TO NEXT PAGE

27. Chloe is graphing her weight loss, which falls on a line perpendicular to $2y = 4x + 3$. What is the slope of the line representing Chloe's weight loss?

(A) $-\frac{2}{3}$

(B) $-\frac{1}{2}$

(C) $\frac{1}{2}$

(D) 2

28. Samantha has two-thirds of a gallon of almond milk and $\frac{7}{12}$ gallon of fruit juice. She has a total of $2\frac{1}{8}$ gallons of beverages in her refrigerator. How many gallons of beverages are neither almond milk nor fruit juice?

(A) $1\frac{1}{4}$

(B) $2\frac{7}{8}$

(C) $1\frac{3}{8}$

(D) $\frac{7}{8}$

29. Dave took four tests in his criminal justice class. He scored 91, 79, 88, and 84. His final exam is worth two test grades, so what grade does Dave need to get on his final exam to get an A (90 percent or better) in the class?

(A) 95

(B) 96

(C) 99

(D) 100

30. Alberto wants to paint one wall in his living room blue. The wall is 7.5 feet high and 15 feet wide. One quart of paint covers exactly 100 square feet. How much paint does Alberto need to cover the entire wall in two coats of paint?

(A) 1.125 quarts

(B) 1.25 quarts

(C) 2 quarts

(D) 2.25 quarts

Part 2: Word Knowledge

1. The teacher's instructions were underlined ambiguous, and I didn't understand what she wanted.
   - (A) clear
   - (B) debatable
   - (C) concise
   - (D) disgusting

2. It's a underlined transient heatwave; the temperatures will return to normal on Monday.
   - (A) short-lived
   - (B) mobile
   - (C) unbearable
   - (D) permanent

3. The word most opposite in meaning to underlined sedentary is
   - (A) hungry.
   - (B) dirt.
   - (C) lazy.
   - (D) active.

4. The soldiers worked in close underlined proximity with civilians while they were deployed.
   - (A) confidence
   - (B) nearness
   - (C) relations
   - (D) obsequiousness

5. underlined Petulant most nearly means
   - (A) bad-tempered.
   - (B) agreeable.
   - (C) floral.
   - (D) friendly.

6. underlined Incredulous most nearly means
   - (A) skeptical.
   - (B) believable.
   - (C) brilliant.
   - (D) remarkable.

7. underlined Gratuitous most nearly means
   - (A) provocative.
   - (B) costly.
   - (C) ridiculous.
   - (D) unwarranted.

8. We plan to underlined boycott the companies that advertise on that website.
   - (A) purchase
   - (B) visit
   - (C) reject
   - (D) patronize

9. Don't believe the underlined fallacy that money can buy you happiness.
   - (A) truth
   - (B) misconception
   - (C) saying
   - (D) argument

10. Foreign diplomats in the U.S. are typically underlined immune from legal action.
    - (A) exempt
    - (B) prone
    - (C) susceptible
    - (D) reluctant

GO ON TO NEXT PAGE

11. Mosaic most nearly means
   (A) wander.
   (B) collage.
   (C) transfusion.
   (D) batter.

12. The most elite soldiers are in the Special Forces.
   (A) snobbish
   (B) overweight
   (C) best
   (D) moderate

13. Mutate most nearly means
   (A) chop.
   (B) maim.
   (C) ignore.
   (D) change.

14. Excerpt most nearly means
   (A) snippet.
   (B) excuse.
   (C) exempt.
   (D) disallow.

15. Nobody could believe that the outrageous candidate made it so far.
   (A) brilliant
   (B) shocking
   (C) charming
   (D) moderate

16. Invariably most nearly means
   (A) always.
   (B) occasionally.
   (C) algebraically.
   (D) theoretically.

17. Encumber most nearly means
   (A) vegetate.
   (B) relax.
   (C) hamper.
   (D) exacerbate.

18. Flair most nearly means
   (A) burn.
   (B) flippancy.
   (C) restriction.
   (D) talent.

19. The stray dog seemed to accept his lot in life with equanimity.
   (A) hopefulness
   (B) composure
   (C) agitation
   (D) confusion

20. Grope most nearly means
   (A) fumble.
   (B) fruit.
   (C) complain.
   (D) fall.

21. Sleek is most opposite in meaning to
   (A) polished.
   (B) shiny.
   (C) clumsy.
   (D) dull.

22. The man's callous comments about his ex-wife made the judge cringe.
   (A) original
   (B) sympathetic
   (C) heartless
   (D) cautious

23. Impervious most nearly means
   (A) waterproof.
   (B) dense.
   (C) repelled.
   (D) proof.

24. Revenue most nearly means
   (A) income.
   (B) taxation.
   (C) musical.
   (D) publicity.

25. Pulverize most nearly means

   (A) transfix.

   (B) grind.

   (C) disseminate.

   (D) transcend.

26. The stranded pilots were in dire need of a communication device.

   (A) inescapable

   (B) frustrated

   (C) urgent

   (D) terrifying

27. Chastise most nearly means

   (A) careful.

   (B) engaged.

   (C) argue.

   (D) scold.

28. The word most opposite in meaning to conspicuous is

   (A) imperceptible.

   (B) garish.

   (C) noticeable.

   (D) quiet.

29. We moved so the kids would have a greater opportunity to get a good education.

   (A) favorability

   (B) chance

   (C) luck

   (D) likelihood

30. Vengeance most nearly means

   (A) forgiveness.

   (B) ignorance.

   (C) punishment.

   (D) vindictiveness.

31. Deplorable most nearly means

   (A) disgraceful.

   (B) honorable.

   (C) gross.

   (D) fanatical.

32. The word most opposite in meaning to recede is

   (A) abate.

   (B) develop.

   (C) dwindle.

   (D) advance.

33. The Wind Talkers could decipher their own secret codes.

   (A) define

   (B) unscramble

   (C) create

   (D) confuse

34. If you keep rereading what you've already read, you'll only protract the process.

   (A) shorten

   (B) write out

   (C) convolute

   (D) lengthen

35. She provided an articulate account of her experience.

   (A) understandable

   (B) long-winded

   (C) expressionless

   (D) disjointed

Part 3: Paragraph Comprehension

TIME: 13 minutes for 15 questions

DIRECTIONS: Paragraph Comprehension is the fourth subtest on the ASVAB. The questions are designed to measure your ability to understand what you read. This section includes one or more paragraphs of reading material, followed by incomplete statements or questions. Read the paragraph and select the choice that best completes the statement or answers the question. Then mark the corresponding space on your answer sheet.

Questions 1 and 2 refer to the following passage, which is from Amphibians and Reptiles of the Rainforests of Southern El Petén, Guatemala *by William E. Duellman.*

In this tropical area having a high amount of rainfall most of the species of amphibians and reptiles have extensive ranges in the wet forests on the Atlantic lowlands of southern México and northern Central America; some species that more frequently are found in sub-humid forests also occur. Ecologically the fauna is divided into five major habitats—aquatic, aquatic margin, fossorial, terrestrial, and arboreal. Forty-two per cent of the 78 species are wholly or partly arboreal. The fauna is most closely related to that in Alta Verapaz, Guatemala, but includes many species that occur in the Tikal-Uaxactún area in northeastern Guatemala.

1. What is *not* a major habitat the author describes?

(A) aquatic

(B) terrestrial

(C) aquatic margin

(D) territorial

2. According to this passage, what percentage of species of amphibians and reptiles are completely or partly arboreal?

(A) 78

(B) 42

(C) 32.76

(D) The passage doesn't say.

Questions 3 through 5 refer to the following passage, which is from Prisoners in Devil's Bog *by Hugh Lloyd.*

He had never before visited one of these commercial palaces and he gazed about him in speechless awe. He found the revolving door so delightful that it seemed like some freakish entertainment in an amusement park, and he indulged himself with the giddy sensation of going around and around in it until a uniformed elevator starter brusquely ordered him out.

Instead, he went in.

Observing the rather ornate cigar and candy booth, he invested in a gooey chocolate bar which he ate while studying the alphabetical list of offices. He was deeply impressed with this imposing directory and experienced a thrill of triumph when at last his searching eyes discovered the name, INTERNATIONAL DETECTIVE AGENCY—7-721-728.

3. Based on the passage, you can assume the man is in

(A) a palace.

(B) an amusement park.

(C) an office building.

(D) an elevator.

4. What is the man in the passage looking for in the office building?

(A) an elevator

(B) a chocolate bar

(C) a building directory

(D) a detective agency

5. What does the man buy?

(A) tickets

(B) a cigar

(C) candy

(D) nothing

Question 6 refers to the following passage, which is from The Cliff Ruins of Canyon de Chelly, Arizona *by Cosmos Mindeleff.*

To the traveler on foot, or even on horseback, Canyon de Chelly is easily accessible from almost any direction. Good trails run northward to the San Juan and northeastward over the Tunicha mountains to the upper part of that river; Fort Defiance is but half a day's journey to the southeast; Tusayan and Zuñi are but three days distant to the traveler on foot; the Navaho often ride the distance in a day or a day and a half. The canyon is accessible to wagons, however, only at its mouth.

6. According to the passage, how long does it take to hike to Tusayan from Canyon de Chelly?

(A) 1.5 days

(B) 3 days

(C) 0.5 days

(D) The passage doesn't say.

Questions 7 and 8 refer to the following passage, which is by Angie Papple Johnston.

General Braxton Bragg, born in 1817 in Warrenton, North Carolina, was a high-profile commander for the Confederacy during the Civil War. Educated at West Point, Bragg led a group of volunteers to capture a federal arsenal in Baton Rouge, Louisiana. Despite the recognition he earned for training his troops, Bragg was almost universally disliked by his peers. One artillery officer, E.P. Alexander, called him "simply muddle-headed." General Nathan Bedford Forrest once called Bragg a scoundrel and a coward (and threatened to slap him). Although most of the actual battles Bragg fought ended in defeat (former general and U.S. Vice President John C. Breckinridge challenged Bragg to a duel after one such lost battle), the U.S. Army installation in Fayetteville, North Carolina — Fort Bragg — is named for the late general, who's been called "the Confederacy's worst general" by a number of historians.

7. According to the passage, why was General Braxton Bragg "the Confederacy's worst general"?

(A) He lost most of the battles he fought.

(B) Few of his peers liked him.

(C) Bragg trained troops.

(D) Both A and B are correct.

8. Where is the military installation named after General Braxton Bragg?

(A) Warrenton, North Carolina

(B) West Point

(C) Fayetteville, North Carolina

(D) Baton Rouge, Louisiana

Question 9 refers to the following passage, which is from Susan B. Anthony: Rebel, Crusader, Humanitarian *by Alma Lutz.*

The attic of the tavern had been finished off for a ballroom with bottles laid under the floor to give a nice tone to the music of the fiddles, and now the young people of the village wanted to hold their dancing school there. Susan's father, true to his Quaker training, felt obliged to refuse, but when they came the second time to tell him that the only other place available was a disreputable tavern where liquor was sold, he relented a little, and talked the matter over with his wife and daughters. Lucy Anthony, recalling her love of dancing, urged him to let the young people come. Finally he consented on the condition that Guelma, Hannah, and Susan would not dance.

9. According to the passage, what made Susan's father reconsider holding dance classes in his ballroom?

(A) It had good acoustics.

(B) Dancing went against his Quaker training.

(C) The only other place available was a disreputable tavern.

(D) He decided that his daughters couldn't dance.

Questions 10 and 11 refer to the following passage, which is from Knights of Art: Stories of the Italian Painters *by Amy Steedman.*

Life was rough and hard in that country home, but the peasant baby grew into a strong, hardy boy, learning early what cold and hunger meant. The hills which surrounded the village were grey and bare, save where the silver of the olive-trees shone in the sunlight, or the tender green of the shooting corn made the valley beautiful in early spring. In summer there was little shade from the blazing sun as it rode high in the blue sky, and the grass which grew among the grey rocks was often burnt and brown. But, nevertheless, it was here that the sheep of the village would be turned out to find what food they could, tended and watched by one of the village boys.

10. According to the passage, what made the valley beautiful?

(A) blue skies and bright sun

(B) cornfields that bloomed in early spring

(C) grass that grew among the rocks

(D) large herds of sheep

11. What does the author of this passage mean by "learning early what cold and hunger meant"?

(A) Winters are uncomfortable in the village.

(B) The village was too hot in the summer, and there was very little food from about June to August.

(C) The boy's family was poor.

(D) The boy was forced to tend sheep during winter.

Question 12 refers to the following passage, which is from Knights of Art: Stories of the Italian Painters *by Amy Steedman.*

The tramontana, that keen wind which blows from over the snow mountains, was sweeping down the narrow streets, searching out every nook and corner with its icy breath. Men flung their cloaks closer round them, and pulled their hats down over their eyes, so that only the tips of their noses were left uncovered for the wind to freeze. Women held their scaldinoes, little pots of hot charcoal, closer under their shawls, and even the dogs had a sad, half-frozen look. One and all longed for the warm winds of spring and the summer heat they loved.

12. According to the passage, why did women carry scaldinoes?

(A) to keep warm

(B) to remember the spring and summer

(C) to bring to the men

(D) The passage doesn't say.

Question 13 refers to the following passage, which is from White Fang *by Jack London.*

The porcupine rolled itself into a ball, radiating long, sharp needles in all directions that defied attack. In his youth One Eye had once sniffed too near a similar, apparently inert ball of quills, and had the tail flick out suddenly in his face. One quill he had carried away in his muzzle, where it had remained for weeks, a rankling flame, until it finally worked out. So he lay down, in a comfortable crouching position, his nose fully a foot away, and out of the line of the tail. Thus he waited, keeping perfectly quiet. There was no telling. Something might happen. The porcupine might unroll.

13. What does "a rankling flame" describe in the context of this passage?

(A) a blister

(B) fire

(C) pain

(D) the porcupine's tail

In order to prevent eye damage, Dr. Bainbridge ordered the distribution of welder's filter glass. Because it was not known exactly how the flash might affect eyesight, it was suggested that direct viewing of the fireball not be attempted even with this protection. The recommended procedure was to face away from ground zero and watch the hills or sky until the fireball illuminated the area. Then, after the initial flash had passed, one could turn around and view the fireball through the filter glass. Despite these well-publicized instructions, two participants did not take precautions. They were temporarily blinded by the intense flash but experienced no permanent vision impairment.

14. Based on the context of the passage, you can assume that the flash is caused by

(A) a house fire.

(B) solar flares.

(C) beacons.

(D) a nuclear explosion.

15. According to the passage, where were people supposed to look during the initial flash?

(A) into welder's glasses

(B) at the hills or sky

(C) at the flash

(D) ground zero

DO NOT TURN THE PAGE UNTIL TOLD TO DO SO STOP **DO NOT RETURN TO A PREVIOUS TEST**

Part 4: Mathematics Knowledge

TIME: 24 minutes for 25 questions

DIRECTIONS: Mathematics Knowledge is the fifth subtest on the ASVAB. The questions are designed to test your ability to solve general mathematical problems. Each question is followed by four possible answers. Decide which answer is correct, and then mark the corresponding space on your answer sheet. Use your scratch paper for any figuring you want to do. You may *not* use a calculator.

1. Which of the following fractions has the least value?

   (A) $\frac{2}{9}$

   (B) $\frac{1}{2}$

   (C) $\frac{5}{6}$

   (D) $\frac{2}{3}$

2. Solve for x: $3x + 8x = 44$

   (A) 4

   (B) 5

   (C) 8.8

   (D) 11

3. Which formula can you use to find the volume of a rectangular prism?

   (A) $V = \frac{1}{2}bh$

   (B) $V = \pi r^2 h$

   (C) $V = lwh$

   (D) $V = 6s^2$

4. What is the approximate circumference of a circle with a radius of 6 centimeters?

   (A) 37.88 cm

   (B) 37.68 cm

   (C) 18.84 cm

   (D) 6.28 cm

5. What is the area of a square measuring 9 feet on one side?

   (A) 36 cubic feet

   (B) 18 square feet

   (C) 81 cubic feet

   (D) 81 square feet

6. Find the perimeter of this figure:

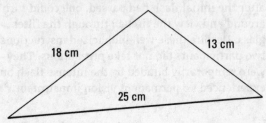

© John Wiley & Sons, Inc.

   (A) 50 cm

   (B) 198 cm

   (C) 56 cm

   (D) 117 cm

7. Find Angle C.

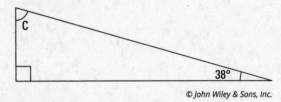

© John Wiley & Sons, Inc.

   (A) 52°

   (B) 38°

   (C) 232°

   (D) 44°

8. Find the approximate volume.

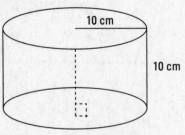

© John Wiley & Sons, Inc.

   (A) 3,000 cubic centimeters

   (B) 314 cubic centimeters

   (C) 3,140 cubic centimeters

   (D) 1,000 cubic centimeters

9. What is the value of *b* when $a = 4$?

$2a + b = 15$

(A) 5.5

(B) 7

(C) 8

(D) 11

10. Solve for *x*: $14(x + 9) = 252$

(A) 4

(B) 9

(C) 16

(D) 27

11. Find the approximate area of the circle.

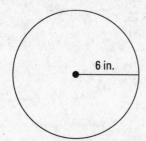

© John Wiley & Sons, Inc.

(A) 110 square inches

(B) 113.04 square inches

(C) 114.03 square inches

(D) 18.84 square inches

12. Find *y*:

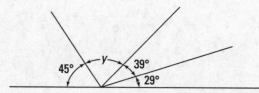

© John Wiley & Sons, Inc.

(A) 67°

(B) 46°

(C) 53°

(D) 21°

13. Solve: $\dfrac{x-6}{4} = \dfrac{x+2}{6}$

(A) 44

(B) 12

(C) 4.4

(D) 22

14. Solve for *y*: $7 + y + 4y \ge 51 + y$

(A) $y \ge 44$

(B) $y \ge 25$

(C) $y \ge 11$

(D) $y \ge 8$

15. Solve: $\dfrac{7}{8} \div x = \dfrac{7}{96}$

(A) 12

(B) 13

(C) 13.5

(D) 7

16. Solve: $18x = 655.5 - x$

(A) 12.5

(B) 17

(C) 34.5

(D) 38.78

17. Find the area of the figure.

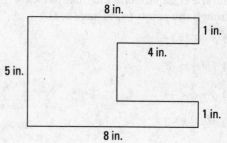

© John Wiley & Sons, Inc.

(A) 30 square inches

(B) 28 square inches

(C) 26 square inches

(D) 25.5 square inches

18. Solve: $4x = 32\dfrac{5}{8}$

(A) $8\dfrac{5}{32}$

(B) $8\dfrac{6}{32}$

(C) $8\dfrac{17}{32}$

(D) $9\dfrac{1}{2}$

GO ON TO NEXT PAGE

19. Simplify: $\sqrt{12a^3b^2}$

(A) $2\sqrt{3}ab$

(B) $2\sqrt{3}a^{\frac{2}{3}}b$

(C) $2b\sqrt{3a^3}$

(D) $2\sqrt{3a^{\frac{3}{2}}b}$

20. Solve for a: $14a = -60 + 2a$

(A) -3.75

(B) 8

(C) 5

(D) -5

21. Express 7,700,000 in scientific notation.

(A) 7.7×10^6

(B) 7.7×10^7

(C) 7.7×10^{-6}

(D) 7.7×6^{10}

22. Find the equation for a line that passes through the points $(6, 7)$ and $(2, 1)$.

(A) $y = \frac{3}{2}(7) - 2$

(B) $7 = \frac{3}{2}x - 2$

(C) $y = \frac{3}{2}x - 4$

(D) $y = \frac{3}{2}x - 2$

23. Identify the appropriate formula to find one unknown length of a side in a right triangle when you know the lengths of the other two sides.

(A) $a = \frac{1}{2}bh$

(B) $a^2 + b^2 = c^2$

(C) $c^2 = ab^2$

(D) $a^3 + b^4 = c^5$

24. Find 35 percent of 200.

(A) 75

(B) 46

(C) 70

(D) 21

25. Solve for a if $b = -5.75$:

$$\frac{3a}{2} + b = 3.25$$

(A) -1.7

(B) 2.5

(C) 7

(D) 6

Chapter 14

Practice Exam 1: Answers and Explanations

D id you do well on the first practice exam? I sure hope so! Use this answer key to score the practice exam in Chapter 13, and check out the answer explanations. If you didn't do well, don't worry — there are three more practice tests in this book to help you hone your English and math skills.

REMEMBER

The AFQT isn't scored based on number correct, number wrong, or even percent of questions correct. Instead, the score is derived by comparing your raw score with the raw score of others who have taken the test before you. In determining the raw score, harder questions are worth more points than easier questions. (For more on scoring, turn to Chapter 2.)

Don't waste time trying to equate your score on this practice test with your potential score on the actual AFQT. It can't be done. Instead, use the results of this practice test to determine which areas you should devote more study time to.

Part 1: Arithmetic Reasoning

Mathematical word problems can be tough. You have to develop a skill for determining which factors are relevant to the problem and then be able to convert those factors into a mathematical formula to arrive at a correct solution. Yikes! No wonder so many math books are on the market! A few good ones that may help are *Basic Math & Pre-Algebra For Dummies* by Mark Zegarelli; *Math Word Problems For Dummies, Algebra I For Dummies,* and *Algebra II For Dummies,* all by Mary Jane Sterling; *Geometry For Dummies* by Mark Ryan; and *SAT II Math For Dummies* by Scott Hatch, JD, and Lisa Zimmer Hatch, MA — all published by Wiley.

Reviewing Chapters 9 and 11 and the additional practice questions in Chapter 12 may also help. Finally, Chapters 21 and 22 may help you improve your scores.

1. B. $2.50

You can create an equation to solve this problem, where c represents coffee.

$$c + 4(1.25) = 7.5$$
$$c + 5 = 7.5$$
$$c + 5 - 5 = 7.5 - 5$$
$$c = 2.5$$

2. C. 324 square inches

The formula to find the area of a square is $A = s^2$, where s represents the length of a side. Replace s with 18 to solve:

$$s^2 = 18^2 = 18 \times 18 = 324$$

The area of the square is 324 square inches.

3. A. 16

It's often helpful to plan your attack on these types of problems by creating your own variables. Let a represent Abigail's age; because Danielle is twice as old, her age is $2a$.

In three years, Abigail will be $a + 3$ years old, and Danielle will be $2a + 3$ years old. The sum of their ages will be 30.

Your equation should represent adding their future ages and setting the sum equal to 30.

$$(a + 3) + (2a + 3) = 30$$
$$3a + 6 = 30$$
$$3a + 6 - 6 = 30 - 6$$
$$3a = 24$$
$$\frac{3a}{3} = \frac{24}{3}$$
$$a = 8$$

Abigail is 8 years old, and the problem tells you that Danielle is twice as old. Multiply Abigail's age by two to find Danielle is now 16.

4. A. $300

First, subtract how much Tammy spent on rims from her total:

$$\$950 - \$500 = \$450$$

Between window tint and the new radio, Tammy spent $450. Let x represent how much she spent on window tint and $2x$ represent how much she spent on the radio; then solve for x:

$$x + 2x = 450$$
$$3x = 450$$
$$\frac{3x}{3} = \frac{450}{3}$$
$$x = 150$$

Remember that x represents how much Tammy spent on window tint. She spent $150 on window tint and twice as much on the radio. Therefore, she spent $300 on the radio.

5. **C. 80**

Let x represent the number you need to find. Your equation looks like this:

$$\frac{1}{2}x + 17 = 57$$

$$\frac{1}{2}x + 17 - 17 = 57 - 17$$

$$\frac{1}{2}x = 40$$

$$\frac{1}{2}x(2) = 40(2)$$

$$x = 80$$

The original number is 80.

6. **C. $1\frac{4}{5}$ cups**

This ratio problem requires you to set a proportion. You don't have to worry about the baking powder, though; this question asks you how much flour you need.

If you can make 10 pancakes with 3 cups of flour, your ratio looks like this:

$$\frac{\text{flour}}{\text{pancakes}} = \frac{3}{10}$$

To find out how much flour you need to make just six pancakes, create an expression that looks like this, letting x represent how much flour you need:

$$\frac{\text{flour}}{\text{pancakes}} = \frac{x}{6}$$

The two ratios are equivalent, so create an equation and cross-multiply to solve for x:

$$\frac{3}{10} = \frac{x}{6}$$

$$10x = 18$$

$$\frac{10x}{10} = \frac{18}{10}$$

$$x = \frac{18}{10}$$

$$x = 1\frac{8}{10} = 1\frac{4}{5}$$

7. **B. 4.4 hours**

Both men are painting the room together, so it's a shared-work problem. Start by considering what portion of the room each man paints per hour. In one hour, Tim paints $\frac{1}{10}$ of the room, because it takes 10 hours for him to paint an entire room. Create an equation to find the total portion of the room painted per hour when they work together.

$$\frac{1}{10} + \frac{1}{8} = x$$

Find a common denominator and solve for x:

$$\frac{1}{10} + \frac{1}{8} = x$$

$$\frac{1}{10}\left(\frac{4}{4}\right) + \frac{1}{8}\left(\frac{5}{5}\right) = x$$

$$\frac{4}{40} + \frac{5}{40} = x$$

$$x = \frac{9}{40}$$

In one hour, the two men paint $\frac{9}{40}$ of the room. Let t stand for the total time they take to paint the room together.

$$\frac{9}{40} = \frac{1}{t}$$
$$9t = 40$$
$$t = \frac{40}{9} \approx 4.4$$

Together, the two men can paint the room in about 4.4 hours. You can also solve this problem using the shared-work formula from Chapter 11.

8. **C. 13 feet**

The area of a rectangle is its length times its width, or $A = lw$. The area and the length are given in the problem, so create an equation to solve for the unknown width. Let w represent the garden's width:

$$156 = 12w$$
$$\frac{156}{12} = \frac{12w}{12}$$
$$w = 13$$

Ebony's garden must be 13 feet wide.

9. **D. 45 and 47**

The question asks you to find two consecutive odd numbers, so Choices (A) and (B) can't be correct. Check the other choices. Choice (C) is $43 + 45 = 88$, and Choice (D) is $45 + 47 = 92$, so Choice (D) is correct.

If you don't read all the answer choices, you'll have to do more math. To solve the problem algebraically, let n represent the first number and $n + 2$ represent the second number. Note that n and $n + 2$ are the variables used to represent any pair of consecutive odd *or* even numbers.

Your equation looks like this:

$$n + (n + 2) = 92$$
$$2n + 2 = 92$$
$$2n + 2 - 2 = 92 - 2$$
$$2n = 90$$
$$\frac{2n}{2} = \frac{90}{2}$$
$$n = 45$$

The first number is 45. Because the next consecutive odd number is 47, Choice (D) is correct. You can double-check your math by adding both numbers together; you get 92.

10. **A. $5.95**

This problem requires you to go through several steps. First, double Davy's monthly allowance because he saved it for two months: $17 \times 2 = \$34$.

The problem tells you Davy spent $\frac{3}{5}$ of his allowance on apps, which means he had $\frac{2}{5}$ left. Figure out how much that is by multiplying:

$$\$34\left(\frac{2}{5}\right) = \$34(0.4) = \$13.60$$

He spent $\frac{1}{8}$ of the remainder, so he has $\frac{7}{8}$ of $13.60 left. Multiply again to see how much money that is:

$$\$13.60\left(\frac{7}{8}\right) = \$13.60(0.875) = \$11.90$$

Davy has half of that left:

$$\$11.90 \div 2 = \$5.95$$

Another way to solve this problem is to multiply all the fractions listed before you multiply by the dollar amount:

$$\frac{2}{5} \cdot \frac{7}{8} \cdot \frac{1}{2} = \frac{\cancel{2}}{5} \cdot \frac{7}{8} \cdot \frac{1}{\cancel{2}} = \frac{7}{40} = 0.175$$
$$0.175(\$34) = \$5.95$$

11. B. $35

The key to this type of problem is to define each variable in the same terms. If you choose to represent each barista with a different variable, you have a single equation with three variables, which is unsolvable.

Start with Tatiana, the person who made the least. Let x represent how much Tatiana made, and because Maria made twice that much, let $2x$ represent Maria's earnings. Let $2x + 12$ represent Pilar's earnings.

The sum of their earnings is $187. Write an equation to represent the sum and solve for x:

$$x + 2x + (2x + 12) = 187$$
$$5x + 12 = 187$$
$$5x + 12 - 12 = 187 - 12$$
$$5x = 175$$
$$\frac{5x}{5} = \frac{175}{5}$$
$$x = 35$$

Tatiana made $35. (And, if you're interested, Maria made $70, while Pilar racked up $82 in tips. Add them all together and you get their total, $187.)

12. A. 48 square inches

The formula to find the area of a triangle is $A = \frac{1}{2}bh$, where A represents area, b represents the length of the base, and h represents the triangle's height. Replace the variables with the values given in the problem and solve:

$$A = \frac{1}{2}(8)(12)$$
$$= \frac{1}{2}(96)$$
$$= 48$$

The area of the triangle is 48 square inches.

13. D. 784 miles

Start by simplifying each exponential term. First, $7^2 = 7 \times 7 = 49$ miles per hour. The car traveled for 2^4 hours, and $2^4 = 2 \times 2 \times 2 \times 2 = 16$. Now multiply the rate by the time to determine that the car traveled 49 mph $\times$ 16 hours = 784 miles.

14. A. 12 minutes

There's plenty of unnecessary information for you to ignore in this problem. First, it doesn't matter what time the start gun fires. Second, it doesn't matter how fast the first runner moves. The problem only asks how long it takes the second runner to reach the finish line, which is 2 miles from the starting point.

You can use a modified form of the distance formula ($d = rt$, where d represents distance, r represents rate, and t represents time) to find out how long it takes the second runner to complete the race:

$$t = \frac{d}{r}$$
$$= \frac{2}{10}$$
$$= \frac{1}{5}$$

Because you're working in miles per hour, the runner reaches the end in one-fifth of an hour, or 12 minutes $(60 \div 5 = 12)$.

15. C. 192

Let x represent the boat's speed, and use the distance formula ($d = rt$, where d represents distance, r represents rate, and t represents time) to create a table. The rate of travel is the boat's speed plus or minus the speed of the current, and the distance is the rate times the time.

	Rate	Time	Distance
Downstream	$x+4$	3	$3(x+4)$
Upstream	$x-4$	4	$4(x-4)$

The problem tells you that the distances are equal, so put set the distances equal to each other and solve for x:

$$3(x+4) = 4(x-4)$$
$$3x + 12 = 4x - 16$$
$$3x + 12 - 12 = 4x - 16 - 12$$
$$3x = 4x - 28$$
$$3x - 4x = -28 + 4x - 4x$$
$$-x = -28$$
$$x = 28$$

The boat's speed is 28 miles per hour. Now use the distance formula with the man's upstream trip (or the downstream trip, which works just as well) to figure out how far the man traveled:

$$d = rt$$
$$= 3(x+4)$$
$$= 3(28+4)$$
$$= 3(32)$$
$$= 96$$

The man traveled 96 miles in one direction, and because the trip back was also 96 miles, he traveled 192 miles round-trip.

16. B. 6

Although it doesn't look like it on the surface, this is a mixture word problem. Let s represent the number of sweatshirts Sadie bought and create a table to help build the correct equation:

	Number	Price per Item	Total
Sweatshirts	s	$27.50	$27.5s$
Jeans	$15-s$	$33.25	$33.25(15-s)$
Total	15		$447

Create an equation by looking at the "Total" column; then solve for s:

$$27.5s + 33.25(15-s) = 447$$
$$27.5s + 498.75 - 33.25s = 447$$
$$-5.75s + 498.75 = 447$$
$$-5.75s + 498.75 - 498.75 = 447 - 498.75$$
$$-5.75s = -51.75$$
$$\frac{-5.75s}{-5.75} = \frac{-51.75}{-5.75}$$
$$s = 9$$

That means Sadie bought nine sweatshirts. Because she bought fifteen items of clothing, the remaining six were jeans.

17. B. 11^{10}

Because the magnification of the eyepiece compounds the magnification of the lens, you multiply the two terms. These two exponential terms have the same base (11), so when multiplying, simply add the exponents. Your work looks like this:

$$11^8 \times 11^2 = 11^{8+2} = 11^{10}$$

18. C. 6 pounds

Let x represent the number of pounds of chocolate that Michael bought. The total cost is the number of pounds times the price per pound, so your equation looks like this:

$$4.5x = 27$$
$$\frac{4.5x}{4.5} = \frac{27}{4.5}$$
$$x = 6$$

Michael bought 6 pounds of chocolate.

19. C. 342.25 cm²

The problem tells you that one diagonal is 18.5 centimeters long and the other is twice that, or 37 centimeters.

The formula to find the area of a kite is $A = \frac{(d_1 \times d_2)}{2}$, where d_1 represents the length of the first diagonal and d_2 represents the length of the second diagonal. Replace the variables and solve:

$$A = \frac{(18.5 \times 37)}{2}$$
$$= \frac{684.5}{2}$$
$$= 342.25 \text{ cm}^2$$

If you don't remember the formula to find the area of a kite, you're definitely not alone — but you can still solve this problem. A kite is a pair of identical triangles stuck together. The base of the triangle is one diagonal, and the height of the triangle is half the other diagonal. Use the formula to find the area of a triangle, and double it:

$$A = 2\left(\frac{1}{2}bh\right) = bh$$

Using this formula, your work looks like this:

$$A = 18.5 \cdot 18.5$$
$$A = 342.25$$

20. **C. 90 inches**

According to the question, the American flag's height-to-width ratio is 1:1.5. For every one unit the flag is high, it must be 1.5 units wide.

Multiply 60 by 1.5 to find out how wide the flag must be at that height:

$$60 \times 1.5 = 90$$

The flag must be 90 inches wide.

21. **C. $24,727.50**

There are at least two ways to solve this problem.

You can multiply the original amount by 1.05 (that's $100\% + 5\%$) to find the new price. Turn the percentage into a decimal:

$$23,550 \times 1.05 = 24,727.50$$

Alternatively, you can figure out 5% of the original price and then add it to the original price:

$$x = 23,550 + (23,550 \times 0.05)$$
$$x = 23,550 + 1,177.5$$
$$x = 24,727.5$$

Remember that you have limited time when you take the ASVAB. The shortest route to the answer is your best bet (unless you forget the shortest route)!

22. **C. 920 feet**

This problem is asking you to find the perimeter of a rectangle. To find perimeter, you add the lengths of all the sides together. In this case, you're adding two sides that measure 300 feet each and two sides that measure 160 feet each.

$$300 + 300 + 160 + 160 = 920$$

You've walked 920 feet.

Alternatively, you can add double the length and double the width: $2(300) + 2(160) = 920$.

Or you can add the length and width, then double the sum: $2(300 + 160) = 920$.

These are all versions of the perimeter formula, and the method you're most comfortable with is the one you should use on the ASVAB.

23. A. 7

Remember that with money problems involving change, your calculations will most likely be easier if you multiply by 100. This is not a necessary step if you find it's quicker to solve using decimals!

Let d represent the number of dimes in Carter's pocket. You know he has 23 coins, so the number of nickels in his pocket is $23 - d$ (because all the coins that aren't dimes must be nickels).

Each dime is worth $0.10, and each nickel is worth $0.05. The sum of the values of the coins equals $1.50, so create an equation and solve for d:

$$0.1d + 0.05(23 - d) = 1.5$$
$$(0.1d \times 100) + (0.05 \times 100)(23 - d) = (1.5 \times 100)$$
$$10d + 5(23 - d) = 150$$
$$5d + 115 = 150$$
$$5d + 115 - 115 = 150 - 115$$
$$5d = 35$$
$$\frac{5d}{5} = \frac{35}{5}$$
$$d = 7$$

Carter has 7 dimes in his pocket.

24. C. 122.7 square inches

The formula to find the area of a circle is $A = \pi r^2$, where A represents area and r represents the circle's radius. A circle's radius is half its diameter, so divide 12.5 by 2 to find the circle's radius is 6.25 inches.

Replace the variable r in the formula with 6.25 and solve, using 3.14 for π:

$$A = 3.14(6.25^2)$$
$$= 3.14(39.0625)$$
$$= 122.65625 \text{ in.}^2$$

Because all the answer choices contain one digit after the decimal point, you'll have to round your answer. 122.65625 rounds up to 122.7.

25. A. 5,188 cubic inches

This problem requires you to solve two volume formulas: One for a cube and one for a rectangular box (or prism, if you want to get fancy about it). When you figure out the volume of each, you'll subtract the cube from the rectangle to figure out how much room Vicki has left.

The formula to find the volume of a cube is $V = s^3$, where V represents volume and s represents the length of one side of the cube. The problem says one side of the music box is 8 inches, so find that volume first:

$$V = 8^3$$
$$= 512 \text{ in.}^3$$

The music box takes up 512 cubic inches.

Finding the volume of Vicki's suitcase requires you to use the formula $V = lwh$, where V represents volume, l represents length, w represents width, and h represents height. Replace the variables with what you know from the problem:

$$V = 10 \times 19 \times 30$$
$$= 5{,}700 \text{ in.}^3$$

Subtract the space the music box will occupy to find out how much room Vicki will have left:

$$5{,}700 - 512 = 5{,}188 \text{ in.}^3$$

26. D. 44

Horses and dogs each have four legs, and kangaroos have two. Let a represent the number of horses and dogs together, because they each have an equal number of legs. Let b represent the number of kangaroos. Let c represent the total number of all the animals' legs. Your equation should look like this:

$$4a + 2b = c$$

Replace the variables with the values you know (there are ten horses and dogs, and two kangaroos):

$$c = 4(10) + 2(2)$$
$$c = 40 + 4$$
$$c = 44$$

Together, these animals have 44 legs.

If you're like many people, though, you didn't create an algebraic formula; you just multiplied and added. That's fine, too — you don't need to create extra work for yourself when you only have a limited time to come up with all the answers.

(And if you were guessing instead of doing the math, you could immediately rule out Choice (C), because there's no way *any* number of animals who have even numbers of legs could total 41.)

27. B. $-\dfrac{1}{2}$

Solve the equation for y to put the equation in slope-intercept form, $y = mx + b$, where m represents the slope of the line and b represents where the line intercepts the y-axis:

$$2y = 4x + 3$$
$$\frac{2y}{2} = \frac{4x + 3}{2}$$
$$y = 2x + \frac{3}{2}$$

The coefficient in front of the x tells you that the slope of this line is 2.

To find the slope of any line that's perpendicular to this one, you need its negative reciprocal. (*Remember:* All pairs of perpendicular lines have negative reciprocal slopes, and all parallel lines have the same slope!) The negative reciprocal of 2 is $-\dfrac{1}{2}$.

28. D. $\frac{7}{8}$

First, figure out how many gallons of fruit juice and almond milk Samantha has in total by adding $\frac{2}{3}$ and $\frac{7}{12}$. Start by finding the lowest common denominator; then add:

$$\frac{2}{3} + \frac{7}{12} = \frac{8}{12} + \frac{7}{12} = \frac{15}{12}$$

Convert your answer to a mixed number and reduce:

$$\frac{15}{12} = 1\frac{3}{12} = 1\frac{1}{4}$$

Samantha has $1\frac{1}{4}$ gallons of almond milk and fruit juice combined. Subtract that from the total number of gallons she has in the fridge by finding a common denominator. In this case, $1\frac{1}{4}$ needs to become $1\frac{2}{8}$:

$$2\frac{1}{8} - 1\frac{2}{8} = \frac{7}{8}$$

29. C. 99

Let x represent what Dave needs to score on his final exam. Remember, there are six tests that count toward his final grade (he's already taken four, and the final exam is worth two). Your equation should look like this:

$$\frac{91 + 79 + 88 + 84 + x + x}{6} = 90$$

Simplify the equation. Then solve for x:

$$\frac{342 + 2x}{6} = 90$$

$$\frac{342 + 2x}{\cancel{6}} \times \frac{\cancel{6}}{1} = 90 \times 6$$

$$342 + 2x = 540$$

$$2x + 342 - 342 = 540 - 342$$

$$2x = 198$$

$$\frac{2x}{2} = \frac{198}{2}$$

$$x = 99$$

Dave needs to score 99 on his final exam to get an A in the class.

30. D. 2.25 quarts

First figure out the area of Alberto's living room wall by using the formula for the area of a rectangle, which is $A = lw$, where A represents area, l represents length, and w represents width:

$$A = 7.5 \times 15$$
$$= 112.5 \text{ ft}^2$$

The area of the wall is 112.5 square feet.

Because Alberto wants to use two coats of paint, he'll need enough paint for twice that, which is 225 square feet.

Each quart of paint covers exactly 100 square feet, so divide the total area by the area covered per quart. Alberto will need 2.25 quarts of paint for this job.

Part 2: Word Knowledge

I hope you did well on this subtest. (I was crossing my fingers the whole time!) If not, you may want to take another gander at Chapter 5 and the practice questions in Chapter 6. Chapters 21 and 22 may also help.

If you need additional study references to improve your vocabulary ability, you may want to consider *Vocabulary For Dummies* by Laurie E. Rozakis, PhD, and *SAT Vocabulary For Dummies* by Suzee Vlk (both published by Wiley).

1. **B. debatable**

   Ambiguous is an adjective that means open to multiple interpretations or having a double meaning.

2. **A. short-lived**

   Transient is an adjective that means lasting for only a short time. It's also used as a noun to refer to a person who's staying or working in a place for a short time.

3. **D. active.**

   Sedentary is an adjective that refers to spending too much time being inactive. It also applies to work that's characterized by a lack of physical activity or to a seated position.

   "Carolyn's sedentary lifestyle contributed to her weight gain."

4. **B. nearness**

   Proximity is a noun that means nearness in space, time, or relationship.

5. **A. bad-tempered.**

   Petulant is an adjective that describes people or their mannerisms as childishly sulky or bad-tempered.

   "He acted like a petulant child when he stormed out of the office like that."

6. **A. skeptical.**

   Incredulous is an adjective that means unwilling (or unable) to believe something.

   "The journalist was incredulous that the politician lied right to her face."

7. **D. unwarranted.**

   Gratuitous is an adjective that means uncalled for or unwarranted. It can also refer to something that's done for free or given freely.

   "The movie was filled with gratuitous violence."

8. **C. reject**

   Boycott is a verb that means to withdraw from commercial or social relations with an organization. It's also a noun that refers to a ban against relations with certain groups or against cooperation with a certain policy.

9. **B. misconception**

   Fallacy is a noun that means a mistaken belief, especially one that's based on an unsound argument.

10. **A. exempt**

Immune is an adjective that describes someone or something as protected or exempt from an obligation or the effects of something.

11. **B. collage.**

Mosaic is a noun that means a picture or pattern produced by arranging multiple small, colored pieces together.

"That beautiful mosaic has been in the entryway since 1910."

12. **C. best**

Elite is a noun that refers to a select part of a group that's superior to the rest.

13. **D. change.**

Mutate is a verb that means to change or cause to change.

"Cancer cells are more likely to mutate than other cells are."

14. **A. snippet.**

Excerpt is a noun that means a short extract from a piece of writing or music, a film, or a broadcast.

"Because the excerpt was so terrible, we decided not to buy the book."

15. **B. shocking**

Outrageous is an adjective that describes someone or something that's shockingly bad or excessive. It can also mean extremely bold, unusual, and startling.

16. **A. always.**

Invariably is an adverb that describes something that happens on every occasion, in every case.

"He was invariably optimistic, even when things weren't going his way."

17. **C. hamper.**

Encumber is a verb that means to restrict or burden someone or something to make free action or movement difficult.

"Those boots will only encumber you when you try walking up that sand dune."

18. **D. talent.**

Flair is a noun that means a special or instinctive talent, ability, or aptitude for doing something well. It can also mean stylishness or originality.

19. **B. composure**

Equanimity is a noun that means mental calmness, composure, and self-possession, especially in a difficult situation.

20. **A. fumble.**

Grope is a verb that means to feel or search blindly or uncertainly.

"The child woke from his nightmare and groped for the light switch."

21. **D. dull.**

Sleek is an adjective that means smooth and glossy.

"She had sleek, blond hair that gleamed in the sun."

22. **C. heartless**

Callous is an adjective that means showing or having an insensitive, cruel disregard for other people. Don't get it mixed up with *callus*, which is what you get on your pencil-gripping fingers when you take too many ASVAB practice tests in a row.

23. **A. waterproof.**

Impervious is an adjective that means not allowing fluid to pass through. It also means unable to be affected by.

"The outer shell of the sleeping bag is impervious, so you can sleep just about anywhere."

24. **A. income.**

Revenue is a noun that means income, especially as it pertains to a company or organization.

"This year's revenue exceeded our goal by $1,500."

25. **B. grind.**

Pulverize is a verb that means to reduce to fine particles.

"The seeds are pulverized into flour during the final step of the process."

26. **C. urgent**

Dire is an adjective that means extremely serious or urgent; it also describes a warning or threat that comes before a disaster.

27. **D. scold.**

Chastise is a verb that means to rebuke or reprimand severely.

"The teacher will definitely chastise you for forgetting your homework for the fifth time this week."

28. **A. imperceptible.**

Conspicuous is an adjective that means standing out so as to be clearly visible. It also means attracting attention.

"The skunk's conspicuous white stripe set off my internal alarm bells, and I ran."

29. **B. chance**

Opportunity is a noun that refers to a set of circumstances that makes it possible to do something.

30. **C. punishment.**

Vengeance is a noun that means punishment inflicted or retribution given for an injury or wrong.

"William the Conqueror's desire for vengeance led him to invade King Harold's domain."

31. A. disgraceful.

Deplorable is an adjective that means deserving strong condemnation.

"The prisoners lived in deplorable conditions while they were incarcerated at Alcatraz."

32. D. advance.

Recede is a verb that means to move back from a previous position.

"If we stay long enough, we can watch the tide recede."

33. B. unscramble

Decipher is a verb that means to convert a text written in code (or a coded signal) into normal language.

34. D. lengthen

Protract is a verb that means to prolong.

35. A. understandable

Articulate is an adjective that means having or showing the ability to speak coherently and fluently; it can refer to a person or to his or her words. It's also used as a verb that means to express an idea or feeling coherently and fluently.

Part 3: Paragraph Comprehension

So, how did you do? If you didn't do very well on this subtest, you may want to engage in some more reading practice. Improving your vocabulary can also help improve your reading comprehension skills; see Chapter 7 for some tips. You may also want to try a few of the practice questions in Chapter 8.

1. D. territorial

The author describes five major habitats: aquatic, aquatic margin, fossorial, terrestrial, and arboreal. Choice (D), territorial, is the only one of the answer choices not on that list.

2. B. 42

The passage says, "Forty-two per cent of the 78 species are wholly or partly arboreal." You don't have to do any math because the question asks you for the percentage of reptiles and amphibians that are arboreal.

3. C. an office building.

The passage calls the space a "commercial palace" and describes the revolving door, and it mentions an "alphabetical list of offices."

4. D. a detective agency

The passage describes the man's "thrill of triumph" when he finds "INTERNATIONAL DETECTIVE AGENCY" on the directory. Although he does see an elevator, buy a chocolate bar, and find the directory, it's the detective agency he wanted to find.

5. C. candy

The passage says, "he invested in a gooey chocolate bar," which means he bought candy.

6. B. 3 days

The passage says, "Tusayan and Zuñi are but three days distant to the traveler on foot."

7. D. Both A and B are correct.

The passage says that General Bragg lost most of the battles he fought ("most of the actual battles Bragg fought ended in defeat") and that he was "almost universally disliked by his peers." The passage also describes what other officers called him, from "muddle-headed" to a scoundrel and a coward.

Although Bragg did train troops, that didn't have anything to do with why he was considered "the Confederacy's worst general."

8. C. Fayetteville, North Carolina

Although each of the locations listed in the answer choices is mentioned in the passage, only one is noted as the location of an installation named after the general. The passage says, "The U.S. Army installation in Fayetteville, North Carolina — Fort Bragg — is named for the late general."

Choice (A), Warrenton, North Carolina, is where General Bragg was born. Choice (B), West Point, is where he learned to operate as an officer in the military, and Choice (D), Baton Rouge, Louisiana, is where Bragg led a group of volunteers to capture a federal arsenal.

9. C. The only other place available was a disreputable tavern.

The passage says Susan's father "relented a little" when the young people of the village asked about using his ballroom a second time because "the only other place available was a disreputable tavern where liquor was sold."

10. B. cornfields that bloomed in early spring

The passage says, "The tender green of the shooting corn made the valley beautiful in early spring."

Although the author mentions the blue skies and bright sun from Choice (A) and the grass that grows between the rocks from Choice (C), she means neither as a compliment. She mentions the sheep, too, but says nothing about them contributing to the valley's beauty.

11. C. The boy's family was poor.

The passage says, "Life was rough and hard in that country home, but the peasant baby grew into a strong, hardy boy." Because the boy was a peasant, and because life was "rough and hard," you can assume that the author means the boy's family was poor.

12. A. to keep warm

The passage says that scaldinoes are "little pots of hot charcoal" that women carried under their shawls. The author describes cold, wintry weather and mentions that men "flung their cloaks closer round them," while "even the dogs had a sad, half-frozen look." Therefore, you can assume that the women carried scaldinoes to keep warm.

13. **C. pain**

The passage says the quill remained in One Eye's muzzle for weeks until it worked its way out — and that One Eye is very careful to stay far enough away from the porcupine's tail so it can't hurt him. Choice (C) is the correct answer because the phrase "a rankling flame" describes the pain the quill caused One Eye.

14. **D. a nuclear explosion.**

The passage doesn't directly say that the flash is from a nuclear explosion, but there are several clues, such as calling the area "ground zero" and saying that "direct viewing of the fireball" should not be attempted, even with welder's glass.

15. **B. at the hills or sky**

The passage says, "The recommended procedure was to face away from ground zero and watch the hills or sky until the fireball illuminated the area."

Part 4: Mathematics Knowledge

This subtest would have been much easier if the ASVAB folks allowed you to use a calculator, wouldn't it? Fortunately, the problems on this subtest are designed so they can be solved using only scratch paper, a good ol' No. 2 pencil, and a little brain sweat.

If you're still having difficulty, give Chapter 9 a gander. *Basic Math & Pre-Algebra For Dummies* by Mark Zegarelli; *Algebra I For Dummies* and *Algebra II For Dummies*, both by Mary Jane Sterling; *Geometry For Dummies* by Mark Ryan; and *SAT II Math For Dummies* by Scott Hatch, JD, and Lisa Zimmer Hatch, MA (all published by Wiley) can also help you improve your math knowledge score. You can find additional practice questions in Chapter 10.

1. **A.** $\frac{2}{9}$

TIP

When a question on the ASVAB asks you to find the fraction with the least (or greatest) value, eliminate obviously wrong answers first. When the numerator is more or less than half its denominator, you have a clearer picture of which answers don't make sense. In this case, finding the lowest common denominator isn't necessary, because Choice (A) is the only one that's less than $\frac{1}{2}$.

If eliminating answers leaves you with two or more choices, find the lowest common denominator so you can see how the fractions compare. In this case, the lowest common denominator of all the choices is 18 (each of the denominators given in the problem is a factor of 18).

Order each fraction based on its new numerator:

$$\frac{2}{9} = \frac{4}{18}$$

$$\frac{1}{2} = \frac{9}{18}$$

$$\frac{5}{6} = \frac{15}{18}$$

$$\frac{2}{3} = \frac{12}{18}$$

Now you can see that because $\frac{2}{9} = \frac{4}{18}$, that's the fraction with the least value.

2. A. 4

Combine like terms. Then isolate the variable x to solve:

$$3x + 8x = 44$$
$$11x = 44$$
$$\frac{11x}{11} = \frac{44}{11}$$
$$x = 4$$

3. C. $V = lwh$

The formula to find the volume of a rectangular prism, or box, is $V = lwh$, where V represents volume, l represents the length of a side, w represents width, and h represents height.

In case you were wondering, Choice (A) is based on the formula to find the area of a triangle, Choice (B) is the formula you need if you're finding the volume of a cylinder, and Choice (D) is based on the formula to find the surface area of a cube.

4. B. 37.68 cm

Using the approximation 3.14 for π, substitute the given information into the formula for the circumference of a circle:

$$C = 12\pi = 12(3.14) = 37.68$$

TIP

Here's a tip that can speed up your problem-solving on the ASVAB: Because the approximation for pi has multiple digits and decimal places, leave calculations in terms of pi until you've solved everything you can in the equation.

5. D. 81 square feet

The formula to find the area of a square is $A = s^2$, where A represents area and s represents the length of a side. All the sides have equal length in a square, so replace the variable s with 9:

$$A = s^2$$
$$= 9^2$$
$$= 9 \times 9$$
$$= 81 \text{ ft}^2$$

Remember, when you're finding the area of something, you're using square measurements — area is two-dimensional, like the flat surface of the ground or a wall. Cubic measurements are three-dimensional, and they relate to volume, like filling up a box or a swimming pool.

6. C. 56 cm

To find the perimeter of any shape, simply add the lengths of all the sides together. The perimeter of this triangle is $13 + 25 + 18 = 56$ centimeters.

7. A. 52°

All the angles in a triangle must add up to 180°. Because this triangle is labeled as a right triangle by the box in the corner, you know that angle is 90°. The question tells you another angle is 38°, so you can figure out the measure of Angle C by adding 90 and 38, then subtracting the total from 180:

$$90 + 38 = 128$$
$$180 - 128 = 52$$

Angle C measures 52°.

8. **C. 3,140 cubic centimeters**

The formula to find the volume of a cylinder is $V = \pi r^2 h$, where V represents volume, r represents the cylinder's radius, and h represents its height.

Replace the variables with the values shown in diagram and use 3.14 to approximate π:

$$V = 3.14\left(10^2\right)(10)$$
$$= 3.14(100)(10)$$
$$= 314(10)$$
$$= 3{,}140 \text{ cm}^3$$

The volume of this right cylinder is 3,140 cubic centimeters.

In many problems, it's easier to leave pi intact so you don't have to work with decimals right away. You could solve this problem this way, too:

$$1{,}000\pi = 1{,}000(3.14) = 3{,}140$$

(Try to remember that you should leave the pi for dessert. I don't want to do it either, but sometimes it's for the best!)

9. **B. 7**

Replace the variable a with 4, and then solve for b:

$$2(4) + b = 15$$
$$8 + b = 15$$
$$b + 8 - 8 = 15 - 8$$
$$b = 7$$

10. **B. 9**

Simplify the equation by distributing the 14. Then solve for x:

$$14(x + 9) = 252$$
$$14x + 126 = 252$$
$$14x + 126 - 126 = 252 - 126$$
$$14x = 126$$
$$\frac{14x}{14} = \frac{126}{14}$$
$$x = 9$$

11. **B. 113.04 square inches**

The formula to find the area of a circle is $A = \pi r^2$, so replace the variable r with the circle's radius (6 inches) and use 3.14 to approximate pi:

$$A = \pi\left(6^2\right)$$
$$= 3.14(36)$$
$$= 113.04 \text{ in.}^2$$

The area of this circle is 113.04 square inches.

12. A. 67°

All the angles on a line must add up to 180°, and the problem gives you three of the four angles measures.

Add all three angles, and then subtract the sum from 180 to find y:

$$45 + 39 + 29 = 113$$
$$180 - 113 = 67$$

The value of y is 67°.

13. D. 22

This problem requires you to cross-multiply to clear the fractions:

$$\frac{x-6}{4} = \frac{x+2}{6}$$
$$6(x-6) = 4(x+2)$$

Then you can isolate x to solve:

$$6x - 36 = 4x + 8$$
$$6x - 36 - 4x = 4x + 8 - 4x$$
$$2x - 36 = 8$$
$$2x - 36 + 36 = 8 + 36$$
$$2x = 44$$
$$\frac{2x}{2} = \frac{44}{2}$$
$$x = 22$$

14. C. $y \geq 11$

Although the $\geq$ can make this inequality look confusing, you'll solve it just like a regular equation. Start by combining like terms (the y, in this case) and then isolate the variable y to solve:

$$7 + y + 4y \geq 51 + y$$
$$7 + 5y \geq 51 + y$$
$$7 + 5y - 7 \geq 51 + y - 7$$
$$5y \geq 44 + y$$
$$5y - y \geq 44 + y - y$$
$$4y \geq 44$$
$$\frac{4y}{4} \geq \frac{44}{4}$$
$$y \geq 11$$

Remember: When solving inequalities, if you divide both sides by a negative number, you must also flip the inequality symbol. If the problem had involved dividing by -4 in the last step (instead of 4), the final answer would have been $y \leq -11$.

15. A. 12

Start by multiplying both sides by x to make the problem look more familiar:

$$\frac{7}{8} \div x = \frac{7}{96}$$
$$\frac{7}{8} \div x \cdot \frac{x}{1} = \frac{7}{96} \cdot \frac{x}{1}$$
$$\frac{7}{8} = \frac{7}{96}x$$

Isolate x by multiplying both sides by the reciprocal of $\frac{7}{96}$ (because the 7s cancel out):

$$\frac{7}{8} = \frac{7}{96}x$$

$$\frac{7}{8} \cdot \frac{96}{7} = x$$

$$\frac{\cancel{7}}{8} \cdot \frac{96}{\cancel{7}} = x$$

$$12 = x$$

16. C. 34.5

Sometimes it's easier to multiply both sides of the problem by 10 right out of the gate to avoid working with decimals. Add x to both sides first so you can skip using the distributive property, and then isolate x to solve:

$$18x = 655.5 - x$$

$$18x + x = 655.5$$

$$19x = 655.5$$

$$19x(10) = (655.5)(10)$$

$$190x = 6,555$$

$$\frac{190x}{190} = \frac{6,555}{190}$$

$$x = \frac{69}{2}$$

$$x = 34.5$$

17. B. 28 square inches

You can see that there's a 4-inch-x-3-inch rectangle cut out of a larger rectangle, so the simplest way to solve this problem is to imagine you're looking at a whole rectangle and find its area first. Then subtract the area of the smaller rectangle to get the final answer.

If you look at the larger rectangle in whole, its length is 5 inches and its width is 8 inches. The formula to find the area of a rectangle is $A = lw$, where l represents length and w represents width. The area of the larger rectangle is $8 \times 5 = 40$ square inches.

The smaller rectangle measures 4 inches wide by 3 inches long. Its area is $4 \times 3 = 12$ square inches.

Subtract the area of the smaller rectangle from the area of the larger rectangle to get your answer: $40 - 12 = 28$ square inches.

18. A. $8\frac{5}{32}$

A problem like this is easier to tackle if you turn $\frac{5}{8}$ into the decimal 0.625 before you start. Once that's done, you can multiply both sides by 1,000 to ditch the decimals and solve:

$$4x = 32\frac{5}{8}$$

$$4x = 32.625$$

$$4x \cdot 1,000 = 32.625(1,000)$$

$$4,000x = 32,625$$

$$\frac{4,000x}{4,000} = \frac{32,625}{4,000}$$

$$x = \frac{261}{32}$$

$$x = 8\frac{5}{32}$$

Because all the answer choices are in fraction form, you didn't have to convert your answer to a decimal.

Here's an even faster approach: Isolate x by dividing both sides by 4, treating the whole number (32) and the fraction separately:

$$4x = 32\frac{5}{8}$$

Whole number part: $32 \div 4 = 8$

Fractional part: $\frac{5}{8} \div 4 = \frac{5}{8} \cdot \frac{1}{4} = \frac{5}{32}$

Add the two parts of the problem back together. The answer is still $8\frac{5}{32}$.

19. C. $2b\sqrt{3a^3}$

To solve this problem, you'll have to separate the variables from the real numbers:

$$\sqrt{12a^3b^2} = \sqrt{12}\sqrt{b^2}\sqrt{a^3}$$

Then break 12 into its primes (2^2 and 3); your work looks like this:

$$2\sqrt{3}\sqrt{b^2}\sqrt{a^3}$$

Break down the variable b, because the square of a squared number is itself, and apply the radical rule $\sqrt[n]{a^m} = a^{\frac{m}{n}}$ to what's left:

$$2b\sqrt{3a^3}$$

20. D. −5

Collect all terms with an a on one side. Then divide both sides by 12 to solve.

$$14a = -60 + 2a$$
$$14a - 2a = -60 + 2a - 2a$$
$$12a = -60$$
$$\frac{12a}{12} = \frac{-60}{12}$$
$$a = -5$$

21. A. 7.7×10^6

Scientific notation requires you to write a number in two parts: A real number between 1 and 10, multiplied by 10 raised to a power. The power shows you how many places to move the decimal point to get back to the original number.

In scientific notation, only one digit goes before the decimal point. For 7,700,000, the decimal point goes after the first 7 but before the second. There are then six digits after the decimal point, which tells you what power you need to use. The answer is 7.7×10^6.

22. D. $y = \frac{3}{2}x - 2$

Remember the point-slope form of a line is $y = mx + b$, where m represents the slope and b represents the point where the line intersects the y-axis. The first thing you need to find is the slope. Use the formula $m = \frac{y_2 - y_1}{x_2 - x_1}$, and plug in the given x and y values given by the coordinates.

$$m = \frac{1-7}{2-6} = \frac{-6}{-4} = \frac{3}{2}$$

Now you have the first piece of the puzzle, so plug it into the equation:

$$y = mx + b$$
$$y = \frac{3}{2}x + b$$

Substitute the given values for x and y from the coordinates of one of the points into the equation and then solve for b. Here are the calculations if you choose the first point:

$$7 = \frac{3}{2}(6) + b$$
$$\frac{3}{2}(6) + b = 7$$
$$9 + b = 7$$
$$9 + b - 9 = 7 - 9$$
$$b = -2$$

Now that you know $b = -2$, you know the complete equation is $y = \frac{3}{2}x - 2$.

You could've used the second set of points to find the equation, too. Either way, the answer is the same.

23. **B.** $\boldsymbol{a^2 + b^2 = c^2}$

Using the Pythagorean theorem, you can find an unknown side's length in a right triangle if you know the lengths of the other two sides.

In this formula, a and b stand for the lengths of the legs, and c stands for the length of the hypotenuse.

24. **C. 70**

Before you work on percentage problems, convert the percentage to a decimal. 35 percent translates into 0.35.

The word *of* in the problem tells you to multiply the two quantities. 35% *of* 200 = 35% times 200:

$$0.35 \times 200 = 70$$

Tip: If you're doing mental math, you could reason that 35 is 35 percent of 100. If you double that to find 35 percent of 200, you'll come up with 70 again. This works because multiplication is commutative. Mathematically, $35 \cdot \frac{1}{100} \cdot 200 = 200 \cdot \frac{1}{100} \cdot 35$, and because 200% is 2, you can double 35 to get the answer on this (or a similar) problem.

25. **D. 6**

The problem tells you that $b = -5.75$, so replace the variable b in the equation with the given value; then simplify:

$$\frac{3a}{2} + b = 3.25$$
$$\frac{3a}{2} + (-5.75) = 3.25$$
$$\frac{3a}{2} - 5.75 + 5.75 = 3.25 + 5.75$$
$$\frac{3a}{2} = 9$$
$$\frac{3a}{2} \times \frac{2}{1} = 9 \times \frac{2}{1}$$
$$3a = 18$$
$$a = 6$$

Answer Key

Part 1: Arithmetic Reasoning

1.	B	7.	B	13.	D	19.	C	25.	A
2.	C	8.	C	14.	A	20.	C	26.	D
3.	A	9.	D	15.	C	21.	C	27.	B
4.	A	10.	A	16.	B	22.	C	28.	D
5.	C	11.	B	17.	B	23.	A	29.	C
6.	C	12.	A	18.	C	24.	C	30.	D

Part 2: Word Knowledge

1.	B	8.	C	15.	B	22.	C	29.	B
2.	A	9.	B	16.	A	23.	A	30.	C
3.	D	10.	A	17.	C	24.	A	31.	A
4.	B	11.	B	18.	D	25.	B	32.	D
5.	A	12.	C	19.	B	26.	C	33.	B
6.	A	13.	D	20.	A	27.	D	34.	D
7.	D	14.	A	21.	D	28.	A	35.	A

Part 3: Paragraph Comprehension

1.	D	4.	D	7.	D	10.	B	13.	C
2.	B	5.	C	8.	C	11.	C	14.	D
3.	C	6.	B	9.	C	12.	A	15.	B

Part 4: Mathematics Knowledge

1.	A	6.	C	11.	B	16.	C	21.	A
2.	A	7.	A	12.	A	17.	B	22.	D
3.	C	8.	C	13.	D	18.	A	23.	B
4.	B	9.	B	14.	C	19.	C	24.	C
5.	D	10.	B	15.	A	20.	D	25.	D

Chapter **15**

Practice Exam 2

The Armed Services Vocational Aptitude Battery (ASVAB) includes four subtests that make up the Armed Forces Qualification Test (AFQT) score: Arithmetic Reasoning, Word Knowledge, Paragraph Comprehension, and Mathematics Knowledge.

The military branches use the AFQT score as an initial qualifier to determine whether the military considers you to be "trainable." Each service has established its own minimum score. You can find much more information about how the AFQT is scored, and how the services use those scores, in Chapter 2.

REMEMBER

You can't take the AFQT by itself. You have to take the entire ASVAB exam, which includes nine total subtests. All the subtests of the ASVAB are used to determine military job qualifications, while the four subtests that make up the AFQT score are used to determine military qualification.

After you complete the entire sample test, check your answers against the answers and explanations in Chapter 16. On the actual AFQT, hard questions are worth more points than easy questions, so you can't score your test by a simple number correct or number wrong. (Chapter 2 explains how the AFQT is scored.)

Consider using this test as a progress check after your first week or two of study. Adjust your study plan accordingly.

Answer Sheet for Practice Exam 2

Part 1: Arithmetic Reasoning

1. Ⓐ Ⓑ Ⓒ Ⓓ	7. Ⓐ Ⓑ Ⓒ Ⓓ	13. Ⓐ Ⓑ Ⓒ Ⓓ	19. Ⓐ Ⓑ Ⓒ Ⓓ	25. Ⓐ Ⓑ Ⓒ Ⓓ
2. Ⓐ Ⓑ Ⓒ Ⓓ	8. Ⓐ Ⓑ Ⓒ Ⓓ	14. Ⓐ Ⓑ Ⓒ Ⓓ	20. Ⓐ Ⓑ Ⓒ Ⓓ	26. Ⓐ Ⓑ Ⓒ Ⓓ
3. Ⓐ Ⓑ Ⓒ Ⓓ	9. Ⓐ Ⓑ Ⓒ Ⓓ	15. Ⓐ Ⓑ Ⓒ Ⓓ	21. Ⓐ Ⓑ Ⓒ Ⓓ	27. Ⓐ Ⓑ Ⓒ Ⓓ
4. Ⓐ Ⓑ Ⓒ Ⓓ	10. Ⓐ Ⓑ Ⓒ Ⓓ	16. Ⓐ Ⓑ Ⓒ Ⓓ	22. Ⓐ Ⓑ Ⓒ Ⓓ	28. Ⓐ Ⓑ Ⓒ Ⓓ
5. Ⓐ Ⓑ Ⓒ Ⓓ	11. Ⓐ Ⓑ Ⓒ Ⓓ	17. Ⓐ Ⓑ Ⓒ Ⓓ	23. Ⓐ Ⓑ Ⓒ Ⓓ	29. Ⓐ Ⓑ Ⓒ Ⓓ
6. Ⓐ Ⓑ Ⓒ Ⓓ	12. Ⓐ Ⓑ Ⓒ Ⓓ	18. Ⓐ Ⓑ Ⓒ Ⓓ	24. Ⓐ Ⓑ Ⓒ Ⓓ	30. Ⓐ Ⓑ Ⓒ Ⓓ

Part 2: Word Knowledge

1. Ⓐ Ⓑ Ⓒ Ⓓ	8. Ⓐ Ⓑ Ⓒ Ⓓ	15. Ⓐ Ⓑ Ⓒ Ⓓ	22. Ⓐ Ⓑ Ⓒ Ⓓ	29. Ⓐ Ⓑ Ⓒ Ⓓ
2. Ⓐ Ⓑ Ⓒ Ⓓ	9. Ⓐ Ⓑ Ⓒ Ⓓ	16. Ⓐ Ⓑ Ⓒ Ⓓ	23. Ⓐ Ⓑ Ⓒ Ⓓ	30. Ⓐ Ⓑ Ⓒ Ⓓ
3. Ⓐ Ⓑ Ⓒ Ⓓ	10. Ⓐ Ⓑ Ⓒ Ⓓ	17. Ⓐ Ⓑ Ⓒ Ⓓ	24. Ⓐ Ⓑ Ⓒ Ⓓ	31. Ⓐ Ⓑ Ⓒ Ⓓ
4. Ⓐ Ⓑ Ⓒ Ⓓ	11. Ⓐ Ⓑ Ⓒ Ⓓ	18. Ⓐ Ⓑ Ⓒ Ⓓ	25. Ⓐ Ⓑ Ⓒ Ⓓ	32. Ⓐ Ⓑ Ⓒ Ⓓ
5. Ⓐ Ⓑ Ⓒ Ⓓ	12. Ⓐ Ⓑ Ⓒ Ⓓ	19. Ⓐ Ⓑ Ⓒ Ⓓ	26. Ⓐ Ⓑ Ⓒ Ⓓ	33. Ⓐ Ⓑ Ⓒ Ⓓ
6. Ⓐ Ⓑ Ⓒ Ⓓ	13. Ⓐ Ⓑ Ⓒ Ⓓ	20. Ⓐ Ⓑ Ⓒ Ⓓ	27. Ⓐ Ⓑ Ⓒ Ⓓ	34. Ⓐ Ⓑ Ⓒ Ⓓ
7. Ⓐ Ⓑ Ⓒ Ⓓ	14. Ⓐ Ⓑ Ⓒ Ⓓ	21. Ⓐ Ⓑ Ⓒ Ⓓ	28. Ⓐ Ⓑ Ⓒ Ⓓ	35. Ⓐ Ⓑ Ⓒ Ⓓ

Part 3: Paragraph Comprehension

1. Ⓐ Ⓑ Ⓒ Ⓓ　　4. Ⓐ Ⓑ Ⓒ Ⓓ　　7. Ⓐ Ⓑ Ⓒ Ⓓ　　10. Ⓐ Ⓑ Ⓒ Ⓓ　　13. Ⓐ Ⓑ Ⓒ Ⓓ
2. Ⓐ Ⓑ Ⓒ Ⓓ　　5. Ⓐ Ⓑ Ⓒ Ⓓ　　8. Ⓐ Ⓑ Ⓒ Ⓓ　　11. Ⓐ Ⓑ Ⓒ Ⓓ　　14. Ⓐ Ⓑ Ⓒ Ⓓ
3. Ⓐ Ⓑ Ⓒ Ⓓ　　6. Ⓐ Ⓑ Ⓒ Ⓓ　　9. Ⓐ Ⓑ Ⓒ Ⓓ　　12. Ⓐ Ⓑ Ⓒ Ⓓ　　15. Ⓐ Ⓑ Ⓒ Ⓓ

Part 4: Mathematics Knowledge

1. Ⓐ Ⓑ Ⓒ Ⓓ　　6. Ⓐ Ⓑ Ⓒ Ⓓ　　11. Ⓐ Ⓑ Ⓒ Ⓓ　　16. Ⓐ Ⓑ Ⓒ Ⓓ　　21. Ⓐ Ⓑ Ⓒ Ⓓ
2. Ⓐ Ⓑ Ⓒ Ⓓ　　7. Ⓐ Ⓑ Ⓒ Ⓓ　　12. Ⓐ Ⓑ Ⓒ Ⓓ　　17. Ⓐ Ⓑ Ⓒ Ⓓ　　22. Ⓐ Ⓑ Ⓒ Ⓓ
3. Ⓐ Ⓑ Ⓒ Ⓓ　　8. Ⓐ Ⓑ Ⓒ Ⓓ　　13. Ⓐ Ⓑ Ⓒ Ⓓ　　18. Ⓐ Ⓑ Ⓒ Ⓓ　　23. Ⓐ Ⓑ Ⓒ Ⓓ
4. Ⓐ Ⓑ Ⓒ Ⓓ　　9. Ⓐ Ⓑ Ⓒ Ⓓ　　14. Ⓐ Ⓑ Ⓒ Ⓓ　　19. Ⓐ Ⓑ Ⓒ Ⓓ　　24. Ⓐ Ⓑ Ⓒ Ⓓ
5. Ⓐ Ⓑ Ⓒ Ⓓ　　10. Ⓐ Ⓑ Ⓒ Ⓓ　　15. Ⓐ Ⓑ Ⓒ Ⓓ　　20. Ⓐ Ⓑ Ⓒ Ⓓ　　25. Ⓐ Ⓑ Ⓒ Ⓓ

Part 1: Arithmetic Reasoning

TIME: 36 minutes for 30 questions

DIRECTIONS: Arithmetic Reasoning is the second subtest of the ASVAB; it comes after General Science, which isn't part of the AFQT. These questions are designed to test your ability to use mathematics to solve various problems that may be found in real life — in other words, math word problems.

Each question is followed by four possible answers. Decide which answer is correct, and then mark the corresponding space on your answer sheet. Use your scratch paper for any figuring you want to do. You may *not* use a calculator.

1. Marty is building a rectangular fence in his backyard and has 200 feet of fencing he can use. If the yard is to be 15 feet wide and he uses all the fencing, how long will the yard be?

   (A) 27 ft
   (B) 72 ft
   (C) 85 ft
   (D) 87 ft

2. Henry is 48 inches tall. His older brother is 25 percent taller. How tall is Henry's brother?

   (A) 60 in.
   (B) 64 in.
   (C) 63 in.
   (D) 73 in.

3. Janet, Alice, and Gabriel are collecting cans for recycling. Altogether, they collected 473 cans. Janet collected 124 cans, and Alice collected 205 cans. How many cans did Gabriel collect?

   (A) 329
   (B) 142
   (C) 144
   (D) 167

4. The floor of Mr. Gilbert's office is in the shape of a rectangle with an area of 168 square feet. The length of the floor is 12 feet. What is the width?

   (A) 12 ft
   (B) 14 ft
   (C) 9 ft
   (D) 16 ft

5. There are 10 decimeters in a meter and 10 meters in a decameter. How many decimeters are there in 3 decameters?

   (A) 3,000
   (B) 0.03
   (C) 300
   (D) 30

6. At 9:00 a.m., the outside temperature was −14° Fahrenheit. By noon, the temperature increased by 21° Fahrenheit. What was the outside temperature at noon?

   (A) 7°
   (B) 6°
   (C) −7°
   (D) −35°

7. An airplane flew a distance of 180 miles in an hour and a half. What was the speed of the plane?

   (A) 120 mph
   (B) 110 mph
   (C) 180 mph
   (D) 270 mph

8. The ratio of cars to trucks is 3:4. There are 15 cars. How many trucks are there?

   (A) 24
   (B) 10
   (C) 12
   (D) 20

GO ON TO NEXT PAGE

9. A grocery store sells raisins for $3.50 per pound and almonds for $4 per pound. Keith bought just enough raisins and almonds to make a 2-pound mixture that is 40 percent raisins. How much did he pay for the raisins?

(A) $2.85

(B) $3.50

(C) $3.20

(D) $2.80

10. Patricia's age is one-third Ms. Chang's age. The sum of their ages is 56 years. What is Ms. Chang's age?

(A) 38

(B) 44

(C) 42

(D) 14

11. Ed worked 10 hours and earned $125. John also worked 10 hours, but his hourly rate is $0.50 less than Ed's hourly rate. How much did John earn for 10 hours of work?

(A) $118.50

(B) $60.00

(C) $119.50

(D) $120.00

12. A game board is in the shape of a square with a perimeter of 60 inches. What is the length of one side of the game board?

(A) 1 ft

(B) 1.25 ft

(C) 1.5 ft

(D) 1.75 ft

13. A recipe calls for $2\frac{3}{4}$ cups of milk, but you have only $1\frac{1}{2}$ cups of milk available. How much more milk do you need for the recipe?

(A) $1\frac{3}{5}$ cups

(B) $1\frac{1}{4}$ cups

(C) $1\frac{1}{5}$ cups

(D) $\frac{3}{4}$ cup

14. Maria invests $2,500 into a savings account. After 1 year, she has earned $100 in interest. What is the annual interest rate for the account?

(A) 4.5 percent

(B) 0.4 percent

(C) 4 percent

(D) 2.5 percent

15. What is the area of the region in this figure?

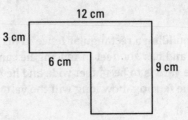

Illustration by Thomson Digital

(A) 72 cm²

(B) 36 cm²

(C) 90 cm²

(D) 30 cm²

16. Martha is teaching her first cooking class. 60 percent of the class — or 21 students — burned their quiche. How many total students are in the class?

(A) 27

(B) 31

(C) 35

(D) 39

17. Keisha walked a distance of 4.5 miles at a rate of 3 miles per hour. She started her walk at 3:40 p.m. What time did she finish her walk?

(A) 4:10 p.m.

(B) 3:55 p.m.

(C) 4:20 p.m.

(D) 5:10 p.m.

18. You earn $9.75 an hour and need to earn at least $150. Which inequality shows the number of hours, h, you must work?

(A) $9.75 < 150h$

(B) $9.75h \geq 150$

(C) $9.75h \leq 150$

(D) $\frac{19.75}{h} \geq 150$

19. Carlos has a model of his father's new truck. The model truck is 32 centimeters long. If the scale of the model is 2 centimeters = 0.25 meters, what is the approximate length of his father's truck?

(A) 4 m

(B) 8 m

(C) 10 m

(D) 12 m

20. Joan is selling 3 paintings. She places them in a row so the cost increases by $15 from left to right. The painting on the far left costs $29. What is the cost of the painting on the far right?

(A) $59

(B) $15

(C) $44

(D) $75

21. Megan is in a hurry to get to her grandmother's Thanksgiving dinner in Wyoming. If she is traveling a constant 50 miles per hour, how many hours will it take her to make the 600-mile trip?

(A) 30 hours

(B) 12 hours

(C) 60 hours

(D) 15 hours

22. On the expressway, where the speed limit is 60 miles per hour, the formula for calculating a speeding fine, F, is $F = 10(x-60)+80$, where x is the speed of the car in miles per hour. If Steve was fined $230 for speeding down the highway, how fast was he driving?

(A) 70 mph

(B) 75 mph

(C) 85 mph

(D) 80 mph

23. Nick recorded the odometer reading of 65,034 before filling his car with gas. The next time he filled his car with gas, the odometer reading was 65,322. He needed 12 gallons of gas to fill his tank. What is the best estimate of the car's gas mileage in miles per gallon (mpg)?

(A) 12 mpg

(B) 24 mpg

(C) 18 mpg

(D) 32 mpg

24. A can of beans is in the shape of a cylinder. The can has a diameter of 8 centimeters and a height of 10 centimeters. What is the volume of the can?

(A) 160π cm^3

(B) 640π cm^3

(C) 80π cm^3

(D) $1,600\pi$ cm^3

25. Matt must pay a $15 co-pay for each of his visits to a chiropractor. Then the insurance company pays 60 percent of the remaining cost of the visit. He made 10 visits to the chiropractor, each costing $305. How much did Matt pay for his chiropractor visits in total?

(A) $2,900

(B) $1,310

(C) $1,160

(D) $1,180

26. Marco can replace a truck tire in 20 minutes. His brother takes 10 minutes longer to do the same job. How long will replacing a truck tire take them if they work together?

(A) 18 minutes

(B) 16 minutes

(C) 12 minutes

(D) 25 minutes

GO ON TO NEXT PAGE

27. Each squeeze of a spray bottle's trigger emits 0.024 ounces of water. Ten squeezes of the trigger emit 2 percent of the total amount of water the bottle holds. How many ounces of water can the bottle hold?

(A) 16 oz

(B) 20 oz

(C) 24 oz

(D) 12 oz

28. A shoe box has a length of 30 centimeters, a width of 15 centimeters, and a height of 10 centimeters. What is the surface area of the shoe box?

(A) 3,600 cm²

(B) 4,500 cm²

(C) 1,800 cm²

(D) 900 cm²

29. Two runners start in the same place and run in opposite directions. The first runner averages 5 miles per hour, and the second runner averages 6 miles per hour. After how many hours will they be 11 miles apart?

(A) 1 hour

(B) 2 hours

(C) 1.5 hours

(D) 1.1 hours

30. The coach bought pepperoni pizzas for the entire soccer team, including himself. Each pizza cost \$12. When they were all finished eating, $2\frac{3}{4}$ pizzas were left over. Each of the 15 players on the team ate a quarter of a pizza, and the coach ate half of a pizza. How much did the coach pay for the pizzas, before tax?

(A) \$72

(B) \$180

(C) \$84

(D) \$88

Part 2: Word Knowledge

TIME: 11 minutes for 35 questions

DIRECTIONS: The Word Knowledge subtest is the third subtest of the ASVAB; it follows Arithmetic Reasoning. The questions are designed to measure your vocabulary knowledge. You'll see three types of questions on this subtest. The first type simply asks you to choose a word or words that most nearly mean the same as the underlined word in the question. The second type includes an underlined word used in a sentence, and you are to choose the word or words that most nearly mean the same as the underlined word, as used in the context of the sentence. The third type of question asks you to choose the word that has the opposite or nearly opposite meaning as the underlined word. Each question is followed by four possible answers. Decide which answer is correct, and then mark the corresponding space on your answer sheet.

1. The word most opposite in meaning to <u>savor</u> is
   (A) deny.
   (B) enjoy.
   (C) detest.
   (D) keep.

2. <u>Lackluster</u> most nearly means
   (A) exuberant.
   (B) benign.
   (C) mediocre.
   (D) sharp.

3. The word most opposite in meaning to <u>participate</u> is
   (A) abstain.
   (B) join.
   (C) contribute.
   (D) shove.

4. The word most opposite in meaning to <u>organize</u> is
   (A) arrange.
   (B) mess up.
   (C) juggle.
   (D) disturb.

5. <u>Unkempt</u> most nearly means
   (A) clean.
   (B) orderly.
   (C) disastrous.
   (D) messy.

6. I knew the <u>preliminary</u> interview was merely to get my foot in the door.
   (A) falling
   (B) first
   (C) closing
   (D) binding

7. The clash between Mary and her mother-in-law was <u>inevitable</u> because of their different values.
   (A) unlikely
   (B) unavoidable
   (C) unrelenting
   (D) unusual

8. Toby took the sunset as a good <u>omen</u> for his new life in Florida.
   (A) fact
   (B) letter
   (C) decree
   (D) sign

9. The <u>frigid</u> wind on the chairlift was enough to give someone frostbite.
   (A) stale
   (B) warm
   (C) cold
   (D) boring

GO ON TO NEXT PAGE

10. No one voted for Michael, because he was such a <u>tyrant</u> last semester.

    (A) leader

    (B) oppressor

    (C) guide

    (D) teacher

11. <u>Counterfeit</u> most nearly means

    (A) authentic.

    (B) soiled.

    (C) phony.

    (D) credible.

12. The word most opposite in meaning to <u>burden</u> is

    (A) relieve.

    (B) bother.

    (C) trouble.

    (D) support.

13. The word most opposite in meaning to <u>animate</u> is

    (A) deflect.

    (B) stir.

    (C) enliven.

    (D) subdue.

14. <u>Plausible</u> most nearly means

    (A) impossible.

    (B) factual.

    (C) reasonable.

    (D) perishable.

15. <u>Pliable</u> most nearly means

    (A) dormant.

    (B) flexible.

    (C) stiff.

    (D) spontaneous.

16. <u>Resignation</u> most nearly means

    (A) approval.

    (B) acceptance.

    (C) denial.

    (D) disbelief.

17. <u>Obliterate</u> most nearly means

    (A) pamper.

    (B) wound.

    (C) destroy.

    (D) control.

18. <u>Heed</u> most nearly means

    (A) betray.

    (B) abide.

    (C) ignore.

    (D) escape.

19. Sean felt <u>immense</u> pride as he accepted the gold medal.

    (A) massive

    (B) contained

    (C) minute

    (D) similar

20. Jenny made a choice to <u>pursue</u> her dream of dancing despite her parents' disapproval.

    (A) follow

    (B) ignore

    (C) mediate

    (D) bring forth

21. I was impressed by how <u>tactful</u> my father was regarding my recent breakup.

    (A) cruel

    (B) oblivious

    (C) sensitive

    (D) doting

22. I loved watching my jock brother <u>endure</u> my sister's ballet recitals.

    (A) tolerate

    (B) approve

    (C) deny

    (D) abstain

23. Charli's <u>longevity</u> during the marathon training was better than she expected.

    (A) brevity

    (B) distance

    (C) number

    (D) endurance

24. The girl had to <u>console</u> her friend, who couldn't stop crying.

    (A) compartment

    (B) comfort

    (C) hide

    (D) push away

25. When the coach claps his hands, we're supposed to <u>disperse</u> to our positions in the field.

    (A) run

    (B) gather

    (C) scatter

    (D) formulate

26. <u>Enshrouded</u> most nearly means

    (A) illuminated.

    (B) enclosed.

    (C) revealed.

    (D) covered.

27. <u>Repudiate</u> most nearly means

    (A) disown.

    (B) waver.

    (C) reclaim.

    (D) adjust.

28. <u>Oblique</u> most nearly means

    (A) forward.

    (B) cordial.

    (C) indirect.

    (D) candid.

29. <u>Acquiesce</u> most nearly means

    (A) agree with.

    (B) argue with.

    (C) hide from.

    (D) move into.

30. <u>Tenuous</u> most nearly means

    (A) stable.

    (B) flimsy.

    (C) firm.

    (D) buoyant.

31. The children were <u>unbridled</u> during playtime, looking more like wild animals than 5-year-olds.

    (A) organized

    (B) relieving

    (C) rampant

    (D) joyous

32. I won't <u>ostracize</u> the new girl just because the other kids are jealous.

    (A) ridicule

    (B) befriend

    (C) exclude

    (D) restrict

33. <u>Replete</u> most nearly means

    (A) full.

    (B) barren.

    (C) meager.

    (D) coarse.

34. <u>Enigma</u> most nearly means

    (A) accessible.

    (B) mystery.

    (C) transparent.

    (D) profound.

35. Carlton stepped in to <u>assuage</u> the patron's fury after a waiter spilled soup on the man.

    (A) pacify

    (B) replace

    (C) order

    (D) determine

Part 3: Paragraph Comprehension

TIME: 13 minutes for 15 questions

DIRECTIONS: Paragraph Comprehension is the fourth subtest on the ASVAB; it comes after Word Knowledge. The questions are designed to measure your ability to understand what you read. In this part of the test, you see one or more paragraphs of reading material, followed by incomplete statements or questions. Read the paragraph and select the choice that best completes the statement or answers the question. Then mark the corresponding space on your answer sheet.

Questions 1 and 2 refer to the following passage.

Dog training isn't for the faint of heart. You have to be tough and let the dog know who's boss, or it'll never listen to anything you say. Sometimes, you have to punish it, and it'll cry or look at you in anger or surprise. If your dog is a puppy, you may have to put it in a crate when you leave the house, which will cause the puppy to whine and become anxious. All these actions can be difficult when you're looking into the face of an adorable dog, so you have to be firm in your resolve even when you feel bad.

1. What is the main point of the passage?

   (A) Crate training is the best way to train a dog.

   (B) Dogs are easy to train.

   (C) All dogs require training.

   (D) Trainers should avoid becoming emotional.

2. In this passage, <u>resolve</u> means

   (A) determination.

   (B) indecision.

   (C) prowess.

   (D) fear.

The sudden death of Dale Earnhardt was a shock to not only the NASCAR community but also the world. His aggressiveness on the track and success behind the wheel made him a well-known figure and a household name. He started his career in 1975, racing as part of the Winston Cup Series in Charlotte, North Carolina. Before his fatal crash in 2001 during the Daytona 500, he won more than 76 races, including one Daytona 500 race in 1998. He shares the record for the most NASCAR Premier Series Championships with Richard Petty and Jimmie Johnson at seven apiece.

3. How many Daytona 500 races did Dale Earnhardt win?

   (A) 7

   (B) 76

   (C) 1

   (D) None of the above

Bipolar disorder is a mental illness that involves acute swings in mood, ranging from a heightened state of mania and an extreme state of depression. More than 4 percent of the population lives with bipolar disorder, which can be a debilitating factor in day-to-day functioning. The cause is still a topic of research for scientists, although they suspect that genetics and environment are responsible, at least in part, for the onset of the illness.

4. As used in this passage, <u>acute</u> most nearly means

   (A) pointed.

   (B) severe.

   (C) sensitive.

   (D) mild.

For a sport to get into the Olympic Games, the International Olympic Committee must first recognize the activity as an official sport, and the sport must have a governing agency that isn't politically affiliated. In 2014, 12 sports were added to the Winter Olympics in Sochi, Russia, but many more have come and gone over the years. For instance, rugby was added and dropped from the games three times between 1900 and 1928. However, the sport was added again to the 2016 Summer Olympics in Rio de Janeiro, Brazil, due to a gap in the roster created by the elimination of softball and baseball from the 2012 Summer Games in London, England.

5. How many times has rugby been added to the roster of Olympic sports?

    (A) 3

    (B) 12

    (C) 4

    (D) 1

6. According to the passage, what country hosted the 2016 Summer Olympics?

    (A) Holland

    (B) England

    (C) Russia

    (D) Brazil

Making bread and cooking are different beasts. You can easily substitute ingredients and improvise the recipe as you go in cooking, but you must use exact ingredients and measurements for bread-making. For example, if you want to use whole-grain flour instead of bread flour, you have to change the ratio of wet ingredients to get the same texture. Cooking is much more flexible than breadmaking.

7. What is the author trying to convey in this paragraph?

    (A) Making bread is easier than cooking.

    (B) Anyone can measure ingredients.

    (C) Breadmaking is more exact than cooking.

    (D) Whole grains are better for cooking.

The history of the bald eagle in the United States is an interesting tale; the national bird came very close to extinction in the mid-20th century. An act of Congress in 1940 barred the trapping and killing of the eagles in the United States, but their numbers continued to decline. It was discovered that the pesticide DDT caused a calcium breakdown in bald eagles, resulting in sterilization or fragile eggshells and therefore low reproduction rates. With the ban of DDT use in 1972, the slow regrowth of the species began. In 1995, the eagles were removed from the endangered species list; in 1998, they were removed from the threatened species list. The bald eagles now live in abundance in North America.

8. In the passage, <u>barred</u> means

    (A) promoted.

    (B) outlawed.

    (C) approved.

    (D) disowned.

9. In what year did the action that eventually led to the growth of the bald eagle population begin?

    (A) 1972

    (B) 1998

    (C) 1995

    (D) 1940

Jill has danced her best many times in front of audiences, but this performance is the most important one of her life. Her audition for the famed Joffrey Ballet company is the end of a long journey of schooling and competitions, all of which were in preparation for this moment. She has spent the last 15 years improving her skills, and she is confident in her ability to achieve her goal. Dancing with the Joffrey Ballet would be a dream come true for Jill.

10. What is the main point of this passage about Jill?

    (A) Jill is a skilled ballet dancer.

    (B) Ballet is Jill's preferred form of exercise.

    (C) Joining the Joffrey Ballet is Jill's life's goal.

    (D) Jill is overly determined.

GO ON TO NEXT PAGE

A good quilt was once simply fluffy, decorative, and cozy, creating the image of a grandmother lovingly sewing patches of material together by hand. Today, however, the art of quilting is more lucrative than just a hobby. National and international quilting contests are regular annual events with hundreds of entrants. The quilts depict a variety of scenes, from landscapes to skylines, and the prizes for best in show can reach up to $10,000. Quilting has become a serious activity for many, and the results are impressive.

11. According to the passage, quilt makers

(A) have plenty of time on their hands.

(B) have opportunities to make a lot of money.

(C) are in short supply.

(D) make quilts only with squares.

For sale: Inflatable lifeboat for use in calm, shallow water. Has some puncture holes on the surface. Water typically fills the bottom, and air must be pumped periodically to avoid sinking. This boat isn't good for water deeper than four feet or for people who don't swim. Asking market price of $200.

12. According to this advertisement, the lifeboat would be safe to use in

(A) a lake.

(B) the ocean.

(C) a river.

(D) None of the above

Questions 13 and 14 refer to the following passage.

A new study indicates that childhood obesity begins in the early years of life. Researchers followed more than 7,500 obese students between kindergarten (age 5) and eighth grade. The findings indicated that two-thirds of the children who were obese in kindergarten remained obese in eighth grade. The study also showed that children who were obese in eighth grade were likely to remain that way into adulthood. The researchers measured the children seven times for height and weight over the period of the study, and determinations of "obese" or "overweight" were made using body mass index levels.

13. Based on the information in the passage, which step might reduce adolescent obesity?

(A) promoting extracurricular activities

(B) removing a child from school

(C) forming a support group for obese children

(D) preventing a child from becoming overweight before the age of 5

14. According to the passage, approximately how many children who participated in the study fell out of the obese range?

(A) one-third

(B) 7,500

(C) two-thirds

(D) 25 percent

Crispin Glover is a cult actor famous for his dark and brooding characters. Finding success first in the thriller *The River's Edge*, he became the most famous nerd in the world with his portrayal of outcast bookworm George McFly in the box-office hit *Back to the Future.* He is often referred to as a shape shifter for his ability to fully become his characters. His role as the slick samurai in the movie adaptation of the TV series *Charlie's Angels* was no exception.

15. In this passage, <u>adaptation</u> can best be defined as

(A) version.

(B) copy.

(C) continuation.

(D) screenplay.

Part 4: Mathematics Knowledge

TIME: 24 minutes for 25 questions

DIRECTIONS: Mathematics Knowledge is the fifth subtest on the ASVAB; it follows Paragraph Comprehension. The questions are designed to test your ability to solve general mathematical problems. Each question is followed by four possible answers. Decide which answer is correct, and then mark the corresponding space on your answer sheet. Use your scratch paper for any figuring you want to do. You may *not* use a calculator.

1. Which number is prime?

(A) 1

(B) 2

(C) 10

(D) 51

2. Which decimal is equal to eleven thousandths?

(A) 1.1

(B) 0.11

(C) 0.011

(D) 0.101

3. $1.091 + 0.19 =$

(A) 1.100

(B) 1.182

(C) 1.281

(D) 1.11

4. An equilateral triangle has a perimeter of 54 feet. What is the length of one side of the triangle?

(A) 18 ft

(B) 16 ft

(C) 27 ft

(D) 162 ft

5. What is 40 percent of 220?

(A) 8.8

(B) 55

(C) 44

(D) 88

6. What is $\frac{26}{8}$ expressed as a decimal?

(A) 4.25

(B) 3.5

(C) 2.75

(D) 3.25

7. Which of the following is equal to $p^3 \times p^{-1}$?

(A) p^2

(B) $2p^2$

(C) p^{-3}

(D) p

8. $\frac{8}{25} - \frac{3}{25} =$

(A) $\frac{5}{50}$

(B) $\frac{1}{5}$

(C) $\frac{1}{4}$

(D) $\frac{5}{0}$

9. For which value of y is the inequality $y + 2 < -6$ true?

(A) -9

(B) -8

(C) 7

(D) 9

10. Simplify: $3(x - 5) + 4x$

(A) $7x - 5$

(B) $7x - 15$

(C) $7x + 35$

(D) $12x - 15$

GO ON TO NEXT PAGE

11. The longest side of a right triangle has a length of 17 feet, and the shortest side has a length of 8 feet. What is the length of the remaining side?

(A) 10 ft

(B) 12 ft

(C) 15 ft

(D) 16 ft

12. What is the result when the quotient of 40 and 20 is decreased by the sum of 1 and 5?

(A) −5.5

(B) 2

(C) 14

(D) −4

13. $15 - 3 \times 2^2 =$

(A) −21

(B) 576

(C) 3

(D) 48

14. What is the least common multiple of 12 and 20?

(A) 2

(B) 60

(C) 120

(D) 240

15. What is the product of $\frac{3}{4}$ and $\frac{8}{7}$?

(A) $\frac{6}{7}$

(B) $\frac{11}{28}$

(C) 1

(D) $\frac{24}{11}$

16. $3(-4)(1)(-2) =$

(A) −24

(B) 12

(C) 18

(D) 24

17. $\sqrt[3]{64} =$

(A) 8 and −8

(B) 4 and −4

(C) 8 only

(D) 4 only

18. $\frac{2}{5} + \frac{1}{3} =$

(A) $\frac{5}{50}$

(B) $\frac{1}{5}$

(C) $\frac{11}{15}$

(D) $\frac{3}{8}$

19. The length of one side of the square is 20 meters. Find the area of the region that is inside the square but outside the circle.

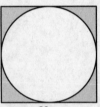

20 m

Illustration by Thomson Digital

(A) 314 m²

(B) 86 m²

(C) 856 m²

(D) 234 m²

20. The sum of three consecutive odd integers is 63. What is the middle number?

(A) 21

(B) 23

(C) 25

(D) 27

21. Solve the equation $x^2 + 4 = 20$ for x.

(A) 16 only

(B) 8 and −8

(C) 4 only

(D) 4 and −4

22. The measure of the supplement of an angle is equal to twice the measure of the angle. What is the measure of the angle?

   (A) 60°

   (B) 30°

   (C) 120°

   (D) 90°

23. Solve for x: $\dfrac{9}{x} = \dfrac{81}{10}$

   (A) 90

   (B) $1\dfrac{1}{9}$

   (C) $\dfrac{1}{9}$

   (D) $2\dfrac{1}{9}$

24. Simplify: $\dfrac{x^2 - 16}{x - 4}$

   (A) $\dfrac{1}{x - 4}$

   (B) $\dfrac{x - 16}{x + 4}$

   (C) $x + 4$

   (D) $x - 4$

25. The measures of the angles of a given quadrilateral are 55, 90, 111, and $2n$. What is the value of n?

   (A) 45°

   (B) 90°

   (C) 110°

   (D) 52°

Chapter 16

Practice Exam 2: Answers and Explanations

The answers and explanations in the following sections help you determine how well you performed on the practice test in Chapter 15 — and give you some hints about where you may have dropped a decimal point or two. Don't worry; it happens to the best of us.

Don't focus too much on scores. On the actual AFQT, harder questions are worth more points than easier questions. The AFQT is one of those rare tests on which you can miss some questions and still max out your test score. As always, use the results to decide where you want to concentrate your study time. Do you need more work on math or reading and verbal skills? This chapter helps you find out.

If you want to skip the explanations for now and see which questions you got right or wrong, go to the Answer Key at the end of the chapter.

Part 1: Arithmetic Reasoning

The Arithmetic Reasoning subtest is not only one of the important subtests that make up the AFQT, but it's also used as a qualification factor for many of the military jobs you can choose from. You may want to glance at *ASVAB For Dummies* by Rod Powers and Angie Papple Johnston (published by Wiley) to see which military jobs require you to do well on this subtest.

If you missed more than five or six questions on this practice test, it's time to dig out that old high-school math textbook and wrap your brain around some math problems. Chapters 9 and 11 can also help you out. Some other great books that may help you score better on this subtest include *Math Word Problems For Dummies*, *Algebra I For Dummies*, and *Algebra II For Dummies*, all by Mary Jane Sterling; *Basic Math & Pre-Algebra For Dummies* by Mark Zegarelli; *Geometry For Dummies* by Mark Ryan; and *SAT II Math For Dummies* by Scott Hatch, JD, and Lisa Zimmer Hatch, MA — all published by Wiley.

1. C. 85 ft

Marty has 200 feet of fencing and wants to fence in a rectangular yard. If the yard is to be 15 feet wide, then use the formula for perimeter to find the length:

$$P = 2(l + w)$$
$$200 = 2(l + 15)$$
$$\frac{200}{2} = \frac{2(l + 15)}{2}$$
$$100 - 15 = l + 15 - 15$$
$$85 = l$$

You can check your work by plugging the numbers for length and width back into the equation to make sure the answer comes out to 200 or less (the total amount of fencing Marty has).

2. A. 60 in.

First, find 25 percent of 48: $0.25(48) = 12$ inches. (Instead of multiplying 48 by 0.25, you can also recognize that 25 percent is equal to $\frac{1}{4}$ of something and simply divide 48 by 4 to arrive at the same answer.) Henry's brother's height is $48 + 12 = 60$ inches.

3. C. 144

Together, Janet and Alice collected 329 cans: $124 + 205 = 329$. Because the group collected 473 cans, subtract Janet and Alice's total to find how many cans Gabriel collected: $473 - 329 = 144$ cans.

4. B. 14 ft

The area formula for a rectangle is $A = lw$, where $A =$ area, $l =$ length, and $w =$ width. Substitute the known values into this formula and then isolate w by dividing both sides by 12:

$$168 = 12w$$
$$\frac{168}{12} = \frac{12w}{12}$$
$$14 = w$$

5. C. 300

A decameter equals 10 meters, so 3 decameters equals 30 meters. Because there are 10 decimeters in a meter, you multiply that number by the total number of meters: $10(30) = 300$ decimeters in a decameter.

6. A. 7°F

Because the temperature increased, add to find the outside temperature at noon:

$$-14 + 21 = 21 + (-14) = 21 - 14 = 7° \text{ Fahrenheit}$$

7. A. 120 mph

The distance formula is $d = rt$, where d is the distance, r is the rate, and t is the time. In this problem, you can save time by using fractions instead of decimals (that's not always the case, though). Turn 1.5 (the time the plane flew) into an improper fraction:

$$1\frac{1}{2} = \frac{3}{2}$$

Replace the variables with the values you know and cancel out everything you can:

$$\frac{180}{\frac{3}{2}} = 180 \cdot \frac{2}{3} = \frac{\overset{60}{\cancel{180}}}{1} \cdot \frac{2}{\underset{1}{\cancel{3}}} = 120$$

If you're not good with fractions, it's okay to stick with the decimal. Substitute the known values into this formula and then isolate r by dividing both sides by 1.5:

$$180 = r(1.5)$$
$$\frac{180}{1.5} = \frac{1.5r}{1.5}$$
$$120 = r$$

8. D. 20

Let $x =$ the number of trucks, and express the two ratios of cars to trucks as a proportion. So $\frac{3}{4} = \frac{15}{x}$ because you know there are 15 cars. Cross-multiply to solve for x.

$$\frac{3}{4} = \frac{15}{x}$$
$$3x = 4(15)$$
$$3x = 60$$
$$\frac{3x}{3} = \frac{60}{3}$$
$$x = 20$$

9. D. $2.80

Forty percent of 2 pounds is $0.4(2) = 0.8$ pounds. The amount he paid for the raisins is $0.8(\$3.50) = \$2.80$.

10. C. 42

If x is Patricia's age, then Ms. Chang's age is $3x$. Set up the equation and solve for x:

$$x + 3x = 56$$
$$4x = 56$$
$$\frac{4x}{4} = \frac{56}{4}$$
$$x = 14$$

Patricia's age is 14, so Ms. Chang's age is $3(14) = 42$. To double-check, add the two ages together to make sure they equal 56 as the problem indicates: $14 + 42 = 56$.

11. D. $120.00

Ed's hourly rate is $125 \div 10 = \$12.50$ per hour. John's hourly rate is $\$12.50 - \$0.50 = \$12$ per hour. For 10 hours of work, John earns $10(\$12) = \$120$.

You can skip working out Ed's hourly rate if you multiply the $0.50 difference in the men's hourly wages by 10 hours of work $(\$0.50 \times 10 = \$5)$ and subtract that from Ed's total earnings: $\$125 - \$5 = \$120$.

TIP

If you find a shortcut that works for you — and that you'll remember on test day — use it. But if you're a little shaky on the details, stick with what you know so you don't make mistakes that drop your AFQT score.

12. B. 1.25 ft

The length of one side of the square game board is $\frac{60}{4} = 15$ inches. There are 12 inches in 1 foot, so 15 inches is 1 foot and 3 inches, or $1\frac{3}{12} = 1\frac{1}{4} = 1.25$ feet.

13. B. $1\frac{1}{4}$ cups

Write each mixed number as an improper fraction. To do so, multiply the denominator by the whole number and then add the result to the numerator:

$$2\frac{3}{4} = \frac{4 \times 2 + 3}{4} = \frac{8+3}{4} = \frac{11}{4}$$
$$1\frac{1}{2} = \frac{2 \times 1 + 1}{2} = \frac{2+1}{2} = \frac{3}{2}$$

Write the fractions using a common denominator, and then subtract to find the amount of milk you need. The common denominator is 4 because 4 is the least common multiple (LCM) of 4 and 2:

$$\frac{11}{4} - \frac{3}{2} = \frac{11}{4} - \frac{6}{4}$$
$$= \frac{11-6}{4}$$
$$= \frac{5}{4}$$
$$= 1\frac{1}{4}$$

Another approach is to add to the first amount $\left(1\frac{1}{2}\right)$ until you reach the second amount $\left(2\frac{3}{4}\right)$. If you add $\frac{1}{2}$ cup, you'll hit an even 2 cups; another $\frac{3}{4}$ cup will bring you to $2\frac{3}{4}$ cups. Add the fractions $\left(\frac{1}{2} + \frac{3}{4}\right)$ to see how much milk you added altogether:

$$\frac{1}{2} + \frac{3}{4} = \frac{2}{4} + \frac{3}{4} = \frac{5}{4} = 1\frac{1}{4}$$

14. C. 4 percent

Use the interest formula $I = prt$, where I is the interest, p is the principal, r is the interest rate (as a decimal), and t is the time in years. Substitute known values into the formula and solve for r.

$$100 = 2,500(r)(1)$$
$$100 = 2,500r$$
$$\frac{100}{2,500} = \frac{2,500r}{2,500}$$
$$r = \frac{1}{25}$$
$$r = 0.04$$

Write 0.04 as a percent by moving the decimal point two places to the right: $0.04 = 4$ percent.

15. **A. 72 cm²**

Divide the region into two rectangles and find the length of the missing sides.

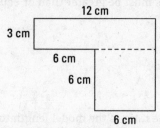

Illustration by Thomson Digital

The formula for the area of a rectangle is $A = lw$. Find the area of the upper rectangle and add it to the area of the lower rectangle.

Upper rectangle: $A = 3(12) = 36$ cm²

Lower rectangle: $A = 6(6) = 36$ cm²

The area of the total region is $36 + 36 = 72$ cm².

16. **C. 35**

If 60 percent of Martha's cooking class is equal to 21 people, you must find the total number of students by using x for the total number of people in the class.

Write the equation like this:

$$0.60 = 21$$

Divide both sides by 0.60:

$$\frac{0.60x}{0.60} = \frac{21}{0.60}$$
$$x = 35$$

There are 35 total students in the class.

You can also set up a proportion if you know that $60\% = \frac{3}{5}$:

$$\frac{3}{5} = \frac{21}{x}$$

Increase the terms of the first fraction to get to the second; you get 21 by multiplying 3 by 7, and multiplying 5 by 7 gives you 35, so $x = 35$.

17. **D. 5:10 p.m.**

The distance formula is $d = rt$, where d is the distance, r is the rate, and t is the time. Substitute the known values and solve for t to find out how long Keisha walked:

$$4.5 = 3t$$
$$\frac{4.5}{3} = \frac{3t}{3}$$
$$1.5 = t$$

One hour and 30 minutes after 3:40 p.m. is 5:10 p.m. Add one hour to 3:40 p.m. to arrive at 4:40 p.m., and then add another 20 minutes to get to 5:00 p.m. Add the remaining 10 minutes to reach 5:10 p.m.

18. B. 9.75h ≥ 150

The amount you earn is the product of your hourly rate and the number of hours worked, which you can express as $9.75h$. Your earnings must be greater than or equal to $150, which is represented by the symbol ≥.

amount earned ≥ $150

$$\$9.75h \geq \$150$$

19. A. 4 m

Let x = the length of Carlos's father's truck. The ratio of the model length to the length of the actual truck should equal the ratio of 2 centimeters to 0.25 m. Set the two ratios equal to each other to make an equation. Cross-multiply to solve for x.

$$\frac{32}{x} = \frac{2}{0.25}$$
$$2x = 32(0.25)$$
$$\frac{2x}{2} = \frac{8}{2}$$
$$x = 4$$

In the equation above, an easy way to multiply 32 by 0.25 is to divide 32 by 4 (because $0.25 = \frac{1}{4}$).

20. A. $59

Use a sequence of numbers to represent the cost of the paintings in order from left to right. The first number on the left is 29. Add 15 to find the cost of the next painting: 29, 44, 59. The painting on the far right costs $59.

If it's easier, round 29 up to 30, add 15 three times, and subtract $1 at the end:

$$\$15 + \$15 + \$15 = \$60$$
$$\$60 - \$1 = \$59$$

21. B. 12 hours

Find how many hours it will take Megan to travel by using the distance formula $(d = rt)$, where $d = 600$ and $r = 50$:

$$600 = 50t$$
$$\frac{600}{50} = \frac{50t}{50}$$
$$t = 12$$

It will take Megan 12 hours to get to her grandmother's house.

22. B. 75 mph

Substitute $F = 230$ into the formula and solve for x:

$$10(x-60)+80 = 230$$
$$10x - 600 + 80 = 230$$
$$10x - 520 = 230$$
$$10x - 520 + 520 = 230 + 520$$
$$10x = 750$$
$$\frac{10x}{10} = \frac{750}{10}$$
$$x = 75$$

23. B. 24 mpg

Subtract to find the number of miles traveled: $65,322 - 65,034 = 288$ miles. The car's gas mileage is the distance traveled divided by the number of gallons of gas used: $\frac{288}{12} = 24$.

24. A. 160π cm^3

The formula for the volume of a cylinder is $V = \pi r^2 h$, where r is the radius and h is the height. The radius of the can is equal to half the diameter: $r = \frac{d}{2} = \frac{8}{2} = 4$. Substitute known values into the formula to find the volume: $V = \pi(4^2)(10) = \pi(16)(10) = 160\pi$.

25. B. $1,310

Subtract the co-pay for one visit from the cost of one visit: $305 - $15 = 290. The insurance company pays 60 percent of the cost after the co-pay, so Matt pays 40 percent of the cost. Find 40 percent of $290: $0.4($290) = 116. Add Matt's portion after the co-pay to the co-pay: $15 + $116 = 131 total for each visit. Multiply Matt's total cost for one visit to the chiropractor by 10: $10($131) = $1,310$.

26. C. 12 minutes

You can figure out how long it will take Marco and his brother to change a tire together by determining how much work each person does in a set amount of time. Use one hour (60 minutes) to keep it simple: Marco can repair one tire in 20 minutes, so he can finish three tires in an hour. His brother can repair two tires in one hour.

In one hour together, they repair

$$\frac{3 \text{ tires}}{1 \text{ hour}} + \frac{2 \text{ tires}}{1 \text{ hour}} = \frac{5 \text{ tires}}{1 \text{ hour}}$$

The number of tires is expressed in the numerator, and the unit of time is expressed in the denominator. Because they can repair five tires in one hour together, divide the 60 minutes of an hour by 5 to get the time it takes them to repair just one:

$$60 \div 5 = 12$$

27. D. 12 oz

First, find out how many ounces of water ten squeezes of the trigger emit: $10(0.024) = 0.24$ ounces. That means 0.24 ounces of water is 2 percent of the total amount of water that the bottle can hold.

Let x = the total number of ounces of water that the bottle will hold. You know that 2 percent of x is equal to 0.24, so write an equation and then solve for x.

$$x = \frac{0.24}{0.02}$$
$$x = \frac{24}{2}$$
$$x = 12$$

28. C. 1,800 cm²

A shoe box is a rectangular box. The formula for the surface area of a rectangular box is $SA = 2lw + 2wh + 2lh$, where l = length, w = width, and h = height. Substitute the known values into the formula and simplify.

$$SA = 2(30)(15) + 2(15)(10) + 2(30)(10)$$
$$= 60(15) + 30(10) + 60(10)$$
$$= 900 + 300 + 600$$
$$= 1,800$$

29. A. 1 hour

You could create an algebraic equation and a chart to solve this problem, but the question is really asking you how far apart the runners will be in one hour. The first runner can run 5 miles per hour, and the second runs 6 miles per hour — and they're running in opposite directions. That means in one hour, they're $5 + 6 = 11$ miles apart.

For more complex problems, algebra comes in handy. You could solve this problem by letting x represent the amount of time the runners take to run 11 miles in opposite directions and then making a chart to help solve the problem.

	Rate	×	Time	=	Distance
Runner 1	5		x		$5x$
Runner 2	6		x		$7x$

Illustration by Thomson Digital

You need to figure out how far each runner ran; you can use a variation of the distance formula, $d = rt$, where d = distance, r = rate, and t = time. The table shows you that Runner 1 will run a distance of $5x$ and Runner 2 will run a distance of $6x$. Because they are running in opposite directions and you want to know when they are 11 miles apart, you add the two distances together and set the sum equal to 11. The equation looks like this:

$$5x + 6x = 11$$
$$11x = 11$$
$$x = 1$$

It will take the runners 1 hour to get 11 miles apart.

30. **c. $84**

Use the amount of pizza eaten to determine how many pizzas the coach bought. Excluding the coach, the team ate $15\left(\frac{1}{4}\right) = \frac{15}{4}$ pizzas. Add the amount of pizza the coach ate and the amount of pizza left over: $\frac{15}{4} + \frac{1}{2} + 2\frac{3}{4}$. Convert the remaining pizza $\left(2\frac{3}{4}\right)$ to an improper fraction: $2\frac{3}{4} = \frac{11}{4}$.

Come up with a common denominator and add to find the total number of pizzas:

$$\frac{15}{4} + \frac{2}{4} + \frac{11}{4} = \frac{15 + 2 + 11}{4}$$
$$= \frac{28}{4}$$
$$= 7$$

For 7 pizzas, the total cost before tax is $7(\$12) = \$84$.

If it's easier, you can add the fractional and whole parts of the pizza separately. If you add the players' pizza as a fraction, the coach's pizza, and the fractional part of the leftover pizza, then add the sum to the whole pizzas, your calculation looks like this:

$$\frac{15}{4} + \frac{1}{2} + \frac{3}{4} = \frac{15}{4} + \frac{2}{4} + \frac{3}{4} = \frac{20}{4} = 5 \text{ pizzas}$$
$$5 \text{ pizzas} + 2 \text{ pizzas} = 7 \text{ pizzas}$$

Part 2: Word Knowledge

The Word Knowledge subtest is nothing more than a vocabulary test. However, it can be hard for some people. The good news is that vocabulary isn't an innate talent. It's something that everyone can improve. If you find you need to improve your vocabulary, see Chapter 5. A couple of other great study references are *Vocabulary For Dummies* by Laurie E. Rozakis (Wiley) and *SAT Vocabulary For Dummies* by Suzee Vlk (Wiley). Additionally, see Chapter 6 for more practice questions.

1. **c. detest.**

   Savor is a verb that means to appreciate something.

   "Simón wanted to savor every bite of the meringue."

2. **c. mediocre.**

   Lackluster is an adjective that means lacking life or energy.

   "The actor gave a lackluster performance during his audition, so he didn't get the part."

3. **A. abstain.**

   Participate is a verb that means to take part in.

   "Marie didn't want to participate in marriage counseling after her husband had an affair."

4. **B. mess up.**

   Organize is a verb that means to coordinate or make orderly.

   "Cheryl took one look at the messy room and began to organize everything into neat stacks."

5. D. messy.

Unkempt is an adjective describing something disorderly.

"Tina's bedroom was so unkempt that Cheryl had to come in and organize it."

6. B. first

Preliminary is an adjective describing something introductory.

7. B. unavoidable

Inevitable is an adjective that means bound to happen.

8. D. sign

Omen is a noun describing something prophetic.

9. C. cold

As used in this sentence, *frigid* is an adjective meaning extremely cold.

10. B. oppressor

Tyrant is a noun describing someone who rules over others unjustly.

11. C. phony.

As used in this sentence, *counterfeit* is an adjective meaning fake or forged.

"When the criminal tried to pay for his dinner with a counterfeit $100 bill, the server called her manager."

12. A. relieve.

Used as a verb, *burden* means to provide a load or a difficult task to someone. It's also a noun that refers to something that's carried, or a duty or responsibility.

"Robert thought that his complaints about work would burden his wife."

13. D. subdue.

Used as a verb, *animate* means to rouse or make lively.

"Playing loud, happy music animated the kids in gymnastics class."

14. C. reasonable.

Plausible is an adjective that means something looks to be true or believable, though it may or may not actually be so.

"The defendant's self-defense claim wasn't plausible, so the prosecutor encouraged the jury to find the man guilty."

15. B. flexible.

Pliable is an adjective that means easily bent or changeable.

"Good leather is pliable, so it won't crack when you mold it into a saddle."

16. B. acceptance.

Resignation is a noun that means a reluctant agreement.

"In the famous movie, William Wallace accepted his terrible fate with resignation."

17. C. destroy.

Obliterate is a verb that means to demolish or annihilate.

"The goal is to obliterate the enemy's communication abilities so they can't conduct military operations."

18. B. abide.

Heed is a verb meaning to take warning or advice in earnest.

"Pilar told Beto to heed her warning about the cat's aggression because she didn't want him to get scratched."

19. A. massive

Immense is an adjective meaning very large or colossal.

20. A. follow

Pursue is a verb meaning to go after something or someone.

21. C. sensitive

Tactful is an adjective that means being thoughtful or delicate.

22. A. tolerate

Endure is a verb that means to bear with patience or tolerate, or to hold out against.

23. D. endurance

In this sentence, *longevity* is a noun meaning a prolonged ability. It can also refer to length of service or tenure, or the length or duration of life.

24. B. comfort

Console is a verb that means to alleviate or lessen grief, sorrow, or disappointment.

25. C. scatter

Disperse is a verb that means to move in different directions.

26. D. covered.

Enshrouded is a verb meaning to encompass or obscure something.

"The sun went down, and soon we were enshrouded in darkness."

27. A. disown.

Repudiate is a verb that means to reject as having no authority or strongly deny something or someone.

"The judge knew he would have to repudiate the man's claim."

28. C. indirect.

Oblique is an adjective meaning not straight or not straightforward.

"The candidate made only oblique references to the scandal."

29. A. agree with.

Acquiesce is a verb meaning to consent by way of giving in.

"Two of the six partners had to acquiesce because the other four (the majority) had already agreed on the plan."

30. B. flimsy.

Tenuous is an adjective describing something weak or lacking substance.

"The man's adult stepson had a tenuous claim to the inheritance, so the court would have to decide one way or the other."

31. C. rampant

Unbridled is an adjective meaning unrestrained.

32. C. exclude

Ostracize is a verb meaning to leave out intentionally.

33. A. full.

Replete is an adjective that means ample or fully supplied.

"The book was replete with detail, describing every character and scene so readers could really envision them."

34. B. mystery.

Enigma is a noun that means something puzzling, not clear, or not understandable.

"The private millionaire, who rarely leaves his house, is an enigma to everyone in town."

35. A. pacify

Assuage is a verb meaning to pacify or lessen the intensity of something.

Part 3: Paragraph Comprehension

The Paragraph Comprehension subtest can be a bit tricky, but you need to get a good score on this subtest if you want to ace the AFQT. Pay special attention to your reading skills if you missed more than a couple of these answers — you need some study time (see Chapter 7). Remember that rereading the paragraph several times to make sure that you have the right answer is perfectly fine. The best method of improving your reading comprehension skills is simply to read more. You can find additional practice questions in Chapter 8.

1. D. Trainers should avoid becoming emotional.

The first sentence states the point: "Dog training isn't for the faint of heart." In other words, sometimes you have to discipline the dog without becoming an emotional wreck.

2. A. determination

The last sentence of the passage lets you know that your *resolve* will be tested because you may feel guilty for training your dog. You have to be very determined to train your pet because pity could make you want to drop everything and play.

3. C. 1

A scan of the passage shows you that it clearly says "including one Daytona 500 race." You can answer questions like these quickly on the ASVAB, so read the question thoroughly, find your answer, and move on.

4. B. severe.

The description of the mood swings states that moods range from a heightened place to an extreme state of depression. *Severe* is the only word that describes the large range experienced.

5. C. 4

The passage states that rugby has been added and dropped three times but was added back in 2016. The first three times plus the most recent equals four times rugby has been added to the Olympic Games.

6. D. Brazil

The passage lists many locations, but careful scanning shows you that the 2016 Olympics were in Rio de Janeiro, Brazil.

7. C. Breadmaking is more exact than cooking.

The paragraph gives examples of how making bread, unlike cooking, uses exact measurements and ratios to get the desired result. The last sentence also states the answer in different terms.

8. B. outlawed.

The paragraph states that the number of bald eagles continued to decline despite trapping and killing having been barred. The term *despite* tells you that *barred* signifies an action against trapping and killing. In fact, the act banned, or outlawed, those practices against the eagle.

9. A. 1972

The passage indicates that DDT was responsible for the decline of the species. Thus, the banning of DDT in 1972 would be the beginning of the repopulation of the bald eagle. You may have been tempted by 1940, but the congressional act didn't contribute to the population regrowth. When an ASVAB question asks you for a specific date, scan the paragraph quickly for numbers; you'll be able to find the answer easily.

10. C. Joining the Joffrey Ballet is Jill's life's goal.

Although many of these things could be true about Jill, the question asks for the main point of the passage. The passage stresses the importance of her audition and how being accepted by the Joffrey Ballet would be "a dream come true," so the main point is that she has been eagerly anticipating this moment for some time.

11. B. have opportunities to make a lot of money.

The paragraph describes the popularity of quilting and mentions contests with best in show prizes reaching $10,000. Therefore, you can assume quilters today can make a good amount of money.

12. **D. None of the above**

Although areas of the other answers may have depths of less than 4 feet, they can all have deeper areas. Because the seller clearly says the lifeboat should not be used by people who cannot swim, it shouldn't be used in open water.

13. **D. preventing a child from becoming overweight before the age of 5**

The information states that children obese at age 5 were more likely to be obese in adolescence. Although the passage doesn't explicitly state that weight management before the age of 5 is desirable, you can reason that from the information provided. The other three answers aren't stated in the passage, so you can quickly rule them out as possible answers.

14. **A. one-third**

The passage states that approximately two-thirds of the children involved in the study remained obese in their later years, so you can reason that one-third became thinner.

15. **A. version**

The movie is based on the TV show, so an *adaptation* is another version of the show.

Part 4: Mathematics Knowledge

Some folks find math to be a breeze and can't understand why the rest of us approach math problems with all the enthusiasm of a trip to the dentist. However, the military considers math skills to be important, and it's right. If you miss more than four or five questions, you should consider brushing up on your basic math skills — Chapter 9 can help with this. As with the Arithmetic Reasoning subtest, the following *For Dummies* books may also be of some help: *Algebra I For Dummies* and *Algebra II For Dummies*, both by Mary Jane Sterling; *Basic Math & Pre-Algebra For Dummies* by Mark Zegarelli; *Geometry For Dummies* by Mark Ryan; and *SAT II Math For Dummies* by Scott Hatch, JD, and Lisa Zimmer Hatch, MA (all published by Wiley). Chapter 10 also has some additional practice questions.

1. **B. 2**

A prime number is a number that is bigger than 1 and has only itself and 1 as factors. The number 2 is the only choice that fits the definition of a prime number.

2. **C. 0.011**

Eleven thousandths is the same as $\frac{11}{1,000}$. To divide a number by 1,000, move the decimal point 3 places to the left: $\frac{11}{1,000} = 0.011$.

3. **C. 1.281**

When adding decimals, arrange the numbers in an addition column with the decimal points lined up:

$$\begin{array}{r} \overset{1}{1.091} \\ +0.19 \\ \hline 1.281 \end{array}$$

When adding the 9s in the hundredths column, remember to carry the 1 to the tenths column.

4. A. 18 ft

An equilateral triangle has three equal sides. The perimeter is the sum of all three sides. To find the length of one side, divide the perimeter by 3: $54 \div 3 = 18$ ft.

5. D. 88

Write 40 percent as a decimal: 40 percent $= 0.4$. Multiply 0.4 by 220: $0.4(220) = 88$.

6. D. 3.25

Divide 26 by 8 using long division.

$$
\begin{array}{r}
3.25 \\
8\overline{)26.00} \\
-24 \\
\hline
20 \\
-16 \\
\hline
40 \\
-40 \\
\hline
0
\end{array}
$$

7. A. p^2

To multiply terms with the same base, add the exponents: $p^{3+(-1)} = p^{3-1} = p^2$.

8. B. $\dfrac{1}{5}$

To subtract fractions with the same denominator, subtract the numerators but keep the denominators the same. You can then simplify the difference $\dfrac{5}{25}$ to $\dfrac{1}{5}$.

$$\frac{8}{25} - \frac{3}{25} = \frac{8-3}{25} = \frac{5}{25} = \frac{1}{5}$$

9. A. −9

Get y alone on one side of the inequality symbol by subtracting 2 from both sides:

$$
\begin{aligned}
y + 2 &< -6 \\
y + 2 - 2 &< -6 - 2 \\
y &< -8
\end{aligned}
$$

So y can be any number less than -8. The only answer choice that is less than -8 is -9.

10. B. $7x - 15$

Use the distributive property to remove the parentheses. Then add the like terms $3x$ and $4x$.

$$
\begin{aligned}
3(x-5) + 4x &= 3x - 15 + 4x \\
&= 7x - 15
\end{aligned}
$$

11. **C. 15 ft**

Use the Pythagorean theorem $a^2 + b^2 = c^2$ to find the length of the remaining side. Remember that the hypotenuse, c, is always the longest side of a right triangle. Let a represent the length of the remaining side.

$$a^2 + 8^2 = 17^2$$
$$a^2 + 64 = 289$$
$$a^2 + 64 - 64 = 289 - 64$$
$$a^2 = 225$$
$$a = \pm\sqrt{225} = \pm 15$$

Use the positive answer because length is always positive.

12. **D. −4**

The quotient of 40 and 20 is $40 \div 20 = 2$. The sum of 1 and 5 is 6. Decrease 2 by 6 using subtraction: $2 - 6 = -4$.

13. **C. 3**

Use the order of operations, which says to simplify inside the parentheses first, compute all exponents, multiply and/or divide from left to right, and then add and/or subtract from left to right. (You might know this order of operations as PEMDAS.) This equation has no parentheses (or other grouping symbols), so start with the exponents:

$$15 - 3 \times 2^2 = 15 - 3 \times 4$$
$$= 15 - 12$$
$$= 3$$

14. **B. 60**

To find the least common multiple (LCM) of two numbers, write out the multiples of each number and find the smallest number that they have in common.

Multiples of 12: 12, 24, 36, 48, 60

Multiples of 20: 20, 40, 60

The LCM is 60.

Another way (and one that could save you precious time on the ASVAB) to tackle this problem is to check which answer choices are divisible by both 12 and 20. Start with the smallest answer choice and you'll find that you can toss Choice (A) right out the window. Try choice (B), and you'll see that it's the correct answer.

15. **A. $\frac{6}{7}$**

Product means multiplication. When multiplying two fractions, multiply the numerators by each other and multiply the denominators by each other.

$$\frac{3}{4} \times \frac{8}{7} = \frac{3 \times 8}{4 \times 7} = \frac{24}{28}$$

Remember to simplify all fractions. Simplify this fraction by dividing the numerator and denominator by the greatest common divisor, 4:

$$\frac{24 \div 4}{28 \div 4} = \frac{6}{7}$$

16. **D. 24**

This question asks for the product of four numbers. You can multiply two numbers at a time. Remember that the product of two numbers with the same sign is positive, and the product of two numbers with different signs is negative.

$$3(-4)(1)(-2) = (-12)(1)(-2)$$
$$= (-12)(-2)$$
$$= 24$$

17. **D. 4 only**

A cube root is a number that when multiplied by itself three times equals the number under the radical sign. Because $4(4)(4) = 64$, 4 is the cube root of 64.

18. **C. $\frac{11}{15}$**

You need to find the common denominator for these two fractions. The common denominator is the least common multiple of 5 and 3.

Multiples of 5: 5, 10, 15

Multiples of 3: 3, 6, 9, 12, 15

The common denominator for these two fractions is 15. Multiply the numerator and denominator of each fraction by the number that makes each denominator 15.

$$\frac{2}{5} + \frac{1}{3} = \frac{2 \cdot 3}{5 \cdot 3} + \frac{1 \cdot 5}{3 \cdot 5}$$
$$= \frac{6}{15} + \frac{5}{15}$$
$$= \frac{6+5}{15}$$
$$= \frac{11}{15}$$

19. **B. 86 m²**

First, find the area of the square by using the formula $A = s^2$, where s is the length of one side of the square. Because $s = 20$ meters, the area of the square is $20^2 = 400$ m².

Next, find the area of the circle by using the formula $A = \pi r^2$, where r is the radius of the circle. Because the diameter of the circle runs the length of one side of the square, the radius is half the length of one side of the square, so $r = 10$ meters. The area of the circle is $A = \pi(10^2) = 3.14(100) = 314$ m².

To find the area of the region inside the square but outside the circle, subtract the area of the circle from the area of the square: $400 - 314 = 86$ m².

20. **A. 21**

Let x represent the middle number. Next, add and subtract 2 (to represent the other odd numbers), written as $(x+2)$ and $(x-2)$.

$$(x+2) + x + (x-2) = 63$$
$$3x = 63$$
$$\frac{3x}{3} = \frac{63}{3}$$
$$x = 21$$

If you're not big on algebra (surprisingly, it's not everyone's favorite subject), you may not need to use it on questions like this one. When you're adding three consecutive odd numbers, you can reason that each number is going to be close to one-third of the sum, 63:

$$\frac{63}{3} = 21$$

Check 21 as your middle number to see if it works:

$$19 + 21 + 23 = 63$$

It does, so Choice (A) is correct.

21. D. 4 and −4

This equation is a quadratic equation because the unknown quantity (x) has an exponent of 2. To solve it, first isolate the variable by subtracting 4 from both sides:

$$x^2 + 4 = 20$$
$$x^2 + 4 - 4 = 20 - 4$$
$$x^2 = 16$$

Next, take the square root of both sides. (With any positive real number, you'll get a positive and negative answer to the square root problem, because when you multiply a negative number by a negative number, you get a positive number.)

$$x = \pm\sqrt{16}$$
$$x = \pm 4$$

22. A. 60°

If two angles are supplementary, the sum of their measures is 180°. Label the angle you're trying to find as x and the supplement as $2x$. You can then set up an equation:

$$x + 2x = 180$$
$$3x = 180$$
$$\frac{x}{3} = \frac{180}{3}$$
$$x = 60$$

23. B. $1\frac{1}{9}$

To solve for x, cross-multiply and isolate the variable:

$$\frac{9}{x} = \frac{81}{10}$$
$$81x = 9(10)$$
$$81x = 90$$
$$\frac{81x}{81} = \frac{90}{81}$$
$$x = \frac{90}{81}$$

Use long division to write the answer as a mixed number.

$$\begin{array}{r} 1 \\ 81\overline{)90} \\ -81 \\ \hline 9 \end{array}$$

The quotient forms the whole number; the remainder, 9, is the numerator of the fraction, and the divisor, 81, is the denominator: $1\frac{9}{81}$. You can simplify this number to $1\frac{1}{9}$.

24. C. $x+4$

The numerator is a difference of two squares. Use the formula $x^2 - a^2 = (x-a)(x+a)$ to factor the numerator. The factor $(x-4)$ cancels out in the numerator and in the denominator.

$$\frac{x^2 - 16}{x-4} = \frac{(x-4)(x+4)}{x-4}$$
$$= \frac{\cancel{(x-4)}(x+4)}{\cancel{x-4}}$$
$$= x+4$$

25. D. 52°

The sum of the angles in a quadrilateral always equals 360°. Write an equation to find the value of n: $55 + 90 + 111 + 2n = 360$.

To solve this equation, isolate the variable:

$$256 + 2n = 360$$
$$256 + 2n - 256 = 360 - 256$$
$$2n = 104$$
$$n = 52$$

Answer Key

Part 1: Arithmetic Reasoning

1.	C	7.	A	13.	B	19.	A	25.	B
2.	A	8.	D	14.	C	20.	A	26.	C
3.	C	9.	D	15.	A	21.	B	27.	D
4.	B	10.	C	16.	C	22.	B	28.	C
5.	C	11.	D	17.	D	23.	B	29.	A
6.	A	12.	B	18.	B	24.	A	30.	C

Part 2: Word Knowledge

1.	C	8.	D	15.	B	22.	A	29.	A
2.	C	9.	C	16.	B	23.	D	30.	B
3.	A	10.	B	17.	C	24.	B	31.	C
4.	B	11.	C	18.	B	25.	C	32.	C
5.	D	12.	A	19.	A	26.	D	33.	A
6.	B	13.	D	20.	A	27.	A	34.	B
7.	B	14.	C	21.	C	28.	C	35.	A

Part 3: Paragraph Comprehension

1.	D	4.	B	7.	C	10.	C	13.	D
2.	A	5.	C	8.	B	11.	B	14.	A
3.	C	6.	D	9.	A	12.	D	15.	A

Part 4: Mathematics Knowledge

1.	B	6.	D	11.	C	16.	D	21.	D
2.	C	7.	A	12.	D	17.	D	22.	A
3.	C	8.	B	13.	C	18.	C	23.	B
4.	A	9.	A	14.	B	19.	B	24.	C
5.	D	10.	B	15.	A	20.	A	25.	D

Chapter 17

Practice Exam 3

I n the sections that follow, you find the four subtests of the Armed Services Vocational Aptitude Battery (ASVAB), which make up the Armed Forces Qualification Test (AFQT) score: Arithmetic Reasoning, Word Knowledge, Paragraph Comprehension, and Mathematics Knowledge.

I note in Chapter 2 that the military services use the scores derived from these four subtests to determine your overall AFQT score and that the AFQT score is the primary factor that decides whether you're qualified to enlist in the military branch of your choice. Remember to use the results of the following practice exam to decide which areas you should dedicate more study to.

Use the answer key and explanations in Chapter 18 to score your practice exam. Remember not to be too concerned with how many you get right and how many you get wrong. Some of the questions on the practice exam are hard, and others are very easy. When you take the actual subtests as part of the ASVAB, harder questions are awarded more points than easier questions.

Consider taking this practice exam about a week before you're scheduled to take the actual ASVAB. Use the results to determine which AFQT subjects need a little extra attention.

Answer Sheet for Practice Exam 3

Part 1: Arithmetic Reasoning

1. Ⓐ Ⓑ Ⓒ Ⓓ
2. Ⓐ Ⓑ Ⓒ Ⓓ
3. Ⓐ Ⓑ Ⓒ Ⓓ
4. Ⓐ Ⓑ Ⓒ Ⓓ
5. Ⓐ Ⓑ Ⓒ Ⓓ
6. Ⓐ Ⓑ Ⓒ Ⓓ

7. Ⓐ Ⓑ Ⓒ Ⓓ
8. Ⓐ Ⓑ Ⓒ Ⓓ
9. Ⓐ Ⓑ Ⓒ Ⓓ
10. Ⓐ Ⓑ Ⓒ Ⓓ
11. Ⓐ Ⓑ Ⓒ Ⓓ
12. Ⓐ Ⓑ Ⓒ Ⓓ

13. Ⓐ Ⓑ Ⓒ Ⓓ
14. Ⓐ Ⓑ Ⓒ Ⓓ
15. Ⓐ Ⓑ Ⓒ Ⓓ
16. Ⓐ Ⓑ Ⓒ Ⓓ
17. Ⓐ Ⓑ Ⓒ Ⓓ
18. Ⓐ Ⓑ Ⓒ Ⓓ

19. Ⓐ Ⓑ Ⓒ Ⓓ
20. Ⓐ Ⓑ Ⓒ Ⓓ
21. Ⓐ Ⓑ Ⓒ Ⓓ
22. Ⓐ Ⓑ Ⓒ Ⓓ
23. Ⓐ Ⓑ Ⓒ Ⓓ
24. Ⓐ Ⓑ Ⓒ Ⓓ

25. Ⓐ Ⓑ Ⓒ Ⓓ
26. Ⓐ Ⓑ Ⓒ Ⓓ
27. Ⓐ Ⓑ Ⓒ Ⓓ
28. Ⓐ Ⓑ Ⓒ Ⓓ
29. Ⓐ Ⓑ Ⓒ Ⓓ
30. Ⓐ Ⓑ Ⓒ Ⓓ

Part 2: Word Knowledge

1. Ⓐ Ⓑ Ⓒ Ⓓ
2. Ⓐ Ⓑ Ⓒ Ⓓ
3. Ⓐ Ⓑ Ⓒ Ⓓ
4. Ⓐ Ⓑ Ⓒ Ⓓ
5. Ⓐ Ⓑ Ⓒ Ⓓ
6. Ⓐ Ⓑ Ⓒ Ⓓ
7. Ⓐ Ⓑ Ⓒ Ⓓ

8. Ⓐ Ⓑ Ⓒ Ⓓ
9. Ⓐ Ⓑ Ⓒ Ⓓ
10. Ⓐ Ⓑ Ⓒ Ⓓ
11. Ⓐ Ⓑ Ⓒ Ⓓ
12. Ⓐ Ⓑ Ⓒ Ⓓ
13. Ⓐ Ⓑ Ⓒ Ⓓ
14. Ⓐ Ⓑ Ⓒ Ⓓ

15. Ⓐ Ⓑ Ⓒ Ⓓ
16. Ⓐ Ⓑ Ⓒ Ⓓ
17. Ⓐ Ⓑ Ⓒ Ⓓ
18. Ⓐ Ⓑ Ⓒ Ⓓ
19. Ⓐ Ⓑ Ⓒ Ⓓ
20. Ⓐ Ⓑ Ⓒ Ⓓ
21. Ⓐ Ⓑ Ⓒ Ⓓ

22. Ⓐ Ⓑ Ⓒ Ⓓ
23. Ⓐ Ⓑ Ⓒ Ⓓ
24. Ⓐ Ⓑ Ⓒ Ⓓ
25. Ⓐ Ⓑ Ⓒ Ⓓ
26. Ⓐ Ⓑ Ⓒ Ⓓ
27. Ⓐ Ⓑ Ⓒ Ⓓ
28. Ⓐ Ⓑ Ⓒ Ⓓ

29. Ⓐ Ⓑ Ⓒ Ⓓ
30. Ⓐ Ⓑ Ⓒ Ⓓ
31. Ⓐ Ⓑ Ⓒ Ⓓ
32. Ⓐ Ⓑ Ⓒ Ⓓ
33. Ⓐ Ⓑ Ⓒ Ⓓ
34. Ⓐ Ⓑ Ⓒ Ⓓ
35. Ⓐ Ⓑ Ⓒ Ⓓ

Part 3: Paragraph Comprehension

1. Ⓐ Ⓑ Ⓒ Ⓓ 4. Ⓐ Ⓑ Ⓒ Ⓓ 7. Ⓐ Ⓑ Ⓒ Ⓓ 10. Ⓐ Ⓑ Ⓒ Ⓓ 13. Ⓐ Ⓑ Ⓒ Ⓓ
2. Ⓐ Ⓑ Ⓒ Ⓓ 5. Ⓐ Ⓑ Ⓒ Ⓓ 8. Ⓐ Ⓑ Ⓒ Ⓓ 11. Ⓐ Ⓑ Ⓒ Ⓓ 14. Ⓐ Ⓑ Ⓒ Ⓓ
3. Ⓐ Ⓑ Ⓒ Ⓓ 6. Ⓐ Ⓑ Ⓒ Ⓓ 9. Ⓐ Ⓑ Ⓒ Ⓓ 12. Ⓐ Ⓑ Ⓒ Ⓓ 15. Ⓐ Ⓑ Ⓒ Ⓓ

Part 4: Mathematics Knowledge

1. Ⓐ Ⓑ Ⓒ Ⓓ   6. Ⓐ Ⓑ Ⓒ Ⓓ 11. Ⓐ Ⓑ Ⓒ Ⓓ 16. Ⓐ Ⓑ Ⓒ Ⓓ 21. Ⓐ Ⓑ Ⓒ Ⓓ
2. Ⓐ Ⓑ Ⓒ Ⓓ   7. Ⓐ Ⓑ Ⓒ Ⓓ 12. Ⓐ Ⓑ Ⓒ Ⓓ 17. Ⓐ Ⓑ Ⓒ Ⓓ 22. Ⓐ Ⓑ Ⓒ Ⓓ
3. Ⓐ Ⓑ Ⓒ Ⓓ   8. Ⓐ Ⓑ Ⓒ Ⓓ 13. Ⓐ Ⓑ Ⓒ Ⓓ 18. Ⓐ Ⓑ Ⓒ Ⓓ 23. Ⓐ Ⓑ Ⓒ Ⓓ
4. Ⓐ Ⓑ Ⓒ Ⓓ   9. Ⓐ Ⓑ Ⓒ Ⓓ 14. Ⓐ Ⓑ Ⓒ Ⓓ 19. Ⓐ Ⓑ Ⓒ Ⓓ 24. Ⓐ Ⓑ Ⓒ Ⓓ
5. Ⓐ Ⓑ Ⓒ Ⓓ 10. Ⓐ Ⓑ Ⓒ Ⓓ 15. Ⓐ Ⓑ Ⓒ Ⓓ 20. Ⓐ Ⓑ Ⓒ Ⓓ 25. Ⓐ Ⓑ Ⓒ Ⓓ

Part 1: Arithmetic Reasoning

TIME: 36 minutes for 30 questions

DIRECTIONS: Arithmetic Reasoning is the second subtest of the ASVAB; it follows General Science. These questions are designed to test your ability to use mathematics to solve various problems that may be found in real life — in other words, math word problems.

Each question is followed by four possible answers. Decide which answer is correct, and then mark the corresponding space on your answer sheet. Use your scratch paper for any figuring you want to do. You may *not* use a calculator.

1. Luis has 15 quarters and 22 dimes. What is the dollar value of these coins?

   (A) $4.95

   (B) $5.95

   (C) $5.85

   (D) $6.05

2. A pool has 4,856 gallons of water. How many gallons of water remain after 919 gallons are drained from the pool?

   (A) 3,917 gallons

   (B) 5,775 gallons

   (C) 3,937 gallons

   (D) 4,937 gallons

3. One mile is equal to 5,280 ft. Use this relationship to estimate the number of feet in 50 miles.

   (A) about 250,000 ft

   (B) about 350,000 ft

   (C) about 25,000 ft

   (D) about 300,000 ft

4. Cooking one package of noodles requires 3 cups of water. How many cups of water do you need to cook one and a half dozen packages of noodles?

   (A) 18 cups

   (B) 20 cups

   (C) 54 cups

   (D) 64 cups

5. A boat is carrying 40 passengers, 18 of whom are male. What is the ratio of male to female passengers?

   (A) $\frac{11}{9}$

   (B) $\frac{9}{11}$

   (C) $\frac{9}{20}$

   (D) $\frac{1}{2}$

6. Minnie earned $175 for 14 hours of work. What is her hourly pay rate?

   (A) $12.00

   (B) $9.50

   (C) $12.50

   (D) $13.25

7. Candace made 42 phone calls during the fundraiser. Fred made 6 fewer calls than Candace. How many calls did Fred make?

   (A) 36

   (B) 48

   (C) 7

   (D) 38

8. A bicycle wheel has a diameter of 32 inches. When the bicycle is upright, how far is the center of the wheel from the ground?

   (A) 8 in.

   (B) 24 in.

   (C) 64 in.

   (D) 16 in.

GO ON TO NEXT PAGE

9. A builder needs 420 nails to build a garage. The nails he wants come in boxes of 50. How many boxes of nails must he buy to build the garage?

(A) 8 boxes

(B) 42 boxes

(C) 9 boxes

(D) 5 boxes

10. Ricardo bought a bottle of flavored water for $2.25. He gave the cashier a $5 bill and got $3.25 in change. Which choice describes this transaction?

(A) Ricardo got $0.50 more change than he should have.

(B) Ricardo got $0.75 more change than he should have.

(C) Ricardo got the right amount of change.

(D) Ricardo got $0.50 less change than he should have.

11. Carl has a day job and a night job. He earns $9.50 an hour at the day job and $12 an hour at the night job. Last week, he worked 8 hours at each job. How much more did he earn from his night job than his day job?

(A) $40

(B) $20

(C) $22

(D) $36

12. One hour into the potluck, there were $9\frac{1}{3}$ pies on the dessert table. Throughout the rest of the lunch, the guests ate $2\frac{1}{6}$ pies. How many pies were left on the table at the end of the potluck?

(A) $7\frac{1}{6}$

(B) $6\frac{1}{6}$

(C) $7\frac{1}{3}$

(D) $6\frac{1}{7}$

13. A sheet of construction paper is three-eightieths of an inch thick. A ream of this paper has 240 sheets. How thick is a ream of paper?

(A) 6 in.

(B) 4.5 in.

(C) 9 in.

(D) 18 in.

14. Mr. Franklin invests $4,000 into a savings account. After one year, he earns $200 in interest. What is the annual interest rate for the account?

(A) 5.5 percent

(B) 4.5 percent

(C) 5 percent

(D) 20 percent

15. How far will a car travel in 90 minutes if it is traveling at a constant speed of 70 miles per hour?

(A) 115 miles

(B) 95 miles

(C) 100 miles

(D) 105 miles

16. The weight in pounds of five different rocks is 8.1, 7.2, 6.5, 4.4, and 10.3. What is the average of the weights of these rocks?

(A) 7.6 pounds

(B) 6.5 pounds

(C) 7 pounds

(D) 7.3 pounds

17. At 3:30 p.m., the outside temperature was −12° Fahrenheit. By 4:45 p.m., the temperature had dropped another 8° Fahrenheit. What was the temperature at 4:45 p.m.?

(A) −20° Fahrenheit

(B) −4° Fahrenheit

(C) −10° Fahrenheit

(D) 4° Fahrenheit

18. One ounce is equal to about 28 grams. Roughly how many grams are in $1\frac{1}{5}$ ounces?

(A) $29\frac{3}{5}$

(B) $33\frac{1}{5}$

(C) $33\frac{3}{5}$

(D) $35\frac{4}{5}$

19. To ride the roller coaster, a person's height (x) in inches must satisfy the inequality $2x - 84 > 0$. A person with which height cannot ride the roller coaster?

(A) 43 in.

(B) 42 in.

(C) 46 in.

(D) Both A and B.

20. The bed of a flatbed truck is in the shape of a rectangle and has an area of 72 square feet. What is the perimeter of the flatbed if the width is 6 feet?

(A) 42 ft

(B) 36 ft

(C) 18 ft

(D) 60 ft

21. Patrick charges $1.25 for every square foot of wall that he paints. A rectangular wall has a length of 25 feet and a height of 10 feet. How much will Patrick charge to paint this wall?

(A) $325.50

(B) $315.00

(C) $312.50

(D) $316.75

22. A coat that originally sold for $80 is on sale at a 20 percent discount. What is the discount price of the coat?

(A) $60.00

(B) $64.00

(C) $72.00

(D) $56.00

23. James is twice as old as Kiki. In 5 years, the sum of their ages will be 28. How old is James now?

(A) 14

(B) 6

(C) 16

(D) 12

24. A rectangular playground is 5 yards longer than it is wide. Its area is 300 square yards. What is the length of the playground?

(A) 15 yd

(B) 20 yd

(C) 14 yd

(D) 25 yd

25. A car lot has 140 new vehicles for sale. The graph shows the percent of the cars that are available in blue, yellow, green, and red. How many more blue cars are available than red cars?

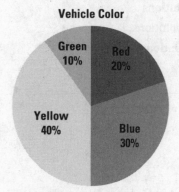

Vehicle Color

Illustration by Thomson Digital

(A) 42

(B) 28

(C) 14

(D) 40

26. Convert $-15°C$ to degrees Fahrenheit. Use the formula $\frac{9}{5}C + 32°$.

(A) 5° Fahrenheit

(B) 10° Fahrenheit

(C) −10° Fahrenheit

(D) 59° Fahrenheit

GO ON TO NEXT PAGE

27. At a grocery store, hot dogs come in packages of 8; hot dog buns come in packages of 6; and small bags of chips come in packages of 16. How many packages of each do you need to buy so you have an equal number of hot dogs, hot dog buns, and bags of chips?

(A) 8 packages of hot dogs, 6 packages of buns, and 3 packages of chips

(B) 6 packages of hot dogs, 8 packages of buns, and 4 packages of chips

(C) 6 packages of hot dogs, 8 packages of buns, and 3 packages of chips

(D) 8 packages of hot dogs, 8 packages of buns, and 12 packages of chips

28. Each wheel on Adam's bicycle has a diameter of 20 inches. When riding down his driveway, Adam moved approximately 6,280 inches. About how many full revolutions did each wheel make during his trip?

(A) 50 revolutions

(B) 100 revolutions

(C) 1,000 revolutions

(D) 500 revolutions

29. Alexa is selling carnival tickets. Each adult ticket costs 40 percent more than a child's ticket. She's sold 10 child tickets and 12 adult tickets for $134. How much does a single adult ticket cost?

(A) $12

(B) $8

(C) $5

(D) $7

30. A parking meter contains $3.40 in quarters, dimes, and nickels. There are 8 nickels and twice as many quarters as dimes. How many quarters are in the parking meter?

(A) 10 quarters

(B) 5 quarters

(C) 15 quarters

(D) 8 quarters

Part 2: Word Knowledge

TIME: 11 minutes for 35 questions

DIRECTIONS: The Word Knowledge subtest is the third subtest of the ASVAB; it follows Arithmetic Reasoning. The questions are designed to measure your vocabulary knowledge. You'll see three types of questions on this subtest. The first type simply asks you to choose a word or words that most nearly mean the same as the underlined word in the question. The second type includes an underlined word used in a sentence, and you are to choose the word or words that most nearly mean the same as the underlined word, as used in the context of the sentence. The third type of question asks you to choose the word that has the opposite or nearly opposite meaning as the underlined word. Each question is followed by four possible answers. Decide which answer is correct, and then mark the corresponding space on your answer sheet.

1. Perjury most nearly means
   (A) order.
   (B) remark.
   (C) oath.
   (D) lie.

2. Dynamic most nearly means
   (A) special.
   (B) vibrant.
   (C) ordinary.
   (D) dull.

3. The word most opposite in meaning to abandon is
   (A) discard.
   (B) maintain.
   (C) remove.
   (D) become.

4. Momentous most nearly means
   (A) major.
   (B) minute.
   (C) heavy.
   (D) brief.

5. Vital most nearly means
   (A) perfect.
   (B) intentional.
   (C) critical.
   (D) deep.

6. Drone most nearly means
   (A) shout.
   (B) hum.
   (C) cackle.
   (D) engage.

7. Stifle most nearly means
   (A) regurgitate.
   (B) reward.
   (C) release.
   (D) restrain.

8. Caroline's new apartment was small but very quaint.
   (A) grand
   (B) charming
   (C) boring
   (D) outlandish

9. Trying to teach the old dog new tricks is futile.
   (A) worthy
   (B) robust
   (C) pointless
   (D) doomed

10. The student's essay about Martians at Thanksgiving was pure drivel.
    (A) poetry
    (B) nonsense
    (C) logic
    (D) fantasy

GO ON TO NEXT PAGE

11. The chef tried to change the negative stereotype against vegetarian cooks.

(A) label

(B) identity

(C) lie

(D) characteristic

12. The word most opposite in meaning to betray is

(A) protect.

(B) deceive.

(C) annoy.

(D) rely.

13. Amble most nearly means

(A) stroll.

(B) navigate.

(C) accelerate.

(D) rush.

14. The skier wanted to garner a few more medals at this year's event.

(A) cherish

(B) generate

(C) gain

(D) display

15. The flat, monotonous section of the cross-country course challenged even the most enthusiastic runners.

(A) varied

(B) manic

(C) exciting

(D) dull

16. The politician's promises were dubious because of his checkered past.

(A) honest

(B) questionable

(C) forthright

(D) manipulative

17. Quarantine most nearly means

(A) gather.

(B) reunite.

(C) isolate.

(D) dispel.

18. The word most opposite in meaning to endorse is

(A) condemn.

(B) approve.

(C) promote.

(D) quibble.

19. Mitigate most nearly means

(A) concede.

(B) enhance.

(C) reduce.

(D) support.

20. Faith was so complacent with her life that she frequently passed up new opportunities.

(A) content

(B) unsatisfied

(C) daring

(D) concerned

21. The word most opposite in meaning to dominate is

(A) control.

(B) govern.

(C) surrender.

(D) ignore.

22. The police officer had to commandeer Julie's bike during a foot chase.

(A) portray

(B) seize

(C) divide

(D) return

23. Vindicate most nearly means

(A) succeed.

(B) blame.

(C) win.

(D) justify.

24. Mrs. Magan was a staunch advocate for animal rights.

(A) smelly

(B) grotesque

(C) devoted

(D) bloated

25. The professor took off points for the colloquial content in the student's midterm paper.

   (A) unique
   (B) commonplace
   (C) avant garde
   (D) intellectual

26. Atrophy most nearly means

   (A) shrivel.
   (B) explode.
   (C) tire.
   (D) awaken.

27. The authorities were on the hunt for the insurgent behind the uprising.

   (A) scout
   (B) partner
   (C) scapegoat
   (D) rebel

28. The choreographer requested they augment the music with a longer section to fit the routine.

   (A) replace
   (B) enlarge
   (C) trade
   (D) diminish

29. Intermittent most nearly means

   (A) regular.
   (B) variable.
   (C) uniform.
   (D) abnormal.

30. The residents were in a quandary after the only bridge accessing their town was destroyed.

   (A) solution
   (B) puzzle
   (C) resolution
   (D) predicament

31. The doctor gave the diagnosis with a stoic demeanor.

   (A) intelligent
   (B) anxious
   (C) unemotional
   (D) overwrought

32. Aversion most nearly means

   (A) distracter.
   (B) dislike.
   (C) goal.
   (D) element.

33. Garish most nearly means

   (A) gaudy.
   (B) frightening.
   (C) boisterous.
   (D) inappropriate.

34. Intrepid most nearly means

   (A) random.
   (B) nervous.
   (C) brave.
   (D) fearful.

35. The word most opposite in meaning to vanquish is

   (A) bemoan.
   (B) conquer.
   (C) crush.
   (D) yield.

DO NOT TURN THE PAGE UNTIL TOLD TO DO SO   STOP   DO NOT RETURN TO A PREVIOUS TEST

Part 3: Paragraph Comprehension

TIME: 13 minutes for 15 questions

DIRECTIONS: Paragraph Comprehension is the fourth subtest on the ASVAB; it comes after Word Knowledge. The questions are designed to measure your ability to understand what you read. In this part of the test, you see one or more paragraphs of reading material, followed by incomplete statements or questions. Read the paragraph and select the choice that best completes the statement or answers the question. Then mark the corresponding space on your answer sheet.

Questions 1 and 2 refer to the following passage.

People are often confused about the difference between the fiddle and the violin. The truth is that there's no difference except for the way they're played. Violins are often part of orchestras, and the music tends more toward classical and composed pieces. The sounds are played fluidly and in long notes. On the other hand, the fiddle is often played in country or bluegrass bands. The notes are more melodic and tend to be shorter and repetitive. Although they sound like separate instruments, the fiddle and violin are the same and can be played in both styles.

1. What is the main point of the passage?

   (A) The violin is not as popular as the fiddle.

   (B) Country music is more entertaining than classical music.

   (C) Violins are used only in orchestras.

   (D) Fiddles and violins are the same instrument.

2. In the passage, the term <u>fluidly</u> most nearly means

   (A) smoothly.

   (B) roughly.

   (C) staccato.

   (D) broken.

Acupuncture is becoming more accepted in modern society as a form of healing; however, the practice of acupuncture has been used for healing in the Eastern world for centuries. The Chinese first began the art of moving *qi* by applying pressure or creating a release in a *chakra*, or energy zone in the body, more than 2,000 years ago. Although acupuncture treatments have taken on a boutique quality, becoming popular features at full-service spas, the ideas behind this ancient form of healing have remained: Moving the stagnant or blocked *qi* in the body allows the life force to move freely and heal the body of physical ailments and medical conditions.

3. What is the author trying to convey with the phrase "boutique quality"?

   (A) Acupuncture is not done properly.

   (B) Acupuncture is done in hair salons.

   (C) Acupuncture has become trendy in spa settings.

   (D) Acupuncture is different in America.

Questions 4 and 5 refer to the following passage.

Researchers from two leading universities in the United States have discovered what may be the answer to the prayers of many parents. Findings reveal that ingesting negligible amounts of peanuts or peanut proteins may help reduce the sensitivity of allergic reactions through contact. The number of children who suffer from peanut allergies in America is in the hundreds of thousands, and many parents live in fear of their children being exposed to peanut oil or other byproducts that could cause severe and sometimes deadly reactions. Researchers say that in order for this treatment to work, daily to weekly doses of peanut products may be required for up to four to five years.

4. How many children in America have peanut allergies?

   (A) less than 1,000

   (B) about 10,000

   (C) hundreds of thousands

   (D) just under a million

5. How could this research help parents of children with peanut allergies?

  (A) It means their children could eat peanuts again.

  (B) It could reduce their anxiety about exposure.

  (C) It could help pay for the medical treatment.

  (D) None of the above.

Residents of suburban communities throughout the western United States are becoming increasingly concerned about coming face-to-face with a mountain lion in their backyards. In the last year, mountain lions have been found prowling neighborhoods in Colorado, Utah, California, and other areas where urban and rural communities rest at the base or within mountainous regions. The main concern for these owners, according to a recent poll, is that their small pets will become prey for the wild animals. Although officials from the Department of Wildlife and Fisheries have provided strategies to protect households, such as clearing the ground of bushes and vegetation to remove possible hiding spots, they say the main cause of the problem is urban sprawl, which continues to displace mountain lions from their natural habitat.

6. According to the passage, why are mountain lions appearing in residential neighborhoods?

  (A) to hide in low bushes

  (B) to eat small pets

  (C) because of urban sprawl

  (D) to access better vegetation

Despite hailing from Chicago, Illinois, in 1927, the Harlem Globetrotters took the name of the Manhattan neighborhood to represent the African American community that was large and prevalent in Harlem, New York. However, the team known for its outlandish antics and moves on the basketball court didn't play in its namesake city until the late 1960s.

7. As used in this paragraph, <u>outlandish</u> most nearly means

  (A) run of the mill.

  (B) perfect.

  (C) bizarre.

  (D) illegal.

Lou Gehrig was known in major league baseball as "The Iron Horse" for his strength and prowess in the batter's box. Gehrig played first base for the New York Yankees from 1923 to 1938. He set many major-league baseball records, including most consecutive games played (2,130), that stood the test of time until the second half of the 20th century. The famed Yankee was diagnosed with a debilitating and fatal disease (now referred to as Lou Gehrig's disease) that attacks the central nervous system. The disease all but shuts down motor function, though the sufferer's mind remains coherent. The greatest first baseman in the history of baseball died in 1941, two years after his diagnosis.

8. How many years did Lou Gehrig play major league baseball?

  (A) 2,130

  (B) 15

  (C) 38

  (D) 20

Questions 9 and 10 refer to the following passage.

Learning to ski is much different for children than for adults. First, adults have farther to fall, so the fear factor is greater. Second, children are still learning about their coordination and can adjust their body positions more quickly than adults can. Third, children follow directions better than adults do. Fourth, adults have a lifetime of injuries that make them afraid of getting hurt, and they heal more slowly than children do. Fifth, children don't worry about health insurance and hefty medical bills if they get hurt.

9. What is the author saying about children in this passage?

  (A) They are more talented.

  (B) They are better skiers.

  (C) They learn to ski more easily.

  (D) They are better at sports.

GO ON TO NEXT PAGE ▶

10. According to the passage, what would make learning to ski easier for adults?

(A) being less fearful

(B) better directions

(C) lessons

(D) better equipment

The drive-in movie theater industry was once a booming pastime, but since its heyday in the late 1950s, the number of drive-ins has been reduced by almost 90 percent. Once a fun weekend activity with the family or a hangout for teens, the drive-in has been reduced to only 500 viable theaters around the country. Experts say that one of the main causes of drive-in decline is growing real estate prices. Perhaps if landowners appreciated the piece of history they had on their property, they would help keep these relics alive for families and teens to enjoy forever.

11. The author is using the word <u>heyday</u> to mean

(A) end.

(B) prime.

(C) country.

(D) farm.

Fidgety children lined in front of the building, eager parents pacing by their sides. Some of the kids were talking to themselves, and some were counting on their fingers or being quizzed by their parents. But on everyone's face was the anticipation of greatness. The national spelling bee was only moments away.

12. According to the passage, some of the children waiting to compete in the spelling bee seemed

(A) bored.

(B) calm.

(C) nervous.

(D) spoiled.

Questions 13 and 14 refer to the following passage.

Perhaps the most famous gymnast of all time is Romanian Nadia Comaneci, who was the first female gymnast to receive a perfect ten score in an Olympic gymnastics competition. She did so at the 1976 Olympic Games in Montreal, Quebec, where she achieved the feat seven times. Her strong suits were the uneven bars and the balance beam, but she often won the top place in the vault and, less often, the floor routine. After her coaches defected during a tour in the United States in 1981, Comaneci, seen as a Romanian national treasure, was heavily guarded and forbidden to travel. She finally found her freedom in 1989 when she defected to the United States. She eventually found a new home in Canada, but she will always be remembered as the 14-year-old phenomenon at the Summer Olympics.

13. Why was Nadia Comaneci considered a phenomenon at the Summer Olympic Games?

(A) She was from Romania.

(B) She excelled at the vault.

(C) She was the youngest gymnast to compete.

(D) She achieved the highest score given in Olympic gymnastics.

14. In what year did Nadia Comaneci defect from Romania?

(A) 1989

(B) 1976

(C) 1980

(D) 1981

Natural gas vehicles (NGVs) are good not only for the environment but also for drivers' wallets. They offer cleaner emissions and better gas mileage than gasoline-burning vehicles, and the price of a gallon of compressed natural gas is more than $1 cheaper than a gallon of gasoline. However, only slightly more than 100,000 NGVs are on the roads in the United States. If Americans knew about these savings, they would likely purchase more NGVs.

15. According to the passage, why do most Americans drive gasoline-burning vehicles?

(A) lack of knowledge about prices

(B) preference for fossil fuel emissions

(C) inability to drive them

(D) high cost of natural gas

DO NOT TURN THE PAGE UNTIL TOLD TO DO SO STOP **DO NOT RETURN TO A PREVIOUS TEST**

Part 4: Mathematics Knowledge

TIME: 24 minutes for 25 questions

DIRECTIONS: Mathematics Knowledge is the fifth subtest on the ASVAB; it follows Paragraph Comprehension. The questions are designed to test your ability to solve general mathematical problems. Each question is followed by four possible answers. Decide which answer is correct, and then mark the corresponding space on your answer sheet. Use your scratch paper for any figuring you want to do. You may *not* use a calculator.

1. $45 - 6 + 15 =$
(A) 24
(B) 54
(C) 35
(D) 0

2. What is 30 percent of 720?
(A) 216
(B) 310
(C) 240
(D) 220

3. In the number 4.5972, which decimal place does the nine occupy?
(A) tenths
(B) hundredths
(C) thousandths
(D) millionths

4. Express the decimal 0.026 as a percent.
(A) 2.6 percent
(B) 0.26 percent
(C) 26 percent
(D) 260 percent

5. What is 234,678 rounded to the nearest thousand?
(A) 234,700
(B) 230,000
(C) 235,000
(D) 200,000

6. In the decimal 845.721, which digit is in the hundredths place?
(A) 8
(B) 4
(C) 7
(D) 2

7. $4! =$
(A) 12
(B) 24
(C) 120
(D) 9

8. Evaluate $\frac{m}{-7}$ if $m = 28$.
(A) −4
(B) 4
(C) 21
(D) −21

9. Solve: $-55 = m - 17$
(A) −38
(B) 38
(C) −72
(D) 935

10. What is the percent increase when 20 is increased to 23?
(A) 3 percent
(B) 17 percent
(C) 15 percent
(D) 7.5 percent

GO ON TO NEXT PAGE

11. Write 0.00000436 using scientific notation.

(A) 4.36×10^6

(B) 4.36×10^{-5}

(C) 436×10^{-6}

(D) 4.36×10^{-6}

12. Which point has coordinates $(-3, 2)$?

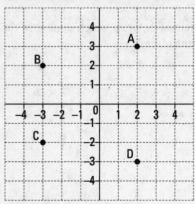

Illustration by Thomson Digital

(A) Point A

(B) Point B

(C) Point C

(D) Point D

13. $5\frac{1}{3} - 4\frac{1}{2} =$

(A) $\frac{1}{6}$

(B) $1\frac{1}{6}$

(C) $\frac{5}{6}$

(D) $1\frac{1}{5}$

14. Simplify: $7(-3m)$

(A) $4m$

(B) $-3 + 7m$

(C) $21m$

(D) $-21m$

15. The lengths of the three sides of a triangle are 14, y, and 6. Which choice could be a value of y?

(A) 19

(B) 21

(C) 25

(D) 31

16. $10 + 2(5 - 3)^2 =$

(A) 48

(B) 18

(C) 26

(D) 36

17. What is 12 divided by $\frac{3}{4}$?

(A) $12\frac{3}{4}$

(B) 9

(C) 16

(D) $\frac{1}{16}$

18. $p^4 = \sqrt{x}$

(A) p^{16}

(B) p^2

(C) p^8

(D) p^4

19. A number is equal to 12 less than the product of 4 and -2.5. What is the number?

(A) -2

(B) -22

(C) 2

(D) 22

20. What are the measures of the three angles of the triangle?

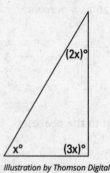

Illustration by Thomson Digital

(A) $30°, 75°, 75°$

(B) $36°, 72°, 108°$

(C) $36°, 54°, 90°$

(D) $30°, 60°, 90°$

21. $\left(3x^2 - 4x + y\right) - \left(2y - 6x^2\right) =$

(A) $9x^x - 4x - y$

(B) $-3x^2 - 4x - y$

(C) $9x^2 - 4x + y$

(D) $-3x^2 - 4x + y$

22. What is the quotient of 4.8×10^{-4} and 1.2×10^{-9}?

(A) 2.5×10^{-3}

(B) 4×10^{5}

(C) 4×10^{-5}

(D) 4×10^{-13}

23. $\sqrt{66 - 2 \cdot 5^2} =$

(A) $2\sqrt{11}$

(B) 10

(C) 4

(D) 40

24. Evaluate $\dfrac{45}{x} - \dfrac{39}{y}$ if $x = -5$ and $y = 3$.

(A) 4

(B) −4

(C) 22

(D) −22

25. The radius of a circle is m centimeters. The radius of another circle is $3 + m$ centimeters. What is the difference of the areas of the two circles?

(A) $\left(9m\pi + 6\pi\right)$ cm^2

(B) 9π cm^2

(C) $\left(9\pi + 6m\pi\right)$ cm^2

(D) $54m^2\pi$ cm^2

Chapter 18
Practice Exam 3: Answers and Explanations

A re you getting tired of math and English yet? I certainly hope not. If you still want more practice after finishing the exams in this book, I recommend you head to your favorite book seller and pick up a copy of *1,001 ASVAB AFQT Practice Questions For Dummies*, written by Angie Papple Johnston (published by Wiley).

Use the answers in the following sections to find out how you did on the AFQT practice exam in Chapter 17. The accompanying explanations tell you how you can get to the correct answer if you got somewhat lost along the way.

Part 1: Arithmetic Reasoning

If you already took three practice AFQT exams, and the temperature is a steady 87 degrees, what is the probability that you got most of the questions right on all four subtests? Okay, that's not a real arithmetic reasoning question (insufficient data, as my computer friends say), but I'm betting you've done pretty well. Now it's time to see how you did on this Arithmetic Reasoning practice subtest.

REMEMBER

If you need more practice doing arithmetic reasoning–type problems, Chapters 9 and 11 are a good place to start. You can also check out *Math Word Problems For Dummies*, *Algebra I For Dummies*, and *Algebra II For Dummies*, all by Mary Jane Sterling; *Geometry For Dummies* and *Calculus For Dummies* both by Mark Ryan; and *Basic Math & Pre-Algebra For Dummies* by Mark Zegarelli — all published by Wiley.

1. **B. $5.95**

    Because you want dollar values, write the value of a quarter as $0.25 and the value of a dime as $0.10. The value of the quarters is $15(\$0.25) = \$3.75$, and the value of the dimes is $22(\$0.10) = \$2.20$. Add to find the answer: $\$3.75 + \$2.20 = \$5.95$.

2. C. 3,937 gallons

This problem just uses simple subtraction. However, remember that this subtraction involves borrowing:

$$
\begin{array}{r}
{\scriptstyle 3\ 18\ 4\ 16} \\
\cancel{4},\cancel{8}\ \cancel{5}\ \cancel{6} \\
-\ \ 9\ \ 1\ \ 9 \\
\hline
3\ \ 9\ \ 3\ \ 7
\end{array}
$$

3. A. 250,000 ft

Because you're estimating, you don't actually need to multiply 5,280 by 50. Instead, round 5,280 down to 5,000 and then multiply: $50(5,000) = 250,000$.

4. C. 54 cups

One dozen is equal to 12 packages, and half of a dozen is 6 packages. You want to find out how much water you need for $12 + 6 = 18$ packages of noodles. Multiply to find the answer: $3(18) = 54$.

5. B. $\frac{9}{11}$

To find this ratio, you need to find the number of female passengers by subtracting the number of males from the total number of passengers: $40 - 18 = 22$ female passengers. Write the ratio of male to female passengers by using a fraction. Simplify by dividing the numerator and denominator by their greatest common factor (GCF, the largest number that will go into both), which is 2:

$$
\frac{\text{male}}{\text{female}} = \frac{18}{22} = \frac{18 \div 2}{22 \div 2} = \frac{9}{11}
$$

6. C. $12.50

To find her hourly pay rate, divide 175 by 14:

$$
\begin{array}{r}
12.5 \\
14\overline{)175.0} \\
\underline{-14} \\
35 \\
\underline{-28} \\
70 \\
\underline{-70} \\
0
\end{array}
$$

Her pay rate is $12.50 an hour.

7. A. 36

If Fred made 6 fewer calls than Candace, you subtract 6 from 42 to find out how many calls Fred made: $42 - 6 = 36$.

8. **D. 16 in.**

The distance between the center of the wheel and the outside of the wheel (where the wheel touches the ground) is the radius. A circle's radius equals half its diameter, so the center is $32 \div 2 = 16$ inches from the ground.

9. **C. 9 boxes**

Divide 420 by 50 to find out how many whole boxes of nails the builder needs: $420 \div 50 = 8$ with a remainder of 20. Eight boxes aren't enough for the project because the builder still needs 20 more nails. The builder needs 9 boxes.

10. **A. Ricardo got $0.50 more change than he should have.**

Subtract $2.25 from $5 to find the amount of change Ricardo should have received: $5 - \$2.25 = \$2.75$. Compare this amount to the change Ricardo actually received ($3.25) to see that he received too much in change. Subtract $2.75 from $3.25 to find the amount of the discrepancy: $\$3.25 - \$2.75 = \$0.50$.

Another approach is to add the cost of the water to the amount of change he received:

$$\$2.25 + \$3.25 = \$5.50$$

That's $0.50 too high, which shows that Ricardo received $0.50 more than he should have.

11. **B. $20**

Multiply to find out how much Carl earned at his day job: $8(\$9.50) = \$76$. Multiply again to find out how much he earned at his night job: $8(\$12) = \$96$. He earned $\$96 - \$76 = \$20$ more at his night job last week.

You can also reason that Carl worked the same number of hours at each job. That means you can find the difference in pay, then multiply it by 8 (the number of hours he worked) to solve this problem:

$$\$12 - \$9.50 = \$2.50$$
$$\$2.50(8) = \$20$$

12. **A. $7\dfrac{1}{6}$**

This problem is easiest to solve if you treat whole numbers and fractions as separate parts:

$$9 \text{ pies} - 2 \text{ pies} = 7 \text{ pies}$$
$$\frac{1}{3} - \frac{1}{6} = \frac{2}{6} - \frac{1}{6} = \frac{1}{6} \text{ pie}$$

That tells you that you have $7\dfrac{1}{6}$ pies left.

13. **C. 9 in.**

A fraction written in words isn't much help, so make it into a fraction: three-eightieths $= \dfrac{3}{80}$. Set up an equation to multiply this fraction by 240, and cross-cancel to save time:

$$\frac{3}{80} \cdot 240 = \frac{3}{80} \cdot \frac{240}{1} = \frac{3}{80_1} \cdot \frac{^3240}{1} = \frac{3}{1} \cdot \frac{3}{1} = \frac{9}{1} = 9$$

14. **C. 5 percent**

Use the interest formula, $I = prt$, where I is the interest, p is the principal, r is the interest rate (as a decimal), and t is the time in years. Substitute the known values into the formula and solve for r:

$$200 = 4,000(r)(1)$$
$$200 = 4,000r$$
$$\frac{200}{4,000} = r$$
$$r = \frac{1}{20} = 0.05$$

Write 0.05 as a percent by moving the decimal point two places to the right: $0.05 = 5$ percent.

15. **D. 105 miles**

The first thing you should notice about this problem is that the speed is in miles per hour but the time traveled is in minutes. You can't solve the problem until you convert the minutes to hours. Fortunately, doing so for this problem is pretty simple: 90 minutes = 1.5 hours. Now you can plug the numbers into the distance formula, $d = rt$ (where d equals distance, r equals rate, and t equals time), using 1.5 for t:

$$d = 70(1.5) = 105 \text{ miles}$$

Another way to look at this problem (especially if you don't remember the distance formula) is to note that the car traveled 70 miles in the first hour and half that distance, or 35 miles, in the next half-hour:

$$70 + \frac{70}{2} = 70 + 35 = 105$$

When you take the ASVAB, find the shortest path to the correct answer and take it.

16. **D. 7.3 pounds**

To find the average, add up all the weights and then divide by 5.

$$\frac{8.1 + 7.2 + 6.5 + 4.4 + 10.3}{5} = \frac{36.5}{5}$$

You can use long division to find the answer.

$$
\begin{array}{r}
7.3 \\
5\overline{)36.5} \\
\underline{-35} \\
15 \\
\underline{-15} \\
0
\end{array}
$$

The average weight is 7.3 pounds.

17. **A. –20° Fahrenheit**

When the temperature drops, you have to subtract. In this case, you want to subtract 8° Fahrenheit from –12° Fahrenheit. If you find subtracting negatives a little confusing, think of it this way: Subtracting 8 from the point labeled –12 means moving 8 units below –12. So $-12 - 8 = -20$.

18. C. $33\frac{3}{5}$ grams

Address the whole numbers and fractions separately to make solving this problem simpler. You know that the whole number (1 ounce) equals about 28 grams, so find out what $\frac{1}{5}$ of 28 grams is:

$$\left(\frac{1}{5}\right)(28 \text{ grams}) = \frac{28}{5} = 5\frac{3}{5} \text{ grams}$$

Add the whole numbers, and then add the fraction to that sum:

$$28 + 5 = 33$$
$$33 + \frac{3}{5} = 33\frac{3}{5}$$

Conversely, you could write $1\frac{1}{5}$ as an improper fraction and multiply it by 28 to arrive at the correct answer:

$$1\frac{1}{5} = \frac{5(1)+1}{5} = \frac{6}{5}$$

Now you can multiply to get the answer:

$$\frac{6}{5} \times 28 = \frac{6}{5} \times \frac{28}{1} = \frac{168}{5} = 33\frac{3}{5}$$

19. B. 42 in.

Based on the problem, you may be able to reason that the shortest person in the answer choices can't ride the roller coaster. You can also solve the inequality by isolating *x*:

$$2x - 84 > 0$$
$$2x > 84$$
$$x > 42$$

If a person's height *x* must be greater than 42, a person with a height of 42 inches can't ride the roller coaster.

REMEMBER

Make sure you read the questions carefully because the folks who write ASVAB questions construct them so you can get hung up on the details. Sometimes you'll need to go back and read the question one more time, after you work out the math, to make sure you're giving the appropriate answer.

20. B. 36 ft

This problem uses two formulas. First, use the area formula, $A = lw$, to find the length *l* of the flatbed. Substitute known values into the formula and solve for *l*:

$$A = lw$$
$$72 = l(6)$$
$$\frac{72}{6} = \frac{6l}{6}$$
$$12 = l$$

Now substitute $w = 6$ and $l = 12$ into the perimeter formula, $P = 2l + 2w$:

$$P = 2(12) + 2(6) = 24 + 12 = 36 \text{ feet}$$

21. **C. $312.50**

The formula to determine the area of a rectangle is $A = lw$. Substitute known values to find the area:

$$A = 10 \times 25 = 250 \text{ square feet}$$

Patrick charges $1.25 per square foot, so he'd require a total of $250(\$1.25) = \$312.50$ to paint the wall.

22. **B. $64.00**

If the coat is 20 percent off, you're paying 80 percent of the original price $(100\% - 20\% = 80\%)$. You can multiply:

$$\$80 \times 0.8 = \$64$$

You can also solve this problem by first finding the amount of the discount: $0.2(80) = \$16$. Then subtract that amount from the original price to find the current cost: $\$80 - \$16 = \$64$. (Both of these approaches work, even when you have to deal with more complicated figures, but the best idea is to find which method is easiest for you — and that you'll be able to remember — on test day.)

23. **D. 12**

Let x = Kiki's age. James is twice as old as Kiki, so his age is $2x$. Kiki's age in 5 years is $x + 5$, and James's age in 5 years is $2x + 5$. In 5 years, the sum of their ages will be 28. Use these expressions to make an equation:

$$x + 5 + 2x + 5 = 28$$
$$3x + 10 = 28$$
$$3x = 18$$
$$x = 6$$

Because Kiki is 6 years old, James's age is $2(6) = 12$.

24. **B. 20 yd**

Let w = the width of the playground. This means that the length is $w + 5$. The formula for the area of a rectangle is $A = lw$. Substitute all known values into the formula and simplify:

$$300 = w(w + 5)$$
$$300 = w^2 + 5w$$
$$0 = w^2 + 5w - 300$$

This is a quadratic equation because it's in the form $ax^2 + bx + c = 0$. You can solve it by factoring. To factor $w^2 + 5w - 300$, or any quadratic equation, you need to think of two numbers that multiply to equal the value of c, or -300 in this case, and add to equal b, which is 5. The only two numbers that fit this description are 20 and -15.

$$0 = w^2 + 5w - 300$$
$$0 = (w + 20)(w - 15)$$

Now set each factor equal to 0 and solve for w:

$$w + 20 = 0$$
$$w = -20$$

$$w - 15 = 0$$
$$w = 15$$

Solving a quadratic equation by factoring produces two solutions. Next, decide which one is correct for this situation. Because a distance can't be negative, the width is 15 yards. The length is $15 + 5 = 20$ yards.

25. **C. 14**

Find the difference in percentages and multiply by the total number of cars:

30% blue − 20% red = 10% more blue cars than red cars

$(10\%)(140) = 14$ cars

You can also solve this problem by reasoning the number of blue cars in the parking lot is equal to $0.3(140) = 42$ and the number of red cars in the parking lot is equal to $0.2(140) = 28$. Subtract the number of red cars from the number of blue cars: $42 - 28 = 14$ more blue cars.

26. **A. 5° Fahrenheit**

Plug the numbers into the formula:

$$F = \frac{9}{5}C + 32°$$
$$= \frac{9}{5}(-15) + 32$$
$$= \frac{9(-15)}{5} + 32$$

First, divide −15 by 5. Remember that a negative number divided by a positive number is negative:

$$F = 9(-3) + 32$$

Next, multiply the result by 9. Remember that a negative number multiplied by a positive number is negative:

$$F = -27 + 32$$

For the final step, add 32 to −27. Remember that adding a negative is the same as subtracting a positive: $32 + (-27) = 32 - 27 = 5°F$.

27. **C. 6 packages of hot dogs, 8 packages of buns, and 3 packages of chips**

This problem involves finding the least common multiple, or LCM, of three numbers. To find the LCM, write out multiples of each number and find the first multiple that they all have in common:

Hot dogs: 8, 16, 24, 43, 40, 48

Buns: 6, 12, 18, 24, 30, 36, 42, 48

Chips: 16, 32, 48

The LCM of 8, 6, and 16 is 48, so you need 48 of each item. For each item, count how many multiples it took to get to 48:

Hot dogs: 8, 16, 24, 43, 40, 48 (6 packages)

Buns: 6, 12, 18, 24, 30, 36, 42, 48 (8 packages)

Chips: 16, 32, 48 (3 packages)

You can take a shortcut in this problem if you noticed that the packages of chips (16) are twice as large as the packages of hot dogs (8). The number of packages of chips must be double the number of packages of hot dogs — and the only answer choice that meets that requirement is Choice (C), which has 6 packages of hot dogs to 3 packages of chips.

Multiply the numbers in Choice (C) by the numbers of items in each package to check:

$$6(8) = 48 \text{ hot dogs}$$
$$8(6) = 48 \text{ buns}$$
$$3(16) = 48 \text{ chips}$$

28. B. 100 revolutions

First, find the circumference of each wheel. The formula for the circumference of a circle is $C = \pi d$. Remember when approximating π, round to 3.14. The circumference of a wheel is $C = 3.14(20) = 62.8$ inches. Every time a wheel makes a full revolution, the bicycle moves approximately 62.8 inches. Divide the total distance traveled by the circumference to find the total number of revolutions: $\frac{6,280}{62.8} = 100$. Each wheel made about 100 full revolutions.

29. D. $7

Let x = the cost of a child's ticket. Alexa has sold a total of $10x$ dollars in children's tickets. An adult ticket costs 40 percent more, which is $0.4x$, so the cost of an adult ticket is $x + 0.4x = 1.4x$. Alexa has sold $12(1.4x)$ dollars in adult tickets. Make an equation and solve for x:

$$10x + 12(1.4x) = 134$$
$$10x + 16.8x = 134$$
$$26.8x = 134$$
$$\frac{26.8x}{26.8} = \frac{134}{26.8}$$
$$x = 5$$

Children's tickets sell for $5, so each adult ticket sells for $1.4($5$) = $7.

30. A. 10 quarters

Let q = the number of quarters and d = the number of dimes. The value of the quarters is $0.25q$, and value of the dimes is $0.10d$. Because you know there are 8 nickels, you know the value of the nickels is $0.5(8)$. The sum of the values of the quarters, dimes, and nickels is equal to 3.40. Start by multiplying the entire equation by 100 to clear the decimals:

$$\left(0.25q + 0.10d + 0.5(8)\right) \cdot 100 = 3.40 \cdot 100$$
$$25q + 10d + 5(8) = 340$$

Because there are twice as many quarters as there are dimes, you can substitute $q = 2d$ into the equation and solve for d:

$$25(2d) + 10d + 5(8) = 340$$
$$50d + 10d + 40 = 340$$
$$60d + 40 = 340$$
$$60d = 300$$
$$d = 5$$

There are 5 dimes, so there are $2(5) = 10$ quarters.

Part 2: Word Knowledge

Scoring well on the Word Knowledge subtest is crucial to scoring high on the AFQT and getting into the military branch of your choice. If your score is weak in this area, spend time reviewing the material and improving your vocabulary (see Chapter 5).

Other great references that can help you improve your score in this area are *Vocabulary For Dummies* by Laurie E. Rozakis and *SAT Vocabulary For Dummies* by Suzee Vlk (both published by Wiley). Plus, see Chapter 6 for more practice questions.

1. D. lie.

Perjury is a noun that means a lie told after taking an oath.

"The man committed perjury by telling the judge he had nothing to do with the crime, despite video evidence to the contrary."

2. B. vibrant.

Used as an adjective, *dynamic* means full of energy and vigorous activity. It's also a noun that means a force that stimulates change or progress.

"The dynamic toddlers ran around the room, laughing and playing."

3. B. maintain.

Used as a verb, *abandon* means to cease or to leave behind.

"The neighbor was afraid the family would abandon their dog."

4. A. major.

Momentous is an adjective that means extremely important or significant.

"The wedding will be a momentous occasion."

5. C. critical.

Vital is an adjective that describes something crucial or very important.

"The commander had the vital task of determining whether to give the 'all clear' signal to her troops."

6. B. hum.

Used as a verb, *drone* means to make a low-pitched humming noise. It's also a noun that means a low, continuous humming sound.

"You can hear the drone of the machinery a mile away from the factory."

7. D. restrain.

Stifle is a verb that means to repress or prevent.

"Ellie had to stifle her laughter during the four-star general's briefing."

8. B. charming

Quaint is an adjective that means having an old-fashioned or pleasant quality.

9. C. pointless

Futile is an adjective that describes something useless or fruitless.

10. B. nonsense

Drivel is a noun that means something foolish or without sense.

11. A. label

Used as a noun, *stereotype* means an oversimplified categorization of a person or group.

12. A. protect.

Betray is a verb that means to harm or to be disloyal.

"A good friend would never betray you by talking about you behind your back."

13. A. stroll.

Amble is a verb that means a leisurely walk for pleasure.

"The parents watched their children amble along the boardwalk, pointing at all the attractions."

14. C. gain

Garner is a verb that means to acquire or gather.

15. D. dull

Monotonous is an adjective that means repetitive or dull.

16. B. questionable

As used in this sentence, *dubious* is an adjective that describes something suspect or untrustworthy.

17. C. isolate.

Used as a verb, *quarantine* means to detain someone from the public or away from others.

"In order to stop the spread of the virus, the CDC had to quarantine the people who had already contracted it."

18. A. condemn.

Endorse is a verb that means to give support to.

"Very few politicians wanted to endorse the presidential candidate."

19. C. reduce.

Mitigate is a verb meaning to lessen or decrease.

"Your platoon sergeant's job is to mitigate the risks you'll face when you're training."

20. A. content

Complacent is an adjective that means unworried or self-satisfied.

21. C. surrender.

Dominate is a verb that means to take over or dictate.

"The king's goal was to dominate all of Europe, so he started to plan for war."

22. B. seize

Commandeer is a verb that means to take or confiscate something by force.

23. D. justify.

Vindicate is a verb that means to prove that something is correct or justified.

"The evidence will vindicate the suspect when it comes out in court."

24. C. devoted

Staunch is an adjective that means loyal or steadfast.

25. B. commonplace

Colloquial is an adjective that describes something usual or informal.

26. A. shrivel.

Atrophy is a verb that means to waste away or deteriorate.

"If you don't exercise, your muscles will atrophy."

27. D. rebel

Insurgent is a noun that represents somebody who rebels against authority.

"An armed insurgent tried to take over the compound, but the local police stopped him."

28. B. enlarge

Augment is a verb that means to add to something or to expand.

29. B. variable.

Intermittent is an adjective that means occurring at sporadic times.

"If you live in Tampa, expect intermittent rain each day during the summer."

30. D. predicament

Quandary is a noun that represents a dilemma or difficult situation.

31. C. unemotional

Stoic is an adjective that describes someone patient or impassive.

32. B. dislike.

Aversion is a noun that means a distaste for something.

"Try to get over your aversion to running before you report to Basic Combat Training." (Seriously.)

33. A. gaudy.

Garish is an adjective that means overly ornate or bright.

"I can't take someone seriously when he's wearing such a garish outfit."

34. C. brave.

Intrepid is an adjective that means courageous or fearless.

"The intrepid storm chasers saw more than five tornadoes that day."

35. D. yield.

Vanquish is a verb that means to overcome or defeat.

"Union soldiers tried hard to vanquish the Confederate artillery unit at Charleston, but they failed."

Part 3: Paragraph Comprehension

Those ASVAB folks sure don't give you much time to read all those paragraphs, do they? But with a little practice, anyone can improve his or her reading speed and comprehension skills. The material in Chapter 7 can be helpful in these endeavors. There are also more practice questions in Chapter 8.

1. D. Fiddles and violins are the same instrument.

Both the opening and closing sentences in this paragraph state the main point. The different styles of music are secondary information.

2. A. smoothly

Fluidly is an adjective that means gracefully or flowingly.

3. C. Acupuncture has become trendy in spa settings.

Although the passage doesn't directly define *boutique*, the use of the term "popular" indicates that Choice (C) is the only choice that makes sense.

4. C. hundreds of thousands

The passage says that the number of children with peanut allergies is in the "hundreds of thousands."

5. B. It could reduce their anxiety about exposure.

The research mentioned in the passage indicates that reduced sensitivity is the possible outcome of the treatment. This reduced sensitivity helps decrease the risk of a negative reaction, which could relieve parents' concerns about a reaction from secondary sources of peanuts.

6. C. because of urban sprawl

The last sentence in the passage specifically states that the main cause is urban sprawl, which refers to the uncontrolled expansion of urban areas into more rural areas, so you can quickly scan and find the answer if you don't remember it from reading.

7. C. bizarre.

Outlandish is an adjective that means peculiar or unusual.

8. B. 15

The passage states that he played with the Yankees from 1923 to 1938. Simple subtraction finds you the correct answer.

9. C. They learn to ski more easily.

The passage provides examples of why children learn to ski more quickly than adults do, but it makes no other judgments about their abilities.

10. A. being less fearful

In the passage, many of the factors that make skiing more difficult for adults involve some kind of fear (fear of falling, fear of injury, fear of medical bills). None of the other answer choices fit the information in the passage.

11. B. prime

Heyday is a noun that means at the height or top of a situation or timeline.

12. C. nervous

The passage describes the fidgety behavior or last-minute preparation of the children as they wait in line. These are signs of nervousness.

13. D. She achieved the highest score given in Olympic gymnastics.

The passage states that Comaneci was the first female gymnast to receive a perfect ten for her performance, which she did seven times at the Montreal games. Choice (D) provides this answer.

14. A. 1989

You can find the answer to this question at the end of the passage, where it specifically states she "found her freedom in 1989 when she defected to the United States."

15. A. lack of knowledge about prices

The passage states that more Americans would likely drive NGVs if they knew about the savings, so their lack of knowledge must be what's keeping them from getting on the NGV bandwagon.

Part 4: Mathematics Knowledge

Many people find the Mathematics Knowledge subtest to be more difficult than the Arithmetic Reasoning subtest, but doing well on this subtest is just as important. If you missed more than a few answers, or you ran out of time before you finished, you have a date with the books (Chapter 9 is a great place to start). Getting in touch with a math teacher at your high school or a local community college (or at least finding a good basic-algebra textbook) can help. You can also try out the following *For Dummies* books: *Algebra I For Dummies* and *Algebra II For Dummies*, both by Mary Jane Sterling; *Geometry For Dummies* by Mark Ryan; *Basic Math & Pre-Algebra For Dummies* by Mark Zegarelli; and *SAT II Math For Dummies* by Scott Hatch, JD, and Lisa Zimmer Hatch, MA (all published by Wiley). Chapter 10 also has some additional practice questions.

1. B. 54

When a numerical expression just has addition and subtraction, the order of operations is flexible. You can work from left to right, like this: $45 - 6 + 15 = 39 + 15 = 54$, or you can add 45 and 15 before you subtract 6. You can use the method you're most comfortable with to find the answer when you encounter a problem like this one.

2. A. 216

Write 30 percent as a decimal: 30 percent $= 0.3$. The word *of* in a word problem means *multiply*, so multiply 0.3 by 720: $0.3(720) = 216$.

3. B. hundredths

The numbers in the decimal system increase as you move from left to right when reading a number. In this case, the number is 4.5972, where the 4 is in the ones place, the 5 is in the tenths place, the 9 is in the hundredths place, the 7 is in the thousandths place, and the 2 is in the ten-thousandths place.

4. A. 2.6 percent

To turn a decimal into a percent, simply move the decimal point two places to the right (which is the same thing as multiplying by 100).

5. C. 235,000

For the given number, 8 is in the ones place, 7 is in the tens place, 6 is in the hundreds place, and 4 is in the thousands place. You round 4 up to 5 because the digit one place to the right of it (6) is 5 or greater. You can round 234,678 to 235,000.

6. D. 2

The first digit after the decimal point is in the tenths place, and the second digit is in the hundredths place. In this problem, the 2 is in the hundredths place.

7. B. 24

4! means the factorial of 4. You find it by multiplying all the whole numbers from 4 down to 1:

$$4 \times 3 \times 2 \times 1 = 24$$

8. A. −4

Evaluate means to substitute the given value of *m* into the expression and then simplify the result. Remember that a positive number divided by a negative number results in a negative number.

$$\frac{28}{-7} = 28 \div (-7) = -4$$

9. A. −38

Isolate the variable, *m*, by adding 17 to each side of the equation.

$$-55 = m - 17$$
$$-55 + 17 = m - 17 + 17$$
$$-38 = m$$

10. C. 15 percent

Subtract the original number from the new number to get the difference: $23 - 20 = 3$.

To find what percent of 20 is 3, divide the difference (3) by the original number (20). This is the percent increase: $3 \div 20 = 0.15 = 15$ percent.

You can also create a fraction and then increase its terms so the denominator is 100 (in this instance, you have to multiply the 20 by 5 to reach 100). Then apply the same multiplier to the numerator to get the right answer:

$$\frac{3}{20} = \frac{x}{100}$$

$$\frac{3(5)}{20(5)} = \frac{15}{100}$$

11. D. 4.36×10^{-6}

A number written in scientific notation is a number between 1 and 10 multiplied by a power of 10. To make a number between 1 and 10, move the decimal point six places to the right to get 4.36. You find the power of 10 by taking the number of spaces you moved the decimal and determining whether it should be positive or negative based on which direction you moved it. Because you moved it to the right (that is, the given number is less than 1), the power of 10 must be negative: 10^{-6}.

12. B. Point B

First, notice that the x-coordinate is −3. This means that from the origin (0, 0), you move to the left three units. The y-coordinate is 2, so you then move up two units. That puts you at Point B.

13. C. $\frac{5}{6}$

Write each mixed number as an improper fraction:

$$5\frac{1}{3} = \frac{3(5)+1}{3} = \frac{15+1}{3} = \frac{16}{3}$$

$$4\frac{1}{2} = \frac{2(4)+1}{2} = \frac{8+1}{2} = \frac{9}{2}$$

The common denominator is 6. Rewrite each fraction with the common denominator:

$$\frac{16}{3} - \frac{9}{2} = \frac{16 \cdot 2}{3 \cdot 2} - \frac{9 \cdot 3}{2 \cdot 3}$$
$$= \frac{32}{6} - \frac{27}{6}$$
$$= \frac{5}{6}$$

14. D. −21m

This is basically just three values being multiplied together: 7, −3, and m. However, because you don't know the value of m, you only need to multiply 7 and −3. Remember that a positive number times a negative number is a negative number:

$$7(-3m) = 7(-3)m = -21m$$

15. A. 19

In any triangle, any side length must be less than the sum of the other two side lengths. So that means y has to be less than $14 + 6 = 20$. All the answer choices are greater than 20 except 19.

16. B. 18

Use the order of operations (PEMDAS), which says to simplify inside the parentheses first, compute all exponents next, multiply and divide from left to right after that, and then add and subtract from left to right:

$$10 + 2(5-3)^2 = 10 + 2(2)^2$$
$$= 10 + 2(4)$$
$$= 10 + 8$$
$$= 18$$

17. C. 16

Remember that dividing by a fraction is the same as multiplying by the reciprocal of the fraction. Dividing 12 by $\frac{3}{4}$ is the same as multiplying 12 by $\frac{4}{3}$.

$$12 \div \frac{3}{4} = 12 \times \frac{4}{3}$$
$$= \frac{12}{1} \times \frac{4}{3}$$
$$= \frac{48}{3}$$
$$= 16$$

Tip: Sometimes you can skip all the calculations and find the most logical answer choice. In this problem, you're dividing by a number that's less than 1, so the answer must be greater than 12. Choices (B) and (D) are out of the question, and Choice (A) is too close to 12 to be correct. The most likely answer is Choice (C).

18. D. p^8

A square root is a number that when multiplied by itself equals the number under the radical sign. Square both sides of the equation to clear the square root. When the base is the same, you add the exponents to multiply, so

$$p^4 = \sqrt{x}$$
$$\left(p^4\right)^2 = \left(\sqrt{x}\right)^2$$
$$\left(p^4\right)\left(p^4\right) = x$$
$$p^{4+4} = x$$
$$p^8 = x$$

19. B. −22

Let x = the number you want to find. Remembering that "12 less than the product" means to subtract 12 from the product, write an equation:

$$x = 4(-2.5) - 12$$

Now, solve the equation, following the order of operations by multiplying first and then subtracting:

$$x = 4(-2.5) - 12$$
$$x = -10 - 12$$
$$x = -22$$

20. D. 30°, 60°, 90°

Remember that for any triangle, the sum of the three angle measures is always 180°. You can make an equation by adding the three expressions shown in the diagram and setting the sum equal to 180°. Then solve the equation.

$$x + 2x + 3x = 180$$
$$6x = 180$$
$$x = 30$$

The measures of the angles are

$$x = 30°$$
$$2x = 2(30°) = 60°$$
$$3x = 3(30°) = 90°$$

21. A. $9x^2 - 4x - y$

For problems like this one, the first thing you want to do is remove the parentheses. Remember that when you have a subtraction sign in front of a set of parentheses, you need to change the sign of all the terms inside the parentheses. Then combine like terms and simplify:

$$(3x^2 - 4x + y) - (2y - 6x^2) = 3x^2 - 4x + y - 2y + 6x^2$$
$$= 9x^2 - 4x - y$$

22. B. 4×10^5

Quotient means division, so first, write this problem as a fraction:

$$\frac{4.8 \times 10^{-4}}{1.2 \times 10^{-9}}$$

Now, separate that fraction into a product of two fractions:

$$\frac{4.8}{1.2} \times \frac{10^{-4}}{10^{-9}}$$

The first fraction simplifies to 4, because $\frac{4.8}{1.2} = 4$. Because the bases are the same in the second fraction, subtract the exponents:

$$\frac{4.8 \times 10^{-4}}{1.2 \times 10^{-9}} = 4 \times 10^{-4-(-9)} = 4 \times 10^{-4+9} = 4 \times 10^5$$

23. C. 4

Simplify everything under the radical sign first, using the order of operations. For this problem, that means computing the exponent first, multiplying next, and then subtracting:

$$\sqrt{66 - 2 \cdot 5^2} = \sqrt{66 - 2 \cdot 25}$$
$$= \sqrt{66 - 50}$$
$$= \sqrt{16}$$

Then find the square root of the result:

$$\sqrt{16} = 4$$

24. D. −22

First, substitute the given values of x and y into the expression: $\frac{45}{-5} - \frac{39}{3}$. Then use the order of operations to simplify. Remember that you have to divide the fractions before you subtract. Also remember that a positive number divided by a negative number produces a negative number:

$$\frac{45}{-5} - \frac{39}{3} = -9 - 13$$
$$= -22$$

25. C. $\left(9\pi + 6m\pi\right)\text{cm}^2$

A good strategy for this problem is to find the area of each circle and then subtract. Use formula for the area of a circle, $A = \pi r^2$.

Area of smaller circle:

$$A_1 = \pi \cdot m^2 = m^2\pi$$

Area of larger circle:

$$A_2 = \pi\left(3 + m\right)^2$$
$$= \pi\left(3 + m\right)\left(3 + m\right)$$
$$= \pi\left(9 + 6m + m^2\right)$$
$$= 9\pi + \pi\left(6m\right) + \pi\left(m^2\right)$$
$$= 9\pi + 6m\pi + m^2\pi$$

Now subtract the area of the smaller circle from the area of the larger circle:

$$9\pi + 6m\pi + m^2\pi - m^2\pi = 9\pi + 6m\pi$$

The answer choices didn't factor out pi, so you can stop your work there. When you see an opportunity to save yourself time on the ASVAB, take it!

Answer Key

Part 1: Arithmetic Reasoning

1.	B	7.	A	13.	C	19.	B	25.	C
2.	C	8.	D	14.	C	20.	B	26.	A
3.	A	9.	C	15.	D	21.	C	27.	C
4.	C	10.	A	16.	D	22.	B	28.	B
5.	B	11.	B	17.	A	23.	D	29.	D
6.	C	12.	A	18.	C	24.	B	30.	A

Part 2: Word Knowledge

1.	D	8.	B	15.	D	22.	B	29.	B
2.	B	9.	C	16.	B	23.	D	30.	D
3.	B	10.	B	17.	C	24.	C	31.	C
4.	A	11.	A	18.	A	25.	B	32.	B
5.	C	12.	A	19.	C	26.	A	33.	A
6.	B	13.	A	20.	A	27.	D	34.	C
7.	D	14.	C	21.	C	28.	B	35.	D

Part 3: Paragraph Comprehension

1.	D	4.	C	7.	C	10.	A	13.	D
2.	A	5.	B	8.	B	11.	B	14.	A
3.	C	6.	C	9.	C	12.	C	15.	A

Part 4: Mathematics Knowledge

1.	B	6.	D	11.	D	16.	B	21.	A
2.	A	7.	B	12.	B	17.	C	22.	B
3.	D	8.	A	13.	C	18.	D	23.	C
4.	A	9.	A	14.	D	19.	B	24.	D
5.	C	10.	C	15.	A	20.	D	25.	C

Chapter 19
Practice Exam 4

When you've taken all four practice AFQT exams in this book, you should be ready to tackle the actual Armed Services Vocational Aptitude Battery (ASVAB) and impress all those military recruiters by acing the four subtests that make up the AFQT. If you still want some more practice after this exam, or you want to study for the other ASVAB subtests as well, might I humbly suggest *ASVAB For Dummies* (Wiley)?

The four sections that follow represent the four subtests of the ASVAB that make up your all-important AFQT score. This is the score that determines whether you're qualified to join the military branch of your choice (see Chapter 2). The four subtests are Arithmetic Reasoning, Word Knowledge, Paragraph Comprehension, and Mathematics Knowledge.

Use the answer key and explanations in Chapter 20 to score the following sections. *Remember:* On the actual ASVAB, harder questions are worth more points than easier questions when you determine your AFQT score.

Consider taking this final practice exam a day or two before the ASVAB to make sure you're ready and to boost your confidence. If you don't score well, you may want to consider asking your recruiter to reschedule your ASVAB test for a later date to give you more time to study.

Ready to get started? Okay, hold your No. 2 pencil in the air. (Not really — your friends might start talking about you.) Ready, set, go!

Answer Sheet for Practice Exam 4

Part 1: Arithmetic Reasoning

1. Ⓐ Ⓑ Ⓒ Ⓓ
2. Ⓐ Ⓑ Ⓒ Ⓓ
3. Ⓐ Ⓑ Ⓒ Ⓓ
4. Ⓐ Ⓑ Ⓒ Ⓓ
5. Ⓐ Ⓑ Ⓒ Ⓓ
6. Ⓐ Ⓑ Ⓒ Ⓓ

7. Ⓐ Ⓑ Ⓒ Ⓓ
8. Ⓐ Ⓑ Ⓒ Ⓓ
9. Ⓐ Ⓑ Ⓒ Ⓓ
10. Ⓐ Ⓑ Ⓒ Ⓓ
11. Ⓐ Ⓑ Ⓒ Ⓓ
12. Ⓐ Ⓑ Ⓒ Ⓓ

13. Ⓐ Ⓑ Ⓒ Ⓓ
14. Ⓐ Ⓑ Ⓒ Ⓓ
15. Ⓐ Ⓑ Ⓒ Ⓓ
16. Ⓐ Ⓑ Ⓒ Ⓓ
17. Ⓐ Ⓑ Ⓒ Ⓓ
18. Ⓐ Ⓑ Ⓒ Ⓓ

19. Ⓐ Ⓑ Ⓒ Ⓓ
20. Ⓐ Ⓑ Ⓒ Ⓓ
21. Ⓐ Ⓑ Ⓒ Ⓓ
22. Ⓐ Ⓑ Ⓒ Ⓓ
23. Ⓐ Ⓑ Ⓒ Ⓓ
24. Ⓐ Ⓑ Ⓒ Ⓓ

25. Ⓐ Ⓑ Ⓒ Ⓓ
26. Ⓐ Ⓑ Ⓒ Ⓓ
27. Ⓐ Ⓑ Ⓒ Ⓓ
28. Ⓐ Ⓑ Ⓒ Ⓓ
29. Ⓐ Ⓑ Ⓒ Ⓓ
30. Ⓐ Ⓑ Ⓒ Ⓓ

Part 2: Word Knowledge

1. Ⓐ Ⓑ Ⓒ Ⓓ
2. Ⓐ Ⓑ Ⓒ Ⓓ
3. Ⓐ Ⓑ Ⓒ Ⓓ
4. Ⓐ Ⓑ Ⓒ Ⓓ
5. Ⓐ Ⓑ Ⓒ Ⓓ
6. Ⓐ Ⓑ Ⓒ Ⓓ
7. Ⓐ Ⓑ Ⓒ Ⓓ

8. Ⓐ Ⓑ Ⓒ Ⓓ
9. Ⓐ Ⓑ Ⓒ Ⓓ
10. Ⓐ Ⓑ Ⓒ Ⓓ
11. Ⓐ Ⓑ Ⓒ Ⓓ
12. Ⓐ Ⓑ Ⓒ Ⓓ
13. Ⓐ Ⓑ Ⓒ Ⓓ
14. Ⓐ Ⓑ Ⓒ Ⓓ

15. Ⓐ Ⓑ Ⓒ Ⓓ
16. Ⓐ Ⓑ Ⓒ Ⓓ
17. Ⓐ Ⓑ Ⓒ Ⓓ
18. Ⓐ Ⓑ Ⓒ Ⓓ
19. Ⓐ Ⓑ Ⓒ Ⓓ
20. Ⓐ Ⓑ Ⓒ Ⓓ
21. Ⓐ Ⓑ Ⓒ Ⓓ

22. Ⓐ Ⓑ Ⓒ Ⓓ
23. Ⓐ Ⓑ Ⓒ Ⓓ
24. Ⓐ Ⓑ Ⓒ Ⓓ
25. Ⓐ Ⓑ Ⓒ Ⓓ
26. Ⓐ Ⓑ Ⓒ Ⓓ
27. Ⓐ Ⓑ Ⓒ Ⓓ
28. Ⓐ Ⓑ Ⓒ Ⓓ

29. Ⓐ Ⓑ Ⓒ Ⓓ
30. Ⓐ Ⓑ Ⓒ Ⓓ
31. Ⓐ Ⓑ Ⓒ Ⓓ
32. Ⓐ Ⓑ Ⓒ Ⓓ
33. Ⓐ Ⓑ Ⓒ Ⓓ
34. Ⓐ Ⓑ Ⓒ Ⓓ
35. Ⓐ Ⓑ Ⓒ Ⓓ

Part 3: Paragraph Comprehension

1. Ⓐ Ⓑ Ⓒ Ⓓ   4. Ⓐ Ⓑ Ⓒ Ⓓ   7. Ⓐ Ⓑ Ⓒ Ⓓ   10. Ⓐ Ⓑ Ⓒ Ⓓ   13. Ⓐ Ⓑ Ⓒ Ⓓ
2. Ⓐ Ⓑ Ⓒ Ⓓ   5. Ⓐ Ⓑ Ⓒ Ⓓ   8. Ⓐ Ⓑ Ⓒ Ⓓ   11. Ⓐ Ⓑ Ⓒ Ⓓ   14. Ⓐ Ⓑ Ⓒ Ⓓ
3. Ⓐ Ⓑ Ⓒ Ⓓ   6. Ⓐ Ⓑ Ⓒ Ⓓ   9. Ⓐ Ⓑ Ⓒ Ⓓ   12. Ⓐ Ⓑ Ⓒ Ⓓ   15. Ⓐ Ⓑ Ⓒ Ⓓ

Part 4: Mathematics Knowledge

1. Ⓐ Ⓑ Ⓒ Ⓓ   6. Ⓐ Ⓑ Ⓒ Ⓓ   11. Ⓐ Ⓑ Ⓒ Ⓓ   16. Ⓐ Ⓑ Ⓒ Ⓓ   21. Ⓐ Ⓑ Ⓒ Ⓓ
2. Ⓐ Ⓑ Ⓒ Ⓓ   7. Ⓐ Ⓑ Ⓒ Ⓓ   12. Ⓐ Ⓑ Ⓒ Ⓓ   17. Ⓐ Ⓑ Ⓒ Ⓓ   22. Ⓐ Ⓑ Ⓒ Ⓓ
3. Ⓐ Ⓑ Ⓒ Ⓓ   8. Ⓐ Ⓑ Ⓒ Ⓓ   13. Ⓐ Ⓑ Ⓒ Ⓓ   18. Ⓐ Ⓑ Ⓒ Ⓓ   23. Ⓐ Ⓑ Ⓒ Ⓓ
4. Ⓐ Ⓑ Ⓒ Ⓓ   9. Ⓐ Ⓑ Ⓒ Ⓓ   14. Ⓐ Ⓑ Ⓒ Ⓓ   19. Ⓐ Ⓑ Ⓒ Ⓓ   24. Ⓐ Ⓑ Ⓒ Ⓓ
5. Ⓐ Ⓑ Ⓒ Ⓓ   10. Ⓐ Ⓑ Ⓒ Ⓓ   15. Ⓐ Ⓑ Ⓒ Ⓓ   20. Ⓐ Ⓑ Ⓒ Ⓓ   25. Ⓐ Ⓑ Ⓒ Ⓓ

Part 1: Arithmetic Reasoning

TIME: 36 minutes for 30 questions

DIRECTIONS: Arithmetic Reasoning is the second subtest of the ASVAB; it follows General Science. These questions are designed to test your ability to use mathematics to solve various problems that may be found in real life — in other words, math word problems.

Each question is followed by four possible answers. Decide which answer is correct, and then mark the corresponding space on your answer sheet. Use your scratch paper for any figuring you want to do. You may *not* use a calculator.

1. One pound is equal to 16 ounces. How many ounces are in 5 pounds?

(A) 21 ounces

(B) 3.2 ounces

(C) 80 ounces

(D) 64 ounces

2. Jason is reading a book that is 180 pages long. He is 40 percent of the way through the book. What page is he on?

(A) page 40

(B) page 72

(C) page 45

(D) page 76

3. If you toss two coins, what is the probability that both coins show tails?

(A) 33 percent

(B) 30 percent

(C) 25 percent

(D) 50 percent

4. In a triangle, one angle has a measure of 40°, and the other two angles have measures equal to each other. What is the measure of one of the two other angles?

(A) 30°

(B) 40°

(C) 80°

(D) 70°

5. Jake's truck gets 22 miles per gallon on the highway. How many miles on the highway can he travel on 4 gallons of gasoline?

(A) 88 miles

(B) 44 miles

(C) 22 miles

(D) 26 miles

6. Sergeant Williams cut a 24-foot rope into smaller ropes, each with a length of 4 feet. How many times did he cut the rope?

(A) 4

(B) 6

(C) 3

(D) 5

7. The refrigerator's temperature dropped from 32° Fahrenheit to 28° Fahrenheit. What is the percent decrease in temperature?

(A) 15 percent

(B) 4 percent

(C) 25 percent

(D) 12.5 percent

8. Carter has $6.70. Dirk has 4 times as much money as Carter. Harriet has half as much money as Dirk. How much money does Harriet have?

(A) $26.80

(B) $13.40

(C) $5.35

(D) $10.70

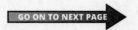

9. The ages of a group of adults are 24, 26, 37, 23, and 40. What is the average age for this group?

(A) 26

(B) 32

(C) 30

(D) 28

10. A pitcher has 2.5 gallons of juice. Twenty-five people share all the juice equally. How much juice does each person get?

(A) 0.1 gallon

(B) 0.25 gallon

(C) 0.01 gallon

(D) 0.2 gallon

11. Timothy's age is one more than twice Sam's age. The sum of their ages is 31. What is Sam's age?

(A) 21

(B) 10

(C) 11

(D) 16

12. The value of a new car depreciates 10 percent each year after it was purchased. What is the car's value two years after it is purchased new if the initial value is $14,000?

(A) $11,340

(B) $11,200

(C) $11,034

(D) $10,955

13. The formula $W = 0.5n + 47$ gives the percent of women (W) in a certain country who owned a laptop computer n years after the year 2000. In what year did 50 percent of women in this country own a laptop computer?

(A) 2004

(B) 2006

(C) 2011

(D) 2008

14. A rhombus has two interior angle measurements of 87° and 93°. Which of the following can be a measure of one of the remaining angles?

(A) 6°

(B) 90°

(C) 93°

(D) 180°

15. To make a certain type of juice, the ratio of water to juice concentrate is 8 to 1. How much concentrate should be added to 6 gallons of water?

(A) $\frac{2}{3}$ gallon

(B) 2 gallons

(C) $1\frac{1}{3}$ gallons

(D) $\frac{3}{4}$ gallon

16. Lillian invests $5,000 into a savings account. After one year, she had earned $100 in interest. What is the annual interest rate for the account?

(A) 0.2 percent

(B) 0.5 percent

(C) 2 percent

(D) 5 percent

17. The number of members in a club has doubled every 2 years. The club started in 2002 with 42 members. How many members were in the club in 2008?

(A) 672

(B) 1,344

(C) 336

(D) 168

18. The high temperature (H) was ten degrees less than twice the low temperature (L). Which equation shows this relationship?

(A) $H = 2L - 10$

(B) $H = 10 - 2L$

(C) $2H = L - 10$

(D) $2H + L = 10$

19. What is the area of the triangle?

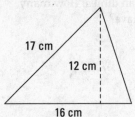

17 cm

12 cm

16 cm

Illustration by Thomson Digital

(A) 136 cm²

(B) 96 cm²

(C) 102 cm²

(D) 45 cm²

20. The table shows how many men and women live in different regions of a town. How many more women live in the West region than men?

	East region	West region	South region
Men	320	110	421
Women	120	262	338

Illustration by Thomson Digital

(A) 110

(B) 372

(C) 262

(D) 152

21. Francis has two jobs. Last week, he earned a total of $314 from both jobs, working 16 hours at the first job and 14 hours at the second job. He earns $10 an hour at his first job. What is his hourly rate at his second job?

(A) $12

(B) $11

(C) $9

(D) $8

22. A bag has a total of 270 red, blue, and green marbles. The ratio of red to blue to green marbles is 1:3:5. How many blue marbles are in the bag?

(A) 30

(B) 90

(C) 150

(D) 50

23. A truck and a car leave from the same place at the same time. The truck takes a road that goes directly north, and the car takes a road that goes directly east. The truck travels at an average speed of 30 miles per hour, and the car travels at an average speed of 40 miles per hour. How far apart are the vehicles 2 hours after departure?

(A) 10 miles

(B) 1,000 miles

(C) 100 miles

(D) 70 miles

24. Evan is twice as old as Joe. In two years, the sum of their ages will be 85. How old is Evan now?

(A) 27

(B) 29

(C) 54

(D) 56

25. Gregory started the day with $45.10 in his wallet. The first thing he did was buy breakfast for himself, which cost $8.50. He left a 20 percent tip. How much did Gregory have left after he paid for breakfast?

(A) $10.20

(B) $34.80

(C) $34.90

(D) $36.60

26. Kendra's first three quiz scores were 7, 6, and 10. On the fourth quiz, she earned twice as much as she did on the fifth quiz. Her average score on the first five quizzes was 7. What was her score on the fourth quiz?

(A) 6.5

(B) 7.5

(C) 4

(D) 8

GO ON TO NEXT PAGE

27. The floor plan of a laboratory is shown. Its area is 126 square meters. What is the length of x?

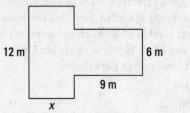

12 m   6 m

9 m

x

Illustration by Thomson Digital

(A) 6 m

(B) 4 m

(C) 5 m

(D) 10 m

28. The company truck weighs 3.5 tons when carrying forty 20-pound cylinder blocks. What is the weight of the truck when it isn't carrying a load?

(A) $3\frac{1}{5}$ tons

(B) $3\frac{7}{10}$ tons

(C) $3\frac{1}{10}$ tons

(D) 4 tons

29. Carla has $4 in quarters and dimes. She has 5 fewer quarters than dimes. How many quarters does she have?

(A) 8

(B) 10

(C) 15

(D) 20

30. A secret building has a front and a rear entrance. The front entrance requires a three-character code, where the first character must be an odd number but the next two characters can be any number 0 through 9. The rear entrance requires a two-character code, where the first character is a letter and the second character can be any number 0 through 9. How many possible entrance codes are there for the rear entrance?

(A) 260

(B) 361

(C) 760

(D) 500

DO NOT TURN THE PAGE UNTIL TOLD TO DO SO   STOP   **DO NOT RETURN TO A PREVIOUS TEST**

Part 2: Word Knowledge

TIME: 11 minutes for 35 questions

DIRECTIONS: The Word Knowledge subtest is the third subtest of the ASVAB; it follows Arithmetic Reasoning. The questions are designed to measure your vocabulary knowledge. You'll see three types of questions on this subtest. The first type simply asks you to choose a word or words that most nearly mean the same as the underlined word in the question. The second type includes an underlined word used in a sentence, and you are to choose the word or words that most nearly mean the same as the underlined word, as used in the context of the sentence. The third type of question asks you to choose the word that has the opposite or nearly opposite meaning as the underlined word. Each question is followed by four possible answers. Decide which answer is correct, and then mark the corresponding space on your answer sheet.

1. <u>Condescend</u> most nearly means
   - (A) share.
   - (B) conjoin.
   - (C) belittle.
   - (D) soften.

2. He's a <u>legend</u> in the bluegrass community, with a career spanning 35 years.
   - (A) star
   - (B) fairytale
   - (C) myth
   - (D) antagonist

3. <u>Lavish</u> most nearly means
   - (A) soapy.
   - (B) thick.
   - (C) meek.
   - (D) extravagant.

4. <u>Retraction</u> most nearly means
   - (A) withdrawal.
   - (B) application.
   - (C) memory.
   - (D) solitude.

5. <u>Decoy</u> most nearly means
   - (A) message.
   - (B) trap.
   - (C) plan.
   - (D) scheme.

6. <u>Obsession</u> most nearly means
   - (A) pastime.
   - (B) piece.
   - (C) fixation.
   - (D) apathy.

7. <u>Brawny</u> most nearly means
   - (A) obese.
   - (B) scrawny.
   - (C) meager.
   - (D) hefty.

8. The word most opposite in meaning to <u>relocate</u> is
   - (A) rearrange.
   - (B) move.
   - (C) continue.
   - (D) remain.

9. Lisa found washing dishes <u>therapeutic</u> because it allowed her to free her mind.
   - (A) astounding
   - (B) healing
   - (C) obstructing
   - (D) injurious

10. Jason was <u>poised</u> to take over as captain this year.
    - (A) perched
    - (B) proper
    - (C) ready
    - (D) unqualified

GO ON TO NEXT PAGE

11. The meaning of the poem was <u>obscure</u> and created a lot of debate.

    (A) clear

    (B) vague

    (C) obvious

    (D) pointed

12. Paolo wasn't ready to deal with the <u>ramifications</u> of his car accident.

    (A) consequences

    (B) prizes

    (C) presentations

    (D) rewards

13. The <u>eccentric</u> minister made the ceremony more enjoyable than your average church wedding.

    (A) foolish

    (B) conventional

    (C) peculiar

    (D) standard

14. The word most opposite in meaning to <u>meander</u> is

    (A) wander.

    (B) hurry.

    (C) dawdle.

    (D) discourage.

15. <u>Volatile</u> most nearly means

    (A) speedy.

    (B) steady.

    (C) unlawful.

    (D) unpredictable.

16. The skaters had obviously done the work to <u>hone</u> their jumps since the last competition.

    (A) tarnish

    (B) maintain

    (C) polish

    (D) contain

17. Cary wanted to <u>broach</u> the topic, but Jeffrey wasn't paying attention.

    (A) mention

    (B) conclude

    (C) kill

    (D) belabor

18. The family was worried when the dog's behavior became <u>erratic</u>.

    (A) irrational

    (B) random

    (C) constant

    (D) even

19. <u>Obsolete</u> most nearly means

    (A) absent.

    (B) old.

    (C) prominent.

    (D) innovative.

20. <u>Decorum</u> most nearly means

    (A) design.

    (B) festivities.

    (C) servitude.

    (D) respectability.

21. My editing style tends to favor <u>brevity</u> over long-winded explanations.

    (A) rudeness

    (B) briefness

    (C) lengthy

    (D) continuous

22. The word most opposite in meaning to <u>mayhem</u> is

    (A) gathering.

    (B) confusion.

    (C) havoc.

    (D) stability.

23. <u>Hiatus</u> most nearly means

    (A) gap.

    (B) inequality.

    (C) mismatch.

    (D) shift.

24. <u>Cynical</u> most nearly means
   (A) friendly.
   (B) hopeful.
   (C) pessimistic.
   (D) depressed.

25. <u>Riddled</u> most nearly means
   (A) mysterious.
   (B) inquisitive.
   (C) full of.
   (D) covered with.

26. Sean was finally released after his <u>larceny</u> conviction four years ago.
   (A) gift
   (B) theft
   (C) help
   (D) skill

27. The word most opposite in meaning to <u>proposition</u> is
   (A) demand.
   (B) suggestion.
   (C) offer.
   (D) plan.

28. The movie gave a <u>poignant</u> portrayal of the fallen soldier.
   (A) lackluster
   (B) traumatic
   (C) moving
   (D) composed

29. I had to take a <u>respite</u> from work or I was never going to rest.
   (A) interval
   (B) start
   (C) end
   (D) continuation

30. The celebrity had to <u>debunk</u> the rumors of his death.
   (A) chide
   (B) shoot down
   (C) alarm
   (D) conceal

31. <u>Adamant</u> most nearly means
   (A) erratic.
   (B) flexible.
   (C) fickle.
   (D) resolute.

32. The word most opposite in meaning to <u>malarkey</u> is
   (A) drivel.
   (B) nonsense.
   (C) justification.
   (D) wisdom.

33. The bobsledder won the bronze medal despite the <u>adversity</u> he had to overcome.
   (A) hardship
   (B) strength
   (C) death
   (D) fortune

34. The <u>defunct</u> band still sold records years after its split.
   (A) rising
   (B) extinct
   (C) promising
   (D) useless

35. <u>Origin</u> most nearly means
   (A) section.
   (B) closure.
   (C) beginning.
   (D) new.

Part 3: Paragraph Comprehension

TIME: 13 minutes for 15 questions

DIRECTIONS: Paragraph Comprehension is the fourth subtest on the ASVAB; it comes after Word Knowledge. The questions are designed to measure your ability to understand what you read. In this part of the test, you see one or more paragraphs of reading material, followed by incomplete statements or questions. Read the paragraph and select the choice that best completes the statement or answers the question. Then mark the corresponding space on your answer sheet.

Questions 1 through 3 refer to the following passage.

"November had come; the crops were in, and barn, buttery, and bin were overflowing with the harvest that rewarded the summer's hard work. The big kitchen was a jolly place just now, for in the great fireplace roared a cheerful fire; on the walls hung garlands of dried apples, onions, and corn; up aloft from the beams shone crook-necked squashes, juicy hams, and dried venison — for in those days deer still haunted the deep forests, and hunters flourished. Savory smells were in the air; on the crane hung steaming kettles, and down among the red embers copper saucepans simmered, all suggestive of some approaching feast."

—Louisa May Alcott

1. In this passage, <u>flourished</u> most nearly means
- **(A)** failed.
- **(B)** prospered.
- **(C)** congregated.
- **(D)** killed.

2. Where is the scene described in the passage taking place?
- **(A)** the kitchen
- **(B)** the forest
- **(C)** the barn
- **(D)** at a feast

3. What is happening in the passage?
- **(A)** The season is changing.
- **(B)** Hunters are looking for deer.
- **(C)** Farmers are harvesting their crops.
- **(D)** A feast is being prepared.

The topic of creating a high-speed rail system in the United States is the focus of the annual High-Speed Rail Summit in Washington, D.C. The purpose of this summit is to determine the most optimal and logical maneuvers that would allow a rail system to succeed on American soil. Critics have long contested the system as an expensive endeavor lacking the appropriate ridership numbers. Regardless, the summit participants will spend two full days hashing out the details to work toward a high-speed rail system in the future.

4. What is the main point of the passage?
- **(A)** to define what a high-speed rail system is
- **(B)** to explain why critics are against a high-speed rail system
- **(C)** to explain the purpose of the High-Speed Rail Summit
- **(D)** to suggest ways to improve ridership on a high-speed rail system

Questions 5 and 6 refer to the following passage.

California is often the location for devastating natural events, such as earthquakes or droughts. However, the aftermath of those events can often be worse than the events themselves. For instance, the near-record drought in 2013 led to a wildfire season that began in May and continued until the end of the year. Fire season typically lasts from September to October, but in 2013, a fire in central California burned thousands of acres of land right before the Christmas holiday. Without rain, the number and severity of wildfires increased in 2013.

5. According to the passage, which of the following is a true statement?

(A) California gets an average amount of rain.

(B) Forest fires are rare.

(C) Firefighters are often able to reduce the damage caused by forest fires.

(D) The 2013 fire season was much longer than normal.

6. What caused the increase in forest fires in 2013?

(A) careless campers

(B) a lack of rain

(C) lightning

(D) heavily vegetated areas

Richard had never had rhythm and didn't enjoy dancing. He only went to the ballroom dance class to watch his wife perform. Then the instructor grabbed Richard's hands, pulling him onto the floor and showing him exactly what to do and how to do it. After that, Richard was dancing like a pro. He realized the secret to dancing wasn't rhythm; it was enjoying moving and being free.

7. According to this passage, Richard's lack of rhythm is

(A) unimportant.

(B) his downfall.

(C) an embarrassment.

(D) hilarious.

Making a good war movie is a tricky business. The subject matter is very dear to the hearts of many people, and accuracy is key. The combat scenes, soldiers, accommodations, and relationships among and throughout the different ranks must all be portrayed well to avoid negative backlash and ensure a profitable film.

8. According to the passage, which of the following is likely to make a war movie profitable?

(A) length

(B) emotional acting

(C) historical accuracy

(D) violence

Anyone can be a world-record holder if he or she has the wits and determination to do so. Guinness World Records has been making record holders out of ordinary citizens since 1955. All that's required is filling out an application stating which record you want to break or make and sending in the evidence of your achievement. If the judges approve of your evidence, you become a world-record holder, and the sky is now the limit.

9. According to the passage, what do you have to do to be recognized by Guinness World Records?

(A) break a record in front of a Guinness judge

(B) file an application and ask to be accepted

(C) prove that you have broken a record

(D) both B and C

Questions 10 and 11 refer to the following passage.

The fervor that each side brings to the Mac versus PC debate is so extreme that you'd think people had a personal stake in the matter. Despite the obvious popularity of Apple products, recent studies have shown that only a small fraction (about 15 percent) of the computers sold each year are Macs. Of course, there's only one Apple company and a multitude of PC manufacturers. Perhaps that's why many feel the Mac operating system is superior to Microsoft Windows. So how do you choose? Price and need are usually the best factors to consider. Why spend a lot of money if all you need is a word processor?

10. As used in this passage, the word <u>fervor</u> most nearly means

(A) passion.

(B) illness.

(C) cruelty.

(D) refreshments.

11. According to the passage, when choosing a new computer, you should consider

(A) a brand's popularity and reliability.

(B) price and need.

(C) popularity and price.

(D) None of the above

GO ON TO NEXT PAGE ▶

If you get a flat tire while driving, stay calm. As long as you have a spare that's full of air, you can fix the problem in no time. The most important thing is to pull off the road to a safe location away from passing cars and with the flat side away from the road, if possible. Use a tire iron to loosen the lug nuts before jacking the car up. Next, place the jack under the vehicle in the appropriate spot and crank it so the car is just a foot or two off the ground. Remove the lug nuts, replace the flat tire with the spare, and put the nuts back on. After you've released the car to the ground, tighten the lug nuts. If you try to tighten the nuts while the wheel is suspended, you won't have the proper resistance to get them as tight as you want. Now you're ready to drive off into the sunset.

12. The author is giving advice on

(A) jack safety.

(B) proper lug nut resistance.

(C) appropriate places to pull off the road.

(D) changing a flat tire.

Questions 13 and 14 refer to the following passage.

The face of tennis was never the same after 14-year-old Venus Williams hit the scene in 1994. After she claimed the distinction of being the first African American woman to rank number one in the world, she and her sister Serena took over. Between the two of them, they dominated the Grand Slam circuit between 2000 and 2012, with 24 Grand Slam singles titles between them and doubles gold medals as a team in the 2000, 2008, and 2012 Summer Olympics. Their athleticism and aggressive playing style have been credited for changing the way women play tennis. They will forever be considered two of the greatest tennis players in history.

13. What year did the Williams sisters *not* win an Olympic gold medal?

(A) 2004

(B) 2000

(C) 2008

(D) 2012

14. How did the Williams sisters change the way women's tennis is played?

(A) by ranking number one

(B) with their uniforms

(C) by being sisters

(D) with their aggressive style

The work of cobblers is very time-consuming. They have to not only find the perfect materials but also size them perfectly, soften the leather for shaping, and attach the leather to the sole. Cobblers use more than 15 techniques when making shoes by hand. Most shoe shoppers have no idea how hard a cobbler's job is.

15. What is the main point of the passage?

(A) Cobblers use many techniques to make shoes.

(B) More people should become cobblers.

(C) Being a cobbler is hard work.

(D) Leather is the only material used to make shoes.

Part 4: Mathematics Knowledge

TIME: 24 minutes for 25 questions

DIRECTIONS: Mathematics Knowledge is the fifth subtest on the ASVAB; it follows Paragraph Comprehension. The questions are designed to test your ability to solve general mathematical problems. Each question is followed by four possible answers. Decide which answer is correct, and then mark the corresponding space on your answer sheet. Use your scratch paper for any figuring you want to do. You may *not* use a calculator.

1. A circle has a diameter of 15 inches. What is its approximate circumference?

(A) 47.1 inches

(B) 30 inches

(C) 55.3 inches

(D) 64.7 inches

2. $4x + 7xy + 6x =$

(A) $17xy$

(B) $10x + 7xy$

(C) $17x + y$

(D) $24x + 7xy$

3. Which is 8 inches less than 3 feet?

(A) 28 in.

(B) 3.5 ft

(C) 32 in.

(D) 2.8 ft

4. Which inequality represents all numbers m that are at least 14?

(A) $m > 14$

(B) $m < 14$

(C) $m \geq 14$

(D) $m \leq 14$

5. An angle has a measure of 37°. What is the measure of its complementary angle?

(A) 63°

(B) 53°

(C) 143°

(D) 163°

6. Round 120,459 to the nearest hundred.

(A) 120,400

(B) 120,460

(C) 120,000

(D) 120,500

7. $\sqrt{16} + \sqrt{100} =$

(A) $\sqrt{116}$

(B) 14

(C) $\sqrt{14}$

(D) 58

8. What is the least common multiple (LCM) of 12 and 14?

(A) 26

(B) 168

(C) 2

(D) 84

9. $\left(\dfrac{2x}{4}\right)^3 =$

(A) $\dfrac{3x^3}{4}$

(B) $\dfrac{x^3}{2}$

(C) $2x^3$

(D) $\dfrac{x^3}{8}$

10. $\dfrac{1}{5} + \dfrac{2}{7} =$

(A) $\dfrac{1}{4}$

(B) $\dfrac{2}{35}$

(C) $\dfrac{3}{12}$

(D) $\dfrac{17}{35}$

GO ON TO NEXT PAGE →

11. Solve the equation $\frac{x^2}{2} = 8$.

(A) 4 only

(B) 4 and −4

(C) 32 only

(D) 8 and −8

12. Fifteen is what percent of 75?

(A) 20 percent

(B) 15 percent

(C) 25 percent

(D) 5 percent

13. $4(x+1)+x$

(A) $x+4$

(B) $5x+4$

(C) $5x+1$

(D) $6x$

14. Eighty-five percent of 320 is

(A) 85

(B) 262

(C) 305

(D) 272

15. Given that $6m = 7n$, what is the ratio of n to m?

(A) $\frac{7}{6}$

(B) $\frac{6}{7}$

(C) $\frac{1}{42}$

(D) $\frac{13}{1}$

16. Two angles of a triangle measure 40° and 100°. What is the name of this kind of triangle?

(A) isosceles

(B) obtuse

(C) equilateral

(D) right

17. What is the length a in the right triangle?

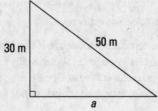

Illustration by Thomson Digital

(A) 48.6 cm

(B) 41.5 cm

(C) 35 m

(D) 40 m

18. Which fraction has the greatest value?

(A) $\frac{1}{4}$

(B) $\frac{7}{12}$

(C) $\frac{2}{3}$

(D) $\frac{5}{9}$

19. What is the product of $\sqrt{81}$ and $\sqrt{121}$?

(A) 9,801

(B) 40

(C) 20

(D) 99

20. What is the value of $(1-x)^3$ if $4x-1=19$?

(A) 64

(B) 125

(C) −124

(D) −64

21. The height of a right cylinder is 8x, and the cylinder's radius is $\frac{x}{2}$. What is the volume of the cylinder?

(A) $2\pi x^3$

(B) $2\pi x^2$

(C) $4\pi x^3$

(D) $4\pi x$

22. If $2p + x + 5q = 14p + 15q$, then $x =$

(A) $12p + 10q$

(B) $12p - 3q$

(C) $7p + 3q$

(D) $10p + 12q$

23. Square A has a perimeter of 8 feet. Square B has an area of 64 square feet. What is the ratio of the area of square A to the area of square B?

(A) $\frac{1}{4}$

(B) $\frac{1}{8}$

(C) $\frac{1}{16}$

(D) $\frac{3}{8}$

24. If $\left(x^9\right)\left(x^3\right) = x^{12}$, then $\left(x^{12}\right) \div \left(x^3\right) =$

(A) x^4

(B) x^{15}

(C) x^9

(D) x^6

25. What is the value of m?

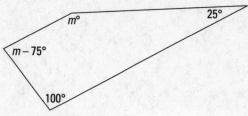

Illustration by Thomson Digital

(A) $155°$

(B) $125°$

(C) $95°$

(D) $80°$

Chapter 20

Practice Exam 4: Answers and Explanations

A re you ready to take the actual ASVAB yet and max out the AFQT score? I sure hope so. I hope you're feeling confident as well. If you still don't feel ready, you may want to look over the practice exams again, until you're comfortable with the types of questions that will be presented on the real test. You may also want to consider reading *ASVAB For Dummies* (Wiley) for two more full-length AFQT practice exams, as well as three full-length ASVAB practice tests.

The answer keys in the following sections tell you how well you did on the final AFQT practice exam. *Remember:* Don't be too concerned about the percent right or wrong. On the actual test, harder questions are worth more points than easier questions when computing your AFQT score, so it's entirely possible to miss a few questions and still max out your AFQT score.

Part 1: Arithmetic Reasoning

How'd you do on this subtest? If you don't feel so good about the results, you may want to postpone taking the real ASVAB until you've gotten some more study time under your belt, and perhaps taken a math course or two at your neighborhood community college. You may also want to take another look at Chapters 9 and 11.

Other great resources to improve your math skills are *Math Word Problems For Dummies, Algebra I For Dummies,* and *Algebra II For Dummies,* all by Mary Jane Sterling; *Geometry For Dummies* by Mark Ryan; *SAT II Math For Dummies* by Scott Hatch, JD, and Lisa Zimmer Hatch, MA; and *Basic Math & Pre-Algebra For Dummies* by Mark Zegarelli — all published by Wiley.

1. C. 80 ounces

Because 1 pound = 16 ounces, you can convert 5 pounds to ounces by multiplying 5 pounds by the conversion factor $\frac{16 \text{ ounces}}{1 \text{ pound}}$. A *conversion factor* is a ratio that represents the relationship between two different units, and in this case, multiplying 5 pounds by the pounds-to-ounces conversion factor looks like this:

$$5 \text{ pounds} \times \frac{16 \text{ ounces}}{1 \text{ pound}} = 5 \times 16 \text{ ounces}$$
$$= 80 \text{ ounces}$$

2. B. page 72

In order to find the page Jason is on, you need to find 40 percent of 180. Write 40 percent as a decimal and multiply by 180: $0.4(180) = 72$. Jason is on page 72.

3. C. 25 percent

There are four possible outcomes: two heads (HH), heads on the first coin and tails on the second (HT), tails on the first coin and heads on the second (TH), and two tails (TT). The desired outcome is TT. The probability is $\frac{1}{4} = 25$ percent.

4. D. 70°

The sum of the angles of any triangle is 180°. You know one of the angles is 40°, so the sum of the remaining two angles is 140° $(180° - 40° = 140°)$. Because the remaining two angles have equal measures, divide 140° by 2 to find the measure of one of the angles:

$$\frac{140°}{2} = 70°$$

5. A. 88 miles

If the truck gets 22 miles per gallon on the highway, that means it can go 22 miles on a gallon of gasoline. Multiply the mileage by 4 to find out how far Jake can travel using 4 gallons of gasoline: $4(22) = 88$ miles.

6. D. 5

After cutting the 24-foot rope into 4-foot lengths, Sergeant Williams would have six smaller ropes. To get these smaller ropes, he'd have to cut the rope five times. The following figure illustrates each of the cuts Sergeant Williams had to make at 4-foot increments. Sometimes drawing a picture can help you solve a problem.

Illustration by Thomson Digital

7. D. 12.5 percent

To calculate percent decrease, divide the change in temperature (4° Fahrenheit) by the original temperature. Then convert the result to a percent:

$$\frac{4}{32} = \frac{1}{8} = 0.125 = 12.5\%$$

8. B. $13.40

First, multiply 4 times $6.70 to find out how much money Dirk has: $4(\$6.70) = \$26.80$. Harriet has half this amount:

$$\frac{1}{2}(\$26.80) = \frac{\$26.80}{2} = \$13.40$$

Tip: Sometimes you can skip the calculations and reason your way to the correct answer. In this case, you know Dirk has 4 times as much money as Carter has, and Harriet has half as much as Dirk does. That means Harriet has twice as much money as Carter has. To find out how much money Harriet has, double Carter's money: $\$6.70 \cdot 2 = \$13.40$.

9. C. 30

To find the average age, add up all the ages and then divide by the number of adults in the group.

$$\frac{24 + 26 + 37 + 23 + 40}{5} = \frac{150}{5} = 30$$

Tip: You can save a little time during the addition step if you pair up numbers with ones digits that add up to 10 or with tens digits that add up to 100. That's the associative property, and here's what it looks like in practice:

$$\frac{(24 + 26) + (37 + 23) + 40}{5} = \frac{50 + (60 + 40)}{5}$$
$$= \frac{150}{5}$$
$$= 30$$

10. A. 0.1 gallon

The word *share* is a clue that this problem uses division, so you need to divide 2.5 by 25.

$$\frac{2.5}{25} = \frac{25}{250} = \frac{1}{10} = 0.1$$

11. B. 10

If x is Sam's age, then Timothy's age is $2x + 1$. Use the fact that the sum of their ages is 31 to set up an equation and solve for x:

$$x + 2x + 1 = 31$$
$$3x + 1 = 31$$
$$3x = 30$$
$$x = 10$$

Sam is 10 years old.

12. A. $11,340

If the car depreciates 10 percent in a year, the car's value after one year is 90 percent of what it was a year earlier. You can multiply the two percentages (0.9 and 0.9) by the car's initial value ($14,000) to figure out how much it's worth two years after purchase:

$$(0.9)(0.9)(\$14,000) = 0.81(\$14,000)$$
$$= \$11,340$$

The value of the car after two years is $11,340.

13. B. 2006

Because you're given a formula, you can substitute the known values and solve for n:

$$W = 0.5n + 47$$
$$50 = 0.5n + 47$$
$$3 = 0.5n$$
$$6 = n$$

The problem states that n represents the number of years after the year 2000, so 50 percent of the women owned a laptop in the year 2006.

14. C. 93°

A rhombus is a quadrilateral, a geometric shape with four sides with interior angles totaling 360°. A rhombus has equal opposite interior angles, so two angles are 93°, and the other two are 87°, totaling 360°.

15. D. $\frac{3}{4}$ gallon

The ratio is 8:1, which means for every 8 gallons of water, you need 1 gallon of concentrate. In this problem, you have only 6 gallons of water, so the amount of concentrate must be less than 1 gallon, which means you can eliminate Choices (B) and (C) right away. (Any time you can rule out incorrect answer choices on the ASVAB, take the opportunity!)

Let x = the amount of concentrate that should be added. Write a proportion using the two ratios and then cross-multiply to solve for x:

$$\frac{8}{1} = \frac{6}{x}$$
$$8x = 6(1)$$
$$x = \frac{6}{8}$$
$$x = \frac{3}{4}$$

16. C. 2 percent

Use the interest formula $(I = prt)$, where I is the interest, p is the principal, r is the interest rate (as a decimal), and t is the time in years. Substitute the known values into the formula and solve for r:

$$100 = 5,000(r)(1)$$
$$100 = 5,000r$$
$$\frac{100}{5,000} = r$$
$$\frac{1}{50} = r$$
$$0.02 = r$$

Write 0.02 as a percent by moving the decimal point two places to the right (which is the same as multiplying by 100): 0.02 = 2 percent.

17. C. 336

To determine club membership over this six-year period, it's best to work in increments. In 2004, after the first two years, the club's membership of 42 had doubled to 84. In 2006, the previous number of members doubled: $2(84) = 168$. Finally, in 2008, membership doubled again: $2(168) = 336$.

You can organize your work in a table:

Year	Number of members
2002	42
2004	2(42) = 84
2006	2(84) = 168
2008	2(168) = 336

Illustration by Thomson Digital

The club had 336 members in 2008.

If you're not a big fan of using tables to organize, try this: The problem tells you that the number of members doubled in 2004, 2006, and 2008. That describes three years in which membership doubled, so multiply the club's membership by 2 three times:

$$42(2)(2)(2) = 42(8) = 336$$

18. **A.** $H = 2L - 10$

First, write twice the low temperature as $2L$. You know that H is 10 less than this amount, or $2L - 10$, so now you have your equation: $H = 2L - 10$.

19. **B.** 96 cm²

The formula for the area of a triangle is $A = \frac{1}{2}bh$, where b is the base and h is the height. The height is drawn perpendicular to the bottom side of the triangle (with a measure of 16 cm), so use the bottom as the base. Substitute $b = 16$ and $h = 12$ into the formula to find the area:

$$A = \frac{1}{2}bh = \frac{1}{2}(16)(12) = 8(12) = 96$$

20. **D.** 152

Looking at the table, you see that 262 women and 110 men live in the West region. To find how many more women there are than men, you need to subtract: $262 - 110 = 152$.

21. **B.** $11

Use Francis's hourly rate and the number of hours worked to find how much he earned at his first job: $16($10) = 160. Subtract that amount from the total pay to find how much he earned at his second job last week: $314 - $160 = 154. Finally, divide $154 by 14 to find the hourly pay at his second job: $154 \div 14 = 11.

22. **B.** 90

If the ratio of red to blue to green marbles is 1:3:5, then there are x red marbles, $3x$ blue marbles, and $5x$ green marbles (x is some common multiple). Write an equation and solve for x:

$$x + 3x + 5x = 270$$
$$9x = 270$$
$$x = 30$$

This solution tells you there are 30 red marbles, which means that there are $3x = 3(30) = 90$ blue marbles.

23. C. 100 miles

First, use the distance formula, $d = rt$ (where d is the distance traveled, r is the rate of speed, and t is the time elapsed), to find how far each vehicle traveled in 2 hours:

Truck: $d = 30(2) = 60$ miles

Car: $d = 40(2) = 80$ miles

Now draw a diagram showing the paths of the two vehicles.

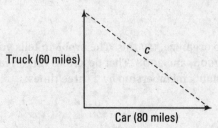

Illustration by Thomson Digital

Looking at the diagram, you see a right triangle with the hypotenuse (*c*) missing, so it's Pythagorean theorem time:

$$c^2 = 60^2 + 80^2$$
$$c^2 = 3,600 + 6,400$$
$$c^2 = 10,000$$
$$c = \pm\sqrt{10,000} = \pm 100$$

Because distance is never negative, you use the positive answer. After 2 hours, the vehicles are 100 miles apart.

24. C. 54

Let Joe's age $= x$. Because Evan is twice as old as Joe, his age can be represented as $2x$. In two years, Joe's age will be $x + 2$, and Evan's age will be $2x + 2$. The sum of their ages together will equal 85.

Write your equation like this and solve for *x*:

$$(x + 2) + (2x + 2) = 85$$
$$3x + 4 = 85$$
$$3x + 4 - 4 = 85 - 4$$
$$3x = 81$$
$$\frac{3x}{3} = \frac{81}{3}$$
$$x = 27$$

Now that you know Joe's age, you can figure out Evan's:

$$27 \times 2 = 54$$

Check by plugging into the formula:

$$(27 + 2) + (2 \times 27 + 2) = 85$$
$$29 + 56 = 85$$

25. **C. $34.90**

First, find out how much of a tip Gregory left by finding 20 percent of $8.50: $0.2($8.50$) = 1.70. The total cost of breakfast after the tip was $8.50 + $1.70 = 10.20. Now, subtract the total amount paid from the amount in Gregory's wallet at the start of the day: $45.10 - $10.20 = 34.90 left over after breakfast.

26. **D. 8**

Let x equal Kendra's score on the fifth quiz. Her score on the fourth quiz was twice that amount, so let $2x$ represent the fourth score. To find the average score, add up all the scores, and then divide by the number of quizzes taken:

$$\frac{7+6+10+2x+x}{5} = 7$$
$$\frac{23+3x}{5} = 7$$
$$23+3x = 35$$
$$3x = 12$$
$$x = 4$$

Her score on the fourth quiz was $2(4) = 8$.

27. **A. 6 m**

For problems like this one, your best bet is to break the odd-shaped figure down into rectangles. You can break this figure into two rectangles and find their areas separately:

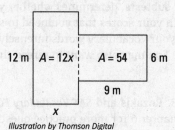

Illustration by Thomson Digital

Because the sum of the two areas is 126, you can write and solve an equation to find x:

$$12x + 54 = 126$$
$$12x = 72$$
$$x = 6$$

28. **C. $3\frac{1}{10}$ tons**

If you remember that 1 ton equals 2,000 pounds, you can work with tons (they're more manageable than pounds in this problem).

Find the total weight of all the cylinder blocks: $20(40) = 800$.

Convert that to tons:

$$\frac{800 \text{ pounds}}{2,000 \text{ pounds/ton}} = \frac{8}{20} = \frac{2}{5} = 0.4 \text{ ton}$$

Subtract the weight of the cylinder blocks from the total weight:

$$3.5 - 0.4 = 3.1 = 3\frac{1}{10} \text{ tons}$$

29. B. 10

Let d equal the number of dimes Carla has; the number of quarters she has is $d - 5$. The values of the dimes and quarters are 10 cents and 25 cents, respectively, and the coins add up to $4 (or 400 cents). Write an equation and solve for d:

$$10d + 25(d - 5) = 400$$
$$10d + 25d - 125 = 400$$
$$35d = 525$$
$$d = 15$$

Carla has 15 dimes, which means she has $15 - 5 = 10$ quarters.

30. A. 260

Ignore the information in the problem for the front entrance; the question asks you to find out how many entrance codes there are for the rear entrance. To find the number of possible codes for the rear entrance, multiply the number of possibilities for each character of the code:

26 possible letters $\times$ 10 possible numbers = 260 possible combinations

Part 2: Word Knowledge

The Word Knowledge subtest, as with all the AFQT subtests, determines whether you qualify for enlistment. If you're not seeing the improvement in your scores that you need to see, work with a partner who can quiz you on vocabulary. Review your vocabulary words intensely, even several times a day, to ensure your success on this subtest. You may also want to reread the information in Chapter 5.

Also check out *Vocabulary For Dummies* by Laurie E. Rozakis and *SAT Vocabulary For Dummies* by Suzee Vlk (both published by Wiley). Finally, see Chapter 6 for more practice questions.

1. C. belittle.

Condescend is a verb that means to talk down to someone.

"Even if you're teaching toddlers, it's important not to condescend to them."

2. A. star

As used in this sentence, *legend* is a noun that refers to someone famous or popular in a certain field.

3. D. extravagant.

Lavish is an adjective that means in abundance.

"The lavish décor made us feel as if we were at a luxury resort."

4. A. withdrawal.

Retraction is a noun that means the taking back of a statement.

"The newspaper printed a retraction when the editors found out the entire story was based on a lie."

5. **B. trap.**

Decoy is a noun that means a distraction or trick.

"Hunters who use a decoy duck tend to have more success than those who don't."

6. **C. fixation.**

Obsession is a noun that means a preoccupation with something or someone.

"Bryan's obsession with cleaning the house drove Tina crazy."

7. **D. hefty.**

Brawny is an adjective that means muscular or appearing strong.

"The brawny weightlifter picked up the 400-pound barbell easily."

8. **D. remain.**

Relocate is a verb that means to change places.

"Many retirees relocate from Michigan to Florida to escape the cold."

9. **B. healing**

Therapeutic is an adjective that describes something relating to good health or beneficial.

10. **C. ready**

As used in this sentence, *poised* is an adjective that means to be in position or prepared.

11. **B. vague**

As used in this sentence, *obscure* is an adjective that means unclear or ambiguous.

12. **A. consequences**

Ramification is a noun that means a result or an outcome.

13. **C. peculiar**

Eccentric is an adjective that describes something or someone unusual or odd.

14. **B. hurry.**

Meander is a verb that means to roam or stroll leisurely, or to follow a winding course (as in a road or river).

"A lot of teenagers meander around the mall for hours without buying anything."

15. **D. unpredictable.**

Volatile is an adjective that means something unstable or explosive.

"The situation became more volatile as the protesters refused to leave, so the police began putting on riot gear."

16. **C. polish**

As used in this sentence, *hone* is a verb that means to improve or perfect something.

17. **A. mention**

Broach is a verb that means to bring up or raise.

18. **B. random**

Erratic is an adjective that describes something inconsistent or frequently changing.

19. **B. old.**

Obsolete is an adjective that means something outdated or no longer in use.

"The version of software you're using is obsolete, so you should upgrade as soon as you can."

20. **D. respectability.**

Decorum is a noun that means appropriate behavior.

"Although the runner-up was unhappy with her position, she maintained decorum and offered the winner her congratulations."

21. **B. briefness**

Brevity is a noun that means conciseness or shortness.

22. **D. stability.**

Mayhem is a noun that means disruption or chaos.

"The fans quickly got out of control, and the entire concert descended into mayhem."

23. **A. gap.**

Hiatus is a noun that means a break or pause in something continuous.

"The professor is taking a short hiatus from teaching after this semester because he needs a break."

24. **C. pessimistic.**

Cynical is an adjective that means distrusting or having a negative outlook.

"Robert's cynical attitude led him to spread negativity through the entire office."

25. **C. full of**

Riddled is an adjective that means containing a lot of something.

"Some of the old buildings on Schofield Barracks are riddled with bullet holes from World War II."

26. **B. theft**

Larceny is a noun that describes the illegal removal of another's possessions.

27. **A. demand.**

Used as a noun, *proposition* means an idea or a proposal.

"The team made their proposition to the company president, who agreed that it was a great idea to hold an annual picnic for employees and their families."

28. **C. moving**

Poignant is an adjective that describes something understanding and emotional.

29. A. interval

Respite is a noun that means a brief break in something or a period of rest.

30. B. shoot down

Debunk is a verb that means to expose false or exaggerated claims.

31. D. resolute.

Adamant is an adjective that means having an unyielding or unwavering opinion.

"The little boy was adamant that the other kids put away the toys when they were finished playing."

32. D. wisdom

Malarkey is a noun that means rubbish or insincere talk.

"Everything the candidate said was malarkey; he didn't mean any of it."

33. A. hardship

Adversity is a noun that represents a difficulty or misfortune.

34. B. extinct

Defunct is an adjective that means no longer in existence.

35. C. beginning.

Origin is a noun that indicates where something started.

"Historians have traced the Roman Empire to its origin during the eighth century BCE."

Part 3: Paragraph Comprehension

If you're struggling with this subtest, remember to take your time when you read the passages. And after you read each question, you can quickly reread the passage just to make sure you're on the money. The information is in the paragraph; you just have to concentrate to pull it out. Turn to Chapter 7 if you still need additional help to pull off a good score on this subtest. You can also find more practice questions in Chapter 8.

1. B. prospered.

Flourished is a verb that means to thrive or do well.

2. A. the kitchen

Although many things are being described in the passage, the scene remains the same: in the "big kitchen."

3. D. A feast is being prepared.

Although Alcott is talking about the harvest and hunting, the only action taking place is the cooking of the feast, as stated in the last sentence: "all suggestive of some approaching feast." Sometimes reading through the answers and eliminating those that are obviously wrong is the best way to answer questions on the ASVAB.

4. **C. to explain the purpose of the High-Speed Rail Summit**

Although the passage touches on many of the other answers, the focus remains on the summit.

5. **D. The 2013 fire season was much longer than normal.**

The passage compares the typical fire season (September to October) to the 2013 fire season (May to December). None of the other choices are addressed.

6. **B. a lack of rain**

The passage states that wildfire season started early due to a drought and later reinforces that the number of fires increased because of a lack of rain.

7. **A. unimportant.**

The last sentence states that the secret to dancing isn't rhythm, so the fact that Richard doesn't have any doesn't matter. The passage never says that Richard is embarrassed by his lack of rhythm or that it has harmed him in any way. Although watching Richard dance may be funny, the passage clearly says that the secret to dancing isn't rhythm; it's "enjoying moving and being free." That means Richard's lack of rhythm is unimportant.

8. **C. historical accuracy**

The passage discusses the aspects that make a good and profitable war movie. It indicates that an accurate portrayal of war is important to "ensure a profitable film," so Choice (C) is the best answer.

9. **D. both B and C**

The passage says aspiring record-holders have to do only two things: complete an application and submit evidence that they have broken the record. Breaking the record in front of a judge isn't required.

10. **A. passion.**

Even if you didn't know what *fervor* meant, the context in which the passage uses it can help you eliminate the incorrect choices. By reading the next part of the sentence, which says, "you'd think people had a personal stake in the matter," you can tell that people take it very seriously. That signifies that each side is passionate about its beliefs.

11. **B. price and need.**

The passage poses the question "So how do you choose?" and then answers it: "Price and need are usually the best factors to consider."

12. **D. changing a flat tire**

This passage gives step-by-step instructions for changing a flat tire. Some of the other answer choices are mentioned, but they're part of the advice given about Choice (D).

13. **A. 2004**

The Summer Olympics occur every four years. The passage lists every Summer Olympic year between 2000 and 2012 except for 2004, so the Williams sisters didn't win that year. When the ASVAB asks you for specific dates, scan the paragraph for them instead of rereading the entire passage.

14. D. with their aggressive style

The end of the passage clearly tells you that the Williams sisters' "athleticism and aggressive playing style have been credited for changing the way women play tennis," which is exactly what the question asked.

15. C. Being a cobbler is hard work.

The first and last sentences both mention the laborious and difficult nature of shoemaking. Choice (A) is a fact mentioned in the passage, but it's in support of the idea that shoemaking is a tough job.

On the ASVAB, many questions are easier than they look. By reading through your answer options, you can see that the passage doesn't say anything about the need for more people to take up cobbling, Choice (B). You can also see that Choice (D) probably isn't correct because the passage doesn't say that leather is the only material used. Though Choice (A) may have tempted you, the passage as a whole is about how tough it is to be a cobbler, making Choice (C) the correct answer.

Part 4: Mathematics Knowledge

If you're missing too many math questions, you may need to take more drastic measures like enrolling in a basic algebra class at a local community college. If your scores are improving, keep hitting the books and testing yourself up until the day of the ASVAB. Chapter 8 will also be a good review.

If you want to increase your math skills, the following *For Dummies* books will help: *Basic Math & Pre-Algebra For Dummies* by Mark Zegarelli; *Algebra I For Dummies* and *Algebra II For Dummies* by Mary Jane Sterling; *Geometry For Dummies* by Mark Ryan; and *SAT II Math For Dummies* by Scott Hatch (all published by Wiley). Chapter 10 also has some additional practice questions.

1. A. 47.1 inches

Using the circumference formula $C = \pi d$, plug in the known values and solve. Remember to round pi to 3.14 when a problem uses the term *approximate*:

$$C = \pi d$$
$$= (3.14)(15)$$
$$= 47.1$$

2. B. $10x + 7xy$

This expression has two like terms: $4x$ and $6x$. Combine them by adding their coefficients:

$$4x + 7xy + 6x = 4x + 6x + 7xy$$
$$= (4 + 6)x + 7xy$$
$$= 10x + 7xy$$

3. A. 28 in.

Convert the 3 feet to inches by multiplying by 12: $3(12) = 36$ inches. Now subtract 8 inches to get the answer: $36 - 8 = 28$.

4. C. $m \geq 14$

"All numbers that are at least 14" means all numbers greater than or equal to 14, which is represented by the symbol $\geq$. The answer is $m \geq 14$.

5. B. 53°

Complementary angles have a sum of 90°. To find the measure of the complement of 37°, subtract from 90°: $90° - 37° = 53°$.

6. D. 120,500

Determine what your rounding digit is; you're rounding to the hundreds place, so you want the hundreds digit. Now look at the number immediately to the right of it. If that number is 4 or less, don't change the rounding digit. If the digit is 5 or more, the rounding digit rounds up by one number. Here, the number in the hundreds place is 4 and the number to the right is 5, so you round up.

7. B. 14

Here, you solve the square roots and then add. The square root of 16 is 4, and the square root of 100 is 10. So $\sqrt{16} + \sqrt{100} = 4 + 10 = 14$.

8. D. 84

One way to find the LCM of two numbers is to list all the multiples of each number and find the smallest number that is common to both:

> 12: 12, 24, 36, 48, 60, 72, 84

> 14: 14, 28, 42, 56, 70, 84

The LCM of 12 and 14 is 84.

Another way is to check the answer choices to find the smallest one that's divisible by 12 and 14. That rules out Choice (C), because it's *too* small, and Choice (A), which isn't a multiple of 14. The next-smallest number is Choice (D), which happens to be the correct answer. If you find it easier to reduce fractions than to use long division, your work will look something like this:

$$\frac{84}{12} = \frac{21}{3} = 7$$
$$\frac{84}{14} = \frac{42}{7} = 6$$

9. D. $\dfrac{x^3}{8}$

First, reduce the fraction inside the parentheses:

$$\left(\frac{2x}{4}\right)^3 = \left(\frac{x}{2}\right)^3$$

Whenever you raise a fraction to a power, the exponent applies to the numerator and the denominator:

$$\left(\frac{x}{2}\right)^3 = \frac{x^3}{2^3} = \frac{x^3}{8}$$

10. D. $\dfrac{17}{35}$

You can solve this problem by multiplying the denominators by each other: $5 \times 7 = 35$.

(Most of the answer choices use 35 as the denominator, so that's a clue that 35 is a good choice.)

Now apply 35 as the common denominator and solve:

$$\frac{1}{5} + \frac{2}{7} = \frac{7}{35} + \frac{10}{35} = \frac{17}{35}$$

If fractions don't come easily to you, find the common denominator, which is the least common multiple of 5 and 7.

Multiples of 5: 5, 10, 15, 20, 25, 30, 35

Multiples of 7: 7, 14, 21, 28, 35

The common denominator for these two fractions is 35. Multiply the numerator and denominator of each fraction by the number that makes each denominator 35; then add:

$$\frac{1}{5} + \frac{2}{7} = \frac{1 \cdot 7}{5 \cdot 7} + \frac{2 \cdot 5}{7 \cdot 5}$$
$$= \frac{7}{35} + \frac{10}{35}$$
$$= \frac{7 + 10}{35}$$
$$= \frac{17}{35}$$

11. B. 4 and −4

First, isolate the variable by multiplying both sides of the equation by 2:

$$\frac{x^2}{2} = 8$$
$$2 \cdot \frac{x^2}{2} = 2 \cdot 8$$
$$x^2 = 16$$

Next, take the square root of both sides of the equation. The *square root rule* says if that $x^2 = k$, then $x = \pm\sqrt{k}$, where k is a number. The $\pm$ symbol indicates that when you take the square root of a number, you get two answers — one positive and one negative. That's because when you square a negative number, you get a positive result; for example, $(-4)^2 = (-4)(-4) = 16$; when you square a positive number, you also get a positive result.

$$x = \pm\sqrt{16}$$
$$x = \pm 4$$

12. A. 20 percent

Begin by writing the problem as a fraction: $\frac{15}{75}$. You can also write an equation if you can't remember how to arrange the fraction. Remember *is* means "equals" and *of* means "multiply," so $15 = x(75)$. Divide both sides by 75 to create the correct fraction. Then divide the numerator by the denominator (you can reduce the fraction to $\frac{3}{15}$ or even $\frac{1}{5}$ first if that makes the division easier): $15 \div 75 = 0.2$. Finally, move the decimal point two spaces to the right, which is the same as multiplying by 100, to express the number as a percent: 20 percent.

13. B. $5x + 4$

To simplify an expression like this one, first use the distributive property to remove the parentheses:

$$4(x + 1) + x = 4x + 4 + x$$

This expression has two like terms: $4x$ and x. Combine the like terms by adding their coefficients:

$$4x + 4 + x = (4+1)x + 4$$
$$= 5x + 4$$

14. **D. 272**

First, write 85 percent as a decimal: $\frac{85}{100} = 0.85$. Next, multiply 0.85 by 320: $0.85(320) = 272$.

15. **B.** $\frac{6}{7}$

The goal here is to use the given equation to find the ratio $\frac{n}{m}$. Start by dividing both sides of the equation by m:

$$6m = 7n$$
$$6 = \frac{7n}{m}$$

To get $\frac{n}{m}$ alone, get rid of the 7 by multiplying both sides by $\frac{1}{7}$ (which the same as dividing both sides by 7):

$$\frac{1}{7} \cdot \frac{6}{1} = \frac{1}{7} \cdot \frac{7n}{m}$$
$$\frac{6}{7} = \frac{1}{7} \cdot \frac{7n}{m}$$
$$\frac{6}{7} = \frac{n}{m}$$

16. **A. isosceles**

The sum of the angles of a triangle is always 180°. To find the measure of the third angle, subtract the known angles from 180°: $180° - 100° - 40° = 40°$. Because two of the angles of the triangle have the same measure, the sides opposite them are the same length. A triangle with two equal sides is an isosceles triangle.

17. **D. 40 m**

Use the Pythagorean theorem $\left(a^2 + b^2 = c^2\right)$ and the known values to find a. Remember, a and b are always the side lengths in the formula, and c is always the hypotenuse:

$$a^2 + 30^2 = 50^2$$
$$a^2 + 900 = 2,500$$
$$a^2 = 1,600$$
$$\sqrt{a^2} = \pm\sqrt{1,600}$$
$$a = \pm 40$$

Use the positive answer because a length is never negative.

18. **C.** $\frac{2}{3}$

On the ASVAB, it pays to rule out obviously wrong answer choices before you start your work. Choice (A) is obviously less than $\frac{1}{2}$, so it can't be correct. Move forward comparing Choices (B), (C), and (D).

Find the least common denominator by taking the least common multiple of all the denominators; in this case, that's 36. Rewrite the fractions with the common denominator, multiplying the numerators and denominators by the number that makes each denominator 36:

$$\frac{7}{12} = \frac{7 \cdot 3}{12 \cdot 3} = \frac{21}{36}$$

$$\frac{2 \cdot 12}{3 \cdot 12} = \frac{24}{36}$$

$$\frac{5}{9} = \frac{5 \cdot 4}{9 \cdot 4} = \frac{20}{36}$$

The greatest fraction is the one with the greatest numerator: $\frac{24}{36} = \frac{2}{3}$.

19. D. 99

The square root of 81 is 9 and the square root of 121 is 11, because $9 \times 9 = 81$ and $11 \times 11 = 121$. The product of those two numbers (9×11) is 99.

20. D. −64

The first thing you need to do is find the value of x by solving the given equation:

$$4x - 1 = 19$$
$$4x = 20$$
$$x = 5$$

Now you can substitute 5 for x in the expression $(1 - x)^3$ and simplify to find the answer. Remember to simplify inside the parentheses before applying exponents.

$$(1 - 5)^3 = (-4)^3$$
$$= (-4)(-4)(-4)$$
$$= -64$$

21. A. $2\pi x^3$

This problem uses the formula for the volume of a right cylinder: $V = \pi r^2 h$. You're given the values of h and r in terms of x, so you can just substitute those values in place of r and h in the formula:

$$V = \pi r^2 h$$
$$= \pi \left(\frac{x}{2}\right)^2 (8x)$$
$$= \pi \left(\frac{x^2}{4}\right)(8x)$$
$$= \frac{\pi \cdot x^2 \cdot 8x}{4}$$
$$= \frac{8\pi x^3}{4}$$
$$= 2\pi x^3$$

22. **A.** $12p + 10q$

Work through the equation, remembering that you can only combine like terms:

$$2p + x + 5q = 14p + 15q$$
$$(2p - 2p) + x + (5q - 5q) = (14p - 2p) + (15q - 5q)$$
$$x = 12p + 10q$$

23. **C.** $\dfrac{1}{16}$

You already know the area of square B, so you need to find the area of square A. To do that, you need to find the side length of square A based on what you know about the square's perimeter. The formula for the perimeter of a square is $P = 4s$. Substitute the known values for square A and then solve for s:

$$P = 4s$$
$$8 = 4s$$
$$2 = s$$

Now you can use the area formula for a square, $A = s^2$:

$$A = s^2$$
$$= (2)^2$$
$$= 4$$

Finally, you can express the ratio of the area of square A to the area of square B with a fraction:

$$\frac{\text{Area of square A}}{\text{Area of square B}} = \frac{4}{64} = \frac{1}{16}$$

24. **C.** x^9

When multiplying exponents, you add. When dividing exponents, you subtract:

$$\left(x^{12}\right) \div \left(x^3\right) = x^{12-3}$$
$$= x^9$$

25. **A.** $155°$

This figure is a quadrilateral, which means the sum of its angles is 360°. Because m is equal to is 360° minus the other three angles, plug in the values and solve:

$$m = 360 - 25 - 100 - (m - 75)$$
$$m = 360 - 25 - 100 - m + 75$$
$$m = 360 - 25 - 25 - m$$
$$m = 360 - 50 - m$$
$$2m = 310$$
$$\frac{2m}{2} = \frac{310}{2}$$
$$m = 155$$

Answer Key

Part 1: Arithmetic Reasoning

1.	C	7.	D	13.	B	19.	B	25.	C
2.	B	8.	B	14.	C	20.	D	26.	D
3.	C	9.	C	15.	D	21.	B	27.	A
4.	D	10.	A	16.	C	22.	B	28.	C
5.	A	11.	B	17.	C	23.	C	29.	B
6.	D	12.	A	18.	A	24.	C	30.	A

Part 2: Word Knowledge

1.	C	8.	D	15.	D	22.	D	29.	A
2.	A	9.	B	16.	C	23.	A	30.	B
3.	D	10.	C	17.	A	24.	C	31.	D
4.	A	11.	B	18.	B	25.	C	32.	D
5.	B	12.	A	19.	B	26.	B	33.	A
6.	C	13.	C	20.	D	27.	A	34.	B
7.	D	14.	B	21.	B	28.	C	35.	C

Part 3: Paragraph Comprehension

1.	B	4.	C	7.	A	10.	A	13.	A
2.	A	5.	D	8.	C	11.	B	14.	D
3.	D	6.	B	9.	D	12.	D	15.	C

Part 4: Mathematics Knowledge

1.	A	6.	D	11.	B	16.	A	21.	A
2.	B	7.	B	12.	A	17.	D	22.	A
3.	A	8.	D	13.	B	18.	C	23.	C
4.	C	9.	D	14.	D	19.	D	24.	C
5.	B	10.	D	15.	B	20.	D	25.	A

5

The Part of Tens

Check out ten tips for getting a better score on the AFQT.

Discover more than ten resources that can give you more information about the military and the ASVAB and help you get ready to take one of the most important exams of your life.

Discover all the enlisted jobs available to you — some you've never heard of — and the minimum line scores the military requires for each.

Chapter 21

Ten Tips for a Better AFQT Score

The U.S. military enlists around 250,000 new troops every year, counting the active and reserve components. And all those men and women share one thing in common: They all earned a qualifying score on the AFQT. (See Chapter 2 for qualifying AFQT scores for each service.)

Many people score very high, which makes their families proud and their recruiters smile. A high score also opens up a new world of special enlistment programs and enlistment incentives that are available only to those who score well on the AFQT.

I'm sure you want to be counted among that group; otherwise, why would you be reading this book? If so, this chapter will be a big help. Here, I list ten surefire ways to maximize your AFQT score and get you on your way to a satisfying and successful military career.

Take Your Time Studying

Don't cram. I don't care whether you call it a "power study," "mega-brain feeding," or "mugging"; study after study has shown that it doesn't work. For example, a 2007 study conducted by University of South Florida psychologist Doug Rohrer determined that last-minute studying reduces retention of material and may hinder the learning process. If you don't plan for adequate study time, your test scores will suffer the consequences.

REMEMBER

Rome wasn't built in a day, but it took only hours for the city to crash and burn. If you develop a solid study plan and stick with it for six to eight weeks, you'll score much higher on the AFQT than if you try to pack four subjects' worth of knowledge into your brain in one or two days. Plus, you won't walk into the testing center with your eyes red and your brain fried.

Make a Study Plan

You wouldn't expect the U.S. military to fight a war without a plan, would you? It would be chaos, and probably nothing would be achieved. The same is true when you're studying for the AFQT (or doing anything else, for that matter). If you try to study without a plan, you'll wind up wandering here and there, reading this and that, but you won't really accomplish anything. Check out Chapter 3 for help developing your individual study plan.

TIP

Start by studying the subjects you find the hardest, and spend extra time on those areas. You're only as strong as your weakest subject. When you focus on the areas where you need the most improvement, you increase your entire score. After you feel confident in your weakest areas, start perfecting and reviewing the areas you consider less problematic.

Use the Practice Exams to Your Advantage

REMEMBER

If you bought this book expecting the practice exams to include the exact same questions you'll see on the ASVAB, I'm afraid I have bad news: You won't see the same questions on the ASVAB that I include in this book (or any other ASVAB/AFQT preparation guide). Giving you the actual questions and answers in advance would be cheating — and illegal. The military classifies ASVAB tests as "official use only." That means only those with an official "need to know" have access to the test questions and answers, and that certainly doesn't include authors of ASVAB AFQT prep books.

The best I can do is to provide you with practice questions that are very similar to the ones you'll see on the ASVAB. In short, don't waste your time trying to memorize the questions and answers on the practice exams.

Even so, the practice exams are a very valuable study tool. Not only do they give you an idea about the type of questions you'll see and the test format, but they're also useful in determining what AFQT subject areas you need to spend the most time on.

REMEMBER

If you've already taken some or all of the exams and you didn't follow a schedule, that's okay, too. The key is to take the exams and learn from them. You may even find repeating each test and comparing your scores helpful. It's a good way to show personal progress.

Memorize Basic Math Formulas

The Arithmetic Reasoning and Mathematics Knowledge subtests require you to know many standard mathematical formulas used in geometry and algebra. As a minimum, you should have the following committed to memory by the time you sit down to take the ASVAB:

>> **Perimeter of a square:** $P = 4s$, where s = one side of the square

>> **Area of a square:** $A = s^2$

>> **Diagonal of a square:** $d = s\sqrt{2}$

>> **Perimeter of a rectangle:** $P = 2l + 2w$, where l = the length and w = the width of the rect-angle; you can also write this formula as $P = 2(l + w)$. (Here's a tip: You can find the perimeter of a shape by adding all its sides.)

» **Area of a rectangle:** $A = lw$

» **Diagonal of a rectangle:** $d = \sqrt{l^2 + w^2}$, where d = the diagonal, l = the length, and w = the width of the rectangle. This formula is the Pythagorean theorem solved for the hypotenuse (c) — it just uses different letters.

» **Perimeter of a triangle:** $P = s_1 + s_2 + s_3$, where s = the length of each side of the triangle

» **Area of a triangle:** $A = \frac{1}{2}bh$, where b = the length of the triangle's base (bottom) and h = the height of the triangle

» **Pythagorean theorem:** $a^2 + b^2 = c^2$

» **Radius of a circle:** $r = \frac{1}{2}d$, where d = the diameter of the circle

» **Diameter of a circle:** $d = 2r$

» **Circumference of a circle:** $C = 2\pi r$ or $C = \pi d$

» **Area of a circle:** $A = \pi r^2$

» **Volume of a cube:** $V = s^3$, where s = the length of one side of the cube

» **Volume of a rectangular prism or box:** $V = lwh$, where l = the length, w = the width, and h = the height of the box. This formula is the area of a rectangle (the base of the box) multiplied by the height.

» **Volume of a cylinder:** $V = \pi r^2 h$, where r = the radius of the cylinder and h = the height of the cylinder; it's really the area of a circle (the base of the cylinder) multiplied by the height.

» **Surface area of a cube:** $SA = 6s^2$

» **Surface area of a rectangular box:** $SA = 2lw + 2wh + 2lh$; you can also write this as $SA = 2(lw + wh + lh)$

» **Distance formula:** $d = rt$, where d = distance, r = rate, and t = time

» **Interest formula:** $I = prt$, where I = interest, p = principal, r = rate, and t = time

Know the Math Order of Operations

When a math problem asks you to perform more than one operation, you need to perform the operations in the correct order:

1. **Start with calculations in brackets or parentheses.**

   Note: When you have *nested* parentheses or brackets — parentheses or brackets inside other parentheses or brackets — do the inner ones first and work your way out.

2. **Work on terms with exponents and roots.**

3. **Do all the multiplication and division, in order from left to right.**

4. **Finish up with addition and subtraction, also in order from left to right.**

TIP

A helpful memory device for the order of operations is "Please Excuse My Dear Aunt Sally" or the acronym PEMDAS. It stands for parentheses, exponents, multiplication and division, and addition and subtraction. Remembering one or both of these will ensure you follow the proper steps in math problems that require you to perform calculations in a certain order.

There are exceptions to the order of operations; sometimes you can juggle the order around to make calculations easier, such as when parentheses appear in a string of numbers you're adding (you can ignore the parentheses in that case). Try to figure out when and why you're allowed to make such exceptions. Chapter 9 fills you in on some properties that may let you choose an order that makes numbers smaller and easier to work with while still giving you the right answer.

TIP

Boost Your Vocabulary

The Word Knowledge subtest is nothing more than a vocabulary test. This subtest contains questions that usually ask you to find the word that is "closest in meaning" to a given word. You may also have to find the *antonym*, or opposite, of a given word. The more words you know, the better you'll do on this subtest. It's that simple. (For details on how to increase your vocabulary, check out Chapter 5.)

Comprehend What You Read

To do well on the Paragraph Comprehension subtest, you must be able to read a paragraph, understand the information, and then correctly answer questions about the material. Generally, paragraph comprehension questions fall into four categories: inferring the main point or idea, analyzing the data, finding specific information, and identifying vocabulary in context. Understanding how to pick apart this information from your reading material is vital to a successful AFQT score.

Sharpen your comprehension daily by reading a paragraph in a book, newspaper, or magazine and then asking a friend to question you about information included in that paragraph.

TIP

Arrive at the Test Site Refreshed and Prepared

Don't let the recruiter schedule you to take the ASVAB until you're sure you're ready. Your recruiter may want to test you as soon as possible so he or she can fill recruiting goals. However, if you don't achieve a qualifying AFQT score, you waste your time, your recruiter's time, and the military's time. *Remember:* You may have to wait for up to six months for a retest. Make sure you're ready. (For more on retesting, turn to Chapter 2.)

The ASVAB test day can be drawn out and overwhelming, especially if nerves and stomach butterflies come out of nowhere or you struggle to use brainpower for an extended period of time. Give yourself a head start against the fatigue factor by arriving well-rested and motivated. Get a good night's sleep on the night before the test. If you're traveling to the test site in a bus or car, get a quick nap during the journey — as long as you're not the one driving, of course!

Try to eat a light meal or snack just before the test, and drink enough water. You don't want to become dehydrated or have your grumbling stomach distract you from solving a quadratic equation.

Watch the Clock

You have a limited amount of time to complete each subtest, but don't worry about it. The more you panic, the more likely you are to make mistakes. Just work at a steady pace, and you'll do fine. Chapter 2 breaks down how much time you have for the number of questions on each subtest (for both the paper and computerized tests).

If you're taking the computerized version of the ASVAB (CAT-ASVAB), you'll see a counter on the screen, counting down the time remaining on the subtest. If you're taking the paper version of the ASVAB, a clock will be clearly visible on the wall, and the test proctor will post the start and stop times of the subtest where you can easily see them.

Most people have plenty of time to complete all the subtests on the computerized and paper versions.

TIP

Don't spend too much time on one question. If you're drawing a blank, make a guess and move on. Keep in mind that if you're taking the CAT-ASVAB, you can't go back to change your answers or review any questions if you finish early, so make your guess a good one! (I explain how to do that in the next section.)

Guess Smart

Despite your extensive study, you may stumble on a question that has you stumped. Prepare Plan B by knowing how to use the process of elimination. If you're stuck on a question, try to eliminate any answers that you know to be wrong instead of making a wild guess. If you can eliminate even one wrong answer, you increase your chances of guessing the right answer from one in four to one in three. If you can eliminate two wrong answers, your chances increase to 50/50. (For more tips on intelligent guessing, see Chapter 4.)

Chapter **22**

Ten Topics to Explore

'll be the first to admit that *ASVAB AFQT For Dummies*, 3rd Edition, is a great book — quite possibly the greatest book ever published (my well-known modesty aside). However, I can't pack everything you need to know about math, vocabulary, reading, and joining the military into 384 pages. You may have to rely on some outside help.

If you need to brush up on some of your skills before taking the ASVAB and maxing out your AFQT score, reading the appropriate chapters in this book is a great place to start. But you may need or want more work in a particular subject area, or you may want to know more about the military or even the entire ASVAB. This chapter helps point you in the right direction. Here I list places you can get additional information.

For More about the ASVAB

This book is about boosting your Armed Forces Qualification Test (AFQT) score, but this score covers only four of the nine ASVAB subtests. The AFQT score is important because it determines whether you're qualified to join the military (see Chapter 2), but the other ASVAB subtests determine which military jobs you qualify for.

If you want to brush up on all the ASVAB subtests, an excellent resource is *ASVAB For Dummies* (Wiley), if I do say so myself. You can pick up a copy at your favorite bookstore, online, or at www.dummies.com.

For More about the Military

If you're thinking about joining the military, presumably you want to learn more about how the military operates. The following websites are great resources:

>> **Department of Defense:** To figure out what the military is up to, you can stop by the official website of the Department of Defense. The site is a treasure-trove of articles and photos about the military. Go to www.defense.gov.

>> **Army recruiting:** If you're thinking about joining the Army, the Army's recruiting website is an essential first stop. Here you can read about Army enlistment qualifications and Army careers and even chat online with an Army recruiter. Visit www.goarmy.com.

>> **Air Force recruiting:** If you want to soar with the eagles (F-15 Eagles, of course), you should check out the Air Force recruiting website at www.airforce.com.

>> **Navy recruiting:** If you aren't the claustrophobic type and you're thinking of a career aboard a submarine (or maybe an aircraft carrier), head to the official Navy site at www.navy.com.

>> **Marine Corps recruiting:** The Marines have a few good men (and women) standing by at the Marine Corps recruiting website to help you become one of the proud few. Check them out at www.marines.com.

>> **Coast Guard recruiting:** The Coast Guard is a military service, but it doesn't belong to the Department of Defense. Instead, it's under the purview of the Department of Homeland Security. You can find out about joining the Coast Guard at www.gocoastguard.com.

For More about Math

The Mathematics Knowledge and Arithmetic Reasoning subtests on the ASVAB make up half of your AFQT score. If you want to do well on these tests but haven't used your math skills since you got a smartphone with a calculator, check out the following resources:

>> **A slew of *For Dummies* math books:** *Math Word Problems For Dummies, Algebra I For Dummies* and *Algebra II For Dummies,* all by Mary Jane Sterling; *Basic Math & Pre-Algebra For Dummies* by Mark Zegarelli; *Geometry For Dummies* by Mark Ryan; and *SAT II Math For Dummies* by Scott Hatch, JD, and Lisa Zimmer Hatch, MA — all published by Wiley — are great places to start. Check your favorite bookstore or visit www.dummies.com.

>> **AAA Math:** AAA Math can help you review math problems from kindergarten through eighth grade levels. The website features a comprehensive set of interactive arithmetic lessons, with unlimited free online practice. Visit www.aaamath.com.

For More about Math Word Problems

Solving math word problems requires a special set of skills. You have to know basic math, analyze the problem, determine how to set up an equation, and then solve it. *Basic Math & Pre-Algebra For Dummies, Algebra I For Dummies, Algebra II For Dummies,* and *Geometry For Dummies* can be a great help in understanding word problems, but you may want to start with *Math Word Problems For Dummies* (see the preceding section). Also, check out Purplemath at www.purplemath.com.

For More about Vocabulary

You can't get a good score on the AFQT without doing well on the Word Knowledge subtest. These resources can help you boost your vocabulary knowledge:

>> *Vocabulary For Dummies* by Laurie E. Rozakis and *SAT Vocabulary For Dummies* by Suzee Vlk (both published by Wiley): Head to your favorite bookstore or www.dummies.com.

>> **Dictionary.com:** This site (www.dictionary.com) offers a new word each day, great word lists, and, well, the entire English dictionary at your fingertips.

>> **Vocabulary.com:** A great resource for themed vocabulary lists, this site (www.vocabulary.com) is teeming with words you can pick apart, define, and use in sentences.

For More about Reading Comprehension

If you need to brush up on your reading skills for the Paragraph Comprehension subtest or you just want to make sense of *War and Peace*, try these sites:

>> **MrNussbaum.com:** This site has dozens of reading comprehension exercises at your fingertips. Take a look at http://mrnussbaum.com/readingpassageindex/.

>> **Resource Room:** This site offers tips, techniques, and exercises to help improve your reading comprehension skills. Go to http://resourceroom.net/Comprehension/index.html.

For More about Test-Taking

The best way to prepare for the AFQT is to develop a sound study plan (see Chapter 3 for advice on developing a study plan). However, even with the best preparation, a question or two may trip you up. Chapter 2 has some great tips to help you take the test. Here are some other resources:

>> **TestTakingTips.com:** This site (http://testtakingtips.com) offers tips and techniques for studying, note taking, reducing test anxiety, and taking tests.

>> **Study Guides and Strategies:** This site gives ten great tips for terrific test taking. Check it out at www.studygs.net/tsttak1.htm.

Playing at Public Libraries

Remember when you learned math and English in high school? You were taught from standard textbooks. Those same textbooks are a great resource to help you review, but have you ever priced a standard textbook in a bookstore? Holy cow! No wonder the American education system always seems to be out of money.

If only you knew a place where you could borrow math and English high-school and college textbooks for free. Wait a minute — you do! It's the public library, and most towns and cities have one. Not only can you borrow standard textbooks, but libraries also offer you a calm and quiet place to study, away from the hustle and bustle and demands of daily life.

Consorting with Colleges

Some people just aren't good at studying on their own. They prefer organized classrooms, specific assignments, and teachers to explain things. If you're one of these people, you may want to consider enrolling in a math, vocabulary, or reading course at your local community college. Who knows? You may even qualify for state or federal student aid and be able to take college courses for free!

TIP

Supplementing your AFQT knowledge through college courses offers a couple of big advantages:

>> If you have a high school equivalency certificate (such as the GED) and get at least 15 college credits, you boost your chances of being accepted for enlistment.

>> If you get more than 30 college credits, you may qualify for advanced enlistment rank.

Trying Out a Tutor

Colleges and universities usually have a group of highly intelligent students who are eager to supplement their incomes by tutoring other students in a variety of subjects. Even if you decide not to enroll in college courses, having the extra company may be helpful. Studying in groups has been proven to help with memory retention.

TIP

To find a tutor in your area, visit the administration office of your local college or university. Or just walk around campus and look at the bulletin boards — students often advertise their tutoring services on fliers.

Appendix

Matching ASVAB Scores to Military Jobs

The military has hundreds of enlisted job opportunities, ranging from washing and sewing clothing items to translating foreign languages. Each of the military services has established its own individual *line score* requirements (a combination of various ASVAB subtest scores) for specific enlisted jobs. The tables in this appendix show the minimum line scores that the services have established for entry-level enlisted jobs.

REMEMBER

Just because you achieve the minimum ASVAB line score for the job of your choice doesn't mean you'll absolutely get that job. Other factors are considered, including the current needs of the service, security clearance qualification, and medical exam results.

The charts in this appendix are as accurate as they can be at press time. However, military jobs and qualification standards are subject to change with little or no notice. For the most up-to-date information and for complete job descriptions and qualification factors, see your local military recruiter.

Army Enlisted Jobs

The Army calls its enlisted jobs *Military Occupational Specialties* (MOSs), and more than 150 such specialties exist for entry-level recruits. Table A-1 shows entry-level Army MOSs and the ASVAB line scores required to qualify for the jobs. Scan the table and see whether you find a job that interests you.

Line scores are abbreviated as follows: Clerical (CL), Combat (CO), Electronics (EL), Field Artillery (FA), General Maintenance (GM), General Technical (GT), Mechanical Maintenance (MM), Operators and Food (OF), Surveillance and Communications (SC), and Skilled Technical (ST). See Chapter 2 for an explanation of which ASVAB subtest scores are used to calculate each of the line scores.

TABLE A-1 Army Enlisted Jobs and Required ASVAB Scores

MOS	Title	Score	MOS	Title	Score	MOS	Title	Score
09L	Interpreter/ Translator	N/A	11B	Infantry	CO-90	11C	Indirect Fire Infantryman	CO-90
12B	Combat Engineer	CO-98	12C	Bridge Crewmember	CO-87	12D	Diver	ST-106 or GM-98 and GT-107
12G	Quarrying Specialist	GM-93	12K	Plumber	GM-88	12M	Firefighter	GM-88
12N	Horizontal Construction Engineer	GM-90	12P	Prime Power Specialist	ST-107, EL-107, and GT-110	12Q	Power Distribution Specialist	EL-93
12R	Interior Electrician	EL-93	12T	Technical Engineer	ST-101	12V	Concrete and Asphalt Equipment Operator	GM-88
12W	Carpentry and Masonry Specialist	GM-88	12Y	Geospatial Engineer	ST-100 and GT-100	13B	Cannon Crewmember	FA-93
13D	Field Artillery Automated Tactical Data Systems Specialist	FA-93	13F	Fire Support Specialist	FA-96	13M	Multiple Launch Rocket System Crewmember	OF-95
13P	Multiple Launch Rocket System Operations/ Fire Direction Specialist	FA-96	13R	Field Artillery Firefinder Radar Operator	SC-98	13T	Field Artillery Surveyor/ Meteorological Crewmember	EL-93
14E	Patriot Fire Control Enhanced Operator/ Maintainer	MM-104	14G	Air Defense Battle Management System Operator	GT-98 and MM-99	14H	Air Defense Early Warning System Operator	GT-98 and MM-99
14S	Air and Missile Defense (AMD) Crewmember	OF-85	14T	PATRIOT Launching Station Enhanced Operator/ Maintainer	OF-92	15B	Aircraft Powerplant Repairer	MM-104
15D	Aircraft Powertrain Repairer	MM-104	15E	Unmanned Aircraft Systems Repairer	EL-93 and MM-104	15F	Aircraft Electrician	MM-104
15G	Aircraft Structural Repairer	MM-104	15H	Aircraft Pneudraulics Repairer	MM-104	15J	OH-58D/ARH Armament/ Electrical/ Avionics Systems Repairer	EL-93 and MM-104

MOS	Title	Score	MOS	Title	Score	MOS	Title	Score
15M	Utility Helicopter Repairer (Reserves only)	MM-105	**15N**	Avionic Mechanic	EL-93	**15P**	Aviation Operations Specialist	ST-91
15Q	Air Traffic Control Operator	ST-101	**15R**	AH-64 Attack Helicopter Repairer	MM-99	**15S**	OH-58D Helicopter Repairer	MM-99
15T	UH-60 Helicopter Repairer	MM-104	**15U**	CH-47 Helicopter Repairer	MM-104	**15W**	Unmanned Aircraft Systems Operator	SC-102
15Y	AH-64D Armament/ Electrical/ Avionics Systems Repairer	EL-98 and MM-104	**18B**	Special Forces Weapons Sergeant	GT-110 and CO-98	**18C**	Special Forces Engineer Sergeant	GT-110 and CO-98
18D	Special Forces Medical Sergeant	GT-107 and CO-98	**18E**	Special Forces Communications Sergeant	GT-110 and SC-98	**19D**	Cavalry Scout	CO-87
19K	M1 Armor Crewman	CO-87	**25B**	Information Technology Specialist	ST-95	**25C**	Radio Operator/ Maintainer	SC-98 and EL-98
25D	Cyber Network Defender	GT-105 and ST-105	**25F**	Network Switching Systems Operator/ Maintainer	SC-105 and EL-102	**25L**	Cable Systems Installer/ Maintainer	SC-89 and EL-89
25M	Multimedia Illustrator	EL-93 and ST-91	**25P**	Microwave Systems Operator/ Maintainer	EL-107	**25Q**	Multichannel Transmission Systems Operator/ Maintainer	EL-98 and SC-98
25R	Visual Information Equipment Operator/ Maintainer	EL-107	**25S**	Satellite Communication Systems Operator/ Maintainer	EL-117	**25U**	Signal Support Systems Specialist	SC-92 and EL-93
25V	Combat Documentation/ Production Specialist	EL-93 and ST-91	**27D**	Paralegal Specialist	CL-105	**29E**	Electronic Warfare Specialist	SC-100, ST-100, and EL-100
31B	Military Police	ST-91	**31D**	Criminal Investigations Special Agent	GT-110 and ST-107	**31E**	Internment/ Resettlement Specialist	ST-95
35F	Intelligence Analyst	ST-101	**35G**	Geospatial Intelligence Imagery Analyst	ST-101	**35M**	Human Intelligence Collector	ST-101
35N	Signals Intelligence Analyst	ST-101	**35P**	Cryptologic Linguist	ST-91	**35Q**	Cryptologic Network Warfare Specialist	ST-112

(continued)

MOS	Title	Score	MOS	Title	Score	MOS	Title	Score
35S	Signals Collector/ Analyst	ST-101	35T	Military Intelligence Systems Maintainer/ Integrator	ST-112	36B	Financial Management Technician	CL-101
37F	Psychological Operations Specialist	GT-107	38B	Civil Affairs Specialist	GT-107	42A	Human Resources Specialist	GT-100 and CL-90
42R	Band Member	N/A	42S	Special Band Musician	N/A	46Q	Public Affairs Specialist	GT-107
46R	Public Affairs Broadcast Specialist Journalist	GT-107	46Q	Public Affairs Specialist	GT-107	56M	Chaplain Assistant	CL-90
68A	Biomedical Equipment Specialist	EL-107	68B	Orthopedic Specialist	ST-101 and GT-107	68D	Operating Room Specialist	ST-91
68E	Dental Specialist	ST-91	68G	Patient Administration Specialist	CL-90	68H	Optical Laboratory Specialist	GM-98
68J	Medical Logistics Specialist	CL-90	68K	Medical Laboratory Specialist	ST-106	68M	Nutrition Care Specialist	OF-95
68N	Cardiovascular Specialist	ST-101 and GT-107	68P	Radiology Specialist	ST-106	68Q	Pharmacy Specialist	ST-95
68R	Veterinary Food Inspection Specialist	ST-95	68S	Preventive Medicine Specialist	ST-101	68T	Animal Care Specialist	ST-91
68V	Respiratory Specialist	ST-102	68W	Healthcare Specialist	ST-101 and GT-107	68X	Mental Health Specialist	ST-101
74D	Chemical, Biological, Radiological, and Nuclear Operations Specialist	ST-100	88H	Cargo Specialist	GM-88	88K	Watercraft Operator	MM-99
88L	Watercraft Engineer	MM-99	88M	Motor Transport Operator	OF-85	88N	Transportation Management Coordinator	CL-95
88P	Railway Equipment Repairer (Reserves only)	MM-97	88T	Railway Section Repairer (Reserves only)	MM-87	88U	Railway Operations Crewmember (Reserves only)	MM-92
89A	Ammunition Stock Control and Accounting Specialist	ST-91	89B	Ammunition Specialist	ST-91	89D	Explosive Ordnance Disposal (EOD) Specialist	ST-110

MOS	Title	Score	MOS	Title	Score	MOS	Title	Score
91A	M1 Abrams Tank System Maintainer	MM-99 or MM-88 and GT-92	91B	Wheeled Vehicle Mechanic	MM-92 or MM-87 and GT-85	91C	Utilities Equipment Repairer	GM-98 or GM-88 and GT-83
91D	Power Generation Equipment Repairer	GM-98 or GM-88 and GT-88	91E	Allied Trade Specialist	GM-98 or GM-88 and GT-92	91F	Small Arms/ Artillery Repairer	GM-93 or GM-88 and GT-85
91G	Fire Control Repairer	EL-98 or EL-93 and GT-88	91H	Track Vehicle Repairer	MM-92 or MM-87 and GT-85	91J	Quartermaster and Chemical Equipment Repairer	MM-92 or MM-87 and GT-85
91L	Construction Equipment Repairer	MM-92 or MM-87 and GT-85	91M	Bradley Fighting Vehicle System Maintainer	MM-99 or MM-88 and GT-92	91P	Artillery Mechanic	MM-99 or MM-88 and GT-88
91S	Stryker Systems Maintainer	MM-92 or MM-87 and GT-85	92F	Petroleum Supply Specialist	CL-86 and OF-85	92G	Food Service Specialist	OF-85
92L	Petroleum Laboratory Specialist	ST-91	92M	Mortuary Affairs Specialist	GM-88	92R	Parachute Rigger	GM-88 and CO-87
92S	Shower/ Laundry and Clothing Repair Specialist	GM-84	92W	Water Treatment Specialist	GM-88	92Y	Unit Supply Specialist	CL-90
94A	Land Combat Electronic Missile System Repairer	EL-102	94D	Air Traffic Control Equipment Repairer	EL-102	94E	Radio and Communications Security Repairer	EL-102
94F	Computer/ Detection Systems Repairer	EL-102	94H	Test Measurement and Diagnostic Equipment Maintenance Support Specialist	EL-107	94M	Radar Repairer	EL-107
94P	Multiple Launch Rocket System Repairer	EL-93	94R	Avionic and Survivability Equipment Repairer	EL-98	94S	Patriot System Repairer	EL-107
94T	Avenger System Repairer	EL-98	94Y	Integrated Family of Test Equipment Operator and Maintainer	N/A			

Air Force Enlisted Jobs

The United States Air Force has about 120 entry-level enlisted jobs for new recruits. The Air Force refers to enlisted jobs as *Air Force Specialty Codes* (AFSCs). Table A-2 shows the Air Force entry-level AFSCs and the line scores required to qualify for each job. The table is organized by AFSC number, so browse the table and see which AFSCs pique your interest.

Line scores are abbreviated as follows: General (G), Electronic (E), Mechanical (M), and Administrative (A). See Chapter 2 for information on which ASVAB subtest scores are used by the Air Force to calculate the various line scores.

TABLE A-2   Air Force Enlisted Jobs and Required ASVAB Scores

AFSC	Title	Score	AFSC	Title	Score	AFSC	Title	Score
1A0X1	In-Flight Refueling	G-55	1A1X1	Flight Engineer	M-47 or E-38	1A2X1	Aircraft Loadmaster	G-57
1A3X1	Airborne Mission Systems	E-70	1A4X1	Airborne Operations	G-55	1A5X1	Airborne Mission Systems	E-70
1A6X1	Flight Attendant	A-28	1A7X1	Aerial Gunner	M-60 or E-45	1A8X1	Airborne Cryptologic Linguist	G-72
1C0X1	Aviation Resource Management	A-45	1C1X1	Air Traffic Control	G-55 and M-55	1C2X1	Combat Control	G-44
1C3X1	Command Post	G-49	1C4X1	Tactical Air Control Party	G-49	1C5X1	Command and Control Battle Management Operations	G-55
1C6X1	Space Systems Operations	E-70	1C7X1	Airfield Management	G-50 and M-40	1N0X1	Operations Intelligence	G-57
1N1X1	Geospatial Intelligence	G-66	1N2X1	Signals Intelligence	G-53	1N3XX	Cryptologic Language Analyst	G-72
1N4X1	Network Intelligence Analyst	G-62	1P0X1	Aircrew Flight Equipment	M-40	1S0X1	Safety	G-62
1T0X1	Survival, Evasion, Resistance, and Escape	G-55	1T2X1	Pararescue	G-44	1U0X1	Career RPA Sensor Operator	G-64 and E-54
1W0X1	Weather	G-66 and E-50	2A0X1	Avionics Test Stations and Components	E-70	2A3X1	Avionics Systems	E-70
2A5X1	Aerospace Maintenance	M-47	2A5X2	Helicopter Maintenance	M-56	2A5X3	Integrated Avionics Systems	E-70
2A6X1	Aerospace Propulsion	M-60	2A6X2	Aerospace Ground Equipment	M-47 and E-28	2A6X3	Aircrew Egress Systems	M-56

AFSC	Title	Score	AFSC	Title	Score	AFSC	Title	Score
2A6X4	Aircraft Fuel Systems	M-47	2A6X5	Aircraft Hydraulic Systems	M-56	2A7X1	Aircraft Metals Technology	M-47
2A7X2	Nondestructive Inspection	M-42	2A7X3	Aircraft Structural Maintenance	M-47	2A7X4	Survival Equipment	M-40
2E0X1	Ground Radar Systems	E-70	2E1X1	Satellite, Wideband, and Telemetry Systems	E-70	2E1X2	Meteorological and Navigations Systems	E-70
2E1X3	Ground Radio Communications	E-70	2E1X4	Visual Imagery and Intrusion Detection Systems	E-70	2E2X1	Network Infrastructure Systems	E-70
2E6X2	Communications Cable and Antenna Systems	M-47	2E6X3	Telephone Systems	E-45	2F0X1	Fuels	M-47 and G-38
2G0X1	Logistics Plans	A-56	2M0X1	Missile Maintenance	E-70	2M0X2	Missile and Space Systems Maintenance	M-47
2M0X3	Missile and Space Facilities	E-50	2P0X1	Precision Measurement Equipment Laboratory	E-70	2R0X1	Maintenance Management Analysis	G-55
2R1X1	Maintenance Management Production	G-44	2S0X1	Materiel Management	A-41 or G-44	2S0X2	Supply Systems Analysis	A-47
2T0X1	Traffic Management	A-35	2T1X1	Vehicle Operations	M-40	2T2X1	Air Transportation	M-47 and A-28
2T3X1	Special Purpose Vehicle and Equipment Maintenance	M-47	2T3X2	Special Vehicle Maintenance	M-40	2T3X5	Vehicle Body Maintenance	M-56
2T3X7	Vehicle Management and Analysis	A-41	2W0X1	Munitions Systems	G-57 and M-60	2W1X1	Aircraft Armament Systems	M-60 or E-45
2W2X1	Nuclear Weapons	M-60	3A0X1	Knowledge Operations Management	A-28	3C0X1	Communication — Computer Systems	G-64
3C0X2	Computer Systems Programming	G-64	3C1X1	Information Systems Technology	E-60	3C1X2	Electromagnetic Spectrum Management	G-44
3C2X1	Network Integration	E-70	3D0X1	Cyber Systems Operations	G-64	3E0X1	Electrical Systems	E-33

(continued)

AFSC	Title	Score	AFSC	Title	Score	AFSC	Title	Score
3E1X1	Heating, Ventilation, AC, Refrigeration	M-47 or E-28	3E2X1	Pavement and Construction Equipment	M-40	3E3X1	Structural	M-47
3E4X1	Water and Fuel Systems Maintenance	M-47 and E-28	3E4X2	Liquid Fuel Systems Maintenance	M-47	3E4X3	Pest Management	G-38
3E5X1	Engineering	G-49	3E6X1	Operations Management	G-44	3E7X1	Fire Protection	G-38
3E8X1	Explosive Ordnance Disposal	G-64 and M-60	3E9X1	Readiness	G-62	3M0X1	Services	G-24
3N0X1	Public Affairs	G-72	3N1X1	Band	G-24 or A-21	3N2X1	Premier Band	G-24 or A-21
3P0X1	Security Forces	G-33	3S0X1	Personnel	A-41	4A0X1	Health Services Management	G-44
4A1X1	Medical Materiel	G-44	4A2X1	Biomedical Equipment	E-70 and M-60	4B0X1	Bioenvironmental Engineering	G-49
4C0X1	Mental Health Services	G-55	4D0X1	Diet Therapy	G-44	4E0X1	Public Health	G-44
4H0X1	Cardiopulmonary Laboratory	G-44	4J0X2	Physical Medicine	G-49	4M0X1	Aerospace and Operational Physiology	G-44
4N0X1	Aerospace Medical Service	G-44	4N1X1	Surgical Service	G-44	4P0X1	Pharmacy	G-44
4R0X1	Diagnostic Imaging	G-44	4T0X1	Medical Laboratory	G-62	4T0X2	Histopathology	G-44
4T0X3	Cytotechnology	G-44	4V0X1	Ophthalmic	G-55	4Y0X1	Dental Assistant	G-44
4Y0X2	Dental Lab	G-66	5J0X1	Paralegal	G-51	5R0X1	Chaplain Assistant	G-44 or A-35
6C0X1	Contracting	G-70	6F0X1	Financial Management and Comptroller	G-57	9S100	Technical Applications Specialist	M-88 and E-85

Navy Enlisted Jobs

The Navy calls its enlisted jobs *ratings* and has about 80 jobs available for entry-level recruits. This branch doesn't use line scores for job-qualification purposes. Instead, the Navy combines scores from the various ASVAB subtests for each of its enlisted ratings.

Table A-3 (in ratings order) shows combinations of ASVAB subtest scores that are required to qualify for Navy enlisted jobs. Peruse the list and see which jobs may best suit you. The ASVAB subtests are abbreviated as follows: General Science (GS), Arithmetic Reasoning (AR), Word Knowledge (WK), Paragraph Comprehension (PC), Auto & Shop Information (AS), Mathematics Knowledge (MK), Mechanical Comprehension (MC), Electronics Information (EI), Assembling Objects (AO), and Verbal Expression (VE).

TABLE A-3 Navy Enlisted Jobs and Required ASVAB Scores

Rating	Title	Score	Rating	Title	Score	Rating	Title	Score
ABE	Aviation Boatswain's Mate — Launch and Recovery Equipment	VE + MR + MK + AS = 184	ABF	Aviation Boatswain's Mate — Fuel	VE + AR + MK + AS = 184	ABH	Aviation Boatswain's Mate — Aircraft Handling	VE + AR + MK + AS = 184
AC	Air Traffic Controller	VE + AR + MK + MC = 220 or VE + MK + MC + CS = 220	AD	Aviation Machinist's Mate	VE + AR + MK + AS = 210 or VE + AR + MK + MC = 210	AE	Aviation Electrician's Mate	AR + MK + EI + GS = 222 or VE + AR + MK + MC = 222
AECF	Advanced Electronics Computer Field	AR + MK + EI + GS = 222	AG	Aerographer's Mate	VE + MK + GS = 162	AIR-CREW	Aircrew Program	VE + AR + MK + MC = 210 or VE + AR + MK + AS = 210
AM	Aviation Structural Mechanic	VE + AR + MK + AS = 210 or VE + AR + MK + MC = 210	AME	Aviation Structural Mechanic — Safety Equipment	VE + AR + MK + AS = 210 or VE + AR + MK + MC = 210	AO	Aviation Ordnanceman	VE + AR + MK + AS = 185 or MK + AS + AO = 140
AS	Aviation Support Equipment Technician	VE + AR + MK + AS = 210 or VE + AR + MK + MC = 210	AT	Aviation Electronics Technician	AR + MK + EI + GS = 222 or VE + AR + MK + MC = 222	AW	Aviation Warfare Systems Operator	VE + AR + MK + MC = 210
AWF	Aircrewman Mechanical	VE + AR + MK + MC = 210 or VE + AR + MK + GS = 210	AWO	Aircrewman Operator	VE + AR + MK + MC = 210 or VE + AR + MK + GS = 210	AWR	Aircrewman Tactical Helicopter	VE + AR + MK + MC = 210 or VE + AR + MK + GS = 210
AWS	Aircrewman Helicopter	VE + AR + MK + MC = 210 or VE + AR + MK + GS = 210	AWV	Aircrewman Avionics	VE + AR + MK + MC = 210 or VE + AR + MK + GS = 210	AZ	Aviation Maintenance Administrationman	VE + AR = 102
BM	Boatswain's Mate	VE + AR + MK + AS = 175 or MK + AS + AO = 135	BU	Builder	AR + MC + AS = 140	CE	Construction Electrician	AR + MK + EI + GS = 201
CM	Construction Mechanic	AR + MC + AS = 158	CS	Culinary Specialist	VE + AR = 88	CS(SS)	Culinary Specialist (Submarine)	AR + MK + EI + GS = 200 or VE + AR + MK + MC = 200

(continued)

TABLE A-3 *(continued)*

Rating	Title	Score	Rating	Title	Score	Rating	Title	Score
CTA	Cryptologic Technician — Administration	VE+MK = 105	CTI	Cryptologic Technician — Interpretive	VE+MK+ GS = 165	CTM	Cryptologic Technician — Maintenance	MK+EI+ GS+AR = 223 (MK > 57 and AR > 57)
CTN	Cryptologic Technician — Networks	AR+2MK+ GS = 222	CTR	Cryptologic Technician — Collection	VE+AR = 109	CTT	Cryptologic Technician — Technical	VE+MK+ GS = 162
DC	Damage Controlman	VE+AR+ MK+AS = 205	EA	Engineering Aide	AR+2MK+ GS = 207	EM	Electrician's Mate	AR+MK+ EI+GS = 252 or VE+AR+ MK+ MC = 252
EN	Engineman	VE+AR+ MK+AS = 195 or VE+ AR+MK+ AO = 200	EO	Equipment Operator	AR+MC+ AS = 140	EOD	Explosive Ordnance Disposal	AR+VE = 109 and MC = 51 or AR+ VE = 100 and MC = 50
ET	Electronics Technician	AR+MK+ EI+GS = 252 or VE+ AR+MK+ MC = 252	ET(SS)	Electronics Technician (Submarine)	AR+MK+ EI+GS = 222	FC	Fire Controlman	AR+MK+ EI+GS = 223
FT(SS)	Fire Control Technician (Submarine)	AR+MK+ EI+GS = 222 or VE+ AR+MK+ MV = 222	GM	Gunner's Mate	AR+MK+ EI+GS = 204	GSE	Gas Turbine Systems Technician — Electrical	VE+AR+ MK+MC = 210 or AR+MK+ EI+GS = 210
GSM	Gas Turbine Systems Technician — Mechanical	VE+AR+ MK+AS = 200 or VE+ AR+MK+ AO = 205	HM	Hospital Corpsman	VE+MK+ GS = 156	HT	Hull Maintenance Technician	AR+MK+ EI+GS = 213
IC	Interior Communications Electrician	AR+MK+ EI+GS = 213	IS	Intelligence Specialist	VE+AR = 108	IT	Information System Technician	AR+2MK+ GS = 222 or AR+ MK+EI+ GS = 222
LN	Legalman	VE+MK = 105	LS	Logistics Specialist	VE+AR = 102	LS (SS)	Storekeeper (Submarine)	AR+MK+ EI+GS = 200 or VE+ AR+MK+ MC = 200
MA	Master at Arms	AR+WK = 98 and WK > 43	MC	Mass Communication Specialist	VE+AR = 115	MM	Machinist's Mate	AR+MK+ EI+GS = 252 or VE+ AR+MK+ MC = 252

Rating	Title	Score	Rating	Title	Score	Rating	Title	Score
MM(SS)	Machinist's Mate (Submarine)	VE+AR+ MK+MC = 210 or VE+ AR+MK+ AS = 210	MN	Mineman	VE+AR+ MK+MC = 210 or VE+ AR+MK+ AS = 210	MR	Machinery Repairman	VE+AR+ MK+AS = 205 or VE+ AR+MK+ MC = 205
MT	Missile Technician	AR+MK+ EI+GS = 222 or VE+ AR+MK+ MC = 222	MU	Musician	N/A	ND	Navy Diver	AR+VE = 103 and MC = 51
NUC	Nuclear Program	AR+MK+ EI+GS = 252 or VE+ AR+MK+ MC = 252	OS	Operations Specialist	VE+MK+ CS = 157 or AR+2MK+ GS = 210	PC	Postal Clerk	VE+AR = 108
PR	Aircrew Survival Equipmentman	VE+AR+ MK+AS = 185 or MK+ AS+AO = 140	PS	Personnel Specialist	VE+MK = 105 or VE+ MK+CS = 157	QM	Quartermaster	VE+AR = 96
RP	Religious Program Specialist	VE+MK = 105 or VE+ MK+CS = 157	SH	Ship Serviceman	VE+AR = 95	SK	Storekeeper	VE+AR = 103
SN(SS)	Seaman (Submarine)	AR+MK+ EI+GS = 210 or VE+ AR+MK+ MC = 200	STG	Sonar Technician (Surface)	AR+MK+ EI+GS = 222 or VE+AR+ MK+MC = 222	STS(SS)	Sonar Technician (Submarine)	AR+MK+ EI+GS = 222 or VE+ AR+MK+ MC = 222
SO	Special Warfare Operator (SEAL)	GS+MC+ EI = 165 or VE+MK+ MC+CS = 220	SW	Steelworker	VE+MC+ AS = 140	TM	Torpedoman's Mate	AR+2MK+ GS = 194
UT	Utilitiesman	AR+MK+ EI+GS = 200	YN	Yeoman	VE+MK = 105 or VE+ MK+CS = 157	YN(SS)	Yeoman (Submarine)	AR+MK+ EI+GS = 200 or VE+ AR+MK+ MC = 200

Marine Corps Enlisted Jobs

The United States Marine Corps needs a few good men (and women) to fill about 140 enlisted entry-level job specialties. Like the Army, the Marine Corps calls its enlisted jobs *Military Occupational Specialties* (MOSs). The Marine Corps has only four line scores, and they're abbreviated in Table A-4 as follows: Clerical (CL), Mechanical Maintenance (MM), Electronics (EL), and General Technical (GT).

TABLE A-4 — Marine Corps Enlisted Jobs and Required ASVAB Scores

MOS	Title	Score	MOS	Title	Score	MOS	Title	Score
0111	Administrative Specialist	CL-100	0161	Postal Clerk	CL-100	0231	Intelligence Specialist	GT-100
0261	Geographic Intelligence Specialist	EL-100	0311	Rifleman	GT-80	0313	LAV Crewman	GT-90
0321	Reconnaissance Marine	GT-105	0331	Machine Gunner	GT-80	0341	Mortarman	GT-80
0351	Basic Infantry Marine	GT-100	0352	Antitank Missileman	GT-100	0411	Maintenance Management Specialist	GT-100
0431	Logistics/ Embarkation Specialist	GT-100	0451	Airborne and Air Delivery Specialist	GT-100	0471	Personnel Retrieval and Processing Specialist	N/A
0472	Personnel Retrieval and Processing Technician	N/A	0481	Landing Support Specialist	MM-100 and GT-95	0511	MAGTF Planning Specialist	GT-110
0612	Tactical Switching Operator	EL-105	0613	Construction Wireman	EL-105	0614	Unit Level Circuit Switch (ULCS) Operator/ Maintainer	EL-100
0621	Field Radio Operator	EL-105	0622	Digital (Multi-Channel) Wideband Transmission Equipment Operator	EL-105	623	Tropospheric Scatter Radio Multi-Channel Equipment Operator	EL-105
0627	Satellite Communications Operator	EL-105	0651	Cyber Network Operator	GT-100	0811	Field Artillery Cannoneer	GT-90
0842	Field Artillery Radar Operator	GT-105	0844	Field Artillery Fire Control Marine	GT-105	0847	Field Artillery Sensor Support Marine	GT-105
0861	Fire Support Marine	GT-100	1141	Electrician	EL-90	1142	Engineer Equipment Electrical Systems Technician	MM-105 and EL-100
1161	Refrigeration and Air Conditioning Technician	MM-105	1171	Water Support Technician	MM-95	1316	Metal Worker	MM-95
1341	Engineer Equipment Mechanic	MM-95	1345	Engineer Equipment Operator	MM-95	1361	Engineer Assistant	GT-100
1371	Combat Engineer	MM-95	1391	Bulk Fuel Specialist	MM-95	1812	M1A1 Tank Crewman	GT-90

MOS	Title	Score	MOS	Title	Score	MOS	Title	Score
1833	Amphibious Assault Vehicle Marine	GT-90	1834	Expeditionary Fighting Vehicle (EFV) Crewman	GT-90	2111	Small Arms Repairer/ Technician	MM-95
2131	Towed Artillery Systems Technician	MM-95	2141	Assault Amphibious Vehicle (AAV) Repairer/ Technician	MM-105	2146	Main Battle Tank (MBT) Repairer/ Technician	MM-105
2147	Light Armored Vehicle (LAV) Repairer/ Technician	MM-105	2148	Expeditionary Fighting Vehicle (EFV) Repairer/ Technician	MM-105	2161	Machinist	MM-105
2171	Electro-Optical Ordnance Repairer	EL-115 and MM-105	2311	Ammunition Technician	GT-100	2336	Explosive Ordnance Disposal Technician	GT-110
2621	Special Communications Signals Collection Operator/ Analyst	GT-100	2631	Electronic Intelligence (ELINT) Intercept Operator/ Analyst	GT-100	2651	Special Intelligence System Administrator/ Communicator	GT-100
2671	Middle East Cryptologic Linguist	GT-105	2673	Asia-Pacific Cryptologic Linguist	GT-105	2674	European Cryptologic Linguist	GT-105
2676	Central Asian Cryptologic Linguist	GT-105	2821	Technical Controller	EL-115	2831	Digital Wideband Repairer	EL-115
2841	Ground Radio Repairer	EL-115	2847	Telephone Systems/ Personal Computer Repairer	EL-115	2862	Electronics Maintenance Technician	EL-115
2871	Calibration Technician	EL-115	2887	Artillery Electronics Technician	EL-115	3043	Supply Administration and Operations Specialist	CL-105
3051	Warehouse Clerk	CL-90	3052	Packaging Specialist	CL-90	3112	Distribution Management Specialist	GT-90
3381	Food Service Specialist	GT-90	3432	Finance Technician	CL-105	3451	Financial Management Resource Analyst	GT-110
3521	Automotive Maintenance Technician	MM-95	3531	Motor Vehicle Operator	MM-85	4113	Marine Corps Community Service Marine	GT-110
4341	Combat Correspondent	GT-110 and VE-45	4421	Legal Services Specialist	CL-110 and GT-105	4612	Combat Camera Production Specialist	GT-100

(continued)

MOS	Title	Score	MOS	Title	Score	MOS	Title	Score
4641	Combat Photographer	GT-100	**4671**	Combat Videographer	GT-100	**55XX**	Band	N/A
5711	Chemical, Biological, Radiological and Nuclear (CBRN) Defense Specialist	GT-110	**5811**	Military Police	GT-100	**5831**	Correctional Specialist	GT-100
5939	Aviation Communication Systems Technician	EL-115	**5948**	Aviation Radar Repairer	EL-115	**5951**	Aviation Meteorological Equipment Technician	EL-110
5952	Air Traffic Control Navigational Aids Technician	EL-110	**5953**	Air Traffic Control Radar Technician	EL-110	**5954**	Air Traffic Control Communications Technician	EL-110
5974	Tactical Data Systems Technician	EL-115	**5979**	Tactical Air Operations/ Air Defense Systems Technician	EL-115	**6042**	Individual Material Readiness List (IMRL) Asset Manager	GT-105
6046	Aircraft Maintenance Administration Specialist	CL-100	**6048**	Flight Equipment Technician	MM-105	**6062**	Aircraft Intermediate Level Hydraulic/ Pneumatic Mechanic	MM-105
6072	Aircraft Maintenance Support Equipment Hydraulic/ Pneumatic/ Structures Mechanic	MM-105	**6073**	Aircraft Maintenance Support Equipment Electrician/ Refrigeration Mechanic	MM-105	**6074**	Cryogenics Equipment Operator	MM-105
6092	Aircraft Intermediate Level Structures Mechanic	MM-105	**6111**	Helicopter/ Tiltrotor Mechanic-Trainee	MM-105	**6113**	Helicopter Mechanic, CH-53	MM-105
6116	Tiltrotor Mechanic, MV-22	MM-105	**6122**	Helicopter Power Plants Mechanic, T-58	MM-105	**6123**	Helicopter Power Plants Mechanic, T-64	MM-105
6124	Helicopter Power Plants Mechanic, T-400/T-700	MM-105	**6132**	Helicopter/ Tiltrotor Dynamic Components Mechanic	MM-105	**6152**	Helicopter/ Tiltrotor Airframe Mechanic, CH-46	MM-105
6153	Helicopter Airframe Mechanic, CH-53	MM-105	**6154**	Helicopter Airframe Mechanic, UH/AH-1	MM-105	**6156**	Tiltrotor Airframe Mechanic, MV-22	MM-105
617X	Helicopter Crew Chief	MM-105	**621X**	Fixed-Wing Aircraft Mechanic	MM-105	**622X**	Fixed-Wing Aircraft Power Plants Mechanic	MM-105

MOS	Title	Score	MOS	Title	Score	MOS	Title	Score
6232	Fixed-Wing Aircraft Flight Mechanic	MM-105	625X	Fixed-Wing Aircraft Airframe Mechanic	MM-105	628X	Fixed-Wing Aircraft Safety Equipment Mechanic	MM-105
63XX	Aircraft Communications/ Navigation/ Radar Systems Technician	EL-105	6423	Aviation Electronic Micro/Miniature Component and Cable Repair Technician	EL-105	6432	Aircraft Electrical/ Instrument/ Flight Control Systems Technician	EL-105
6469	Reconfigurable Transportable Consolidated Automated Support System (RTCASS) Technician	EL-105	6483	Communication/ Cryptographic/ Counter- measures Systems Technician	EL-105	6492	Aviation Precision Measurement Equipment Calibration/ Repair Technician	EL-110
6499	Mobile Facility Technician	EL-105	6511	Aircraft Ordnance Technician	GT-105	6541	Aviation Ordnance Systems Technician	GT-105
6672	Aviation Supply Specialist	CL-100	6694	Aviation Logistics Information Management System (ALIMS) Specialist	EL-115	6842	METOC Analyst Forecaster	GT-105
7011	Expeditionary Airfield Systems Technician	MM-95	7041	Aviation Operations Specialist	CL-100	7051	Aircraft Rescue and Firefighting Specialist	MM-95
7212	Low Altitude Air Defense (LAAD) Gunner	GT-90	7236	Tactical Air Defense Controller	GT-105	7242	Air Support Operations Operator	GT-100
7251	Air Traffic Controller	GT-110	7314	Unmanned Aircraft System (UAS) Operator	GT-105			

Coast Guard Enlisted Jobs

The smallest U.S. Military service, the Coast Guard, has only 19 types of entry-level jobs for enlisted members. Like the Navy, the Coast Guard calls its enlisted jobs *ratings.* Also like the Navy, the Coast Guard doesn't use line scores for job qualification purposes. Instead, it uses the sums of various ASVAB subtest scores.

Table A-5 shows combinations of ASVAB subtest scores that are required to qualify for Coast Guard enlisted jobs. The ASVAB subtests are abbreviated as follows: General Science (GS), Arithmetic Reasoning (AR), Word Knowledge (WK), Paragraph Comprehension (PC), Auto & Shop Information (AS), Mathematics Knowledge (MK), Mechanical Comprehension (MC), Electronics Information (EI), Assembling Objects (AO), and Verbal Expression (VE).

TABLE A-5 Coast Guard Enlisted Jobs and Required ASVAB Scores

Rating	Title	Score	Rating	Title	Score	Rating	Title	Score
AET	Avionics Electrical Technician	AFQT = 65 or MK+EI+ GS = 172 and minimum AR = 52	**AMT**	Aviation Maintenance Technician	AFQT = 65 or AR+MC+ AS+EI = 220 and minimum AR = 52	**AST**	Aviation Survival Technician	AFQT = 65 or VE+MC+ AS = 162 and minimum AR = 52
BM	Boatswain's Mate	AR+VE = 100	**DC**	Damage Controlman	VE+MC+ AS = 155	**EM**	Electrician's Mate	MK+EI+ GS = 153 and minimum AR = 52
ET	Electronics Technician	AFQT = 65 or MK+EI+ GS = 172 and minimum AR = 52	**FS**	Food Service Specialist	VE+AR = 105	**GM**	Gunner's Mate	AR+MK+ EI+GS = 209
HS	Health Services Technician	VE+MK+ GS+AR = 207 and minimum AR = 50	**IS**	Intelligence Specialist	AR+VE = 109	**IT**	Information Systems Technician	AFQT = 65 or MK+EI+ GS = 172 and minimum AR = 52
ME	Maritime Enforcement Specialist	AR+VE = 100	**MK**	Machinery Technician	AR+MC+ AS = 154 or VE+AR = 105	**MST**	Marine Science Technician	VE+AR = 114 and minimum MK = 56
OS	Operations Specialist	VE+AR = 105	**PA**	Public Affairs Specialist	VE+AR = 109 and minimum VE = 54	**SK**	Storekeeper	VE+AR = 105 and minimum VE = 51
YN	Yeoman	VE+AR = 105						

Index

About the Author

Angie Papple Johnston joined the U.S. Army in 2006 as a Chemical, Biological, Radiological, and Nuclear (CBRN) specialist, ready to tackle chemical weapons in a Level-A HAZMAT suit. During her second deployment as part of Operation Iraqi Freedom, Angie became her battalion's public affairs representative, writing press releases and photographing historic moments from Tikrit to Kirkuk.

Angie also served as the Lead Cadre for the Texas Army National Guard's Recruit Sustainment Program (RSP), teaching brand-new privates how to survive Basic Combat Training, Advanced Individual Training, and the Army.

She's currently the CBRN noncommissioned officer-in-charge of an aviation battalion in Washington, D.C., where her favorite things are teaching her soldiers combatives (the Army's version of hand-to-hand combat), doing the occasional ruck march around the airfield, and setting a positive example for the next generation of leaders. She firmly believes that you can learn something from every leader in the military, even if it's how *not* to lead, and that there's nothing more important than leading soldiers from the front through training and mentoring.

Dedication

To Davy, Mom, Dad, D.J., Sassy, and Jesse.

Author's Acknowledgments

Lindsay Lefevere and Vicki Adang: You two are awesome. Thank you for having me on this team.

Danielle Voirol, your contributions have made this book *exponentially* better.

A very special thanks to Suzanne Langebartels, Devin Hyde, and Caleb Leggett for your tremendous help in making this book the best AFQT resource available.

Publisher's Acknowledgments

Executive Editor: Lindsay Sandman Lefevere

Project Manager: Victoria M. Adang

Copy Editor: Danielle Voirol

Technical Editors: Suzanne Langebartels,
Devin Hyde, and Caleb Leggett

Production Editor: Magesh Elangovan

Cover Photos: © CatLane/iStockphoto

Leverage the power

Dummies is the global leader in the reference category and one of the most trusted and highly regarded brands in the world. No longer just focused on books, customers now have access to the dummies content they need in the format they want. Together we'll craft a solution that engages your customers, stands out from the competition, and helps you meet your goals.

Advertising & Sponsorships

Connect with an engaged audience on a powerful multimedia site, and position your message alongside expert how-to content. Dummies.com is a one-stop shop for free, online information and know-how curated by a team of experts.

- Targeted ads
- Video
- Email Marketing
- Microsites
- Sweepstakes sponsorship

20 **MILLION** PAGE VIEWS EVERY SINGLE MONTH

15 MILLION **UNIQUE** VISITORS PER MONTH

43% OF ALL VISITORS ACCESS THE SITE VIA THEIR MOBILE DEVICES

700,000 NEWSLETTER SUBSCRIPTIONS TO THE INBOXES OF

300,000 UNIQUE INDIVIDUALS EVERY WEEK

PERSONAL ENRICHMENT

Staying Sharp dummies

9781119187790
USA $26.00
CAN $31.99
UK £19.99

Facebook dummies
Carolyn Abram

9781119179030
USA $21.99
CAN $25.99
UK £16.99

Guitar dummies
Mark Phillips
Jon Chappell

9781119293354
USA $24.99
CAN $29.99
UK £17.99

Investing dummies
Eric Tyson, MBA

9781119293347
USA $22.99
CAN $27.99
UK £16.99

Beekeeping dummies
Howland Blackiston

9781119310068
USA $22.99
CAN $27.99
UK £16.99

Digital Photography dummies
Julie Adair King

9781119235606
USA $24.99
CAN $29.99
UK £17.99

Meditation dummies
Stephan Bodian

9781119251163
USA $24.99
CAN $29.99
UK £17.99

Pregnancy ALL-IN-ONE dummies

9781119235491
USA $26.99
CAN $31.99
UK £19.99

Samsung Galaxy S7 dummies
Bill Hughes

9781119279952
USA $24.99
CAN $29.99
UK £17.99

iPhone dummies
Edward C. Baig
Bob "Dr. Mac" LeVitus

9781119283133
USA $24.99
CAN $29.99
UK £17.99

Crocheting dummies
Karen Manthey
Susan Brittain

9781119287117
USA $24.99
CAN $29.99
UK £16.99

Nutrition dummies
Carol Ann Rinzler

9781119130246
USA $22.99
CAN $27.99
UK £16.99

PROFESSIONAL DEVELOPMENT

Windows 10 dummies
Andy Rathbone

9781119311041
USA $24.99
CAN $29.99
UK £17.99

AutoCAD dummies
Bill Fane

9781119255796
USA $39.99
CAN $47.99
UK £27.99

Excel 2016 dummies
Greg Harvey, PhD

9781119293439
USA $26.99
CAN $31.99
UK £19.99

QuickBooks 2017 dummies
Stephen L. Nelson, MBA, CPA, MS in Taxation

9781119281467
USA $26.99
CAN $31.99
UK £19.99

macOS Sierra dummies
Bob "Dr. Mac" LeVitus

9781119280651
USA $29.99
CAN $35.99
UK £21.99

LinkedIn dummies
Joel Elad, MBAs

9781119251132
USA $24.99
CAN $29.99
UK £17.99

Windows 10 ALL-IN-ONE dummies
Woody Leonhard

9781119310563
USA $34.00
CAN $41.99
UK £24.99

SharePoint 2016 dummies
Rosemarie Withee
Ken Withee

9781119181705
USA $29.99
CAN $35.99
UK £21.99

Fundamental Analysis dummies
Matt Krantz

9781119263593
USA $26.99
CAN $31.99
UK £19.99

Networking dummies
Doug Lowe

9781119257769
USA $29.99
CAN $35.99
UK £21.99

Office 2016 dummies
Wallace Wang

9781119293477
USA $26.99
CAN $31.99
UK £19.99

Office 365 dummies
Rosemarie Withee
Ken Withee
Jennifer Reed

9781119265313
USA $24.99
CAN $29.99
UK £17.99

Salesforce.com dummies
Liz Kao
Jon Paz

9781119239314
USA $29.99
CAN $35.99
UK £21.99

Coding dummies
Nikhil Abraham

9781119293323
USA $29.99
CAN $35.99
UK £21.99

dummies.com

dummies ®
A Wiley Brand